KB100591

적중 100 plus
2학기 전과정

영어 기출문제집

중 2
능률 | 김성곤

Best Collection

구성과 특징

교과서의 주요 학습 내용을 중심으로 학습 영역별 특성에 맞춰 단계별로 다양한 학습 기회를 제공하여
단원별 학습능력 평가는 물론 중간 및 기말고사 시험 등에 완벽하게 대비할 수 있도록 내용을 구성

Words & Expressions

Step1	Key Words 단원별 핵심 단어 설명 및 풀이
	Key Expression 단원별 핵심 숙어 및 관용어 설명
	Word Power 반대 또는 비슷한 뜻 단어 배우기
	English Dictionary 영어로 배우는 영어 단어
Step2	실력평가 단원별 수시평가 대비 주관식, 객관식 문제풀이
Step3	서술형 대비 학업성취도 및 수행능력평가 대비 서술형 문제풀이

Conversation

Step1	핵심 의사소통 소통에 필요한 주요 표현 방법 요약
	핵심 Check 기본적인 표현 방법 및 활용능력 확인
Step2	대화문 익히기 교과서 대화문 심층 분석 및 확인
Step3	교과서 확인학습 빈칸 채우기를 통한 문장 완성 능력 확인
Step4	기본평가 시험대비 기초 학습 능력 평가
Step5	실력평가 단원별 수시평가 대비 주관식, 객관식 문제풀이
Step6	서술형 대비 학업성취도 및 수행능력평가 대비 서술형 문제풀이

Grammar

Step1	주요 문법 단원별 주요 문법 사항과 예문을 알기 쉽게 설명
	핵심 Check 기본 문법사항에 대한 이해 여부 확인
Step2	기본평가 시험대비 기초 학습 능력 평가
Step3	실력평가 단원별 수시평가 대비 주관식, 객관식 문제풀이
Step4	서술형 대비 학업성취도 및 수행능력평가 대비 서술형 문제풀이

Reading

Step1	구문 분석 단원별로 제시된 문장에 대한 구문별 분석과 내용 설명
	확인문제 문장에 대한 기본적인 이해와 인지능력 확인
Step2	확인학습A 빈칸 채우기를 통한 문장 완성 능력 확인
Step3	확인학습B 제시된 우리말을 영어로 완성하여 작문 능력 키우기
Step4	실력평가 단원별 수시평가 대비 주관식, 객관식 문제풀이
Step5	서술형 대비 학업성취도 및 수행능력평가 대비 서술형 문제풀이
	교과서 구석구석 교과서에 나오는 기타 문장까지 완벽 학습

Composition

|영역별 핵심문제|

단어 및 어휘, 대화문, 문법, 독해 등 각 영역별 기출문제의 출제 유형을 분석하여 실전에 대비하고 연습할 수 있도록 문제를 배열

|단원별 예상문제|

기출문제를 분석한 후 새로운 시험 출제 경향을 더하여 새롭게 출제될 수 있는 문제를 포함하여 시험에 완벽하게 대비할 수 있도록 준비

|서술형 실전 및 창의사고력 문제|

학교 시험에서 점차 늘어나는 서술형 시험에 집중 대비하고 고득점을 취득하는데 만전을 기하기 위한 학습 코너

|단원별 모의고사|

영역별, 단계별 학습을 모두 마친 후 실전 연습을 위한 모의고사

교과서 파헤치기

- **단어Test1~3** 영어 단어 우리말 쓰기, 우리말을 영어 단어로 쓰기, 영영풀이에 해당하는 단어와 우리말 쓰기
- **대화문Test1~2** 대화문 빈칸 완성 및 전체 대화문 쓰기
- **본문Test1~5** 빈칸 완성, 우리말 쓰기, 문장 배열연습, 영어 작문하기 복습 등 단계별 반복 학습을 통해 교과서 지문에 대한 완벽한 습득
- **구석구석지문Test1~2** 지문 빈칸 완성 및 전문 영어로 쓰기

Lesson 5

Give a Helping Hand

의사소통 기능

- 도움 요청하고 답하기
  A: Can you help me move these books?
  B: Sure. / I'm sorry, but I can't.

- 제안하기
  Why don't we donate our clothes to the community center?

언어 형식

- 목적격 관계대명사
  The little black dress **which** she wore in a movie is famous even today.

- 감정을 나타내는 과거분사
  She was **shocked** because their lives were very difficult.

Words & Expressions

교과서

Key Words

- **accident**[ǽksidənt] 명 사고
- **alive**[əláiv] 형 살아 있는, 존속하는
- **beauty**[bjú:ti] 명 아름다움, 미(美)
- **blind**[blaind] 형 눈 먼, 장님의
- **carry**[kǽri] 동 나르다, 운반하다
- **collect**[kəlékt] 동 모으다, 수집하다
- **donate**[dóuneit] 동 기부하다
- **elderly**[éldərli] 형 나이가 지긋한
- **fame**[feim] 명 명성
- **favor**[féivər] 명 호의, 친절
- **feed**[fi:d] 동 먹이를 주다
- **fire**[faiər] 명 화재
- **following**[fálouiŋ] 형 (그) 다음의
- **goodwill ambassador** 친선 대사
- **grass**[græs] 명 풀, 잔디
- **hold**[hould] 동 열다, 개최하다
- **homeless**[hóumlis] 형 집 없는, 노숙자의
- **honor**[ánər] 동 예우하다, 존중하다
- **international**[intərnǽʃənəl] 형 국제적인
- **item**[áitəm] 명 항목, 물품
- **kind**[kaind] 명 종류, 유형

- **luckily**[lʌkili] 부 운이 좋게도, 다행스럽게도
- **medicine**[medisn] 명 약
- **mission**[míʃən] 명 임무, 사명
- **moment**[móumənt] 명 순간, 잠깐
- **nursing home** 양로원
- **plant**[plænt] 동 (식물을) 심다
- **praise**[preiz] 동 칭찬하다
- **raise**[reiz] 동 들어 올리다, (자금을) 모으다
- **realize**[rí:əlàiz] 동 깨닫다, 알아차리다
- **respect**[rispékt] 동 존경하다
- **return**[ritə́:rn] 동 돌아오다, 반납하다
- **saying**[séiiŋ] 명 속담, 격언
- **serve**[sə:rv] 동 (음식을) 제공하다
- **spirit**[spírit] 명 마음, 정신, 영혼
- **statue**[stǽtʃu:] 명 조각상
- **support**[səpɔ́:rt] 동 지지하다, 원조하다
- **survive**[sərváiv] 동 살아남다, 생존하다
- **turning point** 전환점
- **volunteer**[vàləntíər] 형 자원봉사의 명 자원 봉사자
- **walk**[wɔ:k] 동 산책시키다, (사람·동물을) 걷게 하다
- **worldwide**[wə́:rldwaid] 형 세계적인

Key Expressions

- **all the time**: 늘, 내내
- **be going to** 동사원형: ~할 것이다
- **be in a hurry**: 서두르다
- **break one's arm**: 팔이 부러지다
- **clean up**: ~을 치우다, 청소하다
- **fall down**: 넘어지다
- **give a hand**: ~을 돕다
- **hand out**: 나누어 주다
- **have to** 동사원형: ~해야 한다
- **help** 목적어 (**to**) 동사원형: …가 ~하는 것을 돕다

- **hold a party**: 파티를 열다
- **in need**: 어려움에 처한
- **pass away**: 죽다, 사망하다
- **raise money**: 돈을 모금하다
- **search for**: ~을 찾다
- **take care of**: ~을 돌보다
- **thanks to**: ~ 덕분에
- **What[How] about** 동명사 ~?: ~하는 게 어떨까?
- **what kinds of** ~: 어떤 종류의
- **Why don't we** ~?: ~하는 게 어떨까?

Word Power

※ 명사 – 형용사
- **beauty**(아름다움, 미(美)) – **beautiful**(아름다운)
- **favor**(호의, 친절) – **favorable**(호의적인)
- **respect**(존경) – **respectful**(존경심이 가득한, 존경하는), **respectable**(존경할 만한)

※ 서로 반대되는 뜻을 가진 단어
- **alive**(살아 있는, 존속하는) ↔ **dead**(죽은)
- **beauty**(아름다움) ↔ **ugliness**(추함)
- **luckily**(운이 좋게도) ↔ **unluckily**(불행히도)

※ 서로 비슷한 뜻을 가진 단어
- **following**((그) 다음의) : **next**(다음의)
- **collect**(모으다) : **gather**(모으다)
- **thanks to**(~ 덕분에) : **because of, due to**(~ 때문에)
- **pass away**(죽다) : **die**(죽다)

※ 사람의 성격을 묘사할 때 쓸 수 있는 형용사
- **nice[kind/friendly]**(상냥한, 다정한)
- **wise**(현명한)
- **curious**(호기심 많은)
- **funny**(재미있는)
- **polite**(공손한)
- **patient**(끈기 있는)
- **gentle**(온화한)
- **honest**(정직한)
- **creative**(창의적인)
- **generous**(관대한)
- **lively**(쾌활한)

English Dictionary

- **accident** 사고
  → a sudden event that causes damage
  손상[손해]을 유발하는 갑작스러운 일

- **blind**: 눈 먼, 장님의
  → not able to see anything
  어떤 것도 볼 수 없는

- **collect**: 모으다, 수집하다
  → to put things together in one place
  한 장소에 사물들을 함께 두다

- **donate**: 기부하다
  → to give something to help people
  사람들을 돕기 위해 무언가를 주다

- **fame**: 명성
  → the state of being famous
  유명한 상태

- **honor**: 예우하다, 존중하다
  → to treat someone with respect
  존경심을 가지고 누군가를 대하다

- **international**: 국제적인
  → involving more than one country
  하나 이상의 나라를 포함한

- **mission**: 임무, 사명
  → a special task to be accomplished
  달성되어야 할 특별한 일

- **moment**: 순간, 잠깐
  → a particular point in time
  시간 상의 특정한 시점

- **nursing home**: 양로원
  → a place where people who are too old or sick to take care of themselves live
  너무 나이 들거나 병이 들어서 스스로를 돌볼 수 없는 사람들이 사는 장소

- **praise**: 칭찬하다
  → to say nice things about someone
  어떤 사람에 대해 좋은 점을 말하다

- **realize**: 깨닫다, 알아차리다
  → to suddenly know something
  갑자기 무언가를 알다

- **respect**: 존경하다
  → to admire or look up to somebody
  누군가를 존경하거나 우러러보다

- **statue**: 조각상
  → a sculpture of a person made from stone or metal
  돌이나 금속으로 만든 사람의 조각품

- **support**: 지지하다, 원조하다
  → to provide with assistance
  도움을 제공하다

- **survive**: 살아남다, 생존하다
  → to continue to live after something bad happens
  어떤 나쁜 일이 일어난 후에 계속 살다

- **turning point**: 전환점
  → a time when a huge change takes place
  큰 변화가 발생하는 때

- **volunteer**: 자원 봉사자
  → someone who is willing to do a job without getting paid
  돈을 받지 않고 기꺼이 어떤 일을 하는 사람

01 다음 중 성격이 <u>다른</u> 하나를 고르시오.

① creative ② generous ③ lively
④ lucky ⑤ passionate

[02~03] 다음 빈칸에 들어갈 말로 가장 적절한 것을 고르시오.

02
Please don't _____ the animals in the zoo.

① feed ② blow ③ cost
④ fall ⑤ find

03
This box is so heavy that I can't _____ it alone.

① carry ② wear ③ play
④ try ⑤ break

[04~06] 다음 밑줄 친 단어와 바꿔 쓸 수 있는 것을 고르시오.

04
I bought these <u>items</u> at a low price because they are used ones.

① sites ② stops
③ goods ④ markets
⑤ views

05
He <u>died</u> at the hospital last night.

① passed over ② passed away
③ got over ④ gave up
⑤ got back

06
I want to meet many people and travel <u>all over the world</u>.

① nationally ② internationally
③ worldwide ④ global
⑤ variously

07 다음 중 밑줄 친 부분의 뜻풀이가 바르지 <u>않은</u> 것은?

① I'd like to make an <u>international</u> call. (국제적인)
② Her <u>mission</u> was to establish schools for children. (임무)
③ The man keeps his family's tradition <u>alive</u>. (살아 있는)
④ She's gone but her <u>spirit</u> is right here with us. (정신)
⑤ They will <u>raise</u> money to help the poor. (들어 올리다)

[08~09] 다음 영영풀이에 해당하는 단어를 고르시오.

08
a time when a huge change takes place

① turning point ② schedule
③ timetable ④ moment
⑤ honor

09
a particular point in time

① second ② plan
③ moment ④ motive
⑤ respect

01 다음 짝지어진 두 단어의 관계가 같도록 빈칸에 알맞은 단어를 쓰시오. (주어진 철자로 시작할 것)

> luckily: unluckily - a_____ : dead

02 다음 밑줄 친 부분과 의미가 가장 가까운 것을 주어진 철자로 시작하여 쓰시오.

> We'll never forget his <u>soul</u>.

➡ s_____

[03~04] 다음 빈칸에 공통으로 들어갈 말을 쓰시오.

03
> • Can you drive faster? I'm _____ a hurry.
> • I helped the people _____ need.

04
> • The kind girl _____ some money to the poor old man.
> • He came to us and _____ a hand.

05 다음 빈칸에 알맞은 단어를 〈보기〉에서 골라 쓰시오. (형태 변화 가능)

> ┤ 보기 ├
> break   hand   search   take

(1) Please _____ care of my son while I'm not here.

(2) He _____ his arm a week ago.

(3) Santa Claus _____ out gifts to the children last Christmas.

(4) Would you help me _____ for more information about these?

06 우리말에 맞게 주어진 단어를 바르게 배열하시오.

(1) 네 충고 덕택에 기분이 나아졌다.
   (thanks, advice, I, to, your, feel, better)
   ➡ _____

(2) 그녀는 지난달에 세상을 떠났다.
   (month, passed, last, away, she)
   ➡ _____

(3) 정부는 노인들을 후원할 계획을 세웠다.
   (the, the, planned, support, government, elderly, to)
   ➡ _____

(4) 그는 부와 명예 둘 다 얻었다.
   (gained, fame, both, he, and, wealth)
   ➡ _____

07 다음 영영풀이에 해당하는 말을 주어진 철자로 시작하여 쓰시오.

(1)
> not able to see anything

➡ b_____

(2)
> to continue to live after something bad happens

➡ s_____

(3)
> to treat someone with respect

➡ h_____

교과서 Conversation

① 도움 요청하고 답하기

A Can you help me move these books? 이 책들 옮기는 거 도와줄 수 있어?
B Sure. / I'm sorry, but I can't. 그럼. / 미안한데 못할 거 같아.

- 상대방에게 도움을 요청할 때는 'Can you help me ~?'로 시작하는 문장으로 표현할 수 있다. help me 뒤에 동사원형이나 to부정사를 써서 구체적으로 어떤 도움이 필요한지를 밝힌다. 'Can I ask you a favor?'나 'Can you give me a hand?' 등의 표현도 쓸 수 있다.

- 이에 대한 긍정의 대답으로는 'Sure.' 등을, 부정의 대답으로는 'I'm sorry, but I can't.'나 'I'm afraid, but I can't.' 등을 쓴다.

- 도움을 요청할 때 can 대신 would나 could를 써서 'Could you help me ~?'나 'Would you help me ~?' 라고 말하면 공손하고 정중한 느낌을 준다.

도움 요청하기

- Can[Could/Would/Will] you help me (to) 동사원형 ~? (내가 ~하는 거 도와줄 수 있어?)
- Could you please 동사원형 ~? (~해 줄 수 있니?)
- Can you give me a hand to 동사원형?
- Can[May] I ask you a favor? (부탁 좀 해도 될까요?)
- Can[Could] you do me a favor? (부탁 좀 들어 주겠니?)

도움 요청에 답하기

- 수락하기: Sure. / Okay. / Certainly. / No problem. / Go ahead. / All right.
- 거절하기: I'm sorry, but I can't. / No, I'm afraid not.

핵심 Check

1. 다음 우리말에 맞게 대화의 빈칸을 채우시오.

   A: Can you do me a _____? (부탁 좀 해도 될까요?)
   B: Okay. _____ _____. (문제없어요.)

2. 다음 주어진 단어를 이용하여 대화를 완성하시오.

   A: _____? (help, can, wash, you, the dishes, me, to)
   B: Sure.

② 제안하기

Why don't we donate our clothes to the community center? 우리의 옷을 지역 문화 센터에 기부하는 게 어떨까?

- 특정 행동을 함께 하자고 제안할 때는 'Why don't we ~?'로 시작하는 표현을 쓴다. 'How about ~?'이나 'What about ~?' 등의 표현도 쓸 수 있는데, 이때 동사 형태는 'How about donating our clothes?'처럼 전치사 about 뒤에 동명사를 쓰는 것에 유의한다.

- 'Why don't you + 동사 ~?'는 함께 하자는 것은 아니고 상대방에게만 권유하는 것이다.

제안하기

- Why don't we + 동사원형 ~? (~하는 게 어떨까?)
- How[What] about (동)명사 ~?
- Let's 동사원형 ~. (~하자.)

- 상대방의 제안에 응할 때는 'Sure, I'd love to.', 그렇지 않을 때는 'Sorry, but I can't.'로 대답할 수 있다. 허락을 요청하는 말에 거절하는 경우에는, 보통 간단히 이유를 덧붙인다.

핵심 Check

3. 다음 대화의 밑줄 친 부분과 같은 의미가 되도록, 주어진 단어를 이용해 문장을 만드시오.

> A: How about having some ice cream?
> B: Sure, I'd love to.

➡ (Why) _____
(What) _____
(Let's) _____

[4-5] 다음 주어진 어구를 배열하여 대화를 완성하시오.

4.
> A: _____? (the movies, we, tomorrow, why, to, don't, go)
> B: That sounds good.

5.
> A: _____? (school. about, after, how, soccer, playing)
> B: Okay.

Listen & Talk 1 B

B: Hey, Minji! ❶What's wrong with your leg?

G: I ❷broke it last week.

B: Really? What happened?

G: I ❸was in a hurry ❹to catch a train. But I ❺fell down in the street.

B: Oh, that's terrible! ❻Is there anything I can do for you?

G: Well, ❼can you help me carry this bag?

B: Sure.

B: 민지야! 너 다리에 무슨 문제가 있니?
G: 지난주에 부러졌어.
B: 그래? 무슨 일이야?
G: 기차를 타려고 서두르고 있었어. 그런데 길에 넘어졌어.
B: 오, 정말 끔찍하다! 내가 너를 위해 해줄 게 있니?
G: 음, 이 가방을 드는 걸 도와줄 수 있니?
B: 그럼.

❶ 'What's wrong with ～?'는 상대방의 안 좋은 일에 대해 묻는 표현으로 '너 ～에 문제가 있니?'의 뜻이다. 'What's the matter with ～?', 'Is there anything wrong with ～?', 'What happened to ～?' 등의 표현과 바꿔 쓸 수 있다.

❷ broke는 break(부러지다)의 과거형이다.

❸ be in a hurry: 서두르다

❹ to부정사의 부사적 용법 중 목적(～하기 위해서)의 의미로 사용되었다.

❺ fall down: 넘어지다

❻ Is there anything I can do for you?는 '내가 너를 위해 해줄 게 있니?'의 의미로 도움을 제안할 때 쓰는 표현이다. 'Can I give you a hand?', 'May I help you?', 'What can I do for you?', 'Do you need my help?' 등으로 바꿔 쓸 수 있다.

❼ 'Can you help me ～?'는 상대방에게 도움을 요청할 때 사용하는 표현이다. help me 뒤에 동사원형이나 to부정사를 써서 구체적으로 어떤 도움이 필요한지를 밝힌다.

Check(√) True or False

(1) Minji broke her leg last month.   T ☐ F ☐

(2) The boy will help Minji to carry her bag.   T ☐ F ☐

Listen & Talk 2 A

G: ❶What kinds of volunteer activities can we do?

B: ❷Why don't we clean up our town's streets?

G: All right! ❸Let's do it.

G: 우리 어떤 종류의 봉사 활동들을 할 수 있을까?
B: 우리 동네 길거리를 청소하는 게 어때?
G: 좋아! 그러자.

❶ What kinds of ～. 어떤 종류의 volunteer: 자원봉사의; 자원 봉사자

❷ Why don't we ～?: ～하는 게 어떨까? clean up: ～을 치우다, 청소하다

❸ 'Let's 동사원형 ～.'은 '～하자'의 뜻으로, 어떤 일을 제안할 때 사용한다. 'Let's 동사원형 ～.' 외에도 'Why don't we ～?'의 표현을 쓸 수 있다.

Check(√) True or False

(3) They talk about volunteer activities to do.   T ☐ F ☐

(4) They will clean up their town's streets.   T ☐ F ☐

Listen & Talk 1 A

B: Mia, ❶can you help me move these books?

G: Sure. ❷What are you going to do with them?

B: ❸I'm going to ❹donate them to a children's library.

❶ 상대방에게 도움을 요청할 때는 'Can you help me ∼?'로 시작하는 문장으로 표현할 수 있다. help me 뒤에 동사원형이나 to부정사를 써서 구체적으로 어떤 도움이 필요한지를 밝힌다. 'Can I ask you a favor?'나 'Can you give me a hand?' 등의 표현도 쓸 수 있다.

❷ 상대방의 계획에 대하여 물을 때는 'What are you going to do ∼?'로 물을 수 있다. (= What will you do ∼? = What are you planning to do ∼?)

❸ 'What are you going to+동사원형 ∼?'에 대답할 때는 'I'm going to+동사원형'으로 말할 수 있다. 내용상 주어가 바뀔 경우 그에 따라 'be동사'를 바꾸어 써야 한다. be going to 동사원형: ∼할 것이다

❹ donate: 기부하다

Listen & Talk 1 C

B1: Wow! These dogs are so dirty. Jay, can you ❶help me wash them?

B2: Allen, ❷I'm sorry, but I can't. ❸I have to feed the cats now. ❹Why don't you ask Nicky?

B1: Okay! Nicky, ❺can I ask you a favor?

G: Sure, Allen. What is it?

B1: Can you help me wash these dogs?

G: Sure. But I have to ❻walk these dogs first. After that, I will help you.

B1: All right! Thank you.

❶ help는 불완전 타동사로 '∼이 …하는 것을 돕다'의 의미로 사용되었다. 목적격 보어로 to부정사와 동사원형을 쓰는 준사역동사이다. 그러므로 목적격 보어 자리의 wash 대신에 to wash도 가능하다.

❷ 상대방의 요청을 거절할 때 쓰는 표현이다. (=I'm afraid I can't.)

❸ have to 동사원형: ∼해야 한다 feed: 먹이를 주다

❹ 상대방에게 함께 ∼하자고 제안이나 권유할 때에는 'Why don't we+동사원형 ∼?'을 사용할 수 있다. 'Why don't you+동사원형 ∼?'은 함께 하자는 것이 아니고 상대방에게만 권유하는 것이다.

❺ 상대방에게 도움을 요청할 때 'Can you do me a favor?'(나 좀 도와줄 수 있니?)라고 말할 수 있다. 상대방이 도움을 주겠다고 하면 'Can you (please) help me ∼?' 등의 표현을 통하여 구체적인 내용을 말할 수도 있다.

❻ walk: 산책시키다, (사람·동물을) 걷게 하다

Listen & Talk 2 B

G: Good morning, students! ❶As you know, there was a big fire in Mapletown. ❷Why don't we raise money and help the people there? Come to our special event ❸at the school grounds on May 3! Please ❹bring your items and donate them. We will sell your items. Then, we will ❺give all the money to Mapletown. Please ❻give a hand to people in need.

❶ as: (접) ∼과 같이, ∼하는 대로 as you know: 아시다시피 fire: 화재

❷ Why don't we ∼?: ∼하는 게 어떨까? raise money: 돈을 모금하다 raise와 helps는 접속사 and로 연결되어 있다.

❸ at+장소: ∼에, on+날짜: ∼에

❹ bring과 donate는 접속사 and로 연결되어 있는 명령문이므로, 동사원형이 되어야 한다. them = the people in Mapletown

❺ give+간접목적어(∼에게)+직접목적어(∼을, ∼를) = give+직접목적어+to+간접목적어

❻ give a hand: ∼을 돕다 in need: 어려움에 처한

Listen & Talk 2 C

B1: Next Wednesday is Volunteer Day. We ❶cleaned up the park last time. ❷What are we going to do this time?

G: ❸Why don't we visit a nursing home and clean it up?

B2: That's not a bad idea. But I want to do something fun. Why don't we ❹hold a party for the people there?

G: That's a good idea. What can we do at the party?

B1: We can ❺serve some food.

B2: And ❻how about playing some music? I can play the piano.

G: And I can play the cello.

B1: It sounds like a good plan.

❶ clean up: ∼을 치우다, 청소하다

❷ What are we going to do this time?: 이번엔 뭘 할까?

❸ Why don't we ∼?: ∼하는 게 어떨까? nursing home: 양로원 clean up은 구동사이다. 구동사는 동사+부사(up, on, off, over 등)로 이루어져 있다. '동사+부사+목적어'의 어순이나 '동사+목적어+부사'의 어순 둘 다 가능하다. 하지만 목적어 자리에 인칭대명사(it, them)가 올 때는 반드시 '동사+목적어+부사'의 어순으로 쓴다.

❹ hold a party: 파티를 열다

❺ serve: (음식을) 제공하다

❻ 'How about (동)명사 ∼?'는 특정 행동을 제안할 때 사용할 수 있는 표현으로, '∼하는 게 어때?'의 의미이다.

● 다음 우리말과 일치하도록 빈칸에 알맞은 말을 쓰시오.

Listen & Talk 1 A

B: Mia, _____ you _____ _____ move these books?

G: Sure. _____ _____ you _____ to do with them?

B: I'm _____ _____ _____ them to a children's library.

해석

B: Mia, 이 책들 옮기는 거 도와줄 수 있어?
G: 그럼. 너 이 책으로 뭐 할 거야?
B: 나는 이 책을 어린이 도서관에 기부할 거야.

Listen & Talk 1 B

B: Hey, Minji! What's wrong _____ your leg?

G: I _____ _____ last week.

B: Really? What happened?

G: I was in _____ _____ to catch a train. But I _____ _____ in the street.

B: Oh, that's terrible! _____ _____ anything I _____ _____ for you?

G: Well, _____ _____ _____ me carry this bag?

B: Sure.

B: 민지야! 너 다리에 무슨 문제가 있니?
G: 지난주에 부러졌어.
B: 그래? 무슨 일이야?
G: 기차를 타려고 서두르고 있었어. 그런데 길에 넘어졌어.
B: 오, 정말 끔찍하다! 내가 너를 위해 해 줄 게 있니?
G: 음, 이 가방을 드는 걸 도와줄 수 있니?
B: 그럼.

Listen & Talk 1 C

B1: Wow! These dogs are so dirty. Jay, _____ _____ _____ me _____ _____?

B2: Allen, I'm sorry, _____ I can't. I have _____ _____ the cats now. Why _____ _____ ask Nicky?

B1: Okay! Nicky, can I _____ _____ _____ _____?

G: Sure, Allen. What is it?

B1: _____ _____ _____ me wash these dogs?

G: Sure. But I _____ _____ walk these dogs first. After that, I will help you.

B1: All right! Thank you.

B1: 와! 이 개들 정말 더럽다. Jay, 이 개들 씻기는 거 도와줄 수 있니?
B2: Allen, 미안한데 못할 거 같아. 지금 이 고양이들에게 밥 줘야 해. Nicky 한테 물어보는 게 어때?
B1: 알겠어! Nicky, 나 좀 도와줄 수 있니?
G: 물론이지, Allen. 뭔데?
B1: 이 개들 씻기는 거 도와줄 수 있니?
G: 그럼. 근데 나 이 개들 산책 먼저 시켜야 해. 끝나고 나서 도와줄게.
B1: 그래! 고마워.

Listen & Talk 2 A

G: What _____ _____ _____ activities can we do?

B: Why _____ _____ _____ _____ our town's streets?

G: All right! Let's do it.

G: 우리 어떤 종류의 봉사 활동을 할 수 있을까?
B: 우리 동네 길거리를 청소하는 게 어때?
G: 좋아! 그러자.

Listen & Talk 2 B

G: Good morning, students! _____ you know, there _____ a big fire in Mapletown. Why _____ _____ _____ money and help the people there? Come to our special event _____ the school grounds _____ May 3! Please _____ your items and _____ them. We will sell your items. Then, we will give all the money to Mapletown. Please _____ _____ _____ to people in _____.

해석

G: 좋은 아침입니다, 학생 여러분! 아시다시피, Mapletown에 큰 화재가 있었습니다. 우리 돈을 모금해서 그 곳 사람들을 도와주는 게 어떨까요? 5월 3일 학교 운동장에서 열리는 특별 행사에 오세요! 물품들을 가져와서 그것들을 기부해 주세요. 우리는 여러분의 물품들을 팔 것입니다. 그리고, 모든 돈을 Mapletown에 기부할 것입니다. 어려운 사람들에게 도움을 줍시다.

Listen & Talk 2 C

B1: Next Wednesday is Volunteer Day. We _____ _____ the park last time. What are _____ _____ _____ do this time?

G: Why _____ _____ _____ a nursing home and clean _____ _____?

B2: That's not a bad idea. But I want _____ _____ something fun. Why don't we _____ a party for the people there?

G: That's a good idea. _____ can we do at the party?

B1: We can _____ some food.

B2: And how _____ _____ some music? I can play the piano.

G: And I can play the cello.

B1: It sounds _____ a good plan.

B1: 다음 주 수요일이 봉사 활동 날이네. 우리 저번에는 공원을 청소했지. 이번엔 뭘 할까?
G: 양로원 가서 청소하는 건 어때?
B2: 나쁜 생각은 아니야. 근데 좀 재미있는 걸 하고 싶어. 거기 계신 분들을 위해 파티를 여는 게 어떨까?
G: 좋은 생각이야. 우리가 파티에서 뭘 할 수 있지?
B1: 음식을 대접할 수 있지.
B2: 그리고 연주를 하는 게 어때? 나 피아노 칠 수 있어.
G: 나는 첼로를 켤 수 있어.
B1: 아주 좋은 계획 같아.

Do It Yourself A

G1: We have a class activity day next Friday. What do you want _____ _____ on that day?

B: Why _____ we do some _____ _____? We can help others and _____ our community better.

G1: That sounds great, but choosing a good place _____ not easy.

B: We need someone _____ _____ _____ a lot.

G1: I know Sumin _____ _____ a lot. Sumin, can you _____ _____ _____ some good places?

G2: Sure. I usually _____ _____ information on the internet. Why _____ _____ _____ the volunteering website for teens?

B: That's a good idea.

G1: 우리 다음 주 금요일에 학급 활동이 있어. 그 날 어떤 것을 하고 싶니?
B: 우리 자원 봉사 활동들을 해 보는 게 어때? 우리가 다른 사람들을 도울 수 있고, 우리의 지역 사회를 더 좋게 만들 수 있어.
G1: 그거 좋다, 하지만 좋은 장소를 고르는 건 쉽지 않아.
B: 우리는 봉사 활동을 많이 해본 사람이 필요해.
G1: 나는 수민이가 봉사 활동을 많이 한 것을 알고 있어. 수민아, 우리가 좋은 장소들을 찾는 것을 도와주겠니?
G2: 물론. 나는 주로 인터넷에서 정보를 찾아. 십대들을 위한 자원 봉사 웹사이트를 확인해 보는 게 어떠니?
B: 좋은 생각이다.

[01~02] 다음 중 의미하는 바가 <u>다른</u> 하나를 고르시오.

01
① Why don't we go on a bike ride?
② Why don't you go on a bike ride?
③ How about going on a bike ride?
④ Let's go on a bike ride.
⑤ What about going on a bike ride?

02
① Can you help me?
② Can you do me a favor?
③ Can you please help me?
④ Can I ask you a favor?
⑤ Can I give you a hand?

03 다음 대화의 빈칸에 들어갈 말로 적절하지 <u>않은</u> 것은?

> B: Mia, _____ you help me move these books?
> G: Sure. What are you going to do with them?
> B: I'm going to donate them to a children's library.

① can   ② will   ③ should   ④ could   ⑤ would

04 다음 대화의 빈칸에 적절한 것을 고르시오.

> G: What kinds of volunteer activities can we do?
> B: _____
> G: All right! Let's do it.

① Why don't we do volunteer work?
② Why don't we clean up our town's streets?
③ How about going to the movies?
④ Can you help me move these books?
⑤ Is there anything I can do for you?

[01~02] 다음 대화를 읽고 물음에 답하시오.

B: Mia, can you help me (A)_____ these books?

G: Sure. What are you going (B)_____ with (C)_____?

B: I'm going to donate them to a children's library.

01 빈칸 (A)에 들어갈 말로 적절한 것을 <u>모두</u> 고르시오.

① move
② moving
③ to move
④ moved
⑤ having moved

02 빈칸 (B)와 (C)에 들어갈 말로 알맞게 짝지어진 것은?

	(B)	(C)
①	do	it
②	to do	it
③	to do	them
④	doing	it
⑤	doing	them

[03~04] 다음 대화를 읽고 물음에 답하시오.

B: Hey, Minji! What's wrong with your leg?

G: I broke it last week. (①)

B: Really? What happened? (②)

G: I was in a hurry to catch a train. (③)

B: Oh, that's terrible! (④) Is there anything I can do for you?

G: Well, can you help me carry this bag? (⑤)

B: Sure.

03 위 대화의 ①~⑤ 중 주어진 문장이 들어갈 알맞은 곳은?

But I fell down in the street.

①   ②   ③   ④   ⑤

04 위 대화를 읽고 답할 수 <u>없는</u> 질문은?

① How will the boy help the girl?
② When did the girl hurt?
③ Why was the girl in a hurry?
④ Where will they go?
⑤ What did the girl break?

05 다음 짝지어진 대화가 <u>어색한</u> 것은?

① A: Why don't we join the Mozart Club?
   B: That sounds fun. I love music.
② A: Can I give you a hand?
   B: Oh, I'm sorry but I can't.
③ A: Jane, your books look so heavy. Can I help you?
   B: Yes. Thank you.
④ A: Why don't we go to the movies today?
   B: That's a good idea.
⑤ A: Let's go to the movies after school.
   B: Why don't we watch TV at home?

서답형

06 밑줄 친 우리말과 일치하도록 영작하시오.

A: Excuse me. <u>기차표를 사는 거 도와줄 수 있니?</u> (8 단어)
B: Sure.

➡ _____

[07~10] 다음 담화문을 읽고 물음에 답하시오.

G: Good morning, students! (A)_____ you know, there was a big fire in Mapletown. Why don't we raise money and help the people there? Come to our special event at the school grounds on May 3! 물품들을 가져와서 그것들을 기부해 주세요. We will sell your items. Then, we will (B)_____ all the money to Mapletown. Please (C)_____ a hand to people in need.

07 빈칸 (A)에 알맞은 말을 고르시오.

① When ② Although ③ As
④ Since ⑤ For

서답형
08 빈칸 (B)와 (C)에 공통으로 들어갈 말을 쓰시오.

➡ _____

서답형
09 밑줄 친 우리말에 맞게 주어진 단어를 이용해 빈칸을 채우시오.

➡ Please _____.
(your items)

10 위 글을 읽고 알 수 없는 것을 고르시오.

① the purpose of the special event
② where the special event will be held
③ when the special event will be held
④ what items can't be donated
⑤ where the raised money at the special event will be given

[11~13] 다음 대화를 읽고 물음에 답하시오.

B1: Next Wednesday is Volunteer Day. We cleaned up the park last time. What are we going to do this time?

G: Why don't we visit a nursing home and clean it up?

B2: That's not a bad idea. But I want to do something fun. (A)_____

G: That's a good idea. What can we do at the party?

B1: We can serve some food.

B2: 그리고 연주를 하는 게 어때? I can play the piano.

G: And I can play the cello.

B1: It sounds like a good plan.

11 빈칸 (A)에 알맞은 말을 고르시오.

① Why don't we volunteer work at the animal care center?
② Why don't we play the piano?
③ Why don't we clean up the nursing home?
④ Why don't we hold a party for the people there?
⑤ Why don't we play tennis there?

서답형
12 밑줄 친 우리말을 주어진 단어를 이용해 영작하시오.

➡ _____
(music, how, some)

중요
13 위의 대화를 읽고 답할 수 없는 질문은?

① What musical instrument can the girl play?
② What food will they serve to people at a nursing home?
③ When is Volunteer Day?
④ Where are they going to go to do volunteer work?
⑤ What are they going to do at a nursing home?

[01~02] 주어진 문장 뒤에 이어질 대화의 순서를 바르게 배열하시오.

Hey, Minji! What's wrong with your leg?

(A) I was in a hurry to catch a train. But I fell down in the street.
(B) Really? What happened?
(C) Oh, that's terrible!
(D) I broke it last week.

➡ _____

02

Next Wednesday is Volunteer Day. We cleaned up the park last time. What are we going to do this time?

(A) Why don't we visit a nursing home and clean it up?
(B) That's a good idea. What can we do at the party?
(C) That's not a bad idea. But I want to do something fun. Why don't we hold a party for the people there?
(D) We can serve some food.

➡ _____

[03~04] 다음 대화를 읽고 물음에 답하시오.

G1: We have a class activity day next Friday. What do you want to do on that day?
B: Why don't we ①do some volunteer activities? We can help others and ②make our community better.

G1: That sounds great, but ③choosing a good place is not easy.
B: We need someone ④which has volunteered a lot.
G1: I know Sumin ⑤has volunteered a lot. Sumin, 우리가 좋은 장소들을 찾는 것을 도와 주겠니? (help, some, can, places, you, us, good, find, ?)
G2: Sure. I usually search for information on the internet. Why don't we check the volunteering website for teens?
B: That's a good idea.

03 위 대화의 ①~⑤ 중 어색한 것을 골라 고치시오.

➡ _____

_____

04 밑줄 친 우리말에 맞게 괄호 안에 주어진 단어를 알맞게 배열하시오

➡ _____

[05~06] 다음 대화를 읽고 물음에 답하시오.

A: Why don't we (A)_____ volunteer work at the animal care center?
B: Sounds good. What can we do there?
A: We can take care (B)_____ the dogs and cats.

05 빈칸 (A)에 알맞은 말을 쓰시오.

➡ _____

06 빈칸 (B)에 알맞은 전치사를 쓰시오.

➡ _____

교과서
Grammar

> The little black dress **which** she wore in a movie is famous even today. 그녀가 영화에서 입었던 아담한 검은 드레스는 오늘날까지도 유명하다.

■ 관계대명사가 관계대명사절 내에서 목적어의 역할을 할 때 이것을 목적격 관계대명사라고 한다.

■ 목적격 관계대명사는 선행사가 사람이면 who나 whom, that을, 사물이나 동물은 which나 that을 쓴다. 일반적으로 목적격 관계대명사는 생략할 수 있다.

선행사	사람	사물, 동물	사람, 사물, 동물
목적격 관계대명사	who/whom	which	that

- He was the man (**who/whom/that**) I saw on TV. (그는 내가 TV에서 본 남자였다.)
- He showed me the photos (**which/that**) he had taken. (그는 그가 찍은 사진들을 내게 보여주었다.)

■ 목적격 관계대명사절에서는 앞에 있는 관계대명사가 동사의 목적어 역할을 하기 때문에 동사 뒤에 목적어가 없다는 것에 특히 주의해야 한다.
- These are the boys. I like them(=the boys) most in my class.
  = These are the boys (**who/whom/that**) I like most in my class.
- This is the book. I have to read it(=the book).
  = This is the book (**which/that**) I have to read.

■ 목적격 관계대명사가 전치사의 목적어인 경우 전치사는 관계대명사절의 끝에 오거나 관계대명사 앞에 올 수 있다. 전치사가 관계대명사절의 끝에 올 경우에는 관계대명사를 생략할 수 있지만 전치사가 관계대명사 앞에 올 경우에는 관계대명사를 생략하지 않으며 관계대명사 that을 쓸 수 없다.
- I need a chair (**which/that**) I can sit **on**. (나는 내가 앉을 수 있는 의자가 필요하다.)
  = I need a chair **on which** I can sit.
  = I need a chair on that I can sit. (✗)

핵심 Check

1. 다음 괄호 안에서 알맞은 말을 고르시오.
    (1) David is the boy with (whom / that) I often play soccer.
    (2) Tom is reading the book (whom / which) I gave to him.

2 감정을 나타내는 과거분사

> • She was **shocked** because their lives were very difficult. 그녀는 그들의 삶이 매우 어려웠기 때문에 충격을 받았다.

■ 현재분사는 '능동'의 의미를 갖고, 과거분사는 '수동'의 의미를 갖는다.
   • Math is the most **interesting** subject to me. (능동: 수학이 흥미를 불러일으키는 과목이다.) (수학은 내게 가장 흥미로운 과목이다.)
   • I'm **interested** in math. (수동: 내가 흥미를 느끼게 되는 것이다.) (나는 수학에 흥미가 있다.)

■ 감정을 나타내는 타동사의 과거분사는 '~한 감정을 느끼는'이라는 의미로, 주로 사람을 주어로 하여 형용사로 쓰일 때가 많다.
   • I was very **disappointed** at my friends. (나는 내 친구들에게 무척 실망했다.)

■ 주로 사물을 주어로 하여 '~한 감정을 유발하는'의 의미를 나타내는 현재분사와 혼동하지 않도록 유의한다.
   • It can be very **disappointing** to lose important matches. (중요한 경기에서 패하는 것은 매우 실망스러울 수 있다.)

■ 주어가 사람일 때도 현재분사를 쓸 수 있으므로, 의미에 따라 구분하여 쓴다.
   • She was certainly not **boring**. (그녀는 분명히 따분하지 않다.)
   • She was **bored** with hearing about the work. (그녀는 그 일에 관련된 이야기를 듣는 것이 따분했다.)

핵심 Check

2. 다음 괄호 안에서 알맞은 말을 고르시오.

   (1) Look at the (sleeping / slept) dog.

   (2) It was an (exciting / excited) game.

   (3) He showed me a book (writing / written) in English.

   (4) I'm (exciting / excited) to get married.

01 다음 빈칸에 들어갈 말로 알맞지 <u>않은</u> 것을 <u>모두</u> 고르시오.

> The only food _____ they could find was grass.

① who   ② whose   ③ whom
④ that   ⑤ which

02 다음 우리말을 영어로 옮길 때, 빈칸에 알맞은 말이 순서대로 짝지어진 것은?

> • 그 게임은 재미있어 보였지만 나는 곧 내가 그 게임에 흥미가 없다는 것을 알아차렸다.
> → The game looked _____ but soon I noticed that I was not _____ in the game.

① interested – interesting
② interested – interested
③ interesting – interesting
④ interesting – interested
⑤ interest – interest

03 다음 문장에서 어법상 어색한 부분을 바르게 고쳐 쓰시오.

(1) He likes the dog who he adopted last month.

_____ ➡ _____

(2) Anna is the woman which I like most.

_____ ➡ _____

(3) I'm exciting at the thought of going skiing tomorrow.

_____ ➡ _____

adopt: 입양하다
at the thought of: ~을 생각하면, ~ 생각에

04 다음 우리말에 맞게 괄호 안에 주어진 단어를 빈칸에 바르게 배열하시오. (필요하면 어형을 바꿀 것)

> 우리 엄마가 만든 치킨 샐러드는 정말 맛있다. (my mom, is, made, delicious, the chicken salad, very, which)

➡ _____

01 다음 〈보기〉의 밑줄 친 부분과 용법이 다른 것은?

> ┤ 보기 ├
> Lee Jieun is a singer that my partner likes.

① Breakfast is the meal that people eat in the morning.
② People that respect her will come to help her.
③ I want to have a date with a girl who I love.
④ Kate will read the book which her friend wrote.
⑤ This is the TV program that I really wanted to watch.

02 다음 빈칸에 들어갈 수 있는 말이 다른 하나는?

① *The Old Man and the Sea* is the book _____ I have read several times.
② This is the wallet _____ you were looking for.
③ Select the album _____ cover you'd like to change.
④ Billy is my roommate _____ I have lived with for five years.
⑤ This is the cat _____ I like.

03 다음 빈칸에 알맞은 것은?

> She was really _____ at the news.

① surprise
② surprises
③ surprised
④ surprising
⑤ to surprise

04 서답형 주어진 어휘를 이용하여 다음 우리말을 영어로 쓰시오.

> Alex가 나에게 보낸 박스에 드레스가 있다.
> (there, a dress, sent)

➡ _____

_____

05 서답형 다음 괄호 안에서 알맞은 말을 고르시오.

(1) *Tom and Jerry* is a cartoon (who / that) I often watch.
(2) Mike needs someone (who / which) he can trust.
(3) Jane is the girl with (that / whom) I had dinner at the restaurant.
(4) I am not (interested / interesting) in that sort of thing.
(5) The children found the game (interesting / interested).

06 다음 중 어법상 바르지 않은 것은?

① Well, I'm excited.
② The movie was exciting.
③ Mr. Sing said he was pleased with the outcome.
④ The children were frightening at the way their mom yelled.
⑤ I feel scared when I walk home alone.

07 다음 중 어법상 옳은 문장을 고르시오.

① This is the picture I took yesterday with my new camera.
② Seoul Grand Park is a park who my uncle often visits.
③ The book I read it yesterday was very interesting.
④ The student which I am very close with is Steve.
⑤ It is the building at that he has worked for over 5 years.

08 다음 밑줄 친 that의 성격이 나머지 넷과 다른 것은?

① Jiho is eating the fried rice that his sister made.
② The important thing is that we stay on schedule.
③ Ethan never eats food that is sold at a fast food store.
④ Audrey is the only woman that I love.
⑤ The movie that I watched last Sunday was *Alita*.

09 다음 〈보기〉에 주어진 단어를 변형하여 문맥에 맞게 빈칸에 쓰시오. (한 번씩만 쓸 것)

┌─ 보기 ┐
embarrass   scare   shock
└─────────┘

(1) Do not be _____ of bees.
(2) He put me in a very _____ situation.
(3) The members of his team were _____ at the results.

10 다음 두 문장을 한 문장으로 바르게 바꾸지 않은 것을 모두 고르시오.

• *Donald Duck* is a cartoon.
• My partner often watches *Donald Duck*.

① *Donald Duck* is a cartoon which my partner often watches.
② *Donald Duck* is a cartoon that my partner often watches.
③ *Donald Duck* is a cartoon who my partner often watches.
④ *Donald Duck* is a cartoon my partner often watches.
⑤ *Donald Duck* is a cartoon which my partner often watches it.

11 다음 문장에서 생략할 수 있는 것을 찾아 쓰시오.

(1) I met the woman who you ate dinner with last Sunday.
(2) I received an email that my friend in Chicago had sent to me.
(3) Seoul is a city which is full of energy.

➡ (1) _____ (2) _____ (3) _____

12 다음 중 밑줄 친 부분의 쓰임이 잘못된 것은?

① Rina looked bored in the science class.
② Who was the girl that you met in front of the library?
③ The dog which I raise has a long tail.
④ Everyone feels depressing at some time or another.
⑤ Don't be disappointed about such a thing.

서답형

13 다음 두 문장을 관계대명사를 사용하여 한 문장으로 바꾸시오.

(1) • Audrey Hepburn is a person.

　• My partner respects her a lot.

➡ _____

_____

(2) • This is the ID.

　• The spy used the ID before.

➡ _____

(3) • The letter made me happy.

　• You sent the letter to me last week.

➡ _____

_____

(4) • Do you remember the girl?

　• I met her at the party.

➡ _____

_____

(5) • I like the music.

　• I often listen to the music.

➡ _____

_____

(6) • Do you know the girl?

　• Anne is talking to the girl.

➡ _____

_____

중요

14 다음 빈칸에 들어갈 말로 알맞은 것은?

> I don't like English. It is difficult and _____ .

① exciting　　　② excited

③ boring　　　④ bored

⑤ annoyed

15 다음 밑줄 친 부분의 쓰임이 어색한 것은?

① The chicken salad which Lee Yeonbok made is very delicious.

② Winter is the season that comes after autumn.

③ Here are some of the people whom I helped.

④ That man over there is the dentist about that I told you.

⑤ I want to call the boy who I met at the party.

서답형

16 우리말에 맞게 괄호 안의 어휘를 바르게 배열하시오.

(1) 그녀는 그들의 삶이 매우 어려웠기 때문에 충격을 받았다. (she, lives, because, was, were, difficult, shocked, their, very)

➡ _____

(2) 나는 사파리에서 보았던 호랑이를 잊을 수 없다. (I, I, the tiger, safari, saw, which, forget, can't, on)

➡ _____

(3) 여행 가이드로서의 직업에 만족하십니까?
(you, your, are, satisfied, job, tour guide, as, a, with)

➡ _____

서답형

17 다음 빈칸에 amaze의 알맞은 형태를 쓰시오.

(1) People were _____ at the fire.

(2) It is _____ how the sea water looks different each season.

01 다음 그림을 보고 괄호 안에 주어진 어휘를 이용하여 문장을 완성하시오.

(play / excite)

_____ a basketball game makes me
_____.

02 괄호 안에 주어진 말을 바르게 배열하여 문장을 완성하시오.
(단어 하나를 문맥에 맞게 변형할 것.)

(1) (I, you, Latin dance, know, were, didn't, interest, in)

➡ _____

(2) (Emma, test score, her, disappoint, was, at)

➡ _____

(3) (I, highway signs, confuse, think, are, these, very)

➡ _____

(4) (I, a thing, one, no, that, knows, worry, such, am, about)

➡ _____

(5) (he, I, for me, was, was, not, not, bore, bore, so) (For me로 시작할 것)

➡ _____

03 다음 문장에서 어법상 **틀린** 부분을 찾아 바르게 고쳐 쓰시오.

This is the house in that he was born.

_____ ➡ _____

04 다음 두 문장을 관계대명사를 이용하여 한 문장으로 연결하여 쓰시오.

(1) • Jayu Park is a park.
   • My grandfather often visits the park.

➡ _____
_____

(2) • *Tom and Jerry* is a cartoon.
   • My little sister often watches *Tom and Jerry*.

➡ _____
_____

(3) • That is the girl.
   • I saw the girl this morning.

➡ _____

(4) • The girl did not participate in the meeting.
   • I wanted to meet the girl.

➡ _____
_____

(5) • The woman is Ms. Larson.
   • Mom is talking to Ms. Larson.

➡ _____
_____

(6) • Mariel took pictures of Ben and his car.
   • Ben and his car were on the crime scene.

➡ _____
_____

05 잘못된 부분을 바르게 고쳐 문장을 다시 쓰시오.

(1) King Sejong is a person which my brother respects a lot.

➡ _____

_____

(2) This is the bridge who they built about 20 years ago.

➡ _____

_____

(3) The girl talked to a boy whom she met him at the party.

➡ _____

(4) I don't like the movie which I saw it yesterday.

➡ _____

(5) There are many subjects about that people feel little interest.

➡ _____

_____

_____

06 괄호 안에 주어진 어휘를 이용하여 우리말에 맞게 영작하시오.

(1) 나는 어젯밤 잠을 잘 자지 못했기 때문에 하루 종일 매우 피곤했다. (tire, all day, feel, well, because) (I로 시작할 것)

➡ _____

_____

(2) 나는 집에 홀로 남겨지는 것이 두려웠다. (home, to be, at, scare, leave, alone)

➡ _____

(3) 야구 경기를 보는 것은 나를 지루하게 한다. (watch, a baseball game, make, bore)

➡ _____

07 두 문장을 관계대명사를 사용하여 한 문장으로 썼을 때, 빈칸에 해당하는 문장을 쓰시오.

(1) • _____
• My partner often watches *The Smurfs*.
→ *The Smurfs* is a cartoon that my partner often watches.

(2) • _____
• I traveled with my friend.
→ Let me introduce my friend with whom I traveled.

(3) • The key was under the sofa.
• _____
→ The key that Laura was looking for all day long was under the sofa.

(4) • There is a certain reason.
• _____
→ There is a certain reason for which I cannot speak about it.

08 다음 문장을 어법에 맞게 고쳐 쓰시오.

(1) He put me in a very embarrassed situation.

➡ _____

(2) My mom was surprising at the news.

➡ _____

(3) It was shocked that he lied to me.

➡ _____

(4) We were all exciting because my brother made a goal in the soccer game.

➡ _____

_____

Reading

The Spirit of Audrey

<u>During</u> World War II, a little girl and her mother were hungry and
during+특정 기간을 나타내는 명사

sick. The only food <u>that</u> they could find was grass. The little girl felt
선행사 The only food를 수식하는 목적격 관계대명사

<u>scared</u> all the time. Luckily, the girl survived, <u>thanks to</u> the help of
주어인 The little girl의 감정을 나타내는 형용사 ~ 덕택에

others. One of the groups <u>that</u> helped her was UNICEF.
선행사 the groups를 수식하는 주격 관계대명사

<u>Later</u>, the girl became a worldwide movie star. Her name was Audrey
후에

Hepburn.

spirit 마음, 정신
grass 풀, 잔디
all the time 늘, 내내
luckily 운이 좋게도, 다행스럽게도
survive 살아남다, 생존하다
thanks to ~ 덕택에, ~ 때문에
worldwide 세계적인

 확인문제

● 다음 문장이 본문의 내용과 일치하면 T, 일치하지 않으면 F를 쓰시오.

1 During World War II, Hepburn and her mother were hungry and sick. ☐

2 Hepburn survived World War II for herself. ☐

3 One of the groups that helped Hepburn was UNESCO. ☐

4 Hepburn became a worldwide movie star. ☐

<u>When</u> she grew up, Hepburn became a symbol of beauty. She was
접속사(~할 때)

very popular <u>because of</u> her hit movies, <u>such as</u> *My Fair Lady* and
~ 때문에 ~ 와 같은

Roman Holiday. The little black dress <u>which</u> she wore in a movie <u>is</u>
선행사 The little black dress를 수식하는 목적격 관계대명사 주어 The little black dress를 서술하는 동사

famous even today. Many people still love her style.

The autumn of 1987 was <u>a turning point</u> in Hepburn's life. She went
전환점

to <u>an international music festival</u> in Macau. Many people donated
국제 음악 축제

money at <u>the festival</u>, and the money went to UNICEF.
an international music festival

<u>Thanks to</u> her fame, UNICEF collected <u>more</u> money <u>than</u> ever before.
~ 덕택에 비교급 than: ~보다 더

Hepburn realized <u>that</u> her fame could help others, so she became a
목적어에 해당하는 명사절을 이끄는 접속사

UNICEF Goodwill Ambassador.

beauty 아름다움, 미(美)
turning point 전환점
international 국제적인, 국제의
donate 기부하다
fame 명성
collect 모으다, 수집하다
realize 깨닫다
goodwill ambassador 친선 대사

확인문제

● 다음 문장이 본문의 내용과 일치하면 T, 일치하지 <u>않으면</u> F를 쓰시오.

1 When she was young, Hepburn was a symbol of peace. ☐

2 The little black dress which she wore in a movie is famous even today. ☐

3 In spite of her fame, UNICEF collected less money than ever before. ☐

4 Hepburn became a UNICEF Goodwill Ambassador. ☐

First, Hepburn went to Ethiopia in 1988. There, she brought food
to hungry children. She was shocked because their lives were very
difficult. After that, she volunteered in other countries. In 1990, she
visited Vietnam to hand out medicine and support clean drinking water
programs. Her last trip was to Somalia in 1992, and she passed away
the following year.

Many people praised her beauty and style, but Hepburn's real beauty
was her heart. To honor her, UNICEF made a statue, *The Spirit of
Audrey*. People who respect her keep her mission alive.
Her favorite saying shows her mission.

*As you get older, remember you have two hands. One is for helping
yourself, and the other is for helping others.*

hand out 나누어 주다
medicine 약
support 후원하다, 지원하다
pass away 죽다
following (그) 다음의
praise 칭찬하다
honor 예우하다, 존중하다
statue 상, 조각상
respect 존경하다
mission 임무, 사명
alive 살아 있는
saying 속담, 격언

 확인문제

● 다음 문장이 본문의 내용과 일치하면 T, 일치하지 <u>않으면</u> F를 쓰시오.

1 In Ethiopia Hepburn brought food to hungry children. ☐

2 Hepburn was pleased because the children's lives were very comfortable in Ethiopia. ☐

3 In 1990, Hepburn visited Somalia to hand out medicine. ☐

4 In Vietnam Hepburn supported clean drinking water programs. ☐

5 Hepburn passed away in 1993. ☐

6 Hepburn's real beauty was her style. ☐

• 우리말을 참고하여 빈칸에 알맞은 말을 쓰시오.

1 The _____ of Audrey

2 _____ World War II, a little girl and her mother _____ hungry and sick.

3 _____ _____ food _____ they could find _____ grass.

4 The little girl _____ _____ all the time.

5 _____, the girl survived, _____ _____ the help of others.

6 _____ _____ _____ _____ _____ _____ helped her _____ UNICEF.

7 Later, the girl became _____ _____ _____ _____.

8 _____ _____ was Audrey Hepburn.

9 When she grew up, Hepburn became _____ _____ _____ _____.

10 She was very popular _____ _____ her hit movies, _____ _____ *My Fair Lady* and *Roman Holiday*.

11 The little black dress _____ _____ _____ in a movie is famous even today.

12 Many people _____ _____ her style.

13 The autumn of 1987 was _____ _____ _____ in Hepburn's life.

14 She went to _____ _____ _____ _____ in Macau.

15 Many people _____ _____ at the festival, and the money went to UNICEF.

---

1 오드리의 정신

2 제2차 세계 대전 동안, 한 어린 소녀와 그녀의 어머니는 굶주리고 아팠다.

3 그들이 찾을 수 있었던 유일한 음식은 풀뿐이었다.

4 어린 소녀는 내내 겁에 질려 있었다.

5 다행히도, 소녀는 다른 사람들의 도움 덕분에 살아남았다.

6 그녀를 도왔던 단체 중 하나는 유니세프(국제 연합 아동 기금)였다.

7 후에, 소녀는 세계적인 영화배우가 되었다.

8 그녀의 이름은 오드리 헵번이었다.

9 그녀가 자랐을 때, 헵번은 아름다움의 상징이 되었다.

10 그녀는 〈마이 페어 레이디〉와 〈로마의 휴일〉과 같은 흥행 영화들로 인해 매우 인기가 있었다.

11 그녀가 영화에서 입었던 아담한 검은 드레스는 심지어 오늘날까지도 유명하다.

12 많은 사람이 여전히 그녀의 스타일을 사랑한다.

13 1987년 가을은 헵번의 인생 전환점이었다.

14 그녀는 마카오의 한 국제 음악 축제에 갔다.

15 많은 사람이 축제에서 돈을 기부했고, 그 돈은 유니세프로 보내졌다.

16 _____ _____ her fame, UNICEF collected _____ money _____ ever before.

17 Hepburn _____ _____ her fame could help others, so she became _____ _____ _____ _____.

18 First, Hepburn _____ _____ Ethiopia in 1988.

19 There, she _____ food _____ hungry children.

20 She was _____ because their _____ were very difficult.

21 After that, she _____ in other countries.

22 In 1990, she visited Vietnam _____ _____ _____ medicine and _____ clean drinking water programs.

23 Her last trip was _____ Somalia in 1992, and she _____ _____ the _____ year.

24 Many people _____ her beauty and style, but Hepburn's _____ _____ was her heart.

25 _____ _____ her, UNICEF made a statue, *The Spirit of Audrey*.

26 People _____ respect her _____ her mission _____.

27 Her _____ _____ shows her mission.

28 _____ *you* _____ *older, remember you have two hands.*

29 _____ *is for helping* _____ *, and* _____ _____ *is for helping* _____.

16 그녀의 명성 덕분에, 유니세프는 어느 때보다도 더 많은 돈을 모았다.

17 헵번은 자신의 명성이 다른 사람들을 도울 수 있다는 것을 깨닫고, 유니세프 친선 대사가 되었다.

18 먼저, 헵번은 1988년에 에티오피아로 갔다.

19 그곳에서, 그녀는 굶주린 아이들에게 음식을 가져다주었다.

20 그녀는 그들의 삶이 매우 어려웠기 때문에 충격을 받았다.

21 그 후, 그녀는 다른 나라들에서도 봉사하였다.

22 1990년, 그녀는 의약품을 나눠 주고 깨끗한 식수 프로그램을 지원하기 위하여 베트남을 방문하였다.

23 그녀의 마지막 여행은 1992년 소말리아에 간 것이었으며, 이듬해 그녀는 사망하였다.

24 많은 사람이 그녀의 아름다움과 스타일을 칭송했지만, 헵번의 진정한 아름다움은 그녀의 마음이었다.

25 그녀를 기리기 위해, 유니세프는 '오드리의 정신'이라는 동상을 만들었다.

26 그녀를 존경하는 사람들이 그녀의 사명을 이어 나가고 있다.

27 그녀가 가장 좋아했던 구절은 그녀의 사명을 보여 준다.

28 나이가 들어갈수록, 당신에게 손이 두 개가 있다는 것을 기억하라.

29 한 손은 자신을 돕기 위한 것이고, 다른 한 손은 타인을 돕기 위한 것이다.

● 우리말을 참고하여 본문을 영작하시오.

1 오드리의 정신
➡ _____

2 제2차 세계 대전 동안, 한 어린 소녀와 그녀의 어머니는 굶주리고 아팠다.
➡ _____

3 그들이 찾을 수 있었던 유일한 음식은 풀뿐이었다.
➡ _____

4 어린 소녀는 내내 겁에 질려 있었다.
➡ _____

5 다행히도, 소녀는 다른 사람들의 도움 덕분에 살아남았다.
➡ _____

6 그녀를 도왔던 단체 중 하나는 유니세프(국제 연합 아동 기금)였다.
➡ _____

7 후에, 소녀는 세계적인 영화배우가 되었다.
➡ _____

8 그녀의 이름은 오드리 헵번이었다.
➡ _____

9 그녀가 자랐을 때, 헵번은 아름다움의 상징이 되었다.
➡ _____

10 그녀는 〈마이 페어 레이디〉와 〈로마의 휴일〉과 같은 흥행 영화들로 인해 매우 인기가 있었다.
➡ _____

11 그녀가 영화에서 입었던 아담한 검은 드레스는 심지어 오늘날까지도 유명하다.
➡ _____

12 많은 사람이 여전히 그녀의 스타일을 사랑한다.
➡ _____

13 1987년 가을은 헵번의 인생 전환점이었다.
➡ _____

14 그녀는 마카오의 한 국제 음악 축제에 갔다.
➡ _____

15 많은 사람이 축제에서 돈을 기부했고, 그 돈은 유니세프로 보내졌다.
➡ _____

16 그녀의 명성 덕분에, 유니세프는 어느 때보다도 더 많은 돈을 모았다.
➡ _____

17 헵번은 자신의 명성이 다른 사람들을 도울 수 있다는 것을 깨닫고, 유니세프 친선 대사가 되었다.

➡ _____

18 먼저, 헵번은 1988년에 에티오피아로 갔다.

➡ _____

19 그곳에서, 그녀는 굶주린 아이들에게 음식을 가져다주었다.

➡ _____

20 그녀는 그들의 삶이 매우 어려웠기 때문에 충격을 받았다.

➡ _____

21 그 후, 그녀는 다른 나라들에서도 봉사하였다.

➡ _____

22 1990년, 그녀는 의약품을 나눠 주고 깨끗한 식수 프로그램을 지원하기 위하여 베트남을 방문하였다.

➡ _____

23 그녀의 마지막 여행은 1992년 소말리아에 간 것이었으며, 이듬해 그녀는 사망하였다.

➡ _____

24 많은 사람이 그녀의 아름다움과 스타일을 칭송했지만, 헵번의 진정한 아름다움은 그녀의 마음이었다.

➡ _____

25 그녀를 기리기 위해, 유니세프는 '오드리의 정신'이라는 동상을 만들었다.

➡ _____

26 그녀를 존경하는 사람들이 그녀의 사명을 이어 나가고 있다.

➡ _____

27 그녀가 가장 좋아했던 구절은 그녀의 사명을 보여 준다.

➡ _____

28 나이가 들어갈수록, 당신에게 손이 두 개가 있다는 것을 기억하라.

➡ _____

29 한 손은 자신을 돕기 위한 것이고, 다른 한 손은 타인을 돕기 위한 것이다.

➡ _____

[01~04] 다음 글을 읽고 물음에 답하시오.

(A)[During / While] World War II, a little girl and her mother were hungry and sick. The only food that ⓐthey could find (B)[being / was] grass. The little girl felt scared all the time. Luckily, the girl survived, ⓑthanks to the help of others. One of the groups that helped her (C)[was / were] UNICEF. ⓒLate, the girl became a worldwide movie star. Her name was Audrey Hepburn.

서답형

01 위 글의 괄호 (A)~(C)에서 어법상 알맞은 낱말을 골라 쓰시오.

➡ (A)_____ (B)_____ (C)_____

서답형

02 위 글의 밑줄 친 ⓐthey가 가리키는 것을 본문에서 찾아 쓰시오.

➡ _____

03 위 글의 밑줄 친 ⓑthanks to와 뜻이 다른 말을 고르시오.

① due to　　　　② because of
③ instead of　　 ④ owing to
⑤ on account of

중요

04 위 글의 밑줄 친 ⓒ를 알맞은 어형으로 고치시오.

➡ _____

[05~08] 다음 글을 읽고 물음에 답하시오.

When she grew up, Hepburn became a symbol of beauty. She was very popular because of her hit movies, ⓐsuch as *My Fair Lady* and *Roman Holiday*. The little black dress which she wore in a movie is famous even today. Many people still love her style.

The autumn of 1987 was a turning point in Hepburn's life. She went to an international music festival in Macau. Many people donated money at the festival, and the money went to UNICEF. Thanks to her __ⓑ__, UNICEF collected more money than ever before. Hepburn realized ⓒthat her __ⓓ__ could help others, so she became a UNICEF Goodwill Ambassador.

서답형

05 위 글의 밑줄 친 ⓐsuch as와 바꿔 쓸 수 있는 단어를 쓰시오.

➡ _____

서답형

06 본문의 한 단어를 변형하여 위 글의 빈칸 ⓑ와 ⓓ에 공통으로 들어갈 알맞은 단어를 쓰시오.

➡ _____

07 위 글의 밑줄 친 ⓒthat과 문법적 쓰임이 같은 것을 모두 고르시오.

① Kate knows that you like Mike.
② She is the girl that he loves.
③ Give me the pen that is on the desk.
④ He is the man that I met yesterday.
⑤ The point is that he is still careless.

위 글의 Hepburn에 관한 내용으로 적절하지 <u>않은</u> 것은?

① 그녀는 자랐을 때, 아름다움의 상징이 되었다.
② 그녀가 영화에서 입었던 아담한 검은 드레스는 오늘날까지도 유명하다.
③ 1987년 가을에 그녀는 배우로서 쇠퇴기에 들어섰다.
④ 1987년 가을에 그녀는 마카오의 한 국제 음악 축제에 갔다.
⑤ 자신의 명성이 다른 사람들을 도울 수 있다는 것을 깨닫고, 그녀는 유니세프 친선 대사가 되었다.

[09~12] 다음 글을 읽고 물음에 답하시오.

First, Hepburn went to Ethiopia in 1988. (①) There, she brought food to hungry children. (②) She was shocked because their lives were very difficult. (③) In 1990, she visited Vietnam to hand out medicine and support clean drinking water programs. (④) Her last trip was to Somalia in 1992, and she passed away the following year. (⑤)

Many people praised her beauty and style, but Hepburn's real beauty was her heart. To honor her, UNICEF made a statue, *The Spirit of Audrey*. People who respect her keep her mission alive. Her favorite saying shows her mission.

As you get older, remember you have two hands. One is for @<u>helping yourself</u>, and the other is for helping others.

09 위 글의 흐름으로 보아, 주어진 문장이 들어가기에 가장 적절한 곳은?

After that, she volunteered in other countries.

①   ②   ③   ④   ⑤

10 아래 〈보기〉에서 위 글의 밑줄 친 @helping과 문법적 쓰임이 <u>다른</u> 것의 개수를 고르시오.

보기
① I remember <u>posting</u> his letter.
② Would you mind <u>calling</u> back later?
③ He was <u>watching</u> TV in the room.
④ Thank you for <u>visiting</u> my website.
⑤ She smelled something <u>burning</u>.

① 1개   ② 2개   ③ 3개   ④ 4개   ⑤ 5개

11 위 글의 종류로 알맞은 것을 고르시오.

① article   ② diary   ③ book report
④ essay   ⑤ biography

12 위 글의 내용과 일치하지 <u>않는</u> 것은?

① 헵번은 1988년에 에티오피아로 갔다.
② 헵번은 에티오피아에서 의약품을 나눠 주었다.
③ 1990년, 헵번은 베트남을 방문하였다.
④ 헵번의 마지막 여행은 1992년 소말리아에 간 것이었다.
⑤ 헵번은 1993년에 사망하였다.

[13~15] 다음 인터뷰를 읽고 물음에 답하시오.

Reporter: ⓐ was your life during World War II? Can you tell me about it?

Audrey: It was terrible. ⓑ<u>My family and I was hungry and sick.</u> We survived thanks to the help of others.

Reporter: ⓒ did you begin to work for UNICEF?

Audrey: In 1987, a musical festival in Macau changed my life. I learned that my fame could help other people.

Reporter: After that, what did you do?

Audrey: I visited some countries in Africa and Asia and volunteered there.

13 위 인터뷰의 빈칸 ⓐ와 ⓒ에 공통으로 들어갈 알맞은 말을 고르시오.

① How   ② What   ③ When

④ Why   ⑤ Where

서답형

14 위 인터뷰의 밑줄 친 ⓑ에서 어법상 틀린 부분을 찾아 고치시오.

➡ _____

서답형

15 다음 문장에서 위 인터뷰의 내용과 다른 부분을 찾아서 고치시오.

> Audrey visited some countries in Africa and Asia and volunteered there before 1987.

➡ _____

[16~19] 다음 글을 읽고 물음에 답하시오.

First, Hepburn went to Ethiopia in 1988. There, she brought food ⓐ hungry children. She was shocked because their lives were very difficult. After that, she volunteered in other countries. In 1990, she visited Vietnam ⓑto hand out medicine and support clean drinking water programs. Her last trip was ⓐ Somalia in 1992, and she passed away the following year.

Many people praised her beauty and style, but Hepburn's real beauty was her heart. To honor her, UNICEF made a statue, *The Spirit of Audrey*. People who respect her keep her mission alive. Her favorite saying shows her mission.

As you get older, remember you have two hands. One is ⓒ *helping yourself, and the other is* ⓒ *helping others.*

16 위 글의 빈칸 ⓐ와 ⓒ에 들어갈 전치사가 바르게 짝지어진 것은?

① for – by   ② to – by

③ to – for   ④ for – to

⑤ at – for

17 위 글의 밑줄 친 ⓑto hand와 to부정사의 용법이 다른 것을 고르시오. (2개)

① He grew up to be a scientist.

② Do you know how to make it?

③ She was happy to solve the problem.

④ It's time to go to bed.

⑤ They ran fast to win the race.

18 위 글의 내용으로 보아 알 수 없는 것은?

① 헵번은 여러 나라들에서 봉사하였다.

② 많은 사람이 헵번의 아름다움과 스타일을 칭송했다.

③ 헵번은 배우로서는 성공하지 못했다.

④ 헵번을 기리기 위해, 유니세프는 '오드리의 정신'이라는 동상을 만들었다.

⑤ 헵번을 존경하는 사람들이 그녀의 사명을 이어 나가고 있다.

19 위 글을 읽고 대답할 수 없는 질문은?

① When did Hepburn go to Ethiopia?

② In Ethiopia, what did Hepburn bring to hungry children?

③ Why did Hepburn visit Vietnam?

④ When was Hepburn's last trip?

⑤ Where did UNICEF make a statue, *The Spirit of Audrey*?

[20~22] 다음 글을 읽고 물음에 답하시오.

My little big hero is my mom. She was born in 1972. She lives in Seoul.

She smiles a lot and tries to see the good in everything.

My mom had a serious car accident. She was in the hospital for six months. But she was very strong and ⓐfinally got better.

She always helps people in need. She donates money and does volunteer work. She is my big hero!

20 위 글의 밑줄 친 ⓐfinally와 뜻이 다른 것을 모두 고르시오.

① at last
② actually
③ in the end
④ at least
⑤ in the long run

21 글쓴이의 엄마의 성격으로 알맞지 않은 것을 고르시오.

① strong-willed
② selfish
③ friendly
④ charitable
⑤ generous

22 위 글을 읽고 답할 수 없는 질문은?

① Who is the writer's hero?
② What is the writer's mom like?
③ When does the writer's mom feel happy?
④ What was one of the most important moments in the writer's mom's life?
⑤ Why does the writer think that his or her mom is a hero?

[23~25] 다음 글을 읽고 물음에 답하시오.

First, Hepburn went to Ethiopia in 1988. There, she brought food to hungry children.

She was shocked because their lives were very difficult. After that, she volunteered in other countries. In 1990, she visited Vietnam to hand out medicine and support clean ⓐ drinking water programs. Her last trip was to Somalia in 1992, and she passed away the following year.

Many people praised her beauty and style, but Hepburn's real beauty was her heart. To honor her, UNICEF made a statue, *The Spirit of Audrey*. People who respect her keep her mission alive. Her favorite saying shows her mission.

As you get older, remember you have two hands. One is for helping yourself, and the other is for helping others.

23 위 글의 제목으로 알맞은 것을 고르시오.

① Hepburn Visited Ethiopia!
② Hepburn's Real Beauty Was Her Heart!
③ Why Was Hepburn Shocked?
④ People Praised Hepburn's Beauty!
⑤ Hepburn's Favorite Saying

24 위 글의 밑줄 친 ⓐdrinking과 문법적 쓰임이 같은 것을 모두 고르시오.

① I know the girl drinking water there.
② Who was drinking water in the room?
③ I saw a man drinking water in a bus.
④ She enjoys drinking water in summer.
⑤ He is fond of drinking water when he's tired.

서답형
25 다음 질문에 대한 알맞은 대답을 영어로 쓰시오.

Q: What did UNICEF do to honor Hepburn?

➡ _____

[01~03] 다음 글을 읽고 물음에 답하시오.

During ⓐWorld War II, a little girl and her mother were hungry and sick. The only food ⓑ_____ they could find was grass. The little girl felt scared all the time. Luckily, the girl survived, thanks to the help of others. One of the groups that helped her was UNICEF. Later, the girl became a worldwide movie star. Her name was Audrey Hepburn.

01 위 글의 밑줄 친 ⓐWorld War II를 영어로 읽는 법을 쓰시오.

➡ _____

02 위 글의 빈칸 ⓑ에 들어갈 알맞은 말을 쓰시오.

➡ _____

03 다음 빈칸 (A)와 (B)에 알맞은 단어를 넣어 Audrey Hepburn에 대한 소개를 완성하시오.

Audrey Hepburn survived World War II thanks to (A)_____ _____ of others and later became a worldwide (B)_____ _____.

[04~07] 다음 글을 읽고 물음에 답하시오.

When she grew up, Hepburn became a symbol of beauty. She was very popular because of her hit movies, such as *My Fair Lady* and *Roman Holiday*. The little black dress which she wore in a movie is famous even today. Many people still love her style.

The autumn of 1987 was ⓐa turning point in Hepburn's life. She went to an international music festival in Macau. Many people ⓑ_____ money at the festival, and the money went to UNICEF. (A)[In spite of / Thanks to] her fame, UNICEF (B)[collected / corrected] more money (C)[than / then] ever before. ⓒHepburn realized that her fame could help others, so she became a UNICEF Goodwill Ambassador.

04 다음 빈칸 (A)와 (B)에 알맞은 단어를 넣어 ⓐa turning point에 대한 서술을 완성하시오.

Hepburn who was a very popular actress went to an international (A)_____ _____ in Macau in the autumn of 1987. Then she realized that her fame could help others, so she became a (B)_____ _____ _____.

05 주어진 영영풀이를 참고하여 빈칸 ⓑ에 철자 d로 시작하는 단어를 시제에 맞춰 쓰시오.

give to a charity or good cause

➡ _____

06 위 글의 괄호 (A)~(C)에서 문맥이나 어법상 알맞은 것을 골라 쓰시오.

➡ (A)_____ (B)_____ (C)_____

07 위 글의 밑줄 친 ⓒ를 다음과 같이 바꿔 쓸 때 빈칸에 들어갈 알맞은 말을 쓰시오.

➡ _____ Hepburn realized that her fame could help others, she became a UNICEF Goodwill Ambassador.

[08~10] 다음 글을 읽고 물음에 답하시오.

First, Hepburn went to Ethiopia in 1988. There, she brought food to hungry children. She was (A)[shocking / shocked] because their lives were very difficult. After that, she volunteered in other countries. In 1990, she visited Vietnam to hand out medicine and support clean drinking water programs. Her last trip was to Somalia in 1992, and she ⓐpassed away the following year.

Many people praised her beauty and style, but Hepburn's real beauty was her heart. To honor her, UNICEF made a statue, *The Spirit of Audrey.* People who respect her (B)[keep / keeps] her mission alive. Her favorite saying shows her mission.

As you ⓑget older, remember you have two hands. One is for helping yourself, and (C) [another / the other] is for helping others.

08 위 글의 괄호 (A)~(C)에서 어법상 알맞은 낱말을 골라 쓰시오.

➡ (A)_____ (B)_____ (C)_____

09 위 글의 내용과 일치하도록 다음 빈칸 (A)와 (B)에 알맞은 단어를 본문에서 찾아 쓰시오.

Judging from the fact that Hepburn visited many countries and (A)_____ there, Hepburn's real beauty was (B)_____ _____.

10 위 글의 밑줄 친 ⓐpassed away, ⓑget과 바꿔 쓸 수 있는 단어를 각각 쓰시오.

➡ ⓐ _____ ⓑ _____

[11~13] 다음 인터뷰를 읽고 물음에 답하시오.

Reporter: How was your life during World War II? Can you tell me about ⓐit?

Audrey: It was terrible. My family and I were hungry and sick. We survived thanks to the help of others.

Reporter: How did you begin to work for UNICEF?

Audrey: In 1987, a musical festival in Macau changed my life. I learned that my fame could help ⓑother people.

Reporter: After that, what did you do?

Audrey: I visited some countries in Africa and Asia and volunteered there.

11 위 인터뷰의 밑줄 친 ⓐit가 가리키는 것을 본문에서 찾아 쓰시오.
➡ _____

12 위 인터뷰의 밑줄 친 ⓑother people과 바꿔 쓸 수 있는 단어를 본문에서 찾아 쓰시오.

➡ _____

13 다음 빈칸 (A)와 (B)에 공통으로 들어갈 알맞은 단어를 넣어, Audrey가 UNICEF를 위해 일하게 된 이유를 그녀의 어린 시절과 연결하여 완성하시오.

During World War II, Audrey's family and Audrey were hungry and sick. They survived thanks to the (A)_____ of others.

In 1987, after a musical festival in Macau, Audrey learned that her fame could (B)_____ other people, so she began to work for UNICEF.

해석

Presentation Time

Lee Taeseok was a great person. He was a priest and also a doctor. He built
        성직자   build(짓다)의 과거형

hospitals and schools for the people of Tonj. He took care of them and taught
                                              돌보았다   수업을 했다

classes. From this person, I learned that I should help people in need.
        learned의 목적어로 that절이 사용되었다.   어려움에 처한

이태석은 위대한 사람이었다. 그는 성직자이고 또한 의사였다. 그는 톤즈의 사람들을 위해 병원과 학교를 세웠다. 그는 그들을 돌보고 수업을 했다. 이 사람으로부터, 나는 어려움에 처한 사람들을 도와야 한다고 배웠다.

After You Read B

Reporter: How was your life during World War II? Can you tell me about it?
                            during+특정 기간을 나타내는 명사   your life during World War II

Audrey: It was terrible. My family and I were hungry and sick.
        My life during World War II

        We survived thanks to the help of others.
                    ~ 덕택에, ~ 때문에

Reporter: How did you begin to work for UNICEF?
                                = working

Audrey: In 1987, a musical festival in Macau changed my life. I learned that
                                        목적어에 해당하는 명사절을 이끄는 접속사

        my fame could help other people.

Reporter: After that, what did you do?
              앞에 나온 문장을 받는 지시대명사

Audrey: I visited some countries in Africa and Asia and volunteered there.
                                        some countries in Africa and Asia를 가리킨다.

구문해설 · during: ~ 동안, ~ 중에 · terrible: 끔찍한 · survive 살아남다, 생존하다
        · thanks to ~ 덕택에, ~ 때문에 · volunteer: 자원 봉사를 하다

리포터: 제2차 세계 대전 동안 당신의 삶은 어땠습니까? 그것에 대해 말해주실 수 있나요?
오드리: 끔찍했어요. 제 가족과 저는 굶주리고 아팠어요. 우리는 다른 사람들의 도움 덕분에 살아남았어요.
리포터: 당신은 어떻게 유니세프를 위해 일하게 되었나요?
오드리: 1987년에, 마카오의 한 음악 축제가 제 삶을 바꿨어요. 저는 제 명성이 다른 사람들을 도울 수 있다는 것을 알게 되었어요.
리포터: 그 다음에, 무엇을 했나요?
오드리: 아프리카와 아시아의 몇몇 나라들을 방문해서 그곳에서 자원 봉사를 했어요.

Culture Link

Talking Books Program

This is a program that makes audiobooks for blind people. It was started in
                    주격 관계대명사   수동태

1931 in the United States. You just read books and record your voice. These
년도와 넓은 장소 앞에 쓴 전치사 in

audiobooks are given to blind people for free.
        give는 'to+간접목적어'의 형태를 쓴다.   무료로

구문해설 · blind: 눈이 먼, 맹인인 · audiobook: 오디오북 (책의 내용을 녹음한 것)

말하는 책 프로그램

이것은 시각장애인을 위한 오디오북을 만드는 프로그램이다. 이것은 1931년 미국에서 시작되었다. 당신은 책을 읽고 당신의 목소리를 녹음하기만 하면 된다. 이러한 오디오북들은 시각장애인들에게 무료로 주어진다.

01 다음 제시된 단어를 사용하여 자연스러운 문장을 만들 수 없는 것은? (형태 변화 가능)

┤ 보기 ├

elderly   following   homeless
international

① There are many _____ people at the subway station.
② Many younger Koreans offer their seats to _____ people.
③ It's a _____ movement to build houses for the homeless.
④ The _____ police finally caught him.
⑤ I left Madrid last Sunday and arrived in Seoul the _____ day.

02 우리말에 맞게 주어진 철자로 시작하여 빈칸을 완성하시오.

(1) 우리는 그 여행의 모든 순간을 즐겼다.
➡ We enjoyed every m_____ of the trip.
(2) 우리는 그녀의 요리를 칭찬했다.
➡ We p_____ her cooking.
(3) 나는 건강의 소중함을 깨달았다.
➡ I r_____ the value of health.
(4) 내 취미는 우표를 수집하는 것이다.
➡ My hobby is c_____ stamps.

03 다음 영영풀이에 해당하는 단어를 고르시오.

the state of being famous

① wealth   ② favor
③ difficulty   ④ fame
⑤ population

04 빈칸에 들어갈 알맞은 말을 〈보기〉에서 골라 쓰시오. (형태 변화 가능)

┤ 보기 ├

clean   fall   hold   raise

(1) When are you going to _____ a party?
(2) I lost my balance and _____ down.
(3) You should _____ up your room.
(4) He will also _____ money for the World Food Program.

[05~07] 다음 대화를 읽고 물음에 답하시오.

B1: Wow! These dogs are so dirty. Jay, <u>그 개들을 씻기는 거 도와줄 수 있니?</u>(them, you, help, wash, can, me, ?)
B2: Allen, I'm sorry, but I can't. I have to feed the cats now. (A)_____ don't you ask Nicky?
B1: Okay! Nicky, can I ask you a favor?
G: Sure, Allen. (B)_____ is it?
B1: Can you help me wash these dogs?
G: Sure. But I have to walk these dogs first. After that, I will help you.
B1: All right! Thank you.

05 밑줄 친 우리말에 맞게 괄호 안의 단어를 바르게 배열하시오.

➡ _____

06 빈칸 (A)와 (B)에 알맞은 의문사를 쓰시오.

➡ (A) _____, (B) _____

07 대화가 끝난 후 여자아이가 할 일로 가장 알맞은 것을 고르시오.

① 고양이 먹이 주기
② 동물 병원 들르기
③ 개 산책시키기
④ 개 목욕시키기
⑤ 개 집 청소하기

[08~09] 다음 글을 읽고 물음에 답하시오.

G: Good morning, students! As you know, there was a big fire in Mapletown. Why don't we raise money and help the people there? Come to our special event at the school grounds on May 3! Please bring your items and donate them. We will sell your items. Then, we will give all the money to Mapletown. Please give a hand to people in need.

08 밑줄 친 부분과 같은 뜻이 되도록 주어진 단어를 이용해 문장을 완성하시오.

➡ (shall) _____

_____

(let's) _____

09 위 글을 읽고 답할 수 없는 질문은?

① How can they raise money for the people in need?
② Where will the special event be held?
③ When will the special event be held?
④ Where was a big fire?
⑤ When was a big fire in Mapletown?

[10~11] 다음 대화를 읽고 물음에 답하시오.

B: Mia, 이 책들 옮기는 거 도와줄 수 있어?
G: Sure. What are you going to do with them?
B: I'm going to donate them to a children's library.

10 주어진 단어를 이용해 밑줄 친 우리말을 영작하시오.

➡ _____

(these, move, help)

11 다음 영영풀이에 해당하는 단어를 대화에서 찾아 쓰시오.

to give something to help people

➡ _____

12 다음 대화의 빈칸에 알맞은 것은?

A: What do you want to do this afternoon?
B: _____
A: That sounds like fun. Let's go.

① Where do you usually play tennis?
② Why don't we play tennis together?
③ Do you know how to play tennis?
④ Can you tell me how to play tennis?
⑤ Why didn't you play tennis this morning?

13 다음 우리말을 주어진 어휘를 이용하여 영어로 옮기시오.

요가를 하는 것은 나를 느긋하게 해준다.
(do, yoga, make, relax)

➡ _____

14 다음 대화의 빈칸에 알맞은 말이 순서대로 바르게 짝지어진 것을 고르시오.

> A: Juliet was _____ when she knew that Romeo had left her.
>
> B: Yes. It was really _____ .

① interesting – surprised
② shocking – shocking
③ shocked – surprising
④ interested – surprised
⑤ shocked – shocked

15 다음 중 두 문장을 한 문장으로 만들 때 의미가 다른 하나는?

① The little black dress is famous even today. She wore it in a movie.
  → The little black dress which she wore in a movie is famous even today.
② He is the boy. Mary talked about him yesterday.
  → He is the boy about whom Mary talked yesterday.
③ Do you remember the watch? Herold was wearing it.
  → Do you remember the watch that Herold was wearing?
④ Susan is the woman. I helped her on the street.
  → Susan is the woman who helped me on the street.
⑤ The man comes from Finland. Eveline is going to marry him.
  → The man who Eveline is going to marry comes from Finland.

16 다음 중 어법상 옳은 문장을 모두 고르시오.

① The little girl felt scaring all the time.
② I feel relaxed when I listen to classical music.
③ I am bored with the computer game.
④ Riding a roller coaster makes me exciting.
⑤ It was very excited, and I became interested in hockey!

17 〈보기〉의 밑줄 친 which와 용법이 다른 것은? (2개)

> ┤ 보기 ├
> He bought his daughter the bag which she always wanted.

① I will never forget the people that I met in Korea.
② This is the house which Gibson lived in when he was young.
③ I know the boy who helped the old lady cross the road.
④ I ran into the man with whom I had worked for about a year.
⑤ We went to the restaurant which sold delicious Canadian food.

18 주어진 어휘를 이용하여 우리말의 의미에 맞도록 빈칸에 알맞게 쓰시오.

(1) 그녀의 직업은 전혀 재미있지 않았다. 그녀는 매우 지루했다.
  → Her job was not _____ at all. She was so _____ . (interest, bore)
(2) 나는 하루 종일 매우 피곤함을 느꼈다.
  → I felt very _____ all day long. (tire)

19 다음 괄호 안에 주어진 어휘를 사용해 다음을 영작하시오. (that 사용 금지)

(1) 내가 카페에서 본 남자는 Park Jisung이었다. (the man, the café)

➡ _____

(2) 나는 나의 할머니가 입양한 개를 사랑한다. (my grandmother, adopt)

➡ _____

(3) Jason은 그 파티에 대해서 몰랐으므로 정말로 놀랐다. (about, so, really, surprise)

➡ _____

(4) 우리는 사고에 대해 들었을 때 너무 충격 받았다. (so, shock, about, when, the accident)

➡ _____

_____

Reading

[20~21] 다음 글을 읽고 물음에 답하시오.

When she grew up, Hepburn became a symbol of beauty. She was very popular because of her hit movies, such as *My Fair Lady* and *Roman Holiday*. ⓐThe little black dress which she wore in a movie is famous even today. Many people still love her style.

The autumn of 1987 was a turning point in Hepburn's life. She went to an international music festival in Macau. Many people donated money at the festival, and the money went to UNICEF. Thanks to her fame, UNICEF collected more money than ever before. Hepburn realized that her fame could help others, so she became a UNICEF Goodwill Ambassador.

20 위 글의 밑줄 친 ⓐ에서 어법상 생략할 수 있는 단어를 찾아 쓰시오.

➡ _____

---

21 위 글의 내용과 일치하지 <u>않는</u> 것은?

① 헵번은 <마이 페어 레이디>와 <로마의 휴일>과 같은 흥행 영화들로 인해 매우 인기가 있었다.
② 많은 사람들은 헵번의 스타일이 요즘은 구식이라고 생각한다.
③ 1987년 가을 마카오의 한 국제 음악 축제에서 헵번의 명성 덕분에, 유니세프는 어느 때보다도 더 많은 돈을 모았다.
④ 헵번은 자신의 명성이 다른 사람들을 도울 수 있다는 것을 깨달았다.
⑤ 헵번은 유니세프 친선 대사가 되었다.

[22~24] 다음 글을 읽고 물음에 답하시오.

First, Hepburn went to Ethiopia in 1988. There, she brought food to hungry children. She was shocked because their lives were very difficult. After that, she volunteered in other countries. In 1990, she visited Vietnam to hand out medicine and support clean drinking water programs. Her last trip was to Somalia in 1992, and she passed away the following year.

Many people praised her beauty and style, but Hepburn's real beauty was her heart. To honor her, UNICEF made a statue, *The Spirit of Audrey*. ⓐ그녀를 존경하는 사람들이 그녀의 사명을 이어 나가고 있다. Her favorite saying shows her mission.

ⓑ*As you get older, remember you have two hands. One is for helping yourself, and the other is for helping others.*

22 위 글의 밑줄 친 ⓐ의 우리말에 맞게 한 단어를 보충하여, 주어진 어휘를 배열하시오.

> her / respect / alive / mission / keep / people / her

➡ _____

23 위 글의 밑줄 친 ⓑAs와 같은 의미로 쓰인 것을 고르시오

① She works as hard as her mother.
② Do as you would be done by.
③ He came up as I was speaking.
④ As he is honest, everyone likes him.
⑤ Her anger grew as she talked.

24 위 글을 읽고 Hepburn이 방문한 나라와 방문 연도를 순서대로 쓰시오. (나라 이름은 우리말로 쓰시오)

➡ (1) _____, (2) _____,
(3) _____

[25~27] 다음 인터뷰를 읽고 물음에 답하시오.

Reporter: How was your life during World War
II? Can you tell me about it?
Audrey: It was (A)[terrible / terrific]. My family
and I were hungry and sick. We survived
thanks to the help of others.
Reporter: ⓐHow did you begin to work for
UNICEF?
Audrey: In 1987, a musical festival in Macau (B)
[changed / exchanged] my life. I learned
that my fame could help other people.
Reporter: After that, (C)[how / what] did you
do?
Audrey: I visited some countries in Africa and
Asia and volunteered there.

25 위 인터뷰의 괄호 (A)~(C)에서 문맥이나 어법상 알맞은 낱말을 골라 쓰시오.

➡ (A)_____ (B)_____ (C)_____

26 위 인터뷰의 밑줄 친 ⓐ를 다음과 같이 바꿔 쓸 때 빈칸에 들어갈 알맞은 말을 쓰시오.

➡ How did you begin _____ for
UNICEF?

27 위 인터뷰를 읽고 답할 수 없는 질문은?

① How was Audrey's life during World
War II?
② How did Audrey survive World War II?
③ How did Audrey begin to work for
UNICEF?
④ Why did Audrey participate in a musical
festival in Macau?
⑤ What countries did Audrey visit after
she bought to work for UNICEF?

[28~29] 다음 글을 읽고 물음에 답하시오.

For my volunteer work, I helped young
students with math homework. I ⓐdid this at
my community library. ⓑFrom this volunteer
work, I learned that helping others are a great
experience.

28 위 글의 밑줄 친 ⓐdid this가 가리키는 것을 본문에서 찾아 쓰시오.

➡ _____

29 위 글의 밑줄 친 ⓑ에서 어법상 틀린 부분을 찾아 고치시오.

➡ _____

출제율 90%

01 다음 짝지어진 두 단어의 관계가 같도록 빈칸에 알맞은 단어를 쓰시오.

> beauty : beautiful – _____ : favorable

출제율 95%

02 다음 〈보기〉에서 사람의 성격을 묘사할 때 쓸 수 있는 단어의 개수는?

> ┤ 보기 ├
> • beautiful   • friendly   • gentle
> • curious   • polite   • careful
> • outgoing   • patient

① 4개   ② 5개   ③ 6개   ④ 7개   ⑤ 8개

출제율 100%

03 다음 빈칸에 공통으로 들어갈 말을 쓰시오.

> • _____ kinds of movies do you want to see this evening?
> • _____ about enjoying music at home without going outside?

출제율 90%

04 다음 밑줄 친 단어와 뜻이 같은 단어를 모두 고르시오.

> Thanks to you, I won the dancing contest.

① For   ② Because of
③ Without   ④ Despite
⑤ Due to

[05~06] 다음 대화의 순서를 바르게 배열한 것을 고르시오.

출제율 90%

05
> (A) I'm going to donate them to a children's library.
> (B) Mia, can you help me move these books?
> (C) Sure. What are you going to do with them?

① (A) – (C) – (B)   ② (B) – (A) – (C)
③ (B) – (C) – (A)   ④ (C) – (A) – (B)
⑤ (C) – (B) – (A)

출제율 90%

06
> (A) We can play music for the sick children
> (B) Sounds good. What can we do there?
> (C) Why don't we do volunteer work at the children's hospital?

① (A) – (C) – (B)   ② (B) – (A) – (C)
③ (B) – (C) – (A)   ④ (C) – (A) – (B)
⑤ (C) – (B) – (A)

[07~09] 다음 대화를 읽고 물음에 답하시오.

B1: Next Wednesday is Volunteer Day. We cleaned up the park last time. (①)

G: Why don't we ⓐ visiting a nursing home and ⓑ clean up it? (②)

B2: That's not a bad idea. But I want ⓒ doing ⓓ fun something. (③) Why don't we ⓔ held a party for the people there?

G: That's a good idea. (④) What can we do at the party?

B1: We can serve some food.

B2: And how about playing some music? I can play the piano. (⑤)

G: And I can play the cello.

B1: It sounds like a good plan.

07 위 대화의 ①~⑤ 중 주어진 문장이 들어갈 알맞은 곳은?

> What are we going to do this time?

①   ②   ③   ④   ⑤

출제율 95%

08 ⓐ~ⓔ 중 어법상 어색한 것의 개수를 고르시오.

① 1개   ② 2개   ③ 3개   ④ 4개   ⑤ 5개

출제율 90%

09 다음 영영풀이에 해당하는 단어를 위 대화에서 찾아 쓰시오.

> a place where people who are too old or sick to take care of themselves live

➡ _____

[10~12] 다음 대화를 읽고 물음에 답하시오.

G1: We have a class activity day next Friday. What do you want to do on that day? (①)

B: Why don't we (A)_____ some volunteer activities? (②)

G1: That sounds great, but choosing a good place is not easy.

B: We need someone who has volunteered a lot. (③)

G1: I know Sumin has volunteered a lot. Sumin, can you help us find some good places?

G2: Sure. (④) I usually search for information on the internet. (⑤)(B)십대들을 위한 자원 봉사 웹사이트를 확인해 보는 게 어떠니?

B: That's a good idea. (⑤)

출제율 85%

10 위 대화의 ①~⑤ 중 주어진 문장이 들어갈 알맞은 곳은?

> We can help others and make our community better.

①   ②   ③   ④   ⑤

출제율 100%

11 빈칸 (A)에 적절한 것을 고르시오.

① prepare   ② join   ③ do

④ keep   ⑤ have

출제율 95%

12 밑줄 친 (B) 우리말을 주어진 어구를 이용해 영작하시오.

➡ _____

(check, for, why, teens, the volunteering website)

출제율 90%

13 어법상 어색한 것을 바르게 고쳐 문장을 다시 쓰시오.

(1) This is the cell phone who I broke yesterday.

➡ _____

(2) The speed at that everything moved felt strange.

➡ _____

(3) The girl who I met her the other day was very pretty.

➡ _____

(4) I was very worring about his health.

➡ _____

14 다음 두 문장의 의미가 같도록 빈칸에 알맞은 말을 쓰시오.

(1) The game was exciting to me.

= I was _____ about the game.

(2) Jack thinks baseball is boring.

= Jack isn't _____ in baseball.

[15~16] 다음 글을 읽고 물음에 답하시오.

During World War II, a little girl and her mother were hungry and sick. ①The only food ⓐthat they could find was grass. The little girl felt ②excited all the time. ③Luckily, the girl survived, ④thanks to the help of others. One of the groups that helped her was UNICEF. Later, the girl became a ⑤worldwide movie star. Her name was Audrey Hepburn.

15 위 글의 밑줄 친 ①~⑤에서 흐름상 어색한 부분을 찾아 고치시오.

➡ _____

16 위 글의 밑줄 친 ⓐthat과 문법적 쓰임이 다른 것을 모두 고르시오.

① There's a man that wants to see you.

② Is this the farm that they talked about?

③ He said that the story was true.

④ These are the books that you lent me.

⑤ I was afraid that she might be late.

[17~19] 다음 글을 읽고 물음에 답하시오.

When she grew up, Hepburn became a symbol of beauty. She was very popular (A)[because / because of] her hit movies, such as *My Fair Lady* and *Roman Holiday*. The little black dress which she wore in a movie (B)[is / to be] famous even today. Many people still love her style.

(①) The autumn of 1987 was a (C)[turning / turned] point in Hepburn's life. (②) She went to an international music festival in Macau. (③) Many people donated money at the festival, and the money went to UNICEF. (④) Hepburn realized that her fame could help others, so she became a UNICEF Goodwill Ambassador. (⑤)

17 위 글의 괄호 (A)~(C)에서 어법상 알맞은 낱말을 골라 쓰시오.

➡ (A)_____ (B)_____ (C)_____

18 위 글의 흐름으로 보아, 주어진 문장이 들어가기에 가장 적절한 곳은?

> Thanks to her fame, UNICEF collected more money than ever before.

① ② ③ ④ ⑤

19 다음 질문에 대한 알맞은 대답을 주어진 단어로 시작하여 쓰시오. (7~8 단어)

Q: Why did Hepburn become a UNICEF Goodwill Ambassador?

A: Because _____.

[20~22] 다음 글을 읽고 물음에 답하시오.

First, Hepburn went to Ethiopia in 1988. There, she brought food to hungry children. She was shocked because their lives were very difficult. After that, she ⓐ_____ in other countries. In 1990, she visited Vietnam to hand out medicine and support clean drinking water programs. Her last trip was to Somalia in 1992, and she passed away the following year.

Many people praised her beauty and style, but Hepburn's real beauty was her heart. To honor her, UNICEF made a statue, *The Spirit of Audrey*. People who respect her keep her mission alive. Her favorite saying shows ⓑher mission.

As you get older, remember you have two hands. ©*One is for helping you, and the other is for helping others.*

📝 출제율 90%

20 주어진 영영풀이를 참고하여 빈칸 ⓐ에 철자 v로 시작하는 단어를 시제에 맞춰 쓰시오.

> to offer to do something without being forced to do it

➡ _____

📝 출제율 100%

21 위 글의 밑줄 친 ⓑher mission이 가리키는 것을 본문에서 찾아 쓰시오.

➡ _____

📝 출제율 90%

22 위 글의 밑줄 친 ©에서 어법상 틀린 부분을 찾아 고치시오.

➡ _____

[23~25] 다음 인터뷰를 읽고 물음에 답하시오.

Reporter: How was your life during World War II? Can you tell me about it?

Audrey: It was terrible. My family and I were hungry and sick. ⓐ우리는 다른 사람들의 도움 덕분에 살아남았다.

Reporter: How did you begin to work for UNICEF?

Audrey: In 1987, a musical festival in Macau changed my life. I learned that my fame could help other people.

Reporter: After that, what did you do?

Audrey: I visited some countries in Africa and Asia and volunteered ⓑthere.

📝 출제율 100%

23 위 인터뷰의 밑줄 친 ⓐ의 우리말에 맞게 주어진 어휘를 이용하여 8단어로 영작하시오.

> thanks to

➡ _____

📝 출제율 95%

24 위 인터뷰의 밑줄 친 ⓑthere가 가리키는 것을 본문에서 찾아 쓰시오.

➡ _____

📝 출제율 90%

25 위 인터뷰의 내용과 일치하지 <u>않는</u> 것은?

① 제2차 세계 대전 동안 Audrey의 삶은 끔찍했다.
② 제2차 세계 대전 동안 Audrey의 가족과 Audrey는 굶주리고 아팠다.
③ Audrey가 유니세프를 위해 일하게 된 계기는 1987년 마카오의 한 음악 축제였다.
④ Audrey는 유니세프를 위해 일하면서 아프리카와 아시아의 몇몇 나라들을 방문했다.
⑤ Audrey는 아프리카와 아시아의 몇몇 나라들에서 영화배우로 일했다.

[01~02] 다음 대화를 읽고 물음에 답하시오.

B: Hey, Minji! What's wrong ⓐ_____ your leg?

G: I broke it last week.

B: Really? What happened?

G: I was ⓑ_____ a hurry ⓒ_____ catch a train. But I fell ⓓ_____ in the street.

B: Oh, that's terrible! <u>내가 너를 위해 해줄 게 있니?</u>

G: Well, can you help me carry this bag?

01 빈칸 ⓐ~ⓓ에 들어갈 단어를 <보기>에서 찾아 쓰시오.

┌─ 보기 ─────────────────────┐
│   to   down   of   in   for   with   │
└───────────────────────────┘

➡ _____

02 밑줄 친 우리말을 주어진 단어를 이용하여 영어로 옮기시오.

➡ _____

(there, anything)

03 우리말에 맞게 주어진 단어를 이용해 영어로 옮기시오.

┌───────────────────────────────┐
│ G: Good morning, students! As you know, │
│ there was a big fire in Mapletown. (A) │
│ <u>우리가 돈을 모금해서 그곳 사람들을 도와주는</u> │
│ <u>게 어떨까요?</u> Come to our special event │
│ at the school grounds on May 3! Please │
│ bring your items and donate them. We │
│ will sell your items. Then, we will give │
│ all the money to Mapletown. (B)<u>어려운</u> │
│ <u>사람들에게 도움을 주십시오.</u> │
└───────────────────────────────┘

➡ (A) _____

(raise, help, why, there)

(B) _____

(in, please, give, people)

04 두 문장을 관계대명사를 사용하여 한 문장으로 썼을 때 빈칸에 알맞은 문장을 쓰시오.

(1) • This is my aunt.

• _____

➡ This is my aunt about whom I told you.

(2) • This is the cake.

• _____

➡ This is the cake which I made for my family.

(3) • _____

• It was served at the restaurant.

➡ The food that was served at the restaurant was delicious.

(4) • I met the woman.

• _____

➡ I met the woman you ate dinner with last Sunday.

05 다음 두 문장의 의미가 같도록 빈칸에 알맞은 말을 쓰시오.

(1) Nick thinks the result was disappointing.

= Nick was _____ with the result.

(2) Richard thinks *Alita* is exciting.

= Richard is _____ about *Alita*.

[06~08] 다음 글을 읽고 물음에 답하시오.

When she grew up, Hepburn became a symbol of beauty. She was very popular because of her hit movies, such as *My Fair Lady* and *Roman Holiday*. ⓐ<u>그녀가 영화에서 입었던 아담한 검은 드레스는 심지어 오늘날까지도 유명하다.</u> Many people still love her style.

The autumn of 1987 was a turning point in Hepburn's life. She went to an international music festival in Macau. Many people donated money at the festival, and the money went to UNICEF. Thanks to her fame, UNICEF collected more money than ever before. Hepburn realized that her fame could help others, so she became a UNICEF Goodwill Ambassador.

06 다음 문장에서 위 글의 내용과 <u>다른</u> 부분을 찾아서 고치시오.

> Hepburn was very popular because she was a UNICEF Goodwill Ambassador.

➡ _____

_____

_____

07 위 글의 밑줄 친 ⓐ의 우리말에 맞게 한 단어를 보충하여, 주어진 어휘를 배열하시오.

> is / she / the little black dress / today / which / wore / famous / in a movie

➡ _____

_____

08 위 글의 내용과 일치하도록 다음 빈칸에 알맞은 단어를 쓰시오.

> The event which became _____ _____ _____ in Hepburn's life was an international music festival in Macau in the autumn of 1987.

[09~11] 다음 글을 읽고 물음에 답하시오.

First, Hepburn went to Ethiopia in 1988. There, she brought food to hungry children. She was (A)[pleased / shocked] because their lives were very ①difficult. After that, she volunteered in other countries. In 1990, she visited Vietnam to hand out medicine and support clean drinking water programs. Her (B)[last / latest] trip was ②from Somalia in 1992, and she passed away the ③following year.

Many people praised her beauty and style, but Hepburn's ④real beauty was her heart. To honor her, UNICEF made a statue, *The Spirit of Audrey*. People who respect her keep her mission (C)[alive / live]. Her ⑤favorite saying shows her mission.

As you get older, remember you have two hands. One is for helping yourself, and the other is for helping others.

09 위 글의 괄호 (A)~(C)에서 문맥상 알맞은 낱말을 골라 쓰시오.

➡ (A)_____ (B)_____ (C)_____

10 위 글의 밑줄 친 ①~⑤에서 흐름상 <u>어색한</u> 부분을 찾아 고치시오.

➡ _____

11 다음 질문에 대한 알맞은 대답을 영어로 쓰시오. (5 단어)

> Q: In what year did Hepburn pass away?

➡ _____

01 다음 대화의 흐름에 맞게 빈칸을 완성하시오. (제안하기의 표현을 사용할 것)

A: Are you interested in recycled art?

B: Yes, I am.

A: There is a recycled art festival in City Park. _____ go and see some works of recycled art?

B: That's good. _____ (1, how, meet)

A: _____ (afraid) _____ at 2? (meet, what)

B: OK. _____ meet in front of the front gate of City Park.

02 다음 정보를 바탕으로 자신의 영웅에 대한 이야기 카드를 만드시오.

Personal Information
• Who is your hero?: my mom
• When was he/she born?: in 1972
• Where does he/she live?: in Seoul

Personality
What is he/she like?
She smiles a lot and tries to see the good in everything.

Important Moments
What are some of the most important moments in his/her life?
She had a serious car accident.

Reason
Why is he/she your hero?
She always helps people in need.

My little big hero is (A)_____. She was born in 1972. She lives in Seoul. She smiles a lot and tries to see (B)_____ in everything. My mom had a serious (C)_____. She was in the hospital for six months. But she was very strong and finally got better. She always helps people (D)_____. She donates money and does volunteer work. She is my (E)_____!

단원별 모의고사

[01~02] 다음 빈칸에 알맞은 단어를 고르시오.

1

> She _____ music records as a hobby.

① breaks   ② carries

③ honors   ④ serves

⑤ collects

2

> They decided to _____ an essay contest.

① take   ② do   ③ hold

④ get   ⑤ bring

3 다음 우리말과 일치하도록 빈칸을 채우시오. (주어진 철자가 있을 경우 그 철자로 시작할 것)

(1) 많은 사람들이 여왕에게 존경을 표하기 위해 왔다.
   ➡ Many people came to h_____ the queen.

(2) 나는 그 자동차 사고로 다리가 부러졌다.
   ➡ I _____ my leg in the car _____.

(3) 그들은 임무를 성공적으로 완수했다.
   ➡ They finished their _____ successfully.

(4) 광장에는 그 왕의 조각상이 서 있다.
   ➡ The _____ of the king stands in the square.

(5) 그 추락 사고에서 다섯 명만이 살아남았다.
   ➡ Only five people _____ the crash.

4 다음 주어진 문장과 같은 의미가 되도록 빈칸을 채우시오. (3 단어)

> My sister always listens to music.
> ➡ My sister listens to music _____.

[05~06] 다음 대화를 읽고 물음에 답하시오.

B: Hey, Minji! ⓐWhat's wrong with your leg?
G: ⓑI broke it last week.
B: Really? What happened?
G: ⓒI am in a hurry to catch a train. ⓓBut I fell down in the street.
B: ⓔOh, that's terrific! Is there anything I can do for you?
G: Well, 이 가방을 드는 걸 도와줄 수 있니?
B: Sure.

5 ⓐ~ⓔ 중 문법상 또는 흐름상 어색한 부분을 찾아 고치시오. (2개)

➡ _____

6 밑줄 친 우리말을 영작하시오.

➡ _____

7 다음 대화의 빈칸 ⓐ~ⓔ에 들어갈 수 없는 표현을 고르시오.

> B: Mia, ⓐ_____ me ⓑ_____?
> G: ⓒ_____. ⓓ_____ to do with them?
> B: ⓔ_____ donate them to a children's library.

① What are you going

② move these books

③ Of course not

④ can you help

⑤ I'm going to

8 다음 대화의 밑줄 친 우리말을 영작하시오.

> A: 수학 문제 푸는 걸 도와줄 수 있니?
> B: I'm sorry, but I can't.

➡ _____

[09~12] 다음 대화를 읽고 물음에 답하시오.

G1: ⓐ<u>We have a class activity day next Friday.</u>
ⓑ<u>What do you want to do on that day?</u>

B: ⓒ<u>Why don't we do some volunteer</u>
<u>activities?</u> ⓓ<u>We can help others and make</u>
<u>our community better.</u>

G1: That sounds great, ⓔ<u>but choosing a good</u>
<u>place are not easy.</u>

B: (need, we, who, a, someone, volunteered, lot, has)

G1: I know Sumin has volunteered a lot. Sumin, can you help us find some good places?

G2: Sure. I usually search (A)_____ information on the internet. Why don't we check the volunteering website (B)_____ teens?

B: That's a good idea.

09 위 대화의 ⓐ~ⓔ 중에서 어법상 어색한 것을 고르시오.

① ⓐ   ② ⓑ   ③ ⓒ   ④ ⓓ   ⑤ ⓔ

10 괄호 안의 단어를 알맞게 배열하여 영작하시오.

➡ _____

11 빈칸 (A)와 (B)에 공통으로 들어갈 단어를 쓰시오.

➡ _____

12 위 대화의 내용과 일치하지 <u>않는</u> 것은?

① 봉사 활동을 많이 해 본 사람이 필요하다.
② 수민이는 봉사 활동을 위한 좋은 장소를 고르는 것이 쉽지 않다고 생각한다.
③ 남자아이는 봉사활동이 다른 사람들을 돕고 지역 사회를 더 좋게 만들 수 있다고 생각한다.
④ 다음 주 금요일에 학급 활동이 있다.
⑤ 그들은 대화 후에 십대들을 위한 자원 봉사 웹사이트를 확인할 것이다.

13 다음 중 어법상 바르지 <u>않은</u> 것은?

① The man is going to meet the students who he taught a long time ago.
② Everyone was surprised at the fact.
③ Andy bought the same bike that I wanted.
④ This is the backpack which I bought it yesterday.
⑤ I'm really interested in this book. I want to read it.

14 다음 〈보기〉에 주어진 단어를 변형하여 문맥에 맞게 문장을 완성하시오.

┌─── 보기 ├───
│ relax   interest │
└─────────────

(1) Watching movies makes me _____.
(2) They found the game _____.

15 다음 빈칸에 들어갈 알맞은 말을 <u>모두</u> 고르시오.

┌─────────────────────┐
│ The man _____ you met yesterday is a spy. │
└─────────────────────┘

① who   ② whose
③ whom   ④ that
⑤ which

16 괄호 안에 주어진 어휘를 이용하여 우리말을 영작하시오.

(1) 그녀가 읽고 있었던 책이 없어졌다. (missing)

➡ _____

(2) 내가 함께 점심을 먹고 있던 남자는 Yoojin이
였다. (the man, have)

➡ _____

_____

(3) 우리는 그 아름다운 풍경에 놀랐다. (amaze,
at, scenery)

➡ _____

(4) Dan은 재미있는 남자는 아니지만, 그와 있을
때 나는 지루하지 않다. (a funny guy, bore)

➡ _____

_____

17 다음 중 어법상 바르지 <u>않은</u> 것은?

① I am going to go on a trip tomorrow. I'm
so excited.

② I'll give you the butterflies which I
caught yesterday.

③ I met the girl in whom you are
interested.

④ The child was very scared of the
crocodile and began to cry.

⑤ Someone was following me, and I felt
scaring.

[18~19] 다음 글을 읽고 물음에 답하시오.

When she grew up, Hepburn became a
symbol of beauty. She was very popular
because of her hit movies, such as *My Fair
Lady* and *Roman Holiday*. The little black dress
which she wore in a movie is famous even
today. Many people still love her style.

The autumn of 1987 was a turning point in
Hepburn's life. She went to an international
music festival in Macau. Many people donated
money at the festival, and the money went
to UNICEF. Thanks to her fame, UNICEF
collected more money than ever before.
Hepburn realized that her fame could help
others, so she became a UNICEF Goodwill
Ambassador.

18 다음 질문에 대한 알맞은 대답을 빈칸에 쓰시오.

Q: For what reason could UNICEF
collect more money than ever before
in an international music festival in
Macau in the autumn of 1987?

A: It could do so _____ _____
_____ _____.

19 위 글의 주제로 알맞은 것을 고르시오.

① Hepburn's life as a symbol of beauty

② Hepburn's hit movies, such as *My Fair
Lady* and *Roman Holiday*

③ Hepburn's fame and a turning point in
her life

④ an international music festival in Macau

⑤ Hepburn's life as a UNICEF Goodwill
Ambassador

[20~22] 다음 글을 읽고 물음에 답하시오.

First, Hepburn went to Ethiopia in 1988. There, she brought food to hungry children. She was shocked because ⓐunderline{their lives} were very difficult. After that, she volunteered in other countries. In 1990, she visited Vietnam to hand out medicine and support clean drinking water programs. Her last trip was to Somalia in 1992, and she passed away the following year.

Many people praised her beauty and style, but Hepburn's real beauty was her heart. To honor her, UNICEF made a statue, *The Spirit of Audrey*. People ⓑwho respect her keep her mission alive. Her favorite saying shows her mission.

As you get older, remember you have two hands. One is for helping yourself, and the other is for helping ___ⓒ___ .

20 다음 빈칸에 알맞은 단어를 넣어 밑줄 친 ⓐtheir lives가 가리키는 것을 설명하시오.

the lives of _____ in Ethiopia

21 위 글의 밑줄 친 ⓑwho와 문법적 쓰임이 같은 것을 고르시오.

① Who is that woman?
② Who can jump farther, Tom or Bill?
③ Nobody knew who he was.
④ Who do you mean?
⑤ Anyone who wants to come is welcome.

22 위 글의 빈칸 ⓒ에 들어갈 알맞은 말을 고르시오.

① the other　　② others
③ one　　④ your family
⑤ another

[23~25] 다음 글을 읽고 물음에 답하시오.

My little big hero is my mom. She was born in 1972. She lives in Seoul.
She smiles a lot and tries to see the good in everything.
My mom had a serious car accident. She was in the hospital for six months. But she was very strong and finally got better.
She always helps people in need. She donates money and does volunteer work. She is my big hero!

23 위 글의 제목으로 알맞은 것을 고르시오.

① Mom Was Born in 1972!
② Try to See the Good in Everything
③ Mom Had a Serious Car Accident
④ My Little Big Hero
⑤ My Friendly Mom and Me

24 다음 질문에 대한 알맞은 대답을 완전한 문장으로 쓰시오.

Q: How long was the writer's mom in the hospital?

➡ _____

25 위 글의 글쓴이의 엄마에 관한 내용으로 적절하지 않은 것은?

① 서울에 산다.
② 많이 웃는다.
③ 자동차 사고로 몸이 불편하다.
④ 어려움에 처한 사람들을 항상 돕는다.
⑤ 자원 봉사를 한다.

The Best Trip of Your Life

 의사소통 기능

- 계획 묻고 답하기

  A: What are you planning to do on your trip?

  B: I'm planning to go hiking.

- 소요 시간 묻고 답하기

  A: How long does it take to get to school?

  B: It takes 20 minutes.

 언어 형식

- 가주어 It

  It was nice **to relax in a café and read them.**

- 간접의문문

  Do you know **where the first train station in Korea is?**

Words & Expressions

Key Words

- **amazing** [əméiziŋ] 형 놀라운, 멋진
- **amusement park** 놀이공원
- **art museum** 미술관
- **art show** 미술 전시회
- **autumn** [ɔ́ːtəm] 명 가을
- **awesome** [ɔ́ːsəm] 형 매우 멋진
- **block** [blɑk] 명 블록, 구역
- **cafe** [kæféi] 명 카페, 커피숍
- **comic book** 만화책
- **condition** [kəndíʃən] 명 상태, 상황
- **field trip** 견학 여행, 현장 학습
- **foreign** [fɔ́ːrən] 형 외국의
- **get** [ɡet] 동 (장소·위치에) 도착하다, 얻다
- **goods** [ɡudz] 명 상품, 물건
- **hike** [haik] 동 하이킹하다, 도보 여행하다
- **historical** [histɔ́ːrikəl] 형 역사적인, 역사상의
- **history** [hístəri] 명 역사
- **holiday** [hálədèi] 명 휴가, 공휴일, 휴일
- **international** [intərnǽʃənəl] 형 국제적인
- **museum** [mjuːzíəm] 명 박물관, 미술관
- **natural** [nǽtʃərəl] 형 자연의
- **painting** [péintiŋ] 명 그림

- **picture** [píktʃər] 명 사진, 그림
- **plan** [plæn] 동 계획하다 명 계획
- **presentation** [prèzəntéiʃən] 명 발표
- **purpose** [pə́ːrpəs] 명 목적, 목표
- **rafting** [rǽftiŋ] 명 래프팅, 급류 타기
- **relax** [rilǽks] 동 휴식을 취하다, 느긋이 쉬다
- **roller coaster** 롤러코스터
- **rough** [rʌf] 형 거친, 파도가 심한
- **scenery** [síːnəri] 명 풍경, 경치
- **site** [sait] 명 장소
- **stadium** [stéidiəm] 명 경기장, 스타디움
- **stop** [stɑp] 명 멈춤, 정거장, (여행 중) 머무른 곳
- **straight** [streit] 부 똑바로, 일직선으로
- **street food** 길거리 음식
- **take** [teik] 동 (얼마의 시간이) 걸리다, (사진을) 찍다
- **turn** [təːrn] 동 (가는 방향을 바꾸어) 돌다, 돌리다
- **university** [jùːnəvə́ːrsəti] 명 대학교
- **view** [vjuː] 명 전망
- **village** [vílidʒ] 명 마을
- **visit** [vízit] 동 방문하다, 찾아가다
- **Western-style** [wéstərn-stail] 형 서양풍의, 서양식의

Key Expressions

- **a variety of**: 여러 가지의, 다양한
- **at the same time**: 동시에, 한꺼번에
- **be able to** 동사원형: ~할 수 있다
- **be going to** 동사원형: ~할 예정이다
- **be planning to** 동사원형: ~할 계획이다
- **by bus**: 버스로
- **Can you tell me how to get** ~?: ~에 어떻게 가는지 말해 줄 수 있나요?
- **focus on**: (~에) 집중하다, 초점을 맞추다
- **get off**: 내리다, 하차하다
- **get on**: 타다, 승차하다
- **get to** 장소: ~에 도착하다
- **Have a good trip.**: 좋은 여행하길 바라.

- **How can/do I get to** 장소?: ~에 어떻게 갈 수 있어?
- **How long does it take to go** ~?: ~까지 가는 데 얼마나 걸리나요?
- **in front of**: ~ 앞에서
- **It takes (about)** 시간: ~ (정도) 걸려.
- **lots of**: 많은
- **on foot**: 걸어서, 도보로
- **turn off**: (등, 전화기 등을) 끄다
- **What are you going to** 동사원형 ~?: 너는 무엇을 할 거니?
- **What are you planning to** 동사원형 ~?: 너는 무엇을 할 계획이니?
- **no longer**: 더 이상 ~하지 않는

Word Power

※ 어원은 같지만 뜻이 다른 어휘들
- awesome(매우 멋진) – awful(형편없는)
- fun(재미있는, 즐거운) – funny(웃기는, 우스운, 기이한)
- terrible(끔찍한) – terrific(아주 좋은)

※ 서로 비슷한 뜻을 가진 어휘
- amazing(놀라운, 멋진) : incredible(믿을 수 없는)
- goods(상품, 물건) : item(물품)
- site(장소) : place(장소, 곳)
- condition(상태, 상황) : state(상태)
- holiday(휴가) : vacation(휴가)

※ '여행'을 의미하는 다양한 영어 어휘
- trip: 가장 일반적으로 쓰이는 말로, 비교적 짧은 기간의 단거리 여행을 말할 때 주로 쓴다.
- travel: 상대적으로 장기간에 걸친 여행을 말할 때 쓰는 경우가 많다.
- journey: 보다 격식을 갖춘 단어이다.
- voyage: 배를 이용한 장기간의 여행을 의미한다.
- expedition: '탐험, 원정'이라는 말로 어떤 단체나 조직이 구체적인 목적을 가지고 떠나는 여행을 가리킨다.

English Dictionary

- **amusement park**: 놀이공원
  → a place that has many games and rides
  많은 게임이나 탈것들이 있는 장소

- **autumn**: 가을
  → the season after summer and before winter
  여름 후와 겨울 전의 계절

- **awesome**: 매우 멋진
  → wonderful or impressive
  멋지거나 인상적인

- **condition**: 상태, 상황
  → the state of something
  어떤 것의 상태

- **field trip**: 견학 여행, 현장 학습
  → a visit made by students and teachers to learn about something
  학생들과 선생님들이 무엇인가를 배우기 위해 방문하는 것

- **foreign**: 외국의
  → from another country
  다른 나라에서 온

- **goods**: 상품, 물건
  → products for sale
  판매를 위한 물품

- **history**: 역사
  → events that have happened in the past
  과거에 발생한 사건들

- **museum**: 박물관, 미술관
  → a building where historical or artistic objects are displayed
  역사적이거나 예술적인 물건들이 전시되어 있는 건물

- **natural**: 자연의
  → produced by nature
  자연에 의해 만들어진

- **purpose**: 목적, 목표
  → the reason why something is used or done
  어떤 것이 사용되거나 행해지는 이유

- **relax**: 휴식을 취하다, 느긋이 쉬다
  → not to do anything
  아무것도 하지 않다

- **rough**: 거친
  → having a bumpy surface
  울퉁불퉁한 표면을 가진

- **scenery**: 풍경, 경치
  → a beautiful view of nature
  자연의 아름다운 경치

- **site**: 장소
  → a place 장소

- **stadium**: 경기장, 스타디움
  → a large sports field
  규모가 큰 운동 경기장

- **stop**: (여행 중) 머무른 곳
  → a place where one stops during a trip
  여행 중에 멈춘 장소

- **Western-style**: 서양풍의, 서양식의
  → a particular way or form relating to Western countries
  서양 국가들과 관련된 특별한 방식이나 형식

[01~02] 다음 밑줄 친 단어와 바꿔 쓸 수 있는 것을 고르시오.

01

I bought these <u>items</u> at a low price because they are used ones.

① sites ② stops
③ goods ④ markets
⑤ views

02

Somi has <u>many different kinds of</u> chocolate.

① a sort of ② a lot of
③ a variety of ④ a few
⑤ the number of

서답형

03 다음 빈칸에 알맞은 것을 〈보기〉에서 찾아 쓰시오.

┌── 보기 ──┐
amusement park / autumn / condition / scenery / stop

(1) I recommend this beach. It has the most beautiful _____.
(2) The car is in good _____.
(3) The leaves turn red in _____.
(4) They are having fun in the _____.

[04~05] 다음 영영풀이에 해당하는 단어를 주어진 철자로 시작하여 쓰시오.

서답형

04

a_____: wonderful or impressive

05

p_____: the reason why something is used or done

중요

06 다음 중 밑줄 친 부분의 뜻풀이가 바르지 <u>않은</u> 것은?

① I <u>visit</u> my uncle in Cheongju every year. (방문하다)
② Why don't you <u>relax</u> for a moment? (휴식을 취하다)
③ We will go on a <u>field trip</u> to Olympic Park. (현장 학습)
④ It <u>takes</u> about two hours by train from Seoul to Daegu. (가져가다)
⑤ We should get off at the next <u>stop</u>. (정거장)

[07~08] 다음 빈칸에 들어갈 말로 가장 적절한 것을 고르시오.

07

We're going to _____ to the airport very soon.

① do ② have ③ get
④ make ⑤ take

중요

08

The boat sailed through the _____ waves.

① expensive ② different ③ safe
④ far ⑤ rough

01 다음 주어진 영영풀이의 어휘를 빈칸에 써 넣으시오. (5글자)

> products for sale

> They imported expensive _____ from England.

02 다음 밑줄 친 부분과 의미가 가장 가까운 것을 주어진 철자로 시작하여 쓰시오.

> The city has a lot of important historical sites.

➡ p_____

03 다음 우리말에 맞게 주어진 어구를 바르게 배열하시오.

(1) 유진의 바이올린은 낡긴 했지만, 여전히 좋은 상태이다.
(Eugene's, good, is, still, violin, condition, old, in, but)

➡ _____

(2) 그 식당은 다양한 후식이 특징이다.
(variety, desserts, the restaurant, of, a, features)

➡ _____

(3) 너는 공부에 집중해야 한다.
(focus, studies, you, to, on, have, your)

➡ _____

(4) 나는 지난달에 외국을 방문했다.
(last, I, month, a, country, visited, foreign)

➡ _____

04 주어진 단어를 이용해 우리말 해석에 맞게 빈칸을 완성하시오.

(1) 무대를 위한 그의 디자인은 아주 놀라웠다. (amaze)
→ His design for the stage is very _____.

(2) 그들은 자연식품의 신선한 맛을 즐겼다. (nature)
→ They enjoyed the fresh taste of _____ foods.

[05~06] 다음 빈칸에 공통으로 들어갈 말을 쓰시오.

05
- You need to _____ off at the next stop.
- He waited for the lady to _____ on the bus.

06
- Can you tell me _____ to get to the art museum?
- _____ long does it take to go to Busan in a bus?

07 다음 빈칸에 알맞은 단어를 〈보기〉에서 골라 쓰시오. (형태 변화 가능)

┤ 보기 ├
block   cafe   comic book   plan

(1) Those _____ are very popular among teenagers.
(2) I don't have any _____ for today.
(3) City Hall is on the next _____.
(4) Many people are sitting at an outdoor _____.

Conversation

1 계획 묻고 답하기

> **A** What are you planning to do on your trip? 여행에서 뭐 할 계획이니?
> **B** I'm planning to go hiking. 하이킹을 할 계획이야.

- 계획을 물을 때는 동사 plan을 써서 'What are you planning to 동사원형 ~?'으로 물을 수 있다. to부정사 뒤에는 구체적인 활동이나 계획을 나타낸다. 답을 할 때는 마찬가지로 'I'm planning to 동사원형 ~.'을 사용하여 세부 내용을 나타낸다.

- 계획을 물을 때 의문사 What을 쓰지 않고 구체적인 내용으로 물어볼 수도 있다.

계획을 물을 때

- What are you going to 동사원형 ~? (너는 무엇을 할 거니?/너는 무엇을 할 예정이니?)
- What are you planning to 동사원형 ~? (너는 무엇을 할 계획이니?)
- What are your plans for ~? (~에 대한 너의 계획은 무엇이니?)

계획을 대답할 때

- I'm going to 동사원형 ~. (~하려고 해.)
- I'm thinking of 동명사 ~. (~할 생각이야.)
- I'm planning to 동사원형 ~. (~할 계획이야.)

핵심 Check

1. 다음 우리말과 같도록 대화의 빈칸을 채우시오.

   A: _____ planning _____ after school? (너는 방과 후에 무엇을 할 계획이니?)

   B: _____ my history homework. (나는 역시 숙제를 할 계획이야.)

   A: _____ going to do tomorrow? (너는 내일 무엇을 할 거니?)

   B: I'm _____. (나는 영화를 볼 거야.)

2. 괄호 안의 단어들을 바르게 배열하여 대화를 완성하시오.

   A: _____ (weekend, planning, what, this, do, are, to, you, ?)

   B: _____ (in, to, I'm, Seoul, planning, visit, my, grandparents)

② 소요 시간 묻고 답하기

A How long does it take to get to school? 학교에 가는 데 얼마나 걸려?

B It takes 20 minutes. 20분 걸려.

- 어떤 일을 하는 데 소요되는 시간을 물을 때는 'How long does it take?'를 사용한다. 이때 'How long does it take to get to the airport?'에서처럼 to부정사를 이용하여 구체적인 내용을 밝힐 수 있다.

- 답으로는 'It takes ~.'에 시간 표현을 넣어 말한다. 여기서 take는 '(시간이) 걸리다'라는 의미로 사용되었다. 소요 시간을 말할 때 대략적인 시간을 말할 경우에는 시간 앞에 about을 붙여 쓴다. about은 '약, ~쯤'의 의미이다.

  ex) It takes about an hour to get home. (집에 도착하는 데 1시간쯤 걸려.)

소요 시간 묻기

- How long does it take to go to ~? (~에 가는 데 얼마나 걸려?)

소요 시간 대답하기

- It takes (about) 시간. (~ (정도) 걸려.)

핵심 Check

3. 대화가 자연스럽게 이어지도록 배열하시오.

   (1) (A) I usually ride a bike.
       (B) How long does it take?
       (C) How do you go to school?
       (D) It takes about 20 minutes.

       ➡ _____

   (2) (A) It takes about 30 minutes by bus.
       (B) Yes, there's one in Big Mall.
       (C) How long does it take to get there?
       (D) Is there a movie theater around here?
       (E) OK. Thanks.

       ➡ _____

4. 괄호 안의 단어들을 바르게 배열하여 대화를 완성하시오.

   A: _____ (how, does, take, it, long, ?)

   B: _____ (bus, takes, 30, it, by, minutes)

Listen & Talk 1 B

B: We have a long ❶holiday this month. ❷Do you have any plans?

G: ❸I'm going to visit my grandparents in Jeonju.

B: Oh, really? That's nice. ❹What are you planning to do with them?

G: ❺I'm planning to go to Hanok Village with them. How about you?
   ❻What are your plans for the holiday?

B: ❼I'm going to stay home and relax.

G: That's also a good idea!

남: 우리 이번 달에 긴 휴가가 있어. 무슨 계획이라도 있니?
여: 나는 전주에 있는 나의 조부모님을 방문할 예정이야.
남: 아, 그래? 좋구나. 그분들과 어떤 것을 할 계획이야?
여: 그분들과 한옥 마을에 갈 계획이야. 너는 어때? 휴가 때 무슨 계획 있어?
남: 나는 집에 머물면서 쉴 거야.
여: 그것도 좋은 아이디어!

❶ holiday: 휴가, 공휴일, 휴일
❷ 'Do you have any plans (for ~)?'는 계획이나 계획 여부를 물어보는 표현이다. 뒤에 for the long holiday가 생략되어 있다. 'What are you planning to do for the long holiday?', 'What are you going to do for the long holiday?'로 바꾸어 쓸 수 있다.
❸ 계획을 묻는 표현에 'be going to 동사원형(~할 예정이다.)'을 이용해 대답할 수 있다.
❹ them은 your grandparents를 받고 있다. 계획을 물을 때는 동사 plan을 써서 'What are you planning to 동사원형 ~?'으로 물을 수 있다. What are you planning to do with them? = What are you going to do with them?
❺ be planning to 동사원형: ~할 계획이다
❻ 'What are your plans for ~'는 '~에 무슨 계획이 있어?'라는 뜻으로 계획을 묻는 표현이다.
❼ be going to 동사원형: ~할 예정이다 stay(머무르다)와 relax(휴식을 취하다, 느긋이 쉬다)는 접속사 and로 연결되어 있다.

Check(√) True or False

(1) The boy will stay home during the holiday.　　　　T ☐ F ☐

(2) The girl visited her grandparents in Jeonju.　　　　T ☐ F ☐

Listen & Talk 2 A

G: ❶How do you get to school?

B: I go to school ❷by bus.

G: ❸How long does it take to get there?

B: ❹It takes 15 minutes.

여: 너 학교에 어떻게 가니?
남: 버스 타고 가.
여: 거기까지 가는 데 얼마나 걸려?
남: 15분 걸려.

❶ get to 장소: ~에 도착하다
❷ by 교통수단: 교통수단으로 → by bus: 버스로
❸ 특정 장소까지의 소요 시간을 물을 때는 'How long does it take to get ~?'라고 묻는다.
❹ 소요 시간을 묻는 질문의 대답은 'It takes 시간.'으로 대답한다. take: (얼마의 시간이) 걸리다

Check(√) True or False

(3) The boy goes to school by subway.　　　　T ☐ F ☐

(4) The girl asks the boy how he goes to school.　　　　T ☐ F ☐

Listen & Talk 1 A

B: ❶What are you going to do this weekend?

G: ❷I'm going to go to Jeju-do.

B: ❸What are you planning to do there?

G: ❹I'm planning to go hiking on Hallasan.

❶ 'What are you going to 동사원형 ~?'은 '너는 무엇을 할 거니?, 너는 무엇을 할 예정이니?'라는 뜻으로 계획에 대해 물을 때 사용하는 표현이다. (= What will you do this weekend? = What are you planning to do this weekend? = What are you thinking of doing this weekend?) this weekend: 이번 주말

❷ be going to 동사원형: ~할 예정이다

❸ What are you planning to 동사원형 ~?: 뭐 할 계획이야? there는 앞에 나온 Jeju-do를 받는다.

❹ be planning to 동사원형: ~할 계획이다

Listen & Talk 1 C

B: Hi, Nuri. Where is your class going for the ❶field trip tomorrow?

G: Hello, Mike. ❷We are going to the art museum.

B: ❸Sounds interesting. ❹What are you planning to see there?

G: ❺There are three art shows right now. ❻I'm planning to see Vincent van Gogh's paintings. Where is your class going?

B: ❼We are going to the amusement park. ❽I'm excited to ride a roller coaster!

G: That sounds fun. ❾Have a good trip!

❶ field trip: 견학 여행, 현장 학습

❷ be going to 동사원형: ~할 예정이다 art museum: 미술관

❸ 상대방이 한 말에 대하여 '재미있겠다'라는 표현으로 'Sounds interesting.'이나 'How interesting!' 등의 표현을 사용할 수 있다.

❹ What are you planning to 동사원형 ~?: 뭐 할 계획이야? there는 앞에서 나온 the art museum을 의미한다.

❺ there are+복수명사: ~가 있다 art show: 미술 전시회

❻ be planning to 동사원형: ~할 계획이다

❼ amusement park: 놀이공원

❽ 감정을 나타내는 동사의 경우 과거분사는 '~하게 된'의 뜻으로 감정을 느끼는 대상에 쓰인다. 그러므로 excited는 '신이 난'의 의미로 해석한다. to ride a roller coaster는 to부정사의 부사적 용법 중 감정의 원인으로 사용되었다.

❾ Have a good trip!: 좋은 여행하길 바라!

Listen & Talk 2 B

B: Wow, these ❶pictures are so beautiful. Where did you ❷take them?

G: At Riverside Park. There were ❸lots of flowers. ❹You should go there!

B: ❺I want to. ❻How do I get there from our school?

G: ❼Get on bus number 135 and get off at the Riverside Stadium stop. You can see the park ❽in front of the bus stop.

B: ❾How long does it take to get there?

G: It takes 30 minutes.

B: Thanks. I'll go there next weekend.

❶ picture: 사진

❷ take: (사진을) 찍다 them은 pictures를 받는 대명사이다.

❸ lots of: 많은 (= a lot of = many)

❹ 충고하는 표현으로 'You'd better go there!'로 바꾸어 쓸 수 있다.

❺ 'I want to.'뒤에 'go there'가 생략되어 있다.

❻ 찾아가려고 하는 장소를 물을 때 'How do I get 장소부사(to+장소)?'의 표현을 쓸 수 있다.

❼ get on: 타다, 승차하다 get off: 내리다, 하차하다 stop: 정거장

❽ in front of: ~ 앞에서

❾ 특정 장소까지의 소요 시간을 물을 때는 'How long does it take to get ~?'라고 묻는다.

Listen & Talk 2 C

B: Excuse me. How do I get to Hanguk University from here?

W: ❶You can go there by bus or on foot.

B: How long does it take to get there?

W: It takes five minutes by bus and 20 minutes on foot.

B: Oh, then I will walk there. ❷Can you tell me how to get there?

W: Go straight for two blocks, and then ❸turn left. You will see Hanguk University on your right.

B: Go straight for two blocks and turn left. Thank you!

❶ there는 Hanguk University를 의미한다. by bus: 버스로 on foot 걸어서, 도보로

❷ 'Can you tell me how to get ~?'은 길을 물어보는 표현이다. 'How can/do I get ~?'으로 바꾸어 쓸 수 있다.

❸ turn left: 좌회전하다 on your right: 당신의 오른편에

다음 우리말과 일치하도록 빈칸에 알맞은 말을 쓰시오. (주어진 철자가 있으면 그 철자로 시작할 것)

Listen & Talk 1 A

B: _____ _____ _____ going to do _____ weekend?

G: I'm _____ to _____ to Jeju-do.

B: _____ are _____ planning to _____ there?

G: _____ _____ _____ go hiking on Hallasan.

Listen & Talk 1 B

B: We _____ a long holiday _____ month. Do you _____ _____ plans?

G: I'm g_____ to visit my grandparents in Jeonju.

B: Oh, really? That's nice. _____ are you p_____ _____ do _____ them?

G: _____ p_____ to go to Hanok Village _____ _____. How _____ you? What are your _____ _____ the holiday?

B: I'm g_____ to _____ home and _____.

G: That's also a good idea!

Listen & Talk 1 C

B: Hi, Nuri. _____ is your class going for the _____ _____ tomorrow?

G: Hello, Mike. _____ _____ _____ _____ _____ the art museum.

B: Sounds i_____. What are you p_____ _____ _____ there?

G: There _____ three art shows right now. _____ p_____ _____ _____ Vincent van Gogh's paintings. _____ is your class going?

B: _____ _____ _____ _____ the _____ park. I'm _____ to ride a roller coaster!

G: That sounds fun. Have a good trip!

Listen & Talk 2 A

G: _____ do you _____ to school?

B: I go to school _____ bus.

G: _____ _____ does it _____ to _____ there?

B: _____ _____ 15 minutes.

해석

남: 너 이번 주말에 뭐 할 거야?
여: 제주도에 갈 거야.
남: 거기서 뭐 할 계획이야?
여: 한라산에 올라갈 계획이야.

남: 우리 이번 달에 긴 휴가가 있어. 무슨 계획이라도 있니?
여: 나는 전주에 있는 나의 조부모님을 방문할 예정이야.
남: 아, 그래? 좋다. 그분들과 어떤 것을 할 계획이야?
여: 그분들과 한옥 마을에 갈 계획이야. 너는 어때? 휴가 때 무슨 계획 있어?
남: 나는 집에 머물면서 쉴 거야.
여: 그것도 좋은 아이디어다!

남: 안녕, 누리야. 너희 반은 내일 현장 학습으로 어디 가니?
여: 안녕, 마이크. 우리는 미술관에 갈 거야.
남: 재미있겠다. 너 거기서 뭐 볼 계획이니?
여: 지금 3개의 전시회가 있어. 나는 빈센트 반 고흐의 그림을 볼 거야. 너희 반은 어디로 가니?
남: 우리는 놀이동산에 갈 거야. 롤러코스터를 타게 되어 신나!
여: 재미있겠다. 좋은 여행하길 바라!

여: 너 학교에 어떻게 가니?
남: 버스 타고 가.
여: 거기까지 가는 데 얼마나 걸려?
남: 15분 걸려.

Listen & Talk 2 B

B: Wow, these _____ are so _____. _____ did you _____ them?

G: At Riverside Park. There _____ lots _____ flowers. You _____ go there!

B: I want _____. _____ do I _____ there _____ our school?

G: _____ _____ bus number 135 and get _____ at the Riverside Stadium stop. You can _____ the park in _____ of the bus stop.

B: How _____ does it _____ to get there?

G: It _____ 30 minutes.

B: Thanks. I'll go there _____ _____.

Listen & Talk 2 C

B: Excuse me. _____ _____ _____ _____ _____ Hanguk University from here?

W: You can _____ _____ _____ _____ _____ _____ _____.

B: _____ _____ does it _____ to get there?

W: It takes five minutes _____ bus and 20 minutes _____ _____.

B: Oh, then I will walk there. _____ _____ _____ me _____ _____ _____ there?

W: _____ straight for two blocks, and then _____ left. You will see Hanguk University _____ your right.

B: _____ straight _____ two blocks and _____ _____. Thank you!

Do It Yourself A

G: _____ are you p_____ _____ weekend?

B: I'm planning _____ _____ a baseball game in Daegu.

G: _____ _____ going _____ _____ the All-Star Game?

B: Yes. It _____ be fun. Also, _____ planning _____ _____ my friend there.

G: Nice. _____ _____ does it take to get there?

B: It takes _____ _____ _____ express train.

G: Wow, it's _____ faster _____ I thought. I hope you _____ a good trip!

B: Thank you.

해석

남: 와, 이 사진들 너무 예쁘다. 어디서 찍었어?
여: Riverside Park에서. 꽃이 많았어. 넌 거기 꼭 가 봐야 해!
남: 나도 가고 싶어. 학교에서 거기까지 어떻게 가니?
여: 135번 버스를 타고 Riverside Stadium 정류장에서 내리면 돼. 버스 정류장 앞에 공원이 보일 거야.
남: 거기까지 가는 데 얼마나 걸려?
여: 30분 걸려.
남: 고마워. 다음 주말에 그곳에 가야겠다.

남: 실례합니다. 여기서 한국 대학교까지 어떻게 가나요?
여: 버스 타고 가거나 걸어서 갈 수 있어요.
남: 거기까지 가는 데 얼마나 걸리나요?
여: 버스 타면 5분 걸리고, 걸어서는 20분 걸려요.
남: 아, 그러면 걸어서 갈래요. 어떻게 가는지 말해 줄 수 있나요?
여: 2블록 직진한 다음에 좌회전하세요. 그러면 오른쪽에 한국 대학교가 보일 거예요.
남: 2블록 직진해서 좌회전이요. 감사합니다!

여: 이번 주말에 너는 무엇을 할 계획이니?
남: 나는 대구에 야구 경기를 보러 갈 계획이야.
여: 올 스타 경기를 보러 갈 예정이야?
남: 응. 재미있을 거야. 또한, 그곳에서 내 친구를 만날 계획이야.
여: 좋다. 거기까지 가는 데 얼마나 걸리니?
남: 급행열차로 1시간 40분이 걸려.
여: 와, 내가 생각한 것보다 훨씬 더 빠르다. 즐거운 여행이 되길 바랄게.
남: 고마워.

01 대화의 빈칸에 들어갈 말로 적절한 것을 <u>모두</u> 고르시오.

> B: _____
> G: I'm going to go to Jeju-do.

① What did you do last weekend?
② What are you going to do this weekend?
③ Where are you going now?
④ How was your trip to Jeju-do?
⑤ What are you planning to do this weekend?

02 대화의 빈칸에 들어갈 말로 적절한 것을 고르시오.

> G: How do you get to school?
> B: I go to school by bus.
> G: How long does it take to get there?
> B: _____

① I usually take the bus.   ② It arrives at 8.
③ I'd like to go to school by bus. ④ It takes 15 minutes.
⑤ I'm going to school.

03 대화의 빈칸에 들어갈 말로 적절하지 <u>않은</u> 것은?

> G: What are you planning to do this weekend?
> B: I _____ to a baseball game in Daegu.

① am planning to go   ② am going to go
③ am able to go   ④ am thinking of going
⑤ will go

04 다음 중 의미가 <u>다른</u> 하나를 고르시오.

① What are your plans for the holiday?
② What are you going to do for the holiday?
③ What are you doing for the holiday?
④ What are you planning to do for the holiday?
⑤ What are you thinking of doing for the holiday?

[01~03] 다음 대화를 읽고 물음에 답하시오.

B: Wow, these pictures are so beautiful. (①)

G: At Riverside Park. There were lots of flowers. (②) You should go there!

B: (A)I want to. (③) How do I get there from our school?

G: Get on bus number 135 and get off at the Riverside Stadium stop. (④) You can see the park in front of the bus stop.

B: How long does it take to get there? (⑤)

G: It takes 30 minutes.

B: Thanks. I'll go there next weekend.

01 위 대화의 ①~⑤ 중 주어진 문장이 들어갈 알맞은 곳은?

> Where did you take them?

①　　②　　③　　④　　⑤

서답형
02 밑줄 친 문장 (A)에서 뒤에 생략된 것을 대화에서 찾아 쓰시오.

➡ _____

03 위 대화의 내용과 일치하지 <u>않는</u> 것을 고르시오.

① To get to Riverside Park from school, the boy has to take bus number 135.

② The girl took pictures at Riverside Park.

③ It takes 30 minutes to go from school to Riverside Park by bus.

④ The boy is going to Riverside Park this weekend.

⑤ There are a lot of flowers at Riverside Park.

 다음 짝지어진 대화가 <u>어색한</u> 것은?

① A: What are you going to do this weekend?
　 B: I'm going to take a trip with my family.

② A: Are you going to take a taxi?
　 B: Yes, I am.

③ A: Where are you going to go this weekend?
　 B: I'm planning to go to the library to borrow some books.

④ A: How long does it take to get there?
　 B: It is about 5 km.

⑤ A: How do you get to school?
　 B: I go to school on foot.

05 대화의 순서가 올바르게 배열된 것을 고르시오.

> (A) How long does it take to get there?
> (B) I go to school by bus.
> (C) How do you get to school?
> (D) It takes 15 minutes.

① (A) – (C) – (D) – (B)
② (A) – (D) – (B) – (C)
③ (C) – (A) – (D) – (B)
④ (C) – (B) – (A) – (D)
⑤ (C) – (D) – (B) – (A)

[06~08] 다음 대화를 읽고 물음에 답하시오.

B: Excuse me. (A)_____ do I get to Hanguk University from here? (①)

W: You can go there by bus or on foot.

B: (B)_____ does it take to get there? (②)

W: It (C)<u>takes</u> five minutes by bus and 20 minutes on foot. (③)

B: Oh, then I will walk there. (④)

W: Go straight for two blocks, and then turn left. You will see Hanguk University on your right. (⑤)

B: Go straight for two blocks and turn left. Thank you!

06 위 대화의 ①~⑤ 중 주어진 문장이 들어갈 알맞은 곳은?

Can you tell me how to get there?

①   ②   ③   ④   ⑤

07 🔵 중요
빈칸 (A)와 (B)에 들어갈 말이 알맞게 짝지어진 것을 고르시오.

	(A)	(B)
①	How	How long
②	How	How
③	How long	How long
④	How long	How
⑤	How	How far

08 밑줄 친 (C)takes와 같은 의미로 쓰인 것을 <u>모두</u> 고르시오.

① I want to take some pictures.

② It doesn't take much time.

③ Did you take an umbrella in the morning?

④ When I go to school, I take a bus.

⑤ It will take a lot of time to prepare it.

[09~12] 다음 대화를 읽고 물음에 답하시오.

B: We (A)_____ a long holiday this month. Do you (B)_____ any plans?

G: (C)_____ (①)

B: Oh, really? (②) That's nice. What are you planning to do with them? (③)

G: I'm planning to go to Hanok Village with them. How about you? (④)

B: 나는 집에 머물면서 쉴 거야. (⑤)

G: That's also a good idea!

09 🔵 중요
위 대화의 ①~⑤ 중 주어진 문장이 들어갈 알맞은 곳은?

What are your plans for the holiday?

①   ②   ③   ④   ⑤

서답형

10 빈칸 (A)와 (B)에 공통으로 들어갈 말을 쓰시오.

➡ _____

11 빈칸 (C)에 알맞은 말을 고르시오.

① I'm going to go to Jeonju.

② I'm planning to go hiking.

③ I'm going to go to Jeju-do.

④ I'm planning to eat local dishes in Jeonju.

⑤ I'm going to visit my grandparents in Jeonju.

서답형

12 밑줄 친 우리말에 맞게 주어진 단어를 이용해 빈칸을 채우시오.

➡ _____

(stay, going, relax)

Conversation 서술형 시험대비

[01~02] 다음 대화를 읽고 물음에 답하시오.

B: What are you going (A)_____ this weekend?
G: I'm going to go to Jeju-do.
B: What are you planning (B)_____ there?
G: I'm planning to go hiking on Hallasan.

01 빈칸 (A)와 (B)에 공통으로 들어갈 말을 쓰시오.

➡ _____

02 대화의 내용과 일치하도록 빈칸을 채우시오.

| The boy is asking the girl what _____ |
| _____. She _____ |
| _____ Jeju-do and she _____ |
| _____ on Hallasan. |

[03~04] 다음 대화를 읽고 물음에 답하시오.

A: Where will you go?
B: _____
A: _____
B: _____
A: _____
B: ⓐI'm planning to watch a soccer game.

03 위 대화의 빈칸에 들어갈 말의 기호를 순서대로 쓰시오.

(A) It takes 14 hours by plane.
(B) How long does it take to get there?
(C) What are you planning to do there?
(D) I will go to Barcelona.

➡ _____

04 밑줄 친 ⓐ와 같은 뜻이 되도록 주어진 단어를 이용해 영작하시오.

(1) _____ (will)
(2) _____ (go)
(3) _____ (think)

[05~06] 다음 대화를 읽고 물음에 답하시오.

B: Hi, Nuri. Where is your class going for the field trip tomorrow?
G: Hello, Mike. We are going to the art museum.
B: Sounds (A)_____(interest). 너 거기서 뭐 볼 계획이니?
G: There are three art shows right now. I'm planning to see Vincent van Gogh's paintings. Where is your class going?
B: We are going to the amusement park. I'm (B)_____(excite) to ride a roller coaster!
G: That sounds fun. Have a good trip!

05 빈칸 (A)와 (B)를 주어진 단어를 이용하여 채우시오.

➡ (A) _____ (B) _____

06 밑줄 친 우리말에 맞게 영작하시오. (7 단어)

➡ _____

Grammar

① 가주어 it

> - **It** was interesting **to see** all the international goods there. 그곳에서 세계 곳곳의 상품들을 모두 볼 수 있어서 흥미로웠다.
> - **It** is good **to have** friends but bad **to need** them. 친구가 있는 것은 좋다. 그러나 그들이 필요하게 되면 좋지 않다. (서양 속담)

■ 문장의 주어로 쓰인 to부정사가 수식어로 인해 길어진 경우, 보통 to부정사를 뒤로 보내고 대신 주어 자리에 가주어 it을 둔다. 이때 쓰인 it은 가주어이므로 구체적인 뜻이 없으며, '…하는 것은 ~하다'로 해석한다.

- **It** is easy **to use** a fire alarm box. 화재 경보 박스를 이용하는 것은 쉽다.
  = **To use** a fire alarm box is easy.

- **It** is interesting **to learn** a new language. 새로운 언어를 배우는 것은 흥미로운 일이다.
  = **To learn** a new language is interesting.

- **It** is so exciting **to watch** the soccer game with my friends. 나의 친구들과 함께 축구 경기를 관람하는 것은 정말 흥미진진하다.
  = **To watch** the soccer game with my friends is so exciting.

■ to부정사의 의미상 주어가 필요한 경우에는 'for+명사[목적격 대명사]'를 to부정사 앞에 쓴다. 또한 to부정사의 부정은 to부정사 앞에 not[never]을 써서 'not[never]+to V'로 나타내며 '…하지 않는 것은 ~하다'로 해석한다.

- **It** is good for children **to drink** milk often. 어린이들이 우유를 자주 마시는 것은 좋다.

- **It** is important **not to use** your phone while walking. 걸어가면서 전화기를 사용하지 않는 것은 중요하다.

- I had to try hard **not to cry**. 나는 울지 않으려고 무척 노력해야 했어요.

핵심 Check

1. 다음 우리말과 일치하도록 빈칸에 알맞은 말을 쓰시오.

(1) 이 시간에 길에 주차하는 것이 안전한가요?
  ➡ Is _____ _____ _____ park on the street at this time?

(2) 최저 임금으로 가정을 부양하기란 힘들다.
  ➡ _____ is difficult _____ support a family on the minimum wage.

(3) 붐비는 시간에는 차를 안 가지고 나가는 게 중요하다.
  ➡ It is _____ _____ _____ take the car out during rush hours.

② 간접의문문

> • Do you know **where the first train station in Korea is**? 한국 최초의 기차역이 어디인지 아세요?
>
> • Tell me **whether he is at home**. 그가 집에 있는지 말해 줘.

■ 간접의문문이란 의문문이 '의문사+주어+동사' 형태로 다른 문장 안에서 주어, 목적어, 보어 역할을 하는 것을 말한다. 명사처럼 쓰이므로 주로 '…가 ~하는지'로 해석한다.
  • **How he solved it** is unknown. <주어 역할> 그가 그것을 어떻게 해결했는지는 알려지지 않았다.
  • Rob didn't remember **what her name was**. <목적어 역할> Rob는 그녀의 이름이 무엇이었는지 기억하지 못했다.
  • This is **how she solved the problem**. <보어 역할> 이런 식으로 그녀는 그 문제를 처리했다.

■ 의문사가 주어인 경우에는 의문사가 주어 역할을 하므로 직접의문문처럼 '의문사+동사'의 어순임에 유의한다.
  • Do you know **who wrote this book**? 누가 이 책을 썼는지 아니?

■ 간접의문문으로 바꾸어 쓸 때에는 조동사 do를 삭제한다. 이때, 의문문에 쓰인 조동사의 시제를 간접의문문의 동사에 반영해야 한다는 점에 유의해야 한다.
  • Please tell me. + What did you do last night?
  → Please tell me **what you did last night**.

■ 의문사가 없는 경우에는 의문사 대신에 if나 whether를 쓴다.
  • Will you tell me? + Are you hungry?
  → Will you tell me **if[whether] you are hungry**? 배가 고픈지 내게 말해 줄래?

■ believe, imagine, suppose, consider, expect, think, guess 등과 같은 동사가 주절에 있을 경우 간접의문문의 의문사를 문장 맨 앞에 놓는다.
  • Do you think? + Who is he?
  → Do you think who he is? (×)
  → **Who** do you think **he is**? (○) 너는 그가 누구라고 생각하니?

핵심 Check

2. 다음 우리말과 일치하도록 빈칸에 알맞은 말을 쓰시오.

(1) 네가 무엇을 샀는지 말해 줄 수 있니?
 ➡ Can you tell me _____ _____ _____?

(2) 나는 네가 그것을 좋아하는지 궁금해.
 ➡ I wonder _____ _____ _____ it.

(3) 너는 누가 그 경기에서 이길 거라고 생각하니?
 ➡ _____ _____ _____ _____ _____ win the game?

01 다음 두 문장을 한 문장으로 연결할 때 올바른 것은?

> • Do you know? • What is it famous for?

① Do you know what is it famous for?
② Do you know what it is famous for?
③ Do you know it is famous for what?
④ What do you know it is famous for?
⑤ What do you know is it famous for?

02 다음 밑줄 친 부분의 쓰임이 나머지와 다른 하나는?

① For me, it is possible to do ten push-ups.
② It is exciting to fly a model airplane.
③ It's about two miles from here to the beach.
④ It is very difficult to be good at English.
⑤ It's not easy to have meals in space.

03 다음 빈칸에 알맞은 것을 고르시오.

> A: Do you know _____?
> B: It's on the desk.

① where does the book
② where the books are
③ where are the books
④ where is the book
⑤ where the book is

04 주어진 어구를 바르게 배열하여 다음 우리말을 영어로 쓰시오.

(1) 카페에서 휴식을 취하며 그 책들을 읽는 것이 좋았다. (in a café, nice, relax, read, was, the books, it, and, to)

　➡ _____

(2) 한국 최초의 기차역이 어디인지 아세요? (the first train station, Korea, where, you, know, is, do, in, ?)

　➡ _____

01 다음 중 어법상 바르지 <u>않은</u> 것은?

① It is difficult to study English hard every day.
② That's so kind of you to say so.
③ It is not good to watch too much TV.
④ It's important to decide a topic for the presentation.
⑤ Homer wonders why he feels so hungry today.

 02 다음 빈칸에 들어갈 말로 가장 적절한 것은?

> Do you know _____?

① Hammington is from where
② where is Hammington from
③ where Hammington is from
④ is where Hammington from
⑤ from Hammington is where

03 다음 괄호 안에서 알맞은 말을 고르시오.

(1) (It / That) is difficult to say how many people use it.
(2) It is great (to win / win) a race.
(3) For me, it is possible to (stand / standing) on one leg for a minute.
(4) We have no idea when (she left / did she leave) the village.
(5) She knows who (is he / he is).
(6) I don't know (that / if) he will come.

 04 다음 중 밑줄 친 부분의 쓰임이 <u>다른</u> 하나는?

① <u>It</u> is difficult to live without a smartphone.
② <u>It</u> is good to change the water filter every month.
③ <u>It</u>'s common practice to tip 15 percent of the total bill.
④ <u>It</u> was found behind the sofa in the living room.
⑤ <u>It</u> is dangerous for her to climb the mountain.

05 다음 우리말을 영어로 바르게 옮긴 것은?

> 너는 그의 생일이 언제인지 기억하니?

① When do you remember his birthday is?
② When do you remember is his birthday?
③ Do you remember when is his birthday?
④ Do you remember his birthday is when?
⑤ Do you remember when his birthday is?

06 주어진 단어를 활용하여 다음 우리말을 영어로 쓰시오.

> 한국에서 인터넷을 사용하는 것은 어렵지 않다.
> (it, difficult, the Internet)

➡ _____

07 다음 중 밑줄 친 부분의 어순이 올바르지 <u>않은</u> 것은?

① Do you know <u>when World War II ended</u>?
② <u>Why he has bad breath</u> is unknown.
③ I wondered <u>if she would come to the party or not</u>.
④ Tell me <u>if or not you like Jenny</u>.
⑤ I'm not sure <u>whether it is enough or not</u>.

08 다음 중 빈칸에 들어갈 말이 바르게 짝지어진 것은?

> • _____ is no use _____ over spilt milk.

① This – crying
② That – cry
③ That – crying
④ It – cry
⑤ It – crying

09 다음 중 어법상 바르지 <u>않은</u> 것은?

> ①It ②is ③good ④to exercising ⑤every day.

①　　②　　③　　④　　⑤

10 다음 중 어법상 바르지 <u>않은</u> 문장의 개수는?

> ⓐ It's nice of you help the elderly.
> ⓑ Do you know how dogs swim?
> ⓒ I wonder will he come today.
> ⓓ It was difficult for me understanding the story.
> ⓔ It was wonderful to share the moment with you.

① 1개　② 2개　③ 3개　④ 4개　⑤ 5개

11 우리말과 의미가 같도록 빈칸에 들어갈 말로 알맞은 것을 고르시오.

> • 나는 그가 내일 집으로 돌아올지 알 필요가 있어.
> → I need to know _____ back home tomorrow.

① if he will come
② he will come
③ will he come
④ whether he comes
⑤ that he comes

12 다음 중 빈칸에 들어갈 말이 <u>다른</u> 하나는?

① _____ is brave of you to share such personal things about yourself.
② _____ English in a short period is not easy.
③ _____ was careless of you to say such a thing.
④ _____ is great to find cute animals.
⑤ _____ is necessary for you to go there right now.

13 다음 두 문장을 간접의문문으로 바르게 바꾼 것은?

> • Do you know?
> • Who is Leonardo da Vinci?

① Who is Leonardo da Vinci do you know?
② Who do you know is Leonardo da Vinci?
③ Who do you know Leonardo da Vinci is?
④ Do you know who is Leonardo da Vinci?
⑤ Do you know who Leonardo da Vinci is?

14 다음 중 어법상 바르지 <u>않은</u> 것은?

① It is interesting to ride a skateboard.
② It was foolish of her think so.
③ It's important for children to be taught grammar.
④ It is difficult to learn Greek.
⑤ It is fun to learn a foreign language.

서답형
15 다음 문장에서 어법상 어색한 것을 바르게 고쳐 다시 쓰시오.

(1) Ride a motorcycle without a helmet is dangerous.

⇒ _____

(2) It is great make good friends in your life.

⇒ _____

(3) This is not easy to keep a diary in English every day.

⇒ _____

(4) It is important for learn the history of your country.

⇒ _____

(5) The girl is asking where is the nearest bus stop.

⇒ _____

(6) Do you know will the leaves turn yellow in autumn?

⇒ _____

(7) Will you tell me when did you meet her?

⇒ _____

16 다음 빈칸에 들어갈 말로 알맞은 것은?

> I'd like to ask you _____ you're free tonight.

① because   ② that   ③ as
④ if   ⑤ what

17 다음 두 문장이 같도록 할 때 빈칸에 알맞은 것은?

> To understand others fully is not easy.
> → It is not easy _____ others fully.

① understand   ② understands
③ to understanding   ④ to understands
⑤ to understand

18 다음 중 밑줄 친 부분의 쓰임이 <u>다른</u> 하나는?

① It is fun <u>to play</u> volleyball on the beach.
② I was so glad <u>to hear</u> from you again.
③ Mike must be a fool <u>to do</u> such a stupid thing.
④ Carol went to her home country never <u>to return</u>.
⑤ Her grandmother lived <u>to be</u> 110 years old.

서답형
19 그림을 참고하여 다음 빈칸에 알맞은 말을 쓰시오.

> A: Let me know _____ _____ _____ study last night.
> B: I couldn't because of the loud music.

01 다음 두 문장을 하나의 문장으로 바꿔 쓰시오.

(1) Tell me. + What do you want for Christmas?

➡ _____

(2) She asked me. + How much sugar is there in the coke?

➡ _____

(3) Do you know? + Where is Greece on the map?

➡ _____

(4) I wonder. + Is he a singer?

➡ _____

(5) I have no idea. + Will he join us soon?

➡ _____

(6) Do you think? + Where does your soul go after you die?

➡ _____

02 to부정사를 진주어로 하여 주어진 문장과 같은 의미가 되도록 쓰시오.

(1) That high mountain is dangerous to climb.

➡ _____

(2) This road is not safe to walk on as it is very slippery.

➡ _____

(3) He is very smart to teach himself.

➡ _____

03 다음 사진을 참고하여 주어진 대화의 빈칸을 완성하시오.

A: Look at this picture. Do you know (1)_____?

B: Yeah, it's Moai.

A: Could you tell me (2)_____?

B: It is in Easter island in Chile.

04 다음 문장을 가주어 · 진주어 구문으로 바꿔 쓰시오.

(1) To ride on the rough water and enjoy the view at the same time was exciting.

➡ _____
_____

(2) Trying to excuse yourself is no good.

➡ _____

(3) Not to take the car out during rush hours is wise.

➡ _____

(4) Continuing the search is no use.

➡ _____

(5) For Laura to marry such a man is highly regrettable.

➡ _____

05 두 문장을 한 문장으로 만들었을 때, 나머지 한 문장을 쓰시오.

(1) • He is asking.

  + • _____

  → He is asking how long it takes to reach the top.

(2) • The woman was not sure.

  + • _____

  → The woman was not sure if the thief was a man or a woman.

(3) • Do you believe?

  + • _____

  → What do you believe the secret of his success is?

06 다음 문장을 It으로 시작하여 다시 쓰시오.

(1) To read your handwriting is hard.

  ➡ _____

(2) To swim in this river is very dangerous.

  ➡ _____

(3) To read and write Hangeul is very easy.

  ➡ _____

(4) For me to run 1,000 meters in three minutes is impossible.

  ➡ _____

    _____

(5) That she passed the exam is unbelievable.

  ➡ _____

07 다음 문장을 어법에 맞게 고쳐 쓰시오.

(1) This is dangerous to cross this street at night.

  ➡ _____

(2) It is important to not give up.

  ➡ _____

(3) That was believed that Mike told a lie to his friends.

  ➡ _____

(4) The doctor will ask you what did you eat for breakfast.

  ➡ _____

(5) Please let us know are you able to attend.

  ➡ _____

    _____

(6) Do you suppose what they are thinking?

  ➡ _____

08 괄호 안에 주어진 어휘를 이용하여 다음 우리말을 영작하시오.

(1) 그곳의 자연의 아름다움을 보는 것은 매우 놀라웠다. (amazing, so, it, to)

  ➡ _____

(2) 작은 모험을 하는 것이 필요했다. (necessary, take, risks, it, to)

  ➡ _____

(3) Daniel은 그가 어떻게 가수가 되었는지 우리에게 말해 주었다. (become, a singer)

  ➡ _____

(4) 그가 올지 안 올지 의심스럽다. (doubtful, whether, come, or)

  ➡ _____

The Best Moment of the Field Trip

Teacher: Good morning, everyone! How were your field trips last
week? Please tell us about them!
지난주에   =your field trips last week

Busan, Market Heaven

Do you like traditional markets? Then go to Gukje Market in Busan.
=If you like traditional markets,
It is one of the most famous markets in Busan. Do you know what it is
one of the +최상급+복수 명사: ~ 중의 하나
famous for? It is famous for selling a variety of goods from different
'의문사+주어+동사'의 어순으로 쓰인 간접의문문으로, 동사 know의 목적어
countries. It was interesting to see all the international goods there.
가주어   to see 이하는 진주어
We also ate many kinds of street food, such as *Gimbap*, fish cake, and
= like: ~와 같은
Hotteok. Then we walked to Bosu-dong Book Street. Many bookstores
there sell used books.
그곳에 있는   중고 책
We were really excited because we found some old comic books!
~이기 때문에(접속사)
It was nice to relax in a café and read them.
가주어   to relax 이하는 진주어

be famous for ~으로 유명하다
moment 순간
field trip 견학 여행, 현장 학습
traditional 전통적인
a variety of 여러 가지의, 다양한
goods 상품, 제품
bookstore 책방, 서점
comic book 만화책
relax 휴식을 취하다, 느긋이 쉬다

📎 확인문제

- 다음 문장이 본문의 내용과 일치하면 T, 일치하지 <u>않으면</u> F를 쓰시오.

1   Gukje Market is one of the most famous markets in Busan. ☐

2   Gukje Market is famous for selling a variety of goods made in Korea. ☐

3   Many bookstores on Bosu-dong Book Street sell new books. ☐

4   It was nice to relax in a café and read some old comic books. ☐

Gangwon-do, Full of Natural Beauty

There is no place like Gangwon-do for beautiful nature. First, we went to Baengnyong Cave. This 1.8-kilometer-long cave is still in good condition. It was so amazing to see its natural beauty. Near the end of our cave tour, the guide turned off the lights in the cave for a minute. Everything became very dark, so we were able to focus on the sounds there. It was the most amazing experience of the tour! Our next stop was Donggang. We went rafting! It was exciting to ride on the rough water and enjoy the view at the same time.

Incheon, A City of Firsts

Do you know where the first train station in Korea is? How about the first *Jajangmyeon*? The answer is Incheon! This place has many of Korea's firsts. To get there, we went to Incheon Station.

The Jajangmyeon Museum is next to the station. We learned about the history of *Jajangmyeon* there. Later, we walked around Jayu Park, the first Western-style park in Korea. The view from the park was awesome! It was great to see the historical sites of this city from the park.

Teacher: Wow, these places sound great! You all have done a wonderful job on your presentations!

 확인문제

● 다음 문장이 본문의 내용과 일치하면 T, 일치하지 <u>않으면</u> F를 쓰시오.

1 Baengnyong Cave is still in good condition. ☐

2 Near the end of the cave tour, the guide turned on the lights in the cave for a minute. ☐

3 Everything became very dark, so the students couldn't focus on the sounds in the cave. ☐

4 The first train station in Korea is in Incheon. ☐

5 The Jajangmyeon Museum is next to Incheon Station. ☐

6 Jayu Park is the first Eastern-style park in Korea. ☐

condition 상태
focus on ~에 초점을 맞추다
stop 멈춤, (잠시) 머묾
rough 파도가 심한, 거친
at the same time 동시에, 한꺼번에
Western-style 서양풍의, 서양식의
site 장소
presentation 발표, 제출

● 우리말을 참고하여 빈칸에 알맞은 말을 쓰시오.

1 _____ _____ _____ of the Field Trip

2 Teacher: Good morning, everyone! _____ _____ your field trips last week? _____ _____ _____ about them!

3 Busan, _____ _____

4 Do you like _____ _____ ?

5 _____ go to Gukje Market in Busan.

6 It is _____ _____ _____ _____ _____ _____ in Busan.

7 Do you know _____ _____ _____ _____ _____ ?

8 It is famous for selling _____ _____ _____ goods from different countries.

9 It was interesting to see _____ _____ _____ _____ there.

10 We also ate _____ _____ _____ street food, _____ _____ *Gimbap*, fish cake, and *Hotteok*.

11 _____ we walked to Bosu-dong Book Street.

12 Many bookstores there sell _____ _____ .

13 We were _____ _____ because we found some old comic books!

14 It was nice _____ _____ in a café and read them.

15 Gangwon-do, _____ _____ _____ _____

16 There is _____ _____ _____ Gangwon-do for beautiful nature.

17 _____ , we went to Baengnyong Cave.

18 This 1.8-kilometer-long cave is still _____ _____ .

19 It was _____ _____ to see its natural beauty.

1 수학여행에서의 가장 좋았던 순간

2 교사: 안녕하세요, 여러분! 지난 주 수학여행은 어땠나요? 얘기해 봅시다!

3 부산, 시장 천국

4 전통 시장을 좋아하세요?

5 그렇다면 부산에 있는 국제시장으로 가세요.

6 그곳은 부산에서 가장 유명한 시장 중 하나입니다.

7 그곳이 무엇으로 유명한지 아세요?

8 그 시장은 여러 나라에서 온 다양한 제품들을 파는 것으로 유명합니다.

9 그곳에서 세계 곳곳의 제품들을 모두 볼 수 있어서 흥미로웠습니다.

10 우리는 또한 김밥, 어묵 그리고 호떡과 같은 여러 종류의 길거리 음식을 먹었습니다.

11 그러고 나서 우리는 보수동 책방 거리로 걸어갔습니다.

12 그곳의 많은 서점에서는 중고책을 팝니다.

13 우리는 몇 권의 오래된 만화책을 발견해서 정말 신이 났습니다!

14 카페에서 휴식을 취하며 그 책들을 읽는 것이 좋았습니다.

15 강원도, 자연의 아름다움으로 가득한 곳

16 아름다운 자연에 관한 한 강원도만 한 곳이 없습니다.

17 우선, 우리는 백룡동굴로 갔습니다.

18 이 1.8킬로미터 길이의 동굴은 여전히 잘 보존된 상태입니다.

19 그곳의 자연의 아름다움을 보는 것은 매우 놀라웠습니다.

20 Near the end of our cave tour, the guide _____ _____ the lights in the cave _____ _____ _____.

21 Everything became very dark, so we were able to _____ _____ the sounds there.

22 It was _____ _____ _____ _____ of the tour!

23 _____ _____ _____ was Donggang.

24 We _____ _____!

25 It was exciting to ride on the rough water and enjoy the view _____ _____ _____ _____.

26 Incheon, A City of _____

27 Do you know _____ the first train station in Korea _____?

28 _____ _____ the first *Jajangmyeon*?

29 _____ _____ is Incheon!

30 This place has many of _____ _____.

31 _____ _____ _____, we went to Incheon Station.

32 The Jajangmyeon Museum is _____ _____ the station.

33 We learned about _____ _____ _____ _____ there.

34 Later, we walked around Jayu Park, _____ _____ _____ _____ in Korea.

35 The view _____ the park was _____!

36 It was great to see _____ _____ of this city from the park.

37 Teacher: Wow, these places _____ _____!

38 You all have done a wonderful job _____ _____ _____!

---

20 동굴 관광의 끝 무렵, 안내인이 동굴 안의 불을 잠시 껐습니다.

21 모든 것이 매우 어두워져서, 우리는 그곳의 소리에 집중할 수 있었습니다.

22 그것은 여행에서 가장 경이로운 경험이었습니다!

23 우리의 다음 여행지는 동강이었습니다.

24 우리는 래프팅을 하러 갔습니다!

25 급류를 타면서 동시에 경치를 즐기는 것은 흥미진진했습니다.

26 인천, '최초의 것'들의 도시

27 한국 최초의 기차역이 어디인지 아세요?

28 첫 번째 자장면은요?

29 그 답은 인천입니다!

30 이곳에는 한국의 최초의 것들이 많이 있습니다.

31 그곳으로 가기 위하여, 우리는 인천역으로 갔습니다.

32 자장면 박물관은 역 옆에 있습니다.

33 우리는 그곳에서 자장면의 역사에 대하여 배웠습니다.

34 다음에는, 한국 최초의 서구식 공원인 자유 공원을 거닐었습니다.

35 공원에서 바라본 경치는 정말 멋있었습니다!

36 공원에서 이 도시의 역사적인 장소들을 바라보는 것은 아주 좋았습니다.

37 교사: 와, 이 장소들은 멋지게 들리네요!

38 여러분 모두 발표를 훌륭하게 잘했어요!

우리말을 참고하여 본문을 영작하시오.

1 수학여행에서의 가장 좋았던 순간
➡ _____

2 교사: 안녕하세요, 여러분! 지난주 수학여행은 어땠나요? 얘기해 봅시다!
➡ _____

3 부산, 시장 천국
➡ _____

4 전통 시장을 좋아하세요?
➡ _____

5 그렇다면 부산에 있는 국제시장으로 가세요.
➡ _____

6 그곳은 부산에서 가장 유명한 시장 중 하나입니다.
➡ _____

7 그곳이 무엇으로 유명한지 아세요?
➡ _____

8 그 시장은 여러 나라에서 온 다양한 제품들을 파는 것으로 유명합니다.
➡ _____

9 그곳에서 세계 곳곳의 제품들을 모두 볼 수 있어서 흥미로웠습니다.
➡ _____

10 우리는 또한 김밥, 어묵 그리고 호떡과 같은 여러 종류의 길거리 음식을 먹었습니다
➡ _____

11 그러고 나서 우리는 보수동 책방 거리로 걸어갔습니다.
➡ _____

12 그곳의 많은 서점에서는 중고 책을 팝니다.
➡ _____

13 우리는 몇 권의 오래된 만화책을 발견해서 정말 신이 났습니다!
➡ _____

14 카페에서 휴식을 취하며 그 책들을 읽는 것이 좋았습니다.
➡ _____

15 강원도, 자연의 아름다움으로 가득한 곳
➡ _____

16 아름다운 자연에 관한 한 강원도만 한 곳이 없습니다.
➡ _____

17 우선, 우리는 백룡동굴로 갔습니다.
➡ _____

18 이 1.8킬로미터 길이의 동굴은 여전히 잘 보존된 상태입니다.
➡ _____

19 그곳의 자연의 아름다움을 보는 것은 매우 놀라웠습니다.

➡ _____

20 동굴 관광의 끝 무렵, 안내인이 동굴 안의 불을 잠시 껐습니다.

➡ _____

21 모든 것이 매우 어두워져서, 우리는 그곳의 소리에 집중할 수 있었습니다.

➡ _____

22 그것은 여행에서 가장 경이로운 경험이었습니다!

➡ _____

23 우리의 다음 여행지는 동강이었습니다.

➡ _____

24 우리는 래프팅을 하러 갔습니다!

➡ _____

25 급류를 타면서 동시에 경치를 즐기는 것은 흥미진진했습니다.

➡ _____

26 인천, '최초의 것'들의 도시

➡ _____

27 한국 최초의 기차역이 어디인지 아세요?

➡ _____

28 첫 번째 자장면은요?

➡ _____

29 그 답은 인천입니다!

➡ _____

30 이곳에는 한국의 최초의 것들이 많이 있습니다.

➡ _____

31 그곳으로 가기 위하여, 우리는 인천역으로 갔습니다.

➡ _____

32 자장면 박물관은 역 옆에 있습니다.

➡ _____

33 우리는 그곳에서 자장면의 역사에 대하여 배웠습니다.

➡ _____

34 다음에는, 한국 최초의 서구식 공원인 자유 공원을 거닐었습니다.

➡ _____

35 공원에서 바라본 경치는 정말 멋있었습니다!

➡ _____

36 공원에서 이 도시의 역사적인 장소들을 바라보는 것은 아주 좋았습니다.

➡ _____

37 교사: 와, 이곳들은 멋지게 들리네요!

➡ _____

38 여러분 모두 발표를 훌륭하게 잘했어요!

➡ _____

[01~03] 다음 글을 읽고 물음에 답하시오.

ⓐ
_____

Do you like traditional markets? (①) It is one of the most famous markets in Busan. (②) Do you know what it is famous for? (③) It is famous for selling a variety of goods from different countries. (④) ⓑIt was interesting to see all the international goods there. (⑤) We also ate many kinds of street food, such as *Gimbap*, fish cake, and *Hotteok*. Then we walked to Bosu-dong Book Street. Many bookstores there sell used books. We were really excited because we found some old comic books! It was nice to relax in a café and read them.

중요

01 위 글의 빈칸 ⓐ에 들어갈 제목으로 알맞은 것을 고르시오.

① Busan, a Cultural City
② Busan, Market Heaven
③ How to Enjoy Street Food
④ Selling Goods at Gukje Market
⑤ Wow! Look at These Comic Books

중요

02 위 글의 흐름으로 보아, 주어진 문장이 들어가기에 가장 적절한 곳은?

> Then go to Gukje Market in Busan.

①   ②   ③   ④   ⑤

03 위 글의 밑줄 친 ⓑIt과 문법적 쓰임이 같은 것을 모두 고르시오.

① It is time to start for the airport.
② I think it wrong to tell a lie.
③ Is it possible to solve the problem?
④ It is important to exercise every day.
⑤ It is raining too heavily to go out.

[04~07] 다음 글을 읽고 물음에 답하시오.

Incheon, A City of Firsts

Do you know where the first train station in Korea is? ⓐHow about the first *Jajangmyeon*? The answer is Incheon! ⓑ이곳에는 한국의 최초의 것들이 많이 있습니다. To get there, we went to Incheon Station. The Jajangmyeon Museum is next to the station. We learned about the history of *Jajangmyeon* ⓒthere. Later, we walked around Jayu Park, the first Western-style park in Korea. The view from the park was awesome! It was great ⓓto see the historical sites of this city from the park.

서답형

04 위 글의 밑줄 친 ⓐHow about과 바꿔 쓸 수 있는 말을 쓰시오.

➡ _____

서답형

05 위 글의 밑줄 친 ⓑ의 우리말에 맞게 주어진 어휘를 이용하여 7 단어로 영작하시오.

> has, of, firsts

➡ _____

서답형

06 위 글의 밑줄 친 ⓒthere가 가리키는 것을 영어로 쓰시오. (4 단어)

➡ _____

07 위 글의 밑줄 친 ⓓto see와 to부정사의 용법이 같은 것을 고르시오. (2개)

① I am sorry to hear the news.
② To get up early is good for your health.
③ She has many friends to play with.
④ I found it easy to do so.
⑤ I go to school to learn many things.

[08~10] 다음 글을 읽고 물음에 답하시오.

Busan, Market Heaven

Do you like ①traditional markets? Then go to Gukje Market in Busan. It is one of the most famous markets in Busan. Do you know what it is famous for? It is famous for ⓐselling a variety of ②good from different countries. It was interesting to see all the ③ international goods ⓑthere. We also ate many ④kinds of street food, ⑤such as *Gimbap*, fish cake, and *Hotteok*. Then we walked to Bosu-dong Book Street. Many bookstores ⓒ there sell used books. We were really excited because we found some old comic books! It was nice to relax in a café and read them.

서답형

08 위 글의 밑줄 친 ①~⑤에서 문맥상 낱말의 쓰임이 적절하지 <u>않은</u> 것을 찾아 알맞게 고치시오.

➡ _____

09 위 글의 밑줄 친 ⓐselling과 문법적 쓰임이 <u>다른</u> 것을 모두 고르시오.

① Do you know the woman selling *Hotteok* on the street?

② She gave up selling her used books on Bosu-dong Book Street.

③ He is proud of selling his products to different countries.

④ She is selling the popular street food at Gukje Market.

⑤ I want to visit Gukje Market selling various imported things.

서답형

10 다음 빈칸에 위 글의 밑줄 친 ⓑ와 ⓒ의 there가 가리키는 것을 각각 쓰시오.

➡ ⓑ at _____ ⓒ on _____

[11~13] 다음 글을 읽고 물음에 답하시오.

Gangwon-do, Full of Natural Beauty

There is no place like Gangwon-do for ⓐ_____ . First, we went to Baengnyong Cave. This 1.8-kilometer-long cave is still in good condition. It was so amazing to see its natural beauty. Near the end of our cave tour, the guide turned off the lights in the cave for a minute. Everything became very dark, so we were able to focus on the sounds there. It was the most amazing experience of the tour! Our next stop was Donggang. We went rafting! It was exciting to ride on the rough water and enjoy the view at the same time.

11 위 글의 빈칸 ⓐ에 들어갈 알맞은 말을 고르시오.

① delicious food

② various historic sites

③ beautiful nature

④ artificial structures

⑤ traditional performances

서답형

12 주어진 영영풀이에 해당하는 단어를 본문에서 찾아 쓰시오.

a brief stay in the course of a journey

➡ _____

13 위 글을 읽고 대답할 수 <u>없는</u> 질문은?

① Where did the students go first in Gangwon-do?

② How long is the Baengnyong Cave?

③ What did the guide do near the end of the cave tour?

④ Where did the students go after they went to Baengnyong Cave?

⑤ How far is it from Baengnyong Cave to Donggang?

[14~17] 다음 글을 읽고 물음에 답하시오.

Gangwon-do, Full of (A)[Artificial / Natural] Beauty

There is no place like Gangwon-do for beautiful nature. First, we went to Baengnyong Cave. This 1.8-kilometer-long cave is still in good condition. ⓐIt was so amazing to see its natural beauty. Near the end of our cave tour, the guide turned (B)[on / off] the lights in the cave for a minute. Everything became very dark, so we were able to focus on the sounds there. ⓑ<u>It</u> was the most amazing experience of the tour! Our next stop was Donggang. We went rafting! It was exciting to ride on the (C)[rough / tough] water and enjoy the view at the same time.

서답형

14 위 글의 괄호 (A)~(C)에서 문맥상 알맞은 낱말을 골라 쓰시오.

➡ (A)＿＿＿ (B)＿＿＿ (C)＿＿＿

15 위 글의 밑줄 친 ⓐ 대신 쓸 수 있는 문장을 모두 고르시오.

① It was not too amazing to see its natural beauty.
② To see its natural beauty was so amazing.
③ That was amazing enough to see its natural beauty.
④ Seeing its natural beauty was so amazing.
⑤ That was so amazing to see its natural beauty.

중요

16 위 글의 마지막 부분에서 알 수 있는 학생들의 심경으로 가장 알맞은 것을 고르시오.

① satisfied   ② surprised
③ bored   ④ disappointed
⑤ upset

서답형

17 위 글의 밑줄 친 ⓑ가 가리키는 것을 본문에서 찾아 쓰시오.

➡ ＿＿＿＿＿＿＿＿＿＿＿＿＿＿
＿＿＿＿＿＿＿＿＿＿＿＿＿＿
＿＿＿＿＿＿＿＿＿＿＿＿＿＿
＿＿＿＿＿＿＿＿＿＿＿＿＿＿

[18~20] 다음 글을 읽고 물음에 답하시오.

Incheon, A City of Firsts

Do you know where the first train station in Korea is? How about the first *Jajangmyeon*? The answer is Incheon! This place has many of Korea's ＿ⓐ＿. To get there, we went to Incheon Station. The Jajangmyeon Museum is next to the station. We learned about the history of *Jajangmyeon* there. Later, we walked around Jayu Park, the first Western-style park in Korea. The view from the park was awesome! It was great ⓑto see the historical sites of this city from the park.

중요

18 위 글의 빈칸 ⓐ에 들어갈 알맞은 말을 고르시오.

① surprises   ② firsts
③ resources   ④ inventions
⑤ traditions

서답형

19 What did the students learn from the Jajangmyeon Museum? Answer in English in a full sentence.

➡ _____

서답형

20 본문의 내용과 일치하도록 다음 빈칸 (A)~(C)에 알맞은 단어를 쓰시오.

> The students went to places which are related to Korea's firsts such as (A)_____ _____, (B)_____ _____ _____, and (C)_____ _____.

[21~23] 다음 글을 읽고 물음에 답하시오.

Teacher: Good morning, everyone! How were your field trips last week? Please tell us about ⓐthem!

Busan, Market Heaven

Do you like traditional markets? Then go to Gukje Market in Busan. It is one of the most famous markets in Busan. Do you know what it is famous for? It is famous for selling a variety of goods from different countries. It was interesting to see all the international goods there. We also ate many kinds of street food, ⓑsuch as *Gimbap*, fish cake, and *Hotteok*. Then we walked to Bosu-dong Book Street. Many bookstores there sell used books. We were really excited because we found some old comic books! It was nice to relax in a café and read ⓒthem.

서답형

21 위 글의 밑줄 친 ⓐ와 ⓒ의 them이 가리키는 것을 본문에서 찾아 각각 쓰시오.

➡ ⓐ _____

ⓒ _____

서답형

22 위 글의 밑줄 친 ⓑsuch as와 바꿔 쓸 수 있는 한 단어를 쓰시오.

➡ _____

중요

23 위 글의 국제시장에 대한 내용과 일치하지 <u>않는</u> 것은?

① 부산에 있는 전통 시장이다.
② 부산에서 가장 유명한 시장 중 하나이다.
③ 여러 나라에서 온 다양한 제품들을 파는 것으로 유명하다.
④ 그곳에서 세계 곳곳의 상품들을 모두 볼 수 있다.
⑤ 그곳의 많은 서점에서는 중고 책을 판다.

[24~26] 다음 글을 읽고 물음에 답하시오.

I live in Hang-dong, Seoul. There is an old railway. ⓐIt is no longer used. You can walk there and __ⓑ__ pictures of beautiful scenery.

서답형

24 위 글의 밑줄 친 ⓐ를 능동태로 고치시오.

➡ _____

25 위 글의 밑줄 친 ⓐ와 바꿔 쓸 수 <u>없는</u> 문장을 모두 고르시오.

① It is no more used.
② It is not used any longer.
③ It is not used no longer.
④ It is not used any more.
⑤ It is not used no more.

중요

26 위 글의 빈칸 ⓑ에 알맞은 것은?

① get   ② take
③ let   ④ bring
⑤ carry

[01~03] 다음 글을 읽고 물음에 답하시오.

Busan, Market Heaven

Do you like traditional markets? ⓐThen go to Gukje Market in Busan. ⓑ그곳은 부산에서 가장 유명한 시장 중 하나입니다. Do you know what it is famous for? It is famous for selling a variety of goods from different countries. It was (A)[interesting / interested] to see all the international goods there. We also ate many kinds of street food, such as *Gimbap*, fish cake, and *Hotteok*. Then we walked to Bosu-dong Book Street. Many bookstores there sell (B)[using / used] books. We were really (C)[exciting / excited] because we found some old comic books! It was nice to relax in a café and read them.

01 위 글의 밑줄 친 ⓐThen을 If를 사용하여 고치시오.

➡ _____

02 위 글의 밑줄 친 ⓑ의 우리말에 맞게 주어진 어휘를 이용하여 10 단어로 영작하시오.

famous, in Busan

➡ _____

03 위 글의 괄호 (A)~(C)에서 어법상 알맞은 낱말을 골라 쓰시오.

➡ (A) _____ (B) _____ (C) _____

[04~07] 다음 글을 읽고 물음에 답하시오.

Incheon, A City of Firsts

Do you know where the first train station in Korea is? ⓐHow about the first *Jajangmyeon*? The answer is Incheon! ⓑThis place has many of Korea's firsts. To get there, we went to Incheon Station. The Jajangmyeon Museum is next to the station. We learned about the history of *Jajangmyeon* there. Later, we walked around Jayu Park, the first Western-style park in Korea. The view from the park was awesome! It was great to see the historical sites of this city from the park.

04 위 글의 밑줄 친 ⓐ를 다음과 같이 바꿔 쓸 때 빈칸에 들어갈 알맞은 말을 쓰시오.

➡ Do you know _____ the first *Jajangmyeon* in Korea was introduced?

05 위 글의 밑줄 친 ⓑ를 There로 시작하여 고치시오.

➡ _____

06 위 글의 밑줄 친 문장 ⓑ의 many of Korea's firsts의 예를 본문에서 찾아 우리말로 쓰시오. (세 가지)

➡ (1) _____
   (2) _____
   (3) _____

07 What can you see from Jayu Park? Answer in English in a full sentence.

➡ _____
   _____

[08~10] 다음 글을 읽고 물음에 답하시오.

Busan, Market Heaven

Do you like traditional markets? Then go to Gukje Market in Busan. It is one of the most famous markets in Busan. Do you know what it is famous for? It is famous for selling a variety of goods from different countries. It was interesting to see all the international goods there. We also ate many kinds of street food, such as *Gimbap*, fish cake, and *Hotteok*. Then we walked to Bosu-dong Book Street. Many bookstores there sell used books. We were really excited because we found some old comic books! It was nice to relax in a café and read them.

08 다음 문장에서 위 글의 내용과 <u>다른</u> 부분을 찾아서 고치시오.

> • Gukje Market is the most famous market in Busan.

➡ _____

09 위 글을 읽고 학생들이 국제시장에서 한 일을 우리말로 쓰시오. (두 가지)

➡ (1) _____
   (2) _____

10 다음 빈칸에 알맞은 단어를 넣어 보수동 책방에 대한 소개를 완성하시오.

> Many bookstores on Bosu-dong Book Street are famous for selling _____
> _____.

[11~14] 다음 글을 읽고 물음에 답하시오.

Gangwon-do, Full of Natural Beauty

ⓐThere is no place like Gangwon-do for beautiful nature. First, we went to Baengnyong Cave. This 1.8-kilometer-long cave is still in good condition. It was so amazing to see its natural beauty. Near the end of our cave tour, the guide turned off the lights in the cave for a minute. Everything became very dark, so we were able to focus on the sounds there. It was the most amazing experience of the tour! Our next stop was Donggang. We went ___ⓑ___ ! ⓒ급류를 타면서 동시에 경치를 즐기는 것은 흥미진진했습니다.

11 위 글의 밑줄 친 ⓐ를 다음과 같이 바꿔 쓸 때 빈칸에 들어갈 알맞은 말을 쓰시오.

➡ Gangwon-do is the _____ place for beautiful nature.

12 위 글의 빈칸 ⓑ에 raft를 알맞은 형태로 쓰시오.

➡ _____

13 위 글의 밑줄 친 ⓒ의 우리말에 맞게 한 단어를 보충하여, 주어진 어휘를 알맞게 배열하시오.

> the view / to ride / at the same time / it / and / was / enjoy / exciting / the rough water

➡ _____
  _____

14 본문의 내용과 일치하도록 다음 빈칸 (A)와 (B)에 들어갈 알맞은 단어를 본문에서 찾아 쓰시오.

> When the guide turned off the lights, everything became so dark that the students couldn't (A)_____ the natural beauty of the cave, and it was possible for them to focus only on (B)_____ there.

해석

After You Read D

I live in Hang-dong, Seoul. There is an old railway. It is no longer used. You
~에서 살다　　　　　　There is 단수명사: ~가 있다　　　더 이상 ~하지 않는

can walk there and take pictures of beautiful scenery.
사진을 찍다

구문해설 · scenery: 풍경, 경치

나는 서울의 항동에 산다. 거기에는 오래된 철도가 있다. 이것은 더 이상 사용되지 않는다. 너는 그 철길을 걸을 수 있고 예쁜 풍경 사진을 찍을 수도 있다.

Think & Write Step 3

Autumn Walk in Naejangsan

Last autumn, I went to Naejangsan with my family. I rode a cable car to the
지난　　　　　　　　　　　　　　　　　　　　ride의 과거

middle of the mountain. Then, I hiked to the top.
그리고 나서　　　정상까지

At the top, I saw beautiful autumn scenery. I took many pictures. It was
경치　　　　　　　　　　　　가주어

amazing and exciting to see beautiful autumn leaves.
진주어(명사적 용법)

구문해설 · cable car: 케이블 카 · hike: 하이킹[도보 여행]을 가다 · amazing: 놀라운
· exciting: 흥미진진한

내장산에서의 가을 산행
지난 가을, 나는 가족과 함께 내장산에 갔다. 나는 산의 중간까지 케이블 카를 타고 갔다. 그러고 나서, 나는 정상까지 하이킹을 갔다. 정상에서, 나는 아름다운 가을 경치를 보았다. 나는 많은 사진을 찍었다. 아름다운 가을 나뭇잎을 보는 것은 놀랍고 흥미진진했다.

Culture Link

Eco Trip
Some people take trips in nature without hurting the environment. They think
전치사의 목적어로 동명사

it is important to protect nature.
가주어　　　　　　진주어

Volunteer Trip
Some people go on trips for special purposes. They travel to do volunteer
부정사의 부사적 용법(목적)

work. They help local communities or wild animals during their trips.
전치사: 뒤에 명사구가 나옴

History Trip
On this trip, people visit historical sites and learn about history.

During this trip, people can understand the lives of people in the past.
생활, 삶(명사)　　　　　　과거의(형용사구)

구문해설 · take trips: 여행 가다 · go on trips: 여행 가다 · purpose: 목적 · community: 지역[공동] 사회
· historical: 역사(상)의, 역사적인 cf. historic: 역사적으로 유명한 · site: 유적

생태 여행

몇몇 사람들은 자연 속에서 환경을 해치지 않고 여행을 합니다. 그들은 자연을 보호하는 것이 중요하다고 생각합니다.

자원봉사 여행

몇몇 사람들은 특별한 목적을 위해 여행을 갑니다. 그들은 자원봉사를 하기 위해 여행합니다. 그들은 그들의 여행 중에 지역 사회와 야생 동물들을 돕습니다.

역사 여행

이 여행에서 사람들은 역사적인 유적들을 방문하고 역사에 대해 배웁니다. 이 여행 동안 사람들은 과거의 사람들의 삶을 이해할 수 있습니다.

Words & Expressions

1 다음 밑줄 친 단어 중 뜻이 <u>다른</u> 하나를 고르시오.

① You have to <u>get</u> there as soon as possible.
② I will write to you as soon as I <u>get</u> to Canada.
③ You can <u>get</u> the information from the library.
④ If you take a taxi, you can <u>get</u> there in 10 minutes.
⑤ We're never going to <u>get</u> to school on time.

2 다음 빈칸에 알맞은 말을 고르시오.

> Before the presentation, Jobs felt nervous but, _____, excited.

① at one time
② all at once
③ at once
④ at the same time
⑤ at a time

3 다음 빈칸에 공통으로 들어갈 말을 쓰시오.

> • Do you _____ any plans?
> • Nancy, _____ a good trip!

➡ _____

4 다음 〈보기〉의 단어를 사용하여 자연스러운 문장을 만들 수 <u>없는</u> 것은?

> ┤ 보기 ├
> awesome / natural / rough / Western-style

① The mountain road was _____.
② The food chain is a _____ system.
③ Bread is a key element in a _____ breakfast.
④ How many _____ languages can you speak?
⑤ This school is _____ and I like my classmates, too.

Conversation

[05~06] 다음 대화의 빈칸에 알맞은 말을 고르시오.

5

> A: How do you get to school?
> B: I go to school by bus.
> A: _____
> B: It takes 15 minutes.

① What do you take to your school?
② When does your school end?
③ What time do you go to school?
④ How long does it take to get there?
⑤ What do you do after school?

6

> A: What are you planning to do this weekend?
> B: _____

① I had a wonderful time at the beach.
② I'm going to stay at home and get some rest.
③ It wasn't my plan to meet Peter.
④ I'm going to the library to read books now.
⑤ I have been to Jeju-do three times.

[07~10] 다음 대화를 읽고 물음에 답하시오.

G: What are you (A)planning to do this weekend?

B: (①) I'm (B)planning to go to a baseball game in Daegu.

G: Are you going to see the All-Star Game?

B: Yes. (②) It will be fun. Also, I'm planning to visit my friend there. (③)

G: Nice. How long does it take to get there?

B: 고속 열차로 1시간 40분이 걸려. (④)

G: (⑤) I hope you have a good trip!

B: Thank you.

07 위 대화의 ①~⑤ 중 주어진 문장이 들어갈 알맞은 곳은?

> Wow, it's much faster than I thought.

①   ②   ③   ④   ⑤

08 (A)와 (B)의 밑줄 친 planning을 대신하여 바꿔 쓸 수 있는 말을 쓰시오.

➡ _____

09 주어진 단어를 이용하여 밑줄 친 우리말을 영작하시오.

➡ _____

(express train)

10 다음 중 위 대화의 내용과 일치하지 <u>않는</u> 것을 고르시오.

① The boy's friend is in Daegu.

② The boy is going to visit his friend this weekend.

③ The All-Star Game is a baseball game.

④ Thy boy is planning to go to Daegu.

⑤ Thy boy is planning to see the All-Star Game with his friend.

[11~12] 다음 대화를 읽고 물음에 답하시오.

B: We have a long holiday this month. Do you have any plans?

G: I'm going to visit my grandparents in Jeonju.

B: Oh, really? That's nice. What are you planning to do with them?

G: I'm planning to go to Hanok Village with them. How about you? What are your plans for the holiday?

B: I'm going to stay home and relax.

G: That's also a good idea!

11 다음 영영풀이에 해당하는 단어를 위 대화에서 찾아 쓰시오.

> not to do anything

➡ _____

12 다음 중 위 대화를 읽고 답할 수 <u>없는</u> 질문을 고르시오.

① What are they talking about?

② Where do the girl's grandparents live?

③ How long is the holiday?

④ Where is the girl planning to go with her grandparents?

⑤ What is the boy's plan for the holiday?

Grammar

13 다음 문장을 주어진 말로 시작하여 다시 쓰시오.

> You should pay attention to your teacher in class.

➡ It is necessary _____

_____ .

14 다음 중 어법상 바르지 <u>않은</u> 것은?

① It is safe to say that Anna has always loved designing.

② It was exciting to sing in front of many people.

③ She wants to know who the winner is.

④ The woman is asking him where the best restaurant is around here.

⑤ I don't konw if or not Ann's Korean is perfect.

15 다음 밑줄 친 It[it]의 쓰임이 나머지와 <u>다른</u> 하나를 고르시오.

① <u>It</u> is true that the pen is mightier than the sword.

② <u>It</u> is interesting for me to study the habits of birds.

③ <u>It</u> is lucky to have a good friend like Amy.

④ <u>It</u> was Harry Potter that defeated Voltmore.

⑤ <u>It</u> is not good to stay in the house for a long time.

16 다음 우리말을 영어로 바르게 옮긴 것은?

> 내게 길을 안내해 주다니 Amanda는 친절했다.

① It was kind to show me the way for Amanda.

② It was kind Amanda to show me the way.

③ It was kind to show me the way of Amanda.

④ It was kind for Amanda to show me the way.

⑤ It was kind of Amanda to show me the way.

17 다음 문장을 두 문장으로 나누어 쓰시오.

(1) Nobody knows why Lauren left the office early.

➡ _____

(2) It is difficult to understand what the teacher says.

➡ _____

(3) Steve didn't tell me when the movie began.

➡ _____

(4) What do you think the most typical Korean dish is?

➡ _____

(5) Mariel wants to know whether Kate is going to meet Asako.

➡ _____

(6) They wonder if they can borrow a few books today.

➡ _____

18 다음을 간접의문문을 이용하여 한 문장으로 쓰시오.

(1) • I'll tell you.
　• Where has he been since last Monday?

➡ _____

(2) • I'd like to know.
　• Did you meet her?

➡ _____

(3) • Do you think?
　• Where can I find some fruit?

➡ _____

19 괄호 안에 주어진 어휘를 이용하여 다음 우리말을 영작하시오.

(1) 심장이 오른쪽에 있는 것은 비정상적이다. (the heart, abnormal, have, it, to, on)

➡ _____

(2) 물고기를 맨손으로 잡는 것은 어렵다. (with your bare hands, grab, hard, it, to)

➡ _____

(3) 나는 그 소녀가 어디에 사는지 모른다. (the girl, live)

➡ _____

(4) 다음 기차가 언제 오는지 말해 줄 수 있습니까? (could, the next train)

➡ _____

Reading

[20~21] 다음 글을 읽고 물음에 답하시오.

Busan, Market Heaven

Do you like traditional markets? Then go to Gukje Market in Busan. ⓐIt is one of the most famous markets in Busan. Do you know what ⓑit is famous for? ⓒIt is famous for selling a variety of goods from different countries. ⓓIt was interesting to see all the international goods there. We also ate many kinds of street food, such as *Gimbap*, fish cake, and *Hotteok*. ⒜Then we walked to Bosu-dong Book Street. Many bookstores there sell used books. We were really excited because we found some old comic books! ⓔIt was nice to relax in a café and read them.

20 위 글의 밑줄 친 ⓐ~ⓔ 중 가리키는 대상이 같은 것끼리 짝 지어진 것은?

① ⓐ – ⓑ ② ⓑ – ⓓ

③ ⓒ – ⓓ ④ ⓒ – ⓔ

⑤ ⓓ – ⓔ

21 위 글의 밑줄 친 ⒜Then을 After를 사용하여 고치시오.

➡ _____

[22~24] 다음 글을 읽고 물음에 답하시오.

Gangwon-do, Full of Natural Beauty

There is no place like Gangwon-do ⓐ beautiful nature. First, we went to Baengnyong Cave. (①) This 1.8-kilometer-long cave is still ⓑ good condition. (②) It was so amazing to see its natural beauty. (③) Near the end of our cave tour, the guide turned off the lights in the cave for a minute. (④) It was the most amazing experience of the tour! (⑤) Our next stop was Donggang. We went rafting! It was exciting to ride on the rough water and enjoy the view at the same time.

22 위 글의 흐름으로 보아, 주어진 문장이 들어가기에 가장 적절한 곳은?

Everything became very dark, so we were able to focus on the sounds there.

① ② ③ ④ ⑤

23 위 글의 빈칸 ⓐ와 ⓑ에 들어갈 전치사가 바르게 짝지어진 것은?

① on – at ② for – in ③ to – in

④ for – at ⑤ on – to

24 위 글의 내용과 일치하지 않는 것은?

① 먼저, 학생들은 백룡동굴로 갔다.

② 백룡동굴의 길이는 1.8킬로미터이다.

③ 백룡동굴 안은 많이 훼손되어 있었다.

④ 학생들은 동강에 래프팅을 하러 갔다.

⑤ 급류를 타면서 동시에 경치를 즐기는 것은 흥미 진진했다.

[25~27] 다음 글을 읽고 물음에 답하시오.

Incheon, A City of Firsts

Do you know where the first train station in Korea is? How about the first *Jajangmyeon*? The answer is Incheon! This place has many of Korea's firsts. ⓐTo get there, we went to Incheon Station. The Jajangmyeon Museum is next to the station. We learned about the history of *Jajangmyeon* there. (A)[Later / Latter], we walked around Jayu Park, the first Western-style park in Korea. The view from the park was (B)[awful / awesome]! It was great to see the historical sites of this city from the park.

Teacher: Wow, these places sound great! You all have done a wonderful job on your (C) [preparations / presentations]!

25 위 글의 괄호 (A)~(C)에서 문맥상 알맞은 낱말을 골라 쓰시오.

➡ (A)_____ (B)_____ (C)_____

26 위 글의 밑줄 친 ⓐ와 바꿔 쓸 수 없는 문장을 고르시오.

① We went to Incheon Station in order to get there.
② We went to Incheon Station so that we could get there.
③ We went to Incheon Station in order that we might get there.
④ We went to Incheon Station so as that we might get there.
⑤ We went to Incheon Station so as to get there.

27 위 글을 읽고 대답할 수 없는 질문은?

① Where is the first train station in Korea?
② Who made the first *Jajangmyeon* in Korea?
③ Where did the students learn about the history of *Jajangmyeon*?
④ What is the first Western-style park in Korea?
⑤ How was the view from the park?

[28~29] 다음 글을 읽고 물음에 답하시오.

Autumn Walk in Naejangsan

Last autumn, I went to Naejangsan with my family. I rode a cable car to the middle of the mountain. Then, I hiked to the top. At the top, I saw beautiful autumn scenery. I took many pictures. ⓐIt was amazing and exciting to see beautiful autumn leaves.

28 글쓴이가 내장산의 정상에 도달한 방법을 우리말로 쓰시오.

➡ _____

29 위 글의 밑줄 친 ⓐ를 다음과 같이 바꿔 쓸 때 빈칸에 들어 갈 알맞은 말을 쓰시오.

➡ I was _____ and _____ to see beautiful autumn leaves.

출제율 90%

01 다음 짝지어진 두 단어의 관계가 같도록 주어진 철자로 시작하여 빈칸에 알맞은 단어를 쓰시오.

> amazing : incredible – c_____ : state

[02~03] 밑줄 친 단어와 바꿔 쓸 수 있는 단어를 쓰시오.

출제율 90%

02

> I'm not sure if I can do it.

➡ _____ (3 단어)

출제율 95%

03

> The beach is only five minutes away by walking.

➡ _____

출제율 100%

04 다음 빈칸에 공통으로 들어갈 말로 알맞은 것을 쓰시오.

> • It will _____ a long time to download data to my computer.
> • Did you hear that we're going to _____ a field trip?

출제율 85%

05 주어진 문장 이후에 올 대화의 순서가 올바르게 배열된 것을 고르시오.

> We have a long holiday this month. Do you have any plans?

> (A) That's also a good idea!
> (B) Oh, really? That's nice. What are you planning to do with them?
> (C) I'm going to visit my grandparents in Jeonju.
> (D) I'm planning to go to Hanok Village with them. How about you? What are your plans for the holiday?
> (E) I'm going to stay home and relax.`

① (B) – (A) – (C) – (D) – (E)
② (B) – (C) – (D) – (A) – (E)
③ (C) – (A) – (B) – (E) – (D)
④ (C) – (B) – (D) – (E) – (A)
⑤ (C) – (B) – (E) – (A) – (D)

[06~09] 다음 대화를 읽고 물음에 답하시오.

> B: Wow, these pictures are so beautiful. Where did you take them?
> G: At Riverside Park. There were lots ⓐ_____ flowers. You should go there!
> B: I want to. How do I get there ⓑ_____ our school?
> G: Get on bus number 135 and get ⓒ_____ at the Riverside Stadium (A)stop. You can see the park ⓓ_____ front ⓔ_____ the bus stop.
> B: (B)거기까지 가는 데 얼마나 걸려?
> G: It takes 30 minutes.
> B: Thanks. I'll go there next weekend.

출제율 90%

06 다음 영영풀이에 해당하는 단어를 위 대화에서 찾아 쓰시오.

> a large sports field

➡ _____

출제율 100%

07 빈칸 ⓐ~ⓔ에 알맞은 말을 〈보기〉에서 골라 쓰시오.

> ┤ 보기 ├
> from   in   of   off

➡ ⓐ _____, ⓑ _____, ⓒ _____,

ⓓ _____, ⓔ _____

08 밑줄 친 (A)stop과 다른 의미로 쓰인 문장을 <u>모두</u> 고르시오.

① He decided to stop using it.

② I get off at the next stop.

③ Is there a bus stop near the hotel?

④ Drop me at the next stop, please.

⑤ This elevator only stops at the fifth floor and above.

09 밑줄 친 (B)의 우리말을 주어진 말을 이용하여 영작하시오.

(long, get)

➡ _____

[10~12] 다음 대화를 읽고 물음에 답하시오.

B: Excuse me. ①<u>How do I get from Hanguk University to here?</u>

W: You can go there (A)_____ bus or (B)_____ foot.

B: ②<u>How long does it take to get there?</u>

W: It takes five minutes (A)_____ bus and 20 minutes (B)_____ foot.

B: ③<u>Oh, then I will walk there.</u> ④<u>Can you tell me how to get there?</u>

W: ⑤<u>Go straight for two blocks, and then turn left.</u> You will see Hanguk University on your right.

B: Go straight for two blocks and turn left. Thank you!

10 위 대화의 ①~⑤ 중에서 문맥상 어색한 부분을 고르시오.

① ② ③ ④ ⑤

11 빈칸 (A)와 (B)에 적절한 것을 쓰시오.

➡ (A) _____, (B) _____

12 위 대화의 내용과 일치하지 <u>않는</u> 것을 고르시오.

① The boy wants to go to Hanguk University.

② The boy is going to walk to Hanguk University.

③ The woman knows how to get to Hanguk University.

④ When you go to Hanguk University from here, walking is more faster than taking a bus.

⑤ It takes twenty minutes by walking to get to Hanguk University.

13 다음 중 어법상 옳은 것은?

① It is fun to speaking in front of people.

② It is difficult say which way the wind is blowing.

③ It was great for seeing the historical sites of this city from the park.

④ It was scary to play the game on the big rock.

⑤ It is important make plans in advance.

14 다음을 간접의문문을 이용하여 한 문장으로 쓰시오.

(1) Do you know? Who is that tall guy over there?

➡ _____

(2) Tell me. Who made this chocolate cake?

➡ _____

(3) I wonder. Did Marianne get married?

➡ _____

(4) Do you think? Where is Snow White?

➡ _____

15 다음 그림을 보고 주어진 어휘를 이용하여 자신의 생각을 쓰시오.

(for him, do dunk shot, to)

➡ _____

16 다음 밑줄 친 부분의 쓰임이 어색한 것은?

① Do you know <u>why</u> leaves turn red in autumn?

② Luke's mother knew <u>where</u> he kept the comic books.

③ I wonder <u>what</u> there's an easy way to improve my grade.

④ Do you know <u>how</u> many books your brother has?

⑤ I asked her <u>when</u> she had left her home country.

[17~19] 다음 글을 읽고 물음에 답하시오.

Teacher: Good morning, everyone! ⓐ<u>How was your field trips last week?</u> Please tell us about them!

Busan, Market Heaven

Do you like traditional markets? Then go to Gukje Market in Busan. It is one of the most famous markets in Busan. Do you know what it is famous for? It is famous for selling a variety of goods from different countries.

It was interesting to see all the international goods there. We also ate many kinds of street food, such as *Gimbap*, fish cake, and *Hotteok*. Then we walked to Bosu-dong Book Street. Many bookstores there sell used books. We were really excited because we found some old comic books! It was nice ⓑ<u>to relax</u> in a café and read them.

17 위 글의 밑줄 친 ⓐ에서 어법상 틀린 부분을 찾아 고치시오.

➡ _____

18 아래 〈보기〉에서 위 글의 밑줄 친 ⓑto relax와 to부정사의 용법이 다른 것의 개수를 고르시오.

┤ 보기 ├

① They promised <u>to meet</u> in front of the museum at 5.

② I have nothing <u>to write</u> with.

③ She must be a fool <u>to believe</u> such a thing.

④ I wanted <u>to go</u> to Spain.

⑤ This book was too difficult <u>to read</u>.

① 1개 ② 2개 ③ 3개 ④ 4개 ⑤ 5개

19 위 글을 읽고 대답할 수 <u>없는</u> 질문은?

① When did the students go on field trips?

② What was interesting about Gukje Market?

③ What street food did the students eat at Gukje Market?

④ How long did it take to go to Bosu-dong Book Street from Gukje Market?

⑤ What do the bookstores on Bosu-dong Book Street sell?

[20~22] 다음 글을 읽고 물음에 답하시오.

Gangwon-do, Full of Natural Beauty

There is no place ⓐlike Gangwon-do for beautiful nature. First, we went to Baengnyong Cave. This (A)[1.8-kilometer-long / 1.8-kilometes-long] cave is still in good condition. It was so amazing to see its natural beauty. Near the end of our cave tour, the guide turned off the lights in the cave for a minute. Everything became very dark, so we were able to focus on the sounds there. It was the most amazing experience of the tour! Our next stop was Donggang. We went (B)[to raft / rafting]! It was exciting to ride on the rough water and enjoy the view (C)[at the same time / one by one].

출제율 95%

20 위 글의 밑줄 친 ⓐlike와 같은 의미로 쓰인 것을 고르시오.

① She's wearing a dress like mine.

② How did you like the book?

③ There are many things of like shape.

④ I like my coffee strong.

⑤ He responded in like manner.

출제율 90%

21 위 글의 괄호 (A)~(C)에서 문맥이나 어법상 알맞은 낱말을 골라 쓰시오.

➡ (A) _____

(B) _____

(C) _____

출제율 90%

22 Why did the guide turn off the lights in the cave for a minute near the end of the cave tour? Fill in the blanks with suitable words.

➡ Because he[she] wanted to make everything become _____ _____ so that the students could _____ _____ the sounds in the cave.

[23~24] 다음 글을 읽고 물음에 답하시오.

A Perfect Day in Anmyeon-do

Last summer, I went to Anmyeon-do with my family. I swam in the sea with my brothers. Then we caught some crabs on the beach. ⓐ It was awful and fantastic to see the beautiful sunset there.

출제율 90%

23 글쓴이가 지난 여름 안면도에서 한 일을 우리말로 쓰시오. (세 가지)

➡ (1) _____

(2) _____

(3) _____

출제율 90%

24 위 글의 밑줄 친 ⓐ에서 흐름상 어색한 부분을 찾아 고치시오.

➡ _____

[01~02] 다음 대화를 읽고 물음에 답하시오.

A: (A)Where will you go?
B: I will go to Sydney.
A: How long does it take to get there?
B: (B)_____(10시간 반)
A: What are you planning to do there?
B: I'm planning to go surfing.

01 밑줄 친 (A)와 의미가 같도록 주어진 단어를 이용해서 영작하시오.

➡ _____ (plan)
   _____ (go)
   _____ (think)

02 주어진 정보를 이용해 빈칸 (B)에 알맞은 말을 쓰시오.

➡ _____

[03~04] 다음 대화를 읽고 물음에 답하시오.

A: (A)(going, your, where, you, trip, are, for)?
B: I'm going to Seoul.
A: What are you planning to do there?
B: (B)_____
A: That sounds great!

03 괄호 안에 주어진 단어를 알맞게 배열하시오.

➡ _____

04 주어진 영영풀이의 단어의 복수형을 이용해 빈칸 (B)를 채우시오.

> a building where historical or artistic objects are displayed

➡ _____

05 두 문장이 같은 뜻이 되도록 to부정사를 이용하여 문장을 완성하시오.

(1) My grandma has difficulty remembering names.
→ It is difficult _____.
(2) Studying English is boring for most of students.
→ It is boring _____.

06 주어진 두 문장을 한 문장으로 연결하시오.

(1) It is doubtful.
  + Does Anna love me?
  ➡ _____
(2) I'm not sure.
  + Why was Kate so surprised?
  ➡ _____
(3) Cathy knows.
  Who broke the window yesterday?
  ➡ _____
(4) Can you imagine?
  Which book did Jennifer buy?
  ➡ _____

07 다음 문장에서 어법상 어색한 것을 찾아 바르게 고치시오.

(1) It is necessary for John takes another science class.

_____ ➡ _____

(2) That was amazing and exciting to see beautiful autumn leaves!

_____ ➡ _____

(3) Write an interesting storybook is my dream.

_____ ➡ _____

(4) Do you know when does the show start?

_____ ➡ _____

(5) Please let me know if does the bag have some pockets.

_____ ➡ _____

(6) Do you think who runs fastest?

_____ ➡ _____

[08~10] 다음 글을 읽고 물음에 답하시오.

Teacher: Good morning, everyone! (A)[How / What] were your field trips last week? Please tell us about them!

Busan, Market Heaven

Do you like traditional markets? Then go to Gukje Market in Busan. It is one of the most famous (B)[market / markets] in Busan. Do you know what it is famous for? It is famous for selling a variety of goods from different countries. ⓐIt was interesting to see all the international goods there. We also ate many kinds of street food, such as *Gimbap*, fish cake, and *Hotteok*. Then we walked to Bosu-dong Book Street. Many bookstores there sell used books. We were really excited because we (C)[found / founded] some old comic books! It was nice to relax in a café and read them.

08 위 글의 괄호 (A)~(C)에서 문맥이나 어법상 알맞은 낱말을 골라 쓰시오.

➡ (A)_____ (B)_____ (C)_____

09 위 글의 밑줄 친 ⓐ를 다음과 같이 바꿔 쓸 때 빈칸에 들어갈 알맞은 한 단어를 쓰시오.

➡ _____ all the international goods there was interesting.

10 다음 빈칸 (A)와 (B)에 알맞은 단어를 넣어 국제시장에 대한 소개를 완성하시오.

It is a good place for those who like to visit (A)_____ _____, and it is well known for selling various goods which are imported from (B)_____ _____.

01 주어진 조건을 이용하여 대화의 흐름에 맞게 빈칸을 완성하시오.

조건

다음 주말에 대한 계획 / 영화 보기 / 영화관은 걸어서 5분

A: _____

B: I'm planning _____ alone.

A: I don't have any plans for next weekend. Can I join?

B: Of course.

A: _____

B: You can go there by walking.

A: _____

B: It _____.

02 주어진 어구를 활용하여 자신의 생각을 쓰시오.

It is important … / It is necessary … / Do you know …? / I wonder …

(1) _____

(2) _____

(3) _____

(4) _____

03 다음 내용을 바탕으로 자신의 여행기를 쓰시오.

1. Where: Anmyeon-do
2. When: last summer
3. With whom: with my family
4. Activities:
   - swim in the sea
   - catch crabs on the beach
   - see the beautiful sunset
5. Feelings: awesome, fantastic

A Perfect Day in Anmyeon-do

  (A)_____, I went to Anmyeon-do with my family. I (B)_____ in the sea with my brothers. Then we (C)_____ some crabs on the beach. It was (D)_____ and fantastic to see the (E)_____ there.

단원별 모의고사

01 빈칸에 알맞은 단어를 고르시오.

> She turned _____ her cell phone before the movie started.

① off ② out ③ of
④ in ⑤ at

02 다음 제시된 의미에 맞는 단어를 주어진 철자로 시작하여 빈칸에 쓰고, 알맞은 것을 골라 문장을 완성하시오.

> • h_____ : events that have happened in the past
> • s_____ : a beautiful view of nature
> • W_____ : a particular way or form relating to Western countries

(1) We enjoyed the _____ at the beach.
(2) I want to know about the _____ of the Eiffel Tower.
(3) I like _____ houses better than Eastern-style houses.

[03~06] 다음 대화를 읽고 물음에 답하시오.

B: Hi, Nuri. ⓐWhat is your class going for the field trip tomorrow?
G: Hello, Mike. (①) We ⓑare going to the art museum.
B: Sounds ⓒinteresting. (②) ⓓWhere are you planning to see there?
G: (③) There are three art shows right now. I'm planning to see Vincent van Gogh's paintings. Where is your class going?
B: (④) I'm ⓔexciting to ride a roller coaster!
G: That sounds fun. (⑤) Have a good trip!

03 위 대화의 ①~⑤ 중 주어진 문장이 들어갈 알맞은 곳은?

> We are going to the amusement park.

① ② ③ ④ ⑤

04 다음 영영풀이에 해당하는 단어를 위 대화에서 찾아 쓰시오.

> a visit made by students and teachers to learn about something

➡ _____

05 ⓐ~ⓔ 중 문법상 또는 흐름상 어색한 부분이 모두 몇 개인지 고르시오.

① 1개 ② 2개 ③ 3개 ④ 4개 ⑤ 5개

06 위 대화를 읽고 대답할 수 없는 질문을 고르시오.

① When are they going on the field trip?
② Where is the boy going for the field trip?
③ Where is the girl going for the field trip?
④ How will the boy go to the amusement park?
⑤ How many art shows are there in the art museum now?

[07~09] 다음 대화를 읽고 물음에 답하시오.

Hanguk University

B: Excuse me. <u>여기서 한국 대학교까지 어떻게 가나요?</u>(get, how)

W: You can go there by bus or on foot.

B: How long does it take to get there?

W: It takes five minutes by bus and 20 minutes on foot.

B: Oh, then I will walk there. Can you tell me how to get there?

W: (A)_____ You will see Hanguk University on (B)_____.

B: (A)_____ Thank you!

07 남자의 이동 수단과 소요 시간이 바르게 짝지어진 것을 고르시오.

① 버스 - 15분   ② 지하철 - 5분
③ 걷기 - 12분   ④ 버스 - 20분
⑤ 걷기 - 20분

08 밑줄 친 우리말을 괄호 안에 주어진 말을 이용하여 영작하시오.

➡ _____

09 그림을 참고하여 빈칸 (A)와 (B)에 들어갈 말을 쓰시오.

➡ (A) _____
   (B) _____

10 다음 빈칸에 들어갈 말이 바르게 짝지어진 것은?

• It is difficult _____ 1 km without a rest.
• Melinda knows _____ the man is.

① run – that
② to run – if
③ to run – who
④ running – who
⑤ running – if

11 다음 밑줄 친 부분의 쓰임이 나머지 넷과 다른 것은?

① I wonder if my child expresses himself well in English.
② You can catch the train if you go now.
③ Let's wait and see if the market improves.
④ Please tell me if there's anything I can do to help.
⑤ Alex asked me if I wanted a massage.

12 다음 중 어법상 바르지 않은 것은?

① It was not easy to play soccer after it rained lot.
② These days it is essential to learn English.
③ It is exciting to meet a famous person.
④ Is it possible breathe under the water?
⑤ It is important to drink a lot of water for our health.

13 다음 두 문장을 간접의문문을 이용하여 한 문장으로 쓰시오.

(1) I know. + Who won the race?

➡ _____

(2) Do you know? + When will the bus come?

➡ _____

(3) The man is asking her. + How long does it take to get to the mart?

➡ _____

(4) I have no idea. + Do they like it or not?

➡ _____

(5) Do you think? + Who will win the game?

➡ _____

(6) Do you guess? + What does she want to buy?

➡ _____

14 주어진 어휘를 이용하여 다음 우리말을 영작하시오. (to부정사나 간접의문문을 이용하여 쓸 것.)

(1) 우리의 환경을 보호하는 것은 중요하다. (environment, protect, it)

➡ _____

(2) 전통 시장을 구경하는 것은 재미있다. (the traditional market, look around, it)

➡ _____

(3) 롤러코스터를 타는 것은 신나는 일이다. (the roller coaster, exciting, it)

➡ _____

(4) 잠을 충분히 자는 것이 필요하다. (enough sleep, necessary, get, it)

➡ _____

(5) 나는 그 소녀가 어디에 살았었는지 기억하지 못한다. (remember, live)

➡ _____

(6) Anna는 내게 내가 Angelina를 사랑하는지 물었다. (ask, love)

➡ _____

[15~16] 다음 글을 읽고 물음에 답하시오.

Busan, Market Heaven

Do you like traditional markets? Then go to Gukje Market in Busan. It is one of the most famous markets in Busan. ⓐ그곳이 무엇으로 유명한지 아세요? It is famous for selling ⓑ a variety of goods from different countries. It was interesting to see all the international goods there. We also ate many kinds of street food, such as *Gimbap*, fish cake, and *Hotteok*. Then we walked to Bosu-dong Book Street. Many bookstores there sell used books. We were really excited because we found some old comic books! It was nice to relax in a café and read them.

15 위 글의 밑줄 친 ⓐ의 우리말에 맞게 한 단어를 보충하여, 주어진 어휘를 알맞게 배열하시오.

it / what / famous / you / is / know / do / ?

➡ _____

16 위 글의 밑줄 친 ⓑa variety of와 바꿔 쓸 수 있는 단어를 모두 고르시오.

① familiar   ② diverse

③ various   ④ same

⑤ common

[17~19] 다음 글을 읽고 물음에 답하시오.

Ⓐ

ⓐThere is no place like Gangwon-do for beautiful nature. ⓑFirst, we went to Baengnyong Cave. This 1.8-kilometer-long cave is still in good condition. It was so amazing to see its natural beauty. ⓒNear the end of our cave tour, the guide turned off the lights in the cave for a minute. Everything became very dark, so we were able to focus on the sounds Ⓑthere. It was the most amazing experience of the tour! ⓓOur next stop was Donggang. We went rafting! ⓔIt was exciting to ride on the rough water and enjoy the view at the same time.

17 위 글의 빈칸 Ⓐ에 들어갈 제목으로 알맞은 것을 고르시오.

① Gangwon-do, Seafood Heaven
② Baengnyong Cave in Good Condition
③ Focus on the Sounds of Nature
④ Gangwon-do, Full of Natural Beauty
⑤ How about Going Rafting?

18 위 글의 밑줄 친 문장 ⓐ~ⓔ를 사실(Fact)과 견해(Opinion)로 구분하시오.

➡ 사실(Fact): _____
　견해(Opinion): _____

19 위 글의 밑줄 친 Ⓑthere가 가리키는 것을 본문에서 찾아 쓰시오.

➡ _____

[20~22] 다음 글을 읽고 물음에 답하시오.

Incheon, A City of Firsts

Do you know where the first train station in Korea is? How about the first *Jajangmyeon*? The answer is Incheon! This place has (A)[many / much] of Korea's firsts. To (B)[get / get to] there, we went to Incheon Station. (①) The Jajangmyeon Museum is next to the station. (②) We learned about the history of

Jajangmyeon there. (③) The view from the park was awesome! (④) It was great to see the historical sites of this city from the park. (⑤)
Teacher: Wow, these places sound (C)[great / greatly]! You all have done a wonderful job on your presentations!

20 위 글의 흐름으로 보아, 주어진 문장이 들어가기에 가장 적절한 곳은?

> Later, we walked around Jayu Park, the first Western-style park in Korea.

①   ②   ③   ④   ⑤

21 위 글의 괄호 (A)~(C)에서 어법상 알맞은 낱말을 골라 쓰시오.

(A)_____ (B)_____ (C)_____

22 위 글의 내용과 일치하지 <u>않는</u> 것은?

① The first train station in Korea is in Incheon.
② Incheon has many of Korea's firsts.
③ The Jajangmyeon Museum is next to Incheon Station.
④ Jayu Park is the first Eastern-style park in Korea.
⑤ Seeing the historical sites of Incheon from Jayu Park was great.

Lesson

7

On My Way to the Future

 의사소통 기능

- 능력 표현하기
  I'm good at drawing pictures.
- 조언 구하고 답하기
  A: What do I need to do?
  B: You need to read a lot of books.

 언어 형식

- to부정사를 목적격보어로 취하는 동사
  Taeho wants more people to use 3D printed products in the future.

- 조건을 나타내는 접속사 if
  If you keep looking ahead and dreaming big, your future will be bright.

Words & Expressions

교과서

Key Words

- advice [ædváis] 명 충고, 조언
- allow [əláu] 동 허락하다
- amazing [əméiziŋ] 형 대단한, 멋진
- amount [əmáunt] 명 양, 총액
- analyze [ǽnəlàiz] 동 분석하다
- appear [əpíər] 동 나타나다, 보이기 시작하다
- apply [əplái] 동 지원하다, 신청하다
- artificial [á:rtəfíʃəl] 형 인공적인, 인조의
- career [kəríər] 명 진로, 직업
- cartoonist [kɑ:rtú:nist] 명 만화가
- collaborate [kəlǽbərèit] 동 협력하다
- collaboration [kɔ́læbəréiʃən] 명 공동 작업, 협동
- collect [kəlékt] 동 모으다, 수집하다
- consultant [kɔ́nsʌltənt] 명 상담가
- counseling [káunsəliŋ] 명 상담
- creative [kriéitiv] 형 창의적인
- creativity [krì:eitívəti] 명 창의력, 독창력
- customer [kʌ́stəmər] 명 손님, 고객
- decorate [dékərèit] 동 꾸미다, 장식하다
- designer [dizáinər] 명 디자이너, 설계자
- develop [divéləp] 동 발달시키다, 발전하다
- emotion [imóuʃən] 명 감정
- float [flout] 동 (물 위에) 뜨다, 떠다니다
- following [fálouiŋ] 형 다음[아래]에 나오는[언급되는]

- improve [imprú:v] 동 개선하다, 향상시키다
- interpreter [intə́:rpritər] 명 통역사
- kind [kaind] 명 종류
- late-night [léitnàit] 형 심야의
- modeler [mádlər] 명 모형 제작자
- P.E. 명 체육 (physical education)
- patient [péiʃənt] 명 환자
- photographer [fətágrəfər] 명 사진작가, 사진사
- problem-solving 형 문제 해결의
- reason [rí:zn] 명 이유, 원인
- reduce [ridjú:s] 동 줄이다, 감소시키다
- reviewer [rivjú:ər] 명 (책 · 영화 등의) 논평가
- route [ru:t] 명 경로, 노선
- scientist [sáiəntist] 명 과학자
- self-driving car 자율주행차
- skill [skil] 명 기능, 기술
- software [sɔ́:ftwɛ̀ər] 명 소프트웨어
- space [speis] 명 우주, 공간
- specialist [spéʃəlist] 명 전문가
- strength [streŋkθ] 명 힘, 강점, 장점
- talent [tǽlənt] 명 (타고난) 재능, 재주
- upcycle [ʌ́psaikl] 동 (폐품 등을) 다시 쓸 수 있게 만들다
- waste material 쓰레기, 폐기물

Key Expressions

- be good at ~을 잘하다
- be planning to 동사원형 ~할 계획이다
- come true 이루어지다, 실현되다
- fill out (서식 등을) 작성하다, (정보를) 기입하다, 채우다
- first of all 무엇보다도
- help out 도와주다, 거들다
- keep a diary 일기를 쓰다

- look ahead (앞일을) 내다보다, 예견하다
- need to 동사원형 ~할 필요가 있다
- print out 출력하다
- take care of ~을 돌보다
- wait for ~을 기다리다
- what else 그 외에 무엇, 그 밖에 무엇

Word Power

※ 명사 – 동사
- [ ] **advice**(충고, 조언) – **advise**(충고하다)
- [ ] **analysis**(분석) – **analyze**(분석하다)

※ 서로 비슷한 뜻을 가진 어휘
- [ ] **allow**(허락하다) – **permit**(허락하다, 허가하다)
- [ ] **space**(우주) – **universe**(우주)
- [ ] **strength**(강점, 장점) – **strong point**(장점)
- [ ] **collaborate**(협력하다) – **work together**(함께 일하다)
- [ ] **specialist**(전문가) – **expert**(전문가)

※ 동사 – 행위자
- [ ] **design**(디자인하다, 설계하다) – **designer**(디자이너, 설계자)
- [ ] **consult**(상담하다) – **consultant**(상담가)
- [ ] **interpret**(해석하다, 통역하다) – **interpreter**(통역사)
- [ ] **model**(모형[견본]을 만들다) – **modeler**(모형 제작자)
- [ ] **photograph**(~의 사진을 찍다, 촬영하다) – **photographer**(사진작가, 사진사)
- [ ] **review**(논평[비평]하다) – **reviewer**((책·영화 등의) 논평가)

English Dictionary

- [ ] **analyze** 분석하다
  → to study in detail 자세히 연구하다
- [ ] **apply** 지원하다, 신청하다
  → to give someone papers that say you want to do something
  어떤 것을 하기를 원한다고 말하는 서류를 제출하다
- [ ] **artificial** 인공적인, 인조의
  → not natural; created by humans
  자연적이지 않은, 인간에 의해 만들어진
- [ ] **career** 진로, 직업
  → a job that requires special skills or training
  특별한 기술이나 훈련을 요구하는 직업
- [ ] **counseling** 상담
  → advice that is given to someone to help them with their problems
  문제 해결을 돕기 위해 누군가에게 주어지는 조언
- [ ] **creativity** 창의력, 독창력
  → the ability to think of or create something new
  새로운 것을 생각해 내거나 만들어 내는 능력
- [ ] **develop** 발달시키다, 발전하다
  → to grow or become more advanced
  좀 더 진보된 상태로 되거나 변화되다
- [ ] **fill out** (서식 등을) 작성하다, (정보를) 기입하다, 채우다
  → to write down information on a form
  서식에 정보를 적어 넣다
- [ ] **float** (물 위에) 뜨다, 떠다니다
  → to stay up on water 물 위에 머무르다
- [ ] **improve** 개선하다, 향상시키다

  → to make something better
  어떤 것을 더 좋게 만들다
- [ ] **late-night** 심야의
  → late at night 밤 늦게
- [ ] **look ahead** (앞일을) 내다보다, 예견하다
  → to think about what might happen in the future
  미래에 발생할지도 모르는 것에 대해 생각하다
- [ ] **modeler** 모형 제작자
  → a person who makes something based on something else
  다른 어떤 것에 기초해서 어떤 것을 만들어 내는 사람
- [ ] **patient** 환자
  → a person who receives medical care
  치료를 받는 사람
- [ ] **reviewer** (책·영화 등의) 논평가
  → a person who writes opinions about the quality of a book, movie, or product 책, 영화, 상품의 질에 대한 의견을 쓰는 사람
- [ ] **route** 경로, 노선
  → a way between two places 두 장소 사이의 길
- [ ] **specialist** 전문가
  → a person who has a special skill
  특별한 기술을 가진 사람
- [ ] **strength** 강점, 장점
  → an advantageous quality or ability
  유리한 특성이나 능력
- [ ] **talent** (타고난) 재능, 재주
  → a natural ability to do something well
  어떤 것을 잘하는 타고난 능력

Step2

Words & Expressions 시험대비 실력평가

01 다음 중 성격이 <u>다른</u> 하나를 고르시오.

① cartoonist ② customer
③ photographer ④ consultant
⑤ designer

[02~04] 다음 빈칸에 들어갈 말로 가장 적절한 것은?

02
This food contains no _____ colors.

① annual ② cheerful ③ fake
④ creative ⑤ artificial

03
How can I _____ my writing skills?

① require ② design ③ develop
④ expect ⑤ allow

04
_____ a diary is a good way to practice writing.

① Keeping ② Improving ③ Reducing
④ Decorating ⑤ Allowing

05 다음 영영풀이에 해당하는 단어를 고르시오.

a person who writes opinions about the quality of a book, movie, or product

① judge ② writer ③ artist
④ reviewer ⑤ movie director

06 다음 대화의 빈칸에 들어갈 말을 고르시오.

A: Can you sing?
B: Yes. I'm pretty _____ at singing.

① able ② proud ③ work
④ good ⑤ bad

07 다음 중 밑줄 친 부분의 뜻풀이가 바르지 <u>않은</u> 것은?

① Sam likes to <u>collect</u> fallen leaves every autumn. (모으다)
② A balloon <u>modeler</u> showed an airplane made with balloons only. (모델)
③ Chess seems to improve <u>problem-solving</u> skills. (문제 해결의)
④ The leaves on trees <u>reduce</u> pollution. (줄이다)
⑤ I think my <u>talent</u> is taking pictures of people. (재능, 재주)

08 다음 밑줄 친 단어와 바꿔 쓸 수 있는 것을 고르시오.

Weather <u>specialists</u> said the rainy season will last for more than 10 days.

① experiences ② scientists
③ experts ④ professions
⑤ strangers

1 다음 밑줄 친 부분과 의미가 비슷한 것을 주어진 철자로 시작하여 쓰시오.

> The <u>strong point</u> of my job is high paycheck.

➡ s_____

[02~03] 다음 빈칸에 공통으로 들어갈 말을 쓰시오.

02
> • The park's officials want to _____ them safe.
> • _____ a diary so that you can write down your thoughts.

 3
> • I need someone to take care _____ my little girl after school.
> • First _____ all, you need to calm down.

04 다음 빈칸에 들어갈 말을 〈보기〉에서 찾아 쓰시오.

> ┤ 보기 ├
> amount   career   emotion   reason

(1) You need to control your _____s.
(2) Recycling can save large _____s of energy.
(3) The man chose acting as a(n) _____.
(4) What is the _____ for your visit?

05 다음 그림을 보고 대화의 빈칸을 알맞게 채우시오. (한 칸에 한 단어임)

> A: Would you please _____ _____ your information?
> B: Sure.

06 다음 우리말에 맞게 주어진 단어를 바르게 배열하시오.

(1) 우리는 실패의 원인을 분석할 필요가 있다. (need, of, we, failure, analyze, to, the, the, cause)
   ➡ _____

(2) 너는 영어 실력을 향상시킬 필요가 있다. (you, your, English, improve, need, to)
   ➡ _____

(3) 나의 장점은 나 자신을 믿는다는 것이다. (in, strength, that, I, my, is, myself, believe)
   ➡ _____

(4) 내 아들은 노래에 재능이 있다. (has, singing, my, a, for, son, talent)
   ➡ _____

(5) 너 야식 먹고 싶니? (late-night, you, snack, want, a, do)
   ➡ _____

Conversation

① 능력 표현하기

I'm good at drawing pictures. 나는 그림을 잘 그려.

- 능력을 말할 때 'be good at ~'을 사용해서 '~을 잘한다'는 의미를 나타낼 수 있다. 전치사 at 다음에는 math, baseball 등의 명사나 dancing, playing the piano 등 동명사(구)를 쓰면 된다.

- '내 생각에는 ~'이라는 의미의 'I think ~.'를 활용하면 자신의 능력을 좀 더 겸손하게 표현할 수 있다.

- 자신이 '~에 능숙하지 못하다'고 능력을 부정할 때는 be동사 뒤에 not을 붙여 부정문을 만들며 'be not good at ~ing'의 형태가 된다.

능력 여부 묻기

- Are you good at (동)명사? (너는 ~하는 것을 잘하니?)
- Can you 동사원형 (well)? (너는 ~을 (잘) 할 수 있니?)
- Are you able to 동사원형? (너는 ~을 할 수 있니?)
- Do you know how to 동사원형? (너는 ~하는 방법을 아니?)

능력 표현하기

- Yes, I am. / Yes, I can 동사원형.
- I know how to 동사원형.
- I am able to 동사원형.
- I'm (pretty) good at ~.

능력 부인하기

- (No,) I'm not. / (No,) I can't 동사원형 (well).
- I don't know how to 동사원형.
- Not really.
- I'm not able to 동사원형.
- I'm not good at ~.
- I'm poor at ~.

핵심 Check

1. 다음 우리말을 보고 대화의 빈칸을 채우시오.

   A: Are you _____ the piano? (너는 피아노 연주를 잘하니?)

   B: Yeah, I think so. (응. 그렇다고 생각해.)

2. 다음 주어진 단어를 이용하여 대화를 완성하시오.

   A: _____? (taking, good, pictures, are, at, you)

   B: No, but _____. (good, it, is, my, brother, at)

2 조언 구하고 답하기

> **A** What do I need to do? 뭘 해야 하니?
> **B** You need to read a lot of books. 책을 많이 읽어야 해.

■ 상대방에게 조언을 구할 때는 'What do I need to do?', 'What do you suggest?', 'What should I do to 동사원형?' 등의 표현을 쓸 수 있다.

■ 조언을 구하는 질문에 대해 답할 때는 'You need to 동사원형', 'I suggest (that) you ~.', '(I think) you have to[should] 동사원형 ~.'을 이용하여 답을 할 수 있다. 이때 조동사 have to나 must는 어투가 다소 강한 느낌을 줄 수 있다는 것을 유의한다.

조언을 구할 때

- What do I need to do?
- What do you suggest?
- What should I do to ~?
- How can I ~?
- What can I do to ~?

조언을 할 때

- You need to ~.
- I suggest (that) you ~.
- (I think (that)) You should/have to ~.
- Make sure you ~.

■ I suggest (that) ~.에서 접속사 that은 생략할 수 있으며, 뒤따르는 절의 동사는 동사원형을 쓴다.

■ 'Why don't you ~?'나 'How[What] about ~?'의 제안하는 표현을 이용하여 조언을 할 수도 있다.

핵심 Check

3. 다음 우리말을 보고 대화의 빈칸을 채우시오.

A: What do I _____ lose weight? (살을 빼기 위해서 뭘 해야 하니?)

B: You should exercise every day. (매일 운동을 해야 해.)

4. 다음 대화의 밑줄 친 부분과 같은 의미가 되도록, 주어진 단어를 이용하여 영작하시오.

A: <u>What do I need to do to improve my English skills?</u>

B: You need to keep a diary in English.

➡ (can, how) _____

(suggest, what) _____

Listen & Talk 1 A

G: ❶Let's play basketball.

B: Well… ❷I'm not good at playing basketball. Are you?

G: Yes, ❸I think I am. ❹What are you good at?

B: ❺I'm good at playing soccer.

G: Okay, then let's play soccer.

G: 우리 농구하자.
B: 음… 나는 농구를 잘하지 못해. 너는 잘하니?
G: 응, 내 생각에 나는 잘하는 것 같아. 넌 어떤 것을 잘해?
B: 나는 축구를 잘해.
G: 그래, 그러면 축구를 하자.

❶ 'Let's ～'는 '～하자'라고 제안을 할 때 사용된다. 이 외에도 'Why don't we ～?'의 표현을 쓸 수 있다.

❷ 능력을 말하는 'be good at(～을 잘하다)'에서 자신이 '～에 능숙하지 못하다'라고 능력을 부정할 때는 be동사 뒤에 not을 붙여 부정문을 만들어 'be not good at ～ing'의 형태가 된다.

❸ 'I think I am.' 뒤에 'good at playing basketball'이 생략되어 있다.

❹ 무엇을 잘하는지 묻는 표현으로 'What can you do (well)?', 'What are you able to do?'로 바꿔 쓸 수 있다.

❺ 능력을 말할 때 'be good at ～'을 사용해서 '～을 잘한다'는 의미를 나타낼 수 있다. 전치사 at 다음에는 (동)명사가 나올 수 있다.

Check(√) True or False

(1) The boy can play basketball well. T ☐ F ☐

(2) The girl is going to play basketball. T ☐ F ☐

(3) The girl is good at playing basketball. T ☐ F ☐

Listen & Talk 2 A

B: ❶I want to be a scientist. ❷What do I need to do?

W: ❸You need to study science. ❹And you need to develop your problem-solving skills.

B: 저는 과학자가 되고 싶어요. 저는 어떤 것을 해야 할까요?
W: 과학 공부를 해야 돼요. 그리고 문제 해결 능력을 개발할 필요가 있어요.

❶ be a scientist: 과학자가 되다

❷ 'What do I need to do?'는 '저는 어떤 것을 해야 할까요?'의 뜻으로 의미상 뒤에 'to be a scientist'가 생략되어 있다. 같은 의미로 쓸 수 있는 문장으로는 'What do you suggest?', 'What should I do?', 'How can I be a scientist?' 등이 있다.

❸ need to 동사원형; ～할 필요가 있다

❹ develop: 발달시키다, 발전하다 problem-solving: 문제 해결의

Check(√) True or False

(4) Problem-solving skills are important to become a scientist. T ☐ F ☐

(5) The boy wants to be a science teacher. T ☐ F ☐

(6) The woman suggests that the boy should study science. T ☐ F ☐

Listen & Talk 1 B

B: Jessica, ❶what are you going to do for the school talent show?

G: ❷I didn't decide yet. ❸What am I good at?

B: You're good at dancing, aren't you?

G: Not really. But I think I'm good at singing. I like singing very much.

B: Really? Actually, ❹I'm planning to play rock music with my band. ❺Why don't you sing for us?

G: Sure, I'd love to.

❶ be going to 동사원형: ~할 것이다 What are you going to do?: 뭐 할 거야? talent: (타고난) 재능, 재주

❷ decide: 결정하다 yet: 아직

❸ What am I good at?: 나 어떤 것을 잘하지?

❹ be planning to 동사원형: ~할 계획이다(= be going to 동사원형)

❺ 어떤 일을 하기를 제안하거나 권유하고자 할 때, '~하는 게 어때?'라는 의미로 'Why don't you+동사원형 ~?'을 쓴다.

Listen & Talk 2 B

G: Jason, I read your paper. It was so ❶amazing!

B: ❷Thank you for saying that. I'm trying hard ❸to improve my writing skills. I want to be a writer someday.

G: Really? I want to write well ❹like you. ❺What do I need to do?

B: You need to read a lot of books. Reading makes your writing better.

G: What else do I need to do?

B: Well, I write almost every day. Why don't you start ❻keeping a diary?

G: Thank you for your advice. I'll start today.

❶ amazing: 대단한, 멋진

❷ Thank you 뒤의 전치사 for 다음에는 고마워하는 이유가 나온다. Thank you for saying that.: 그렇게 말해 줘서 고마워.

❸ to부정사의 부사적 용법(목적)으로 '~하기 위해서'의 의미로 사용되었다.

❹ like는 전치사로 '~처럼'의 의미이다.

❺ 'What do I need to do?'는 '뭘 해야 하니?' 의미로 조언을 구할 때 하는 표현이다.

❻ keep a diary: 일기를 쓰다

Listen & Talk 1 C

B: Mom, ❶I need to fill out this form for tomorrow's career counseling program. Could you help me?

W: Sure. Let me see. You already wrote your dream job and hobby.

B: Yes, ❷I want to be a P.E. teacher, and my hobby is watching sports games. But writing my strengths is hard. What am I good at?

W: Well, I think you have lots of strengths. ❸First of all, you are good at playing baseball, aren't you?

B: Oh, yes. I'm good at playing baseball.

W: And you have many other strengths.

B: You're right. I also work well with other people. And I'm good at listening to people.

W: Right! You're good at so many things.

B: Thanks, Mom.

❶ need to 동사원형: ~할 필요가 있다 fill out: (서식 등을) 작성하다, (정보를) 기입하다, 채우다

❷ P.E.: 체육(physical education) 'my hobby is watching sports games.'에서 'watching sports games'는 'is'의 보어로 사용되었다.

❸ first of all: 무엇보다도

Listen & Talk 2 C

G: Hello, Mr. Watson! Thank you for doing this interview.

M: Sure, no problem.

G: This interview is for students ❶who want to be food stylists. ❷Can you tell me about your job?

M: Sure. You may see pictures of food in books or on TV. A food stylist decorates food to look good for pictures or movies.

G: I want to be a food stylist like you. What do I need to do?

M: You need to learn about many kinds of food.

G: ❸What else do I need to do?

M: You need to study art, too. ❹Creativity is important.

G: All right! Thank you for your time, Mr. Watson.

❶ who는 주격 관계대명사로 앞의 students를 수식하고 있다.

❷ 어떤 것에 대한 설명을 요청할 때 'Can you tell me about ~?'이나 'Can you explain ~?'으로 말할 수 있다.

❸ What else: 그 외에 무엇을

❹ creativity: 창의력, 독창력

다음 우리말과 일치하도록 빈칸에 알맞은 말을 쓰시오. (주어진 철자가 있으면 그 철자로 시작할 것)

Listen & Talk 1 A

G: Let's _____ basketball.

B: Well… I'm _____ _____ at playing basketball. Are you?

G: Yes, I think I am. _____ _____ _____ good at?

B: I'm good _____ _____ soccer.

G: Okay, then _____ play soccer.

Listen & Talk 1 B

B: Jessica, what are you going _____ _____ for the school talent show?

G: I didn't _____ yet. _____ _____ I good at?

B: You're _____ _____ dancing, aren't you?

G: Not really. But I think I'm _____ _____ _____. I like singing very much.

B: Really? Actually, I'm planning _____ _____ rock music with my band. _____ _____ _____ sing for us?

G: Sure, I'd love to.

Listen & Talk 1 C

B: Mom, I _____ _____ _____ _____ this form for tomorrow's career counseling program. Could you help me?

W: Sure. Let me see. You already _____ your dream job _____ hobby.

B: Yes, I want to _____ a _____, and my hobby is _____ sports games. But _____ my _____ is hard. _____ _____ _____ at?

W: Well, I think you have _____ of strengths. _____ _____ all, you _____ _____ _____ playing baseball, _____ _____?

B: Oh, yes.

W: And you have many other _____.

B: You're right. I also _____ well with other people. And I'm good _____ _____ _____ people.

W: Right! _____ _____ so many things.

B: Thanks, Mom.

해석

G: 우리 농구하자.
B: 음... 나는 농구를 잘하지 못해. 너는 잘하니?
G: 응, 내 생각에 나는 잘하는 것 같아. 넌 어떤 것을 잘해?
B: 나는 축구를 잘해.
G: 그래, 그러면 축구를 하자.

B: Jessica, 학교 재능 발표회에서 뭐 할 거야?
G: 아직 결정 안 했어. 나 어떤 것을 잘하지?
B: 너 춤 잘 추잖아, 그렇지 않니?
G: 사실 그렇지 않아. 하지만 내 생각에는 나는 노래를 잘해. 나는 노래하는 것을 매우 좋아해.
B: 정말? 사실 나 우리 밴드와 록 음악을 연주할 계획이야. 우리를 위해 노래해 주는 게 어때?
G: 그래, 좋아.

B: 엄마, 저 내일 있을 진로 상담 프로그램을 준비하기 위해 이 양식을 작성해야 해요. 저 좀 도와주시겠어요?
W: 물론이지. 어디 보자. 이미 하고 싶은 직업과 취미는 적었구나.
B: 네. 저는 체육 선생님이 되고 싶어요. 제 취미는 스포츠 경기 보는 거예요. 하지만, 제 강점을 적는 것은 어려워요. 저는 무엇을 잘하죠?
W: 음, 나는 네게 많은 강점이 있다고 생각해. 무엇보다도 너는 야구를 잘하잖니, 그렇지 않니?
B: 아, 맞아요. 저는 야구를 잘해요.
W: 그리고 너는 다른 강점들도 가지고 있단다.
B: 맞아요. 저는 다른 사람들과 협업을 잘해요. 그리고 사람들의 이야기를 잘 들어 줘요.
W: 그렇지! 너는 아주 많은 것들을 잘한단다.
B: 감사해요, 엄마.

Listen & Talk 2 A

B: I _____ _____ _____ a scientist. _____ do I need to do?

W: You _____ _____ study science. And you need to _____ your _____ skills.

Listen & Talk 2 B

G: Jason, I read your paper. It was so _____!

B: Thank you for saying that. I'm _____ hard _____ _____ my writing skills. I want to be a _____ someday.

G: Really? I _____ to write well _____ you. _____ _____ _____ need _____ do?

B: You need to read a lot of books. _____ _____ _____ _____ _____.

G: What _____ do I need to do?

B: Well, I write almost every day. Why _____ you start _____ a diary?

G: Thank you for your _____. I'll start today.

Listen & Talk 2 C

G: Hello, Mr. Watson! Thank you _____ doing this interview.

M: Sure, no problem.

G: This interview is for students _____ _____ _____ _____ _____ stylists. Can you tell me about your job?

M: Sure. You may see pictures of food in books or on TV. A food stylist _____ food _____ _____ good for pictures or movies.

G: I want _____ _____ _____ _____ _____ _____ like you. _____ do I _____ to do?

M: You _____ _____ _____ about many _____ of food.

G: What _____ do I need to do?

M: You need to study art, too. _____ is important.

G: All right! _____ you _____ your time, Mr. Watson.

해석

B: 저는 과학자가 되고 싶어요. 저는 어떤 것을 해야 할까요?

W: 과학 공부를 해야 돼요. 그리고 문제 해결 능력을 개발할 필요가 있어요.

G: Jason, 나 너의 글을 읽었어. 아주 놀라웠어!

B: 그렇게 말해 줘서 고마워. 나는 내 글쓰기 기량을 발전시키려고 노력하고 있어. 언젠가 작가가 되고 싶어.

G: 정말? 나도 너처럼 글을 잘 쓰고 싶어. 뭘 해야 하니?

B: 책을 많이 읽어야 해. 독서가 네 글쓰기를 더 좋게 만들거든.

G: 다른 건 또 뭘 해야 할까?

B: 음, 나는 거의 매일 글을 쓰고 있어. 일기 쓰기를 시작하는 건 어때?

G: 조언 고마워. 오늘부터 시작할게.

G: 안녕하세요, Watson 씨! 오늘 인터뷰 감사해요.

M: 네, 문제 없어요.

G: 이 인터뷰는 푸드 스타일리스트가 되고 싶어 하는 학생들을 위한 것이에요. 당신의 직업에 대해 말씀해 주시겠어요?

M: 그럼요. 아마 여러분은 책이나 TV에서 음식 사진을 보셨을 겁니다. 푸드 스타일리스트는 사진이나 영화에서 음식이 맛있어 보이도록 장식하는 일을 합니다.

G: 저도 Watson 씨와 같은 푸드 스타일리스트가 되고 싶어요. 뭘 해야 하나요?

M: 많은 종류의 음식에 대해 배워야 해요.

G: 다른 건 뭘 해야 하죠?

M: 미술 공부도 해야 해요. 창의력이 중요하거든요.

G: 알겠습니다! 시간 내 주셔서 감사합니다, Watson 씨.

01 다음 대화의 빈칸에 알맞지 <u>않은</u> 것은?

> B: I want to be a scientist. _____
> W: You need to study science. And you need to develop your problem-solving skills.

① What can I do? ② Is there something else to do?
③ What should I do? ④ What do you suggest?
⑤ What do I need to do?

[02~03] 다음 대화의 빈칸에 알맞은 것은?

02

> G: I want to be a food stylist like you. What do I need to do?
> M: _____

① You have to make a shopping list.
② You need to learn about many kinds of food.
③ You should exercise every day.
④ You need to design a blog about Korean culture.
⑤ You should explain the styles about cultures.

03

> A: What are you good at?
> B: _____

① I don't like sports. ② I'm not good at drawing.
③ I'm not a talented cook. ④ I will be a good teacher.
⑤ I'm good at playing soccer.

04 다음 대화의 밑줄 친 부분의 의도로 적절한 것을 고르시오.

> G: Jason, I read your paper. It was so amazing!
> B: Thank you for saying that. I'm trying hard to improve my writing skills. I want to be a writer someday.
> G: Really? I want to write well like you. <u>What do I need to do?</u>
> B: You need to read a lot of books. Reading makes your writing better.

① 희망이나 소망 묻기 ② 능력 여부 묻기 ③ 설명 요청하기
④ 하고 싶은 것 묻기 ⑤ 조언 구하기

[01~02] 다음 짝지어진 대화가 <u>어색한</u> 것은?

01
① A: What are you good at?
  B: I'm good at fixing things.
② A: Are you good at soccer?
  B: Yes, I think so.
③ A: What should we do?
  B: We need to find water to drink first.
④ A: You are so good at drawing.
  B: No, thanks. Do you draw pictures, too?
⑤ A: How can I get better grades?
  B: You should study harder.

02
① A: Are you good at telling jokes?
  B: No, I'm not good at it.
② A: Jiho, what do I need to do to play the piano like you?
  B: Well, I think you're right.
③ A: What's your advice?
  B: You should exercise every day.
④ A: What should I do to become a good writer?
  B: You need to read many books first.
⑤ A: What can I do to get better grades?
  B: You need to take good notes in class.

[03~06] 다음 대화를 읽고 물음에 답하시오.

B: Mom, I need to fill (A)_____ this form for tomorrow's career counseling program. Could you help me?
W: Sure. Let me see. You already wrote your dream job and hobby.
B: Yes, I want to be a P.E. teacher, and my hobby is watching sports games. But writing my strengths is hard. What am I good at?
W: Well, I think you have lots of (B)strengths. First of all, you are good at playing baseball, aren't you?
B: Oh, yes. I'm good at playing baseball.
W: And you have many other strengths.
B: You're right. I also work well with other people. And I'm good at listening to people.
W: Right! (C)너는 아주 많은 것들을 잘한단다. (so, things, at, you, good, many, are)
B: Thanks, Mom.

03 빈칸 (A)에 들어갈 말로 적절한 것을 고르시오.
  ① at   ② on   ③ out
  ④ with   ⑤ from

04 밑줄 친 (B)와 같은 의미로 쓰이지 <u>않은</u> 것은?
① Focus on your <u>strengths</u> to boost your self-confidence.
② A person using <u>strengths</u> is creative, energetic, and productive.
③ Climbing an ice wall requires much physical <u>strength</u>.
④ His <u>strength</u> lies in his honesty.
⑤ His height is his <u>strength</u> in basketball.

서답형
05 밑줄 친 (C)의 우리말에 맞게 괄호 안에 주어진 단어를 알맞게 배열하시오

➡ _____

서답형
06 다음 영영풀이에 해당하는 단어를 대화에서 찾아 쓰시오.

advice that is given to someone to help them with their problems

➡ _____

[07~10] 다음 대화를 읽고 물음에 답하시오.

G: Jason, I read your paper. It was so amazing!

B: Thank you for saying that. I'm trying hard to improve my writing skills. (①) I want to be a (A)_____ someday.

G: Really? I want to write well like you. What do I need to do? (②)

B: You need to read a lot of books. Reading makes your writing better. (③)

G: (B)_____

B: Well, I write almost every day. (④) Why don't you start keeping a diary?

G: (⑤) I'll start today.

중요
07 위 대화의 ①~⑤ 중 주어진 문장이 들어갈 알맞은 곳은?

Thank you for your advice.

①   ②   ③   ④   ⑤

08 빈칸 (A)에 들어갈 적절한 말을 고르시오.

① writer   ② designer   ③ singer
④ painter   ⑤ lawyer

09 빈칸 (B)에 들어갈 말로 적절한 것을 고르시오.

① How can I write?
② What do you need to do?
③ What else do I need to do?
④ How often do you draw?
⑤ What skills do I need to develop?

중요
10 위 대화의 내용과 일치하지 않는 것은?

① The girl thinks Jason is good at writing.
② Jason thinks reading lots of books is helpful to improve writing skills.
③ Jason doesn't write every day.
④ The girl's writing is not as good as the boy's.
⑤ The girl thinks Jason's paper is excellent.

서답형
11 빈칸 (A)와 (B)에 들어갈 말로 적절한 것을 고르시오.

A: (A)_____
B: I'm good at drawing pictures.
A: (B)_____
B: I want to be an artist.

ⓐ What do I need to do?
ⓑ What are you good at?
ⓒ Why don't you draw pictures?
ⓓ What am I good at?
ⓔ What do you want to be in the future?
ⓕ How about becoming an artist?

➡ (A) _____
   (B) _____

[01~02] 다음 대화의 순서를 바르게 배열하시오.

01

> (A) I want to be a food stylist like you. What do I need to do?
> (B) What else do I need to do?
> (C) You need to study art, too. Creativity is important.
> (D) You need to learn about many kinds of food.

➡ _____

02

> (A) You need to learn about the human body.
> (B) Then how about becoming a nurse?
> (C) What are you good at?
> (D) That sounds good. What do I need to do to become a nurse?
> (E) I'm good at taking care of people.

➡ _____

[03~04] 다음 대화를 읽고 물음에 답하시오.

> G: Let's play basketball.
> B: Well... I'm not good at playing basketball. (A)Are you?
> G: Yes, I think I am. What are you good at?
> B: (B)_____
> G: Okay, then let's play soccer.

03 밑줄 친 (A) 뒤에 생략된 부분을 위의 대화에서 찾아 쓰시오.

➡ _____

04 빈칸 (B)에 들어갈 적절한 말을 위의 대화의 단어를 이용하여 쓰시오.

➡ _____

[05~06] 다음 대화를 읽고 물음에 답하시오.

> G: Jason, I read your paper. It was so amazing!
> B: Thank you for saying that. I'm trying hard to improve my writing skills. I want to be a writer someday.
> G: Really? I want to write well like you. (A)<u>내가 뭘 해야 하니?</u>
> B: You need to read a lot of books. (B)<u>독서가 네 글쓰기를 더 좋게 만들거든.</u>(better, makes, reading, writing, your)
> G: What else do I need to do?
> B: Well, I write almost every day. Why don't you start keeping a diary?
> G: Thank you for your advice. I'll start today.

05 밑줄 친 (A)의 우리말을 주어진 단어를 이용하여 영작하시오.

➡ _____ (need, what)

06 밑줄 친 (B)의 우리말에 맞게 괄호 안에 주어진 단어를 알맞게 배열하시오.

➡ _____

07 밑줄 친 우리말을 주어진 단어를 이용하여 영작하시오.

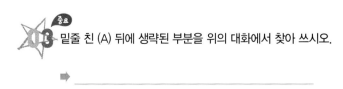

> G: Let's play badminton.
> B: Well... 나는 배드민턴을 잘하지 못해. (good, play) Are you?
> G: Yes, I think I am.

➡ _____

Grammar

1 to부정사를 목적격보어로 취하는 동사

> • Taeho **wants** more people **to use** 3D printed products in the future. 태호는 미래에 더 많은 사람이 3D 프린터로 출력된 제품들을 사용하기를 원합니다.
>
> • Would you **ask** her **to call** me tonight? 오늘밤 저에게 전화해 달라고 그녀에게 부탁해 주시겠어요?

- 동사 다음에 목적어와 to부정사가 쓰여 '목적어가 …하는 것을 ~하다'라는 의미를 나타낸다. 이때 목적어를 설명해 주는 to부정사를 목적격보어라고 하고 이런 문장 유형을 5형식이라고 한다. 동사에 따라 목적격보어로 to부정사를 쓰기도 하고, 동사원형을 쓰기도 한다.

- 목적격보어로 to부정사를 쓰는 동사에는 advise, allow, ask, tell, cause, enable, encourage, expect, force, get, help, need, order, persuade, require, teach, want, would like 등이 있다.

  • I **asked** him **to mail** the letter. 나는 그에게 편지를 부쳐달라고 부탁했다.

  • I **expect** her **to help** me. 나는 그녀가 나를 도와줄 것으로 기대하고 있다.

- 목적격보어로 쓰인 to부정사의 부정형은 'not to 동사원형'으로 쓴다.

  • He **advised** me **not to go** there. 그는 나에게 거기에 가지 말라고 충고했다.

- 목적격보어로 동사원형을 쓰는 동사에는 make, have, let 등이 있다.

  • I will **have** him **do** it. 나는 그가 그것을 하게 할 것이다.

핵심 Check

1. 괄호 안에서 알맞은 것을 고르시오.

   (1) I want Sumin (to be / be) nicer to me.

   (2) She told me (to return / returned) this book by Friday.

   (3) Will you help him (to clear / clearing) the table?

2. 다음 우리말에 맞게 빈칸에 알맞은 말을 쓰시오.

   • 그녀의 성공에 힘입어 나도 똑같은 걸 시도했다.

   ➡ Her success encouraged me _____ _____ the same thing.

2 조건을 나타내는 접속사 if

- **If** you keep looking ahead and dreaming big, your future will be bright. 만약 당신이 계속 앞을 내다보고 꿈을 크게 꾼다면, 당신의 미래는 밝을 것입니다.

- I will start tomorrow **if** it is fine. 나는 날씨가 좋으면 내일 출발하겠다.

■ if는 '만약 ~한다면'이라는 뜻의 조건을 나타내는 부사절을 이끄는 접속사로 한 문장을 다른 문장에 연결해 준다. 접속사가 사용된 문장에서 접속사가 붙은 절을 종속절, 접속사가 붙지 않은 나머지 절을 주절이라고 하는데, 주절이 먼저 나올 수도 있고 종속절이 먼저 나올 수도 있다. if절이 앞에 올 경우, 부사절 뒤에 쉼표(,)를 붙인다.

- **If** you want, you can look around.
= You can look around **if** you want. 원한다면 둘러보아도 좋아.

■ 시간이나 조건의 접속사가 이끄는 부사절에서는 실제로는 미래의 일을 나타내더라도 will을 쓰지 않고 현재시제를 쓴다.

- **If** it rains tomorrow, we will stay home. 내일 비가 오면 우리는 집에 있을 거예요.

- **After** I find out, I'll let you know at the next class. 확인해서 다음 수업시간에 알려 줄게요.

■ 접속사 unless
'만약 ~하지 않는다면'의 뜻으로 'if ~ not'과 같은 의미이다.

- You'll miss the bus **unless** you walk more quickly.
= You'll miss the bus **if** you **don't** walk more quickly. 더 빨리 걷지 않으면 버스를 놓칠 거야.

■ if절이 명사 역할을 하는 경우도 있으며 (이때 if는 whether와 같은 의미이다.) 이때는 '~인지 아닌지'로 해석하며 미래를 나타낼 때에는 미래시제를 써야 한다.

- I wonder **if** he **will** come. 나는 그가 올지 궁금하다.

핵심 Check

3. 괄호 안에서 알맞은 것을 고르시오.

(1) You can catch the train (if / unless) you leave now.

(2) If it (will rain / rains) tomorrow, we will put off the picnic.

(3) I don't know if he (will come / comes) tomorrow.

01 다음 문장에서 어법상 어색한 부분을 바르게 고치시오.

(1) When can I expect you be back?

_____ ➡ _____

(2) He told me to not lose heart.

_____ ➡ _____

(3) It is difficult to do unless you aren't a professional.

_____ ➡ _____ ,

_____ ➡ _____

(4) You will fail if you won't work harder.

_____ ➡ _____

02 다음 우리말을 영어로 옮길 때, 빈칸에 알맞은 것이 순서대로 짝지어진 것은?

• 그가 그녀를 거기로 태워다 주면 그녀는 그에게 돈을 줄 것이다.
→ She _____ him some money if he _____ her there.

① will give – will drive   ② will give – drives
③ gives – will drive   ④ gives – drives
⑤ gave – drove

03 괄호 안의 동사를 어법에 맞게 빈칸에 쓰시오.

(1) She asked me _____ her advice. (give)
(2) I want you _____ us. (join)
(3) I told him _____ it immediately. (do)
(4) The teacher made me _____ my homework. (do)

04 다음 우리말에 맞게 빈칸에 알맞은 말을 쓰시오.

(1) 그들은 내가 더 노력하기를 기대한다.
➡ They expect me _____ _____ harder.
(2) 네가 아무런 계획이 없다면, 우리는 쇼핑을 갈 수 있다.
➡ _____ you don't have any plans, we can go shopping.

01 다음 중 어법상 어색한 문장은?

① My mom let me eat ice cream for dessert.
② Why don't you go home if you feel ill?
③ Are you going to allow us to ask personal questions?
④ If Jina comes to my birthday party, I will be happy.
⑤ They advised him leave the place as soon as possible

02 다음 우리말을 바르게 영작한 것은?

> 유나는 나에게 그녀와 함께 수학 동아리에 가입하자고 했다.

① Yuna asked me join the math club with her.
② Yuna asked me joined the math club with her.
③ Yuna asked me to join the math club with her.
④ Yuna asked me joining the math club with her.
⑤ Yuna asked me to joining the math club with her.

03 다음 괄호 안에서 알맞은 것을 고르시오.

(1) Mr. Lee told his children (to be / be) quiet.
(2) I want Mijin (to study / studying) harder.
(3) If you (will smile /smile) at people, they will smile back at you.

04 빈칸에 들어갈 말을 순서대로 바르게 연결한 것은?

> • _____ you speak too fast, your classmates will not understand you.
> • Don't smoke in front of elders _____ you are invited to do so.

① If   –   if
② If   –   unless
③ Unless   –   if
④ Unless   –   unless
⑤ When   –   however

05 다음 빈칸에 알맞은 것은?

> I ordered him _____ silent in the hall.

① be   ② was   ③ is
④ to be   ⑤ being

06 다음 중 어법상 어색한 문장을 고르시오.

① If Hanbin will join our soccer club, I will play soccer with him.
② I will close this meeting unless you have further questions.
③ If you feel sick, take this medicine quickly.
④ If help is needed, what can people do?
⑤ Unless you start now, you'll be late.

07 다음 문장의 빈칸에 알맞지 않은 것은?

> Her mom _____ her to marry him.

① wanted   ② made   ③ asked
④ advised   ⑤ expected

[08~09] 다음 중 어법상 옳은 것을 고르시오.

08 ① I asked the man take my suitcase to the room.
② He advised me seeing a doctor right away.
③ I want you to share your ideas with your classmates.
④ His mom allowed them watched TV after dinner.
⑤ They made me to say the same thing over and over again.

09 ① If I'm wrong, you should tell me the right answer.
② Unless you go to the aquarium, you can see a lot of fish and sea animals.
③ If you won't have lunch, you will feel hungry soon.
④ I don't know if she comes home next weekend.
⑤ The work will not be done if you do it now.

중요
10 다음 빈칸에 공통으로 들어갈 말을 쓰시오.

• I wonder _____ she received my letter or not.
• You should visit there _____ you want to enjoy a beautiful view of Toronto.

➡ _____

11 괄호 안에 주어진 동사를 어법에 맞게 빈칸에 쓰시오.

(A) My teacher advised us _____ some rest. (get)
(B) What will big data allow us _____ in the future? (do)

중요
12 다음 밑줄 친 부분의 의미가 <u>다른</u> 하나는?

① I would like to hear it <u>if</u> there is a good reason for that.
② Do you happen to know <u>if</u> there's a pay phone around here?
③ <u>If</u> you don't use your smartphone before bed, you can sleep well.
④ <u>If</u> you have any questions, call me right away.
⑤ <u>If</u> Ella makes some mistakes, will Chris help her?

서답형
13 주어진 어구를 이용하여 다음 우리말을 영어로 쓰시오.

(1) 나는 네가 아무한테도 그것에 관해 말을 안 했으면 좋겠어. (want, tell, anybody, that)
➡ _____

(2) 그 의사는 나에게 패스트푸드를 그만 먹으라고 조언했다. (advise, eat, junk food)
➡ _____

(3) 오늘 밤에 비가 오면, 나는 집에 머물 것이다. (rain, home, it, stay, at)
➡ _____

(4) 답을 모르겠다면, 저에게 물어보세요. (the answer, know, ask, unless)
➡ _____

[14~15] 다음 중 어법상 어색한 부분을 찾아 바르게 고친 것은?

14

> Jessie ①told me ②send an email ③to Mr. Smith as ④soon ⑤as possible.

① told → tell
② send → to send
③ to → for
④ soon → sooner
⑤ as → than

15

> ①If Jimin ②will come to school ③early, I ④will exercise with ⑤her.

① If → Unless
② will come → comes
③ early → lately
④ will exercise → exercise
⑤ her → she

서답형

16 다음 빈칸에 들어갈 괄호 안에 주어진 동사의 형태가 다른 하나는?

① When do you want me _____ the package? (send)
② He made me _____ in the street for an hour last night. (stand)
③ Ann didn't allow them _____ a taxi. (take)
④ She got her two boys _____ a cake exactly in half. (divide)
⑤ Jenny asked him _____ the ants away from the food. (keep)

17 다음 중 어법상 바르지 않은 것은?

> ①He ②got ③his car ④to wash ⑤ yesterday.

①   ②   ③   ④   ⑤

서답형

18 다음 우리말과 같은 뜻이 되도록 if를 이용하여 두 문장을 연결하시오.

> 단어를 좋아하면 십자말풀이가 재미있어.
> • Crossword puzzles are fun to do.
> • You enjoy words.

➡ _____
_____

서답형

19 다음 문장에서 어법상 어색한 부분을 찾아 바르게 고쳐 다시 쓰시오.

(1) My family expects me come home by 9 p.m.
➡ _____

(2) His illness forced him canceling his visit.
➡ _____

(3) Yesterday my boss even had me to walk his dog.
➡ _____

(4) We don't have enough people to get the work do.
➡ _____

(5) If Mina will teach me English, I will help her with math.
➡ _____

(6) If you will keep looking ahead and dreaming big, your future is bright.
➡ _____
_____

(7) I forget things if I mark them down.
➡ _____

Grammar 서술형 시험대비

01 다음 두 문장이 비슷한 의미를 갖도록 빈칸을 알맞은 말로 채우시오.

(1) Mr. Taylor let her go back home early.
➡ Mr. Taylor allowed her _____ back home early.

(2) She said that I should focus on my studies.
➡ She advised me _____ on my studies.

(3) The doctor told me that I should stop smoking.
➡ The doctor advised me _____ smoking.

(4) Juliet said to her, "Don't go out late at night."
➡ Juliet warned her _____ out late at night.

(5) Steve said to Donald, "Great. Keep writing a diary in English."
➡ Steve encouraged Donald _____ writing a diary in English.

02 괄호 안에 주어진 어휘를 이용하여 문장을 완성하시오.

(1) _____, I will cook some food for her. (come, Juhee, my birthday party, 7 단어)

(2) _____, I will buy you a new computer. (volunteer, a month, work, do, for, 8 단어)

(3) _____, you'll be late for the meeting. (the subway, take, 5 단어)

03 다음 중 어법상 어색한 부분을 찾아 바르게 고쳐 다시 쓰시오.

(1) I want Jimin coming to school early.
➡ _____

(2) The teacher told the students respected each other.
➡ _____

(3) How much would it cost to have the camera repair?
➡ _____

(4) Her little black dress and pretty hat made her to look chic.
➡ _____

(5) If you won't hurry, you will miss the train.
➡ _____

(6) You will achieve everything you want if you will work hard.
➡ _____

(7) Unless you don't have anything to wear, wear my coat.
➡ _____

04 괄호 안에 주어진 동사를 어법에 맞게 빈칸에 쓰시오.

When would you like me _____ work? (start)

05 다음 두 문장이 같은 의미가 되도록 빈칸에 알맞은 말을 쓰시오.

(1) Amanda told him that he must not forget to turn off the machine.
➡ Amanda warned him _____ to turn off the machine.

(2) I think that Sumi had better join our soccer club.
➡ I want Sumi _____ our soccer club.

(3) The captain told his soldiers that they should leave the city immediately.
➡ The captain ordered his soldiers _____ the city immediately.

(4) Morris told Joseph that he should exercise regularly.
➡ Morris advised Joseph _____ regularly.

(5) Her parents hoped that she would become a good figure skater.
➡ Her parents expected her _____ a good figure skater.

06 다음 괄호 안에 주어진 동사를 어법에 맞게 빈칸에 쓰시오.

(1) If Sumi _____ our soccer club, I _____ her my soccer ball. (join, give)

(2) I'm not sure if Santa _____ me a nice gift or not. (give)

(3) Unless you _____ it up, I _____ you give it up. (give, make)

07 다음 두 문장의 뜻이 같도록 빈칸에 알맞은 말을 쓰시오.

(1) Sign the paper, and the bank will lend you money.
➡ _____ you sign the paper, the bank will lend you money.

(2) Hold the bar tight, or you will fall to the ground.
➡ _____ you hold the bar tight, you will fall to the ground.

08 다음 우리말을 괄호 안에 주어진 어휘를 이용하여 주어진 단어 수대로 영작하시오.

(1) 내가 내일 6시에 나오지 않으면, 나를 깨워줘. (come out, wake up, 12 단어) (종속절로 시작할 것)
➡ _____

(2) 내가 전화를 받지 않으면, 내 동생에게 전화해라. (my phone, answer, call, sister, 8 단어) (종속절로 시작할 것)
➡ _____

(3) 우리가 밤새 걸으면, 내일 그곳에 도착할 거야. (get, all night, 10 단어) (주절로 시작할 것)
➡ _____

(4) 나는 나의 엄마가 나에게 새 휴대전화를 사주시길 원한다. (my mom, cell phone, 11 단어)
➡ _____

(5) 그녀는 나에게 자기와 친구가 되어 달라고 요청했다. (ask, become friends, 8 단어)
➡ _____

(6) 그녀는 대학에 가라고 아들을 격려했다. (encourage, go, college, 8 단어)
➡ _____

(7) 그를 5시에 여기로 오게 하시오. (have, 6 단어)
➡ _____

Jobs of the Future

2020s: Self-driving cars will be on the market.

2030s: People will have robots that do everything for them.
　　　　　　　　　　　　　　　주격 관계대명사

2030s: 3D printers in every home will print out almost everything.
　　　　　　　　　　 every + 단수명사　　　　　출력하다

2050s: People will take space trips.

2050s: People will live under the sea or in floating cities.

Look at the pictures above. Do these ideas surprise you? You can see
　　　　　　　　　　　　위에 있는　　　=Are you surprised at these ideas?
that our lives will be very different in the future. As our lives change,
접속사　　　　　　　　　　　　　　미래에는　　　~함에 따라(비례) life의 복수형
many new jobs will appear. What kind of job do you want? What will
your future life be like? The following people looked ahead and chose
　　　　　　　　~와 같다　　　　다음의　　　　　(앞일을) 내다보았다
jobs that will be important in the future.
　　=which
Let's read about their jobs!

Do you see the flower pot that Sujin made? It was made from old
　　　　　　　　　　　목적격 관계대명사(=which)　　　과거수동태
street flags. She is an upcycling designer. She works with waste
materials to make new products. Her products show people that old
　　　부사적 용법(목적)　　　　　　　　접속사 that이 명사절을 이끌어 show의 목적어 역할을 하고 있다.
materials can be useful in new ways. Upcycling can reduce the amount
of waste in the future. To become an upcycling designer, you should be
　　　　　　　　　　부사적 용법의 to부정사 (목적)
creative and learn about art.

market 시장
almost 거의
float: 떠다니다
appear: 나타나다, 보이기 시작하다
look ahead: (앞일을) 내다보다, 예견하다
product 제품
in the future 미래에
amount 양
creative 창의적인

 확인문제

● 다음 문장이 본문의 내용과 일치하면 T, 일치하지 않으면 F를 쓰시오.

1　In 2020s, self-driving cars will be on the market. ☐

2　In 2050s, people will live under the sea or in the universe. ☐

3　Sujin works with new materials to make new products. ☐

4　Upcycling can reduce the amount of waste in the future. ☐

Have you ever heard of 3D modelers? Taeho, a 3D modeler, works
현재완료 경험 용법   └ 동격 관계 ┘
for a company that makes artificial hands and legs. Taeho uses special
              주격 관계대명사(=which)
software to print out new hands and legs. They are made specially for
        부사적 용법(목적)   수동태
patients. If you are good at computer programming and art, you can
              ~을 잘하다
be a 3D modeler. Taeho wants more people to use 3D printed products
              want는 to부정사를 목적격 보어로 취하는 동사: 동사+목적어+to V
in the future.

Jihye is a big data specialist. She works on many projects. For
example, last year, she made bus routes. To find the best night routes,
예를 들어   부사적 용법의 to부정사(목적)
she needed to collect smartphone use data and taxi use patterns from
                                      datum의 복수형
late-night travelers. Then she analyzed this information to create the
                                              부사적 용법의 to부정사(목적)
most useful routes. Now Jihye is working with an online shopping
useful의 최상급
mall. She is collecting data from customers to find out the best styles
                                      부사적 용법의 to부정사(목적)
for them. She knows big data allows us to learn more about our daily
                      allow+목적어+to부정사: ~가 …하도록 허락하다
lives. If you want to become a big data specialist, you should develop
조건절을 이끄는 접속사
your math and problem-solving skills!

Think about yourself and prepare for your future. If you keep
          재귀대명사   조건의 부사절에서 현재시제가 미래시제를 대신한다.
looking ahead and dreaming big, your future will be bright.
keep ~ing: 계속해서 ~하다

modeler: 모형 제작자
artificial: 인위적인, 인조의
patient: 환자
specialist: 전문가(= expert)
route: 길, 경로
collect 모으다, 수집하다
data 데이터
late-night: 심야의
analyze: 분석하다
develop: 개발하다, 성장[발달]시키다

확인문제

● 다음 문장이 본문의 내용과 일치하면 T, 일치하지 않으면 F를 쓰시오.

1 Taeho is a 3D modeler. ☐

2 Taeho uses a special hardware to print out new hands and legs. ☐

3 Though you aren't good at computer programming and art, you can be a 3D modeler. ☐

4 Jihye, a big data specialist, works on many projects. ☐

5 Last year, Jihye made bus routes. ☐

6 Jihye knows big data allows us to learn more about our future. ☐

● 우리말을 참고하여 빈칸에 알맞은 말을 쓰시오.

1 Jobs _____ _____ _____

2 2020s: Self-driving cars will _____ _____ _____ _____.

3 2030s: People will have robots _____ do everything for them.

4 2030s: 3D printers in every home _____ _____ _____ almost everything.

5 2050s: People will _____ _____ _____.

6 2050s: People will live _____ _____ _____ or _____ _____ _____.

7 Look at the pictures _____.

8 Do these ideas _____ you?

9 You can see that our lives will be very different _____ _____ _____.

10 _____ our lives change, many new jobs _____ _____.

11 _____ _____ _____ _____ do you want?

12 What will your future life _____ _____?

13 The following people _____ _____ and _____ _____ that will be important in the future.

14 _____ _____ about their jobs!

15 Do you see the flower pot _____ _____ _____?

16 It _____ _____ old street flags.

17 She is an _____ _____.

18 She works with _____ to make new products.

19 Her products show people that old materials can be useful _____ _____ _____.

20 Upcycling can reduce _____ _____ _____ _____ in the future.

21 _____ _____ an upcycling designer, you should be _____ and learn about art.

1 미래의 직업

2 2020년대: 자율주행차들이 시장에 나올 것이다.

3 2030년대: 사람들은 그들을 위하여 모든 것을 하는 로봇을 갖게 될 것이다.

4 2030년대: 모든 가정의 3D 프린터가 거의 모든 것을 출력해낼 것이다.

5 2050년대: 사람들은 우주여행을 할 것이다.

6 2050년대: 사람들은 바다 밑이나 수상 도시에서 살 것이다.

7 위의 그림들을 보세요.

8 이 생각들이 놀랍습니까?

9 당신은 미래에 우리의 삶이 매우 달라질 것을 볼 수 있습니다.

10 우리의 삶이 변화함에 따라 새로운 직업들이 많이 생겨날 것입니다.

11 당신은 어떤 직업을 원하세요?

12 미래의 당신 삶은 어떤 모습일까요?

13 다음의 사람들은 앞을 내다보고 미래에 중요하게 될 직업을 선택하였습니다.

14 그들의 직업에 관하여 읽어 봅시다!

15 수진이 만든 화분이 보이시나요?

16 이것은 거리의 낡은 깃발들로 만들어졌습니다.

17 그녀는 업사이클링 디자이너입니다.

18 그녀는 새로운 제품을 만들기 위해 폐기물을 가지고 작업합니다.

19 그녀의 제품들은 낡은 재료가 새로운 방식으로 유용해질 수 있다는 것을 사람들에게 보여줍니다.

20 업사이클링은 미래에 쓰레기의 양을 줄일 수 있습니다.

21 업사이클링 디자이너가 되려면 당신은 창의적이어야 하며 미술을 배워야 합니다.

22 _____ _____ _____ _____ of 3D modelers?

23 Taeho, a 3D modeler, _____ _____ a company _____ _____ artificial hands and legs.

24 Taeho uses _____ _____ to print out new hands and legs.

25 They are made _____ _____ _____ .

26 If you _____ _____ _____ computer programming and art, you can be a 3D modeler.

27 Taeho wants more people _____ _____ 3D printed products in the future.

28 Jihye is a _____ _____ _____ .

29 She _____ _____ many projects.

30 _____ _____ , last year, she made bus routes.

31 To find the best night routes, she needed to collect smartphone use data and _____ _____ _____ from _____ _____ .

32 Then she _____ this information _____ _____ the most useful routes.

33 Now Jihye is _____ _____ an online shopping mall.

34 She is _____ _____ _____ customers to find out the best styles for them.

35 She knows big data _____ _____ _____ _____ more about our daily lives.

36 If you want to become a big data specialist, you should _____ your math and _____ _____ !

37 Think about _____ and _____ _____ your future.

38 If you _____ ahead and _____ big, your future will be bright.

22 3D 모형 제작자에 관하여 들어 본 적이 있으신가요?

23 3D 모형 제작자인 태호는 인공 손과 다리를 만드는 회사에서 일합니다.

24 태호는 새 손과 다리를 출력하기 위하여 특별한 소프트웨어를 사용합니다.

25 그것들은 환자를 위하여 특별히 제작됩니다.

26 만약 당신이 컴퓨터 프로그래밍이나 미술을 잘한다면, 3D 모형 제작자가 될 수 있습니다.

27 태호는 미래에 더 많은 사람들이 3D 프린터로 출력된 제품들을 사용하기를 원합니다.

28 지혜는 빅데이터 전문가입니다.

29 그녀는 많은 프로젝트에서 일합니다.

30 예를 들어, 작년에 그녀는 버스 노선을 만들었습니다.

31 최적의 심야 노선을 찾기 위하여, 그녀는 심야에 이동하는 사람들의 스마트폰 이용 정보와 택시 이용 패턴을 수집할 필요가 있었습니다.

32 그런 다음 그녀는 그 정보를 분석하여 가장 유용한 노선을 만들었습니다.

33 현재 지혜는 온라인 쇼핑몰과 작업하고 있습니다.

34 그녀는 소비자들에게 맞는 최적의 스타일을 찾기 위하여 그들로부터 데이터를 수집하고 있습니다.

35 그녀는 빅데이터가 우리에게 일상생활에 관하여 더 많이 알게 해 준다는 것을 알고 있습니다.

36 만약 당신이 빅데이터 전문가가 되고 싶다면, 수학과 문제 해결 능력을 계발해야 합니다!

37 자신에 대하여 생각해 보고 미래를 준비하세요.

38 만약 당신이 계속 앞을 내다보고 꿈을 크게 꾼다면, 당신의 미래는 밝을 것입니다.

● 우리말을 참고하여 본문을 영작하시오.

1 미래의 직업

➡ _____

2 2020년대: 자율주행차들이 시장에 나올 것이다.

➡ _____

3 2030년대: 사람들은 그들을 위하여 모든 것을 하는 로봇을 갖게 될 것이다.

➡ _____

4 2030년대: 모든 가정의 3D 프린터가 거의 모든 것을 출력해 낼 것이다.

➡ _____

5 2050년대: 사람들은 우주여행을 할 것이다.

➡ _____

6 2050년대: 사람들은 바다 밑이나 수상 도시에서 살 것이다.

➡ _____

7 위의 그림들을 보세요.

➡ _____

8 이 생각들이 놀랍습니까?

➡ _____

9 당신은 미래에 우리의 삶이 매우 달라질 것을 볼 수 있습니다.

➡ _____

10 우리의 삶이 변화함에 따라 새로운 직업들이 많이 생겨날 것입니다.

➡ _____

11 당신은 어떤 직업을 원하세요?

➡ _____

12 미래의 당신 삶은 어떤 모습일까요?

➡ _____

13 다음의 사람들은 앞을 내다보고 미래에 중요하게 될 직업을 선택하였습니다.

➡ _____

14 그들의 직업에 관하여 읽어 봅시다!

➡ _____

15 수진이 만든 화분이 보이시나요?

➡ _____

16 이것은 거리의 낡은 깃발들로 만들어진 것입니다.

➡ _____

17 그녀는 업사이클링 디자이너입니다.

➡ _____

18 그녀는 새로운 제품을 만들기 위해 폐기물을 가지고 작업합니다.
➡ _____

19 그녀의 제품들은 낡은 재료가 새로운 방식으로 유용해질 수 있다는 것을 사람들에게 보여줍니다.
➡ _____

20 업사이클링은 미래에 쓰레기의 양을 줄일 수 있습니다.
➡ _____

21 업사이클링 디자이너가 되려면 당신은 창의적이어야 하며 미술을 배워야 합니다.
➡ _____

22 3D 모형 제작자에 관하여 들어 본 적이 있으신가요?
➡ _____

23 3D 모형 제작자인 태호는 인공 손과 다리를 만드는 회사에서 일합니다.
➡ _____

24 태호는 새 손과 다리를 출력하기 위하여 특별한 소프트웨어를 사용합니다.
➡ _____

25 그것들은 환자를 위하여 특별히 제작됩니다.
➡ _____

26 만약 당신이 컴퓨터 프로그래밍이나 미술을 잘한다면, 3D 모형 제작자가 될 수 있습니다.
➡ _____

27 태호는 미래에 더 많은 사람들이 3D 프린터로 출력된 제품들을 사용하기를 원합니다.
➡ _____

28 지혜는 빅데이터 전문가입니다.
➡ _____

29 그녀는 많은 프로젝트에서 일합니다.
➡ _____

30 예를 들어, 작년에 그녀는 버스 노선을 만들었습니다.
➡ _____

31 최적의 심야 노선을 찾기 위하여, 그녀는 심야에 이동하는 사람들의 스마트폰 이용 정보와 택시 이용 패턴을 수집할 필요가 있었습니다.
➡ _____

32 그런 다음 그녀는 그 정보를 분석하여 가장 유용한 노선을 만들었습니다.
➡ _____

33 현재 지혜는 온라인 쇼핑몰과 작업하고 있습니다.
➡ _____

34 그녀는 소비자들에게 맞는 최적의 스타일을 찾기 위하여 그들로부터 데이터를 수집하고 있습니다.
➡ _____

35 그녀는 빅데이터가 우리에게 일상생활에 관하여 더 많이 알게 해 준다는 것을 알고 있습니다.
➡ _____

36 만약 당신이 빅데이터 전문가가 되고 싶다면, 수학과 문제 해결 능력을 계발해야 합니다!
➡ _____

37 자신에 대하여 생각해 보고 미래를 준비하세요.
➡ _____

38 만약 당신이 계속 앞을 내다보고 꿈을 크게 꾼다면, 당신의 미래는 밝을 것입니다.
➡ _____

[01~04] 다음 글을 읽고 물음에 답하시오.

Look at the pictures above. Do these ideas surprise you? You can see that our lives will be very different in the future. ⓐAs our lives change, many new jobs will (A)[appear / disappear]. What kind of job do you want? (B)[How / What] will your future life be like? The following people looked (C)[ahead / behind] and chose jobs that will be important in the future. Let's read about their jobs!

01 위 글의 밑줄 친 ⓐAs와 같은 의미로 쓰인 것을 고르시오.

① As he is honest, everyone trusts him.
② He runs as fast as you run.
③ Her anger grew as she talked.
④ They treat him as a child.
⑤ Do in Rome as the Romans do.

서답형
02 위 글의 괄호 (A)~(C)에서 문맥이나 어법상 알맞은 낱말을 골라 쓰시오.

➡ (A)_____ (B)_____ (C)_____

서답형
03 Where will people be able to live in the 2050s? Fill in the blanks with the suitable words.

> ➡ They will be able to live not only on land but also _____ or _____ .

중요
04 위 글의 내용과 일치하지 않는 것은?

① They will begin to sell self-driving cars in the 2020s.
② In the 2030s, robots will do everything for people.
③ In the 2030s, we will be able to print out almost everything with our 3D printers in our home.
④ Our lives will always be the same in the future, too.
⑤ We will see many new jobs appear in the future.

[05~07] 다음 글을 읽고 물음에 답하시오.

Have you ever heard of 3D modelers? ⓐTaeho, a 3D modeler, works for a company what makes artificial hands and legs. Taeho uses special software ⓑto print out new hands and legs. They are made specially for patients. If you are good at computer programming and art, you can be a 3D modeler. Taeho wants more people to use 3D printed products in the future.

서답형
05 위 글의 밑줄 친 ⓐ에서 어법상 틀린 부분을 찾아 고치시오.

➡ _____

06 위 글의 밑줄 친 ⓑto print와 to부정사의 용법이 다른 것을 고르시오. (3개)

① I need someone to help me.

② It is difficult for me to answer the question.

③ This book is easy to read.

④ Do you know how to use this machine?

⑤ She must be smart to solve the problem.

서답형

07 다음 빈칸 (A)~(C)에 알맞은 단어를 넣어 태호의 직업에 대한 소개를 완성하시오.

> His Job: He is (A)_____.
>
> About the Job: He (B)_____
> _____
>
> To Get the Job: You (C)_____
> _____.

[08~10] 다음 글을 읽고 물음에 답하시오.

Jihye is a big data ⓐspecialist. She works on many projects. For example, last year, she made bus routes. To find the best night routes, she needed to collect smartphone use data and taxi use patterns from late-night travelers. Then she analyzed this information to create the most useful routes. Now Jihye is working with an online shopping mall. She is collecting data from customers to find out the best styles for ⓑthem. She knows big data allows us to learn more about our daily lives. If you want to become a big data specialist, you should develop your math and problem-solving skills!

Think about yourself and prepare for your future. ⓒIf you will keep looking ahead and dreaming big, your future will be bright.

08 위 글의 밑줄 친 ⓐspecialist와 바꿔 쓸 수 있는 말을 모두 고르시오.

① expert   ② amateur

③ beginner   ④ professional

⑤ outsider

서답형

09 위 글의 밑줄 친 ⓑthem이 가리키는 것을 본문에서 찾아 쓰시오.

➡ _____

서답형

10 위 글의 밑줄 친 ⓒ에서 어법상 틀린 부분을 찾아 고치시오.

➡ _____

[11~13] 다음 글을 읽고 물음에 답하시오.

Do you see the flower pot that Sujin made? It was made from old street flags. She is a(an) ⓐ___. She works with waste materials to make new products. Her products show people that old materials can be useful in new ways. Upcycling can reduce the amount of waste in the future. To become an upcycling designer, you should be creative and learn about art.

11 위 글의 빈칸 ⓐ에 들어갈 알맞은 말을 고르시오.

① florist

② upcycling designer

③ garbage collector

④ recycling programmer

⑤ garbage bag designer

12 위 글의 내용과 어울리는 표어를 고르시오.

① No more environmental pollution!

② Let's buy recycled products.

③ Don't waste waste.

④ Be a wise consumer.

⑤ Don't buy disposable products.

13 위 글을 읽고 알 수 없는 것을 고르시오.

① 수진이 만든 화분의 재료

② 화분 제작에 걸린 시간

③ 수진이 하는 일

④ 수진의 제품이 사람들에게 보여주는 것

⑤ 수진의 직업에 필요한 자격 요건

[14~16] 다음 글을 읽고 물음에 답하시오.

Hello, everyone. My name is Soin Kim. I'm ⓐ(excite) to tell you about my job. I am a computer programmer, and I work at a software company. I develop new software for computers there. I work with many people from different countries. I chose this job because I am ⓑ(interest) in math and science. To become a computer programmer, I studied computer science and developed my problem-solving skills. If you have a dream, work hard for ⓒit. Then it will come true someday.

서답형

14 위 글의 밑줄 친 ⓐ와 ⓑ에 주어진 단어를 각각 알맞은 형태로 쓰시오.

➡ ⓐ _____ ⓑ _____

서답형

15 위 글의 밑줄 친 ⓒit이 가리키는 것을 본문에서 찾아 쓰시오.

➡ _____

16 위 글을 읽고 대답할 수 없는 질문은?

① What is Soin's job and where does she work?

② What does Soin usually do at the company?

③ Who does Soin work with?

④ When did Soin begin to work?

⑤ What did Soin do to get this job?

[17~19] 다음 글을 읽고 물음에 답하시오.

2020s • Self-driving cars will be on the market.

2030s • People will have robots that do everything for ⓐthem.
• 3D printers in every home will print out almost everything.

2050s • People will take space trips.
• People will live under the sea or in floating cities.

Look at the pictures above. Do these ideas surprise you? You can see that our lives will be very   (A)   in the future. As our lives change, many new jobs will appear. What kind of job do you want? What will your future life be like? The following people looked ahead and chose jobs that will be important in the future. Let's read about their jobs!

17 위 글의 빈칸 (A)에 들어갈 알맞은 말을 고르시오.

① difficult   ② simple

③ similar   ④ common

⑤ different

서답형

18 위 글의 밑줄 친 ⓐthem이 가리키는 것을 본문에서 찾아 쓰시오.

➡ _____

19 위 글을 읽고, 다음 중 자신의 미래 모습에 대한 설명이 옳지 <u>않은</u> 사람을 고르시오.

> 수민: I don't like driving, so I will buy a self-driving car in the 2020s.
>
> 희정: I'm a little bit lazy, so in the 2030s, I'm willing to buy a robot to do everything for me.
>
> 진수: I will live forever because 3D printers that can print out everything will print out me, too.
>
> 호진: I'm adventurous, so I'm looking forward to taking a trip to the universe in the 2050s.
>
> 지혜: I like the blue sky, so I will move to the floating city in the 2050s.

① 수민   ② 희정   ③ 진수   ④ 호진   ⑤ 지혜

[20~22] 다음 글을 읽고 물음에 답하시오.

Jihye is a big data specialist. She works on many projects. For example, last year, she made bus routes. To find the best night routes, she needed to collect smartphone use data and taxi use patterns from late-night travelers. Then she analyzed this information to create the most useful routes. Now Jihye is working with an online shopping mall. She is collecting data from customers to find out the best styles ⓐ them. She knows big data allows us ⓑ more about our daily lives. If you want to become a big data specialist, you should develop your math and problem-solving skills!

Think about yourself and prepare ⓒ your future. If you keep looking ahead and dreaming big, your future will be bright.

20 위 글의 빈칸 ⓐ와 ⓒ에 공통으로 들어갈 전치사를 고르시오.

① from   ② to   ③ in
④ for   ⑤ on

21 위 글의 빈칸 ⓑ에 learn을 알맞은 형태로 쓰시오.

➡ _____

22 What did Jihye do as a big data specialist last year? Answer in English in a full sentence. (4 words)

➡ _____

[23~25] 다음 글을 읽고 물음에 답하시오.

Hello, everyone. My name is Soin Kim. I'm excited to tell you about my job. I am a computer programmer, and I work at a software company. I develop new software for computers ⓐ<u>there</u>. I work with many people from different countries. I chose this job because I am interested in math and science. To become a computer programmer, I studied computer science and developed my problem-solving skills. If you have a dream, work hard for it. ⓑ<u>Then it will come true someday.</u>

23 위 글의 밑줄 친 ⓐthere와 바꿔 쓸 수 있는 말을 본문에서 찾아 쓰시오.

➡ _____

24 위 글의 밑줄 친 문장 ⓑ를 다음과 같이 바꿔 쓸 때 빈칸에 들어갈 알맞은 단어를 쓰시오.

➡ Then it will be _____ someday.

25 Why did Soin choose her job? Answer in English in a full sentence.

➡ _____

_____

[01~03] 다음 글을 읽고 물음에 답하시오.

Look at the pictures above. ⓐDo these ideas surprise you? You can see that our lives will be very different in the future. As our lives change, many new jobs will appear. What kind of job do you want? What will your future life be like? The following people (A)looked (　　) and chose jobs that will be important in the future. Let's read about their jobs!

중요
01 위 글의 밑줄 친 (A)가 다음과 같은 뜻이 되도록 빈칸에 철자 a로 시작하는 단어를 쓰시오.

> • considered what would happen in the future
> • foresaw

➡ _____

02 What changes will come to us in the 2030s? Answer in English in a full sentence.

➡ _____

_____

중요
03 위 글의 밑줄 친 문장 ⓐ를 수동태로 바꾸시오.

➡ _____

[04~06] 다음 글을 읽고 물음에 답하시오.

Do you see the flower pot that Sujin made? It was made from old street flags. She is an upcycling designer. She works with ⓐwaste materials to make ⓑnew products. ⓒHer products show people that new materials can be useful in old ways. Upcycling can reduce the amount of waste in the future. To become an upcycling designer, you should be creative and learn about art.

04 위 글의 밑줄 친 ⓐwaste materials와 ⓑnew products의 예를 본문에서 찾아 쓰시오.

➡ ⓐ _____ ⓑ _____

중요
05 위 글의 밑줄 친 ⓒ에서 흐름상 어색한 부분을 찾아 고치시오.

➡ _____

고난이도
06 다음 빈칸 (A)~(C)에 알맞은 단어를 넣어 수진의 직업에 대한 소개를 완성하시오.

Her Job: She is (A)_____.
About the Job: She (B)_____ _____.
To Get the Job: You (C)_____ _____.

[07~09] 다음 글을 읽고 물음에 답하시오.

Have you ever heard of 3D modelers? Taeho, a 3D modeler, (A)[work / works] for a company (B)[that / where] makes artificial hands and legs. Taeho uses special software to print out new hands and legs. They are made specially for patients. If you are good (C)[at / for] computer programming and art, you can be a 3D modeler. ⓐTaeho wants more people using 3D printed products in the future.

07 위 글의 괄호 (A)~(C)에서 문맥이나 어법상 알맞은 낱말을 골라 쓰시오.

➡ (A) _____ (B) _____ (C) _____

08 위 글에서 man-made와 같은 뜻의 단어를 찾아 쓰시오.

➡ _____

09 위 글의 밑줄 친 ⓐ에서 어법상 틀린 부분을 찾아 고치시오.

_____ ➡ _____

[10~13] 다음 글을 읽고 물음에 답하시오.

Jihye is a big data specialist. She works on many projects. For example, last year, she made bus routes. ⓐTo find the best night routes, she needed to collect smartphone use data and taxi use patterns from late-night travelers. Then she analyzed this information to create the most useful routes. Now Jihye is working with an online shopping mall. She is collecting data from customers to find out the best styles for them. ⓑ그녀는 빅데이터가 우리에게 일상생활에 관하여 더 많이 알게 해 준다는 것을 알고 있습니다. If you want to become a big data specialist, you

should develop your math and problem-solving skills!

Think about yourself and prepare for your future. If you keep __(A)__ ahead and __(B)__ big, your future will be bright.

10 위 글의 빈칸 (A)와 (B)에 look과 dream을 각각 알맞은 형태로 쓰시오.

➡ (A) _____ (B) _____

11 위 글의 밑줄 친 ⓐ를 다음과 같이 바꿔 쓸 때 빈칸에 들어갈 알맞은 말을 쓰시오.

(1) _____ the best night routes
(2) _____ the best night routes

12 위 글의 밑줄 친 ⓑ의 우리말에 맞게 한 단어를 보충하여, 주어진 어휘를 알맞게 배열하시오.

big data / our daily lives / us / learn / she / about / allows / more / knows

➡ _____
_____

13 Answer in English in a full sentence.

(1) What did Jihye need to do to find the best night routes?
(2) What did Jihye do to create the most useful routes?

➡ (1) _____
_____
(2) _____

After You Read D

Taehun Kim is a movie reviewer. He writes articles about new movies. He

chose this job because he loves watching movies.
　　　　　　　　= as, since　　　　　= to watch

To get this job, he read many books to improve his writing skills. He also
부사적 용법의 to부정사(목적)　　　　　　　　　　　be동사, 조동사 뒤, 일반동사 앞에 위치

watched many different types of movies.

구문해설 • reviewer: (책·연극·영화 등의) 논평가[비평가] • article: (신문·잡지의) 글, 기사
• chose: choose의 과거 • improve: 향상시키다

해석

김태훈은 영화 비평가이다. 그는 새로운 영화에 대한 기사를 쓴다. 그는 영화 보는 것을 매우 좋아하기 때문에 이 직업을 선택했다. 이 직업을 얻기 위해 그는 글쓰기 기술을 향상시키려고 많은 책들을 읽었다. 그는 또한 많은 다른 유형의 영화들을 보았다.

Culture Link

Personal Brand Consultant

A personal brand consultant creates a personal brand for their customers. They
　　　　　　　　　　　　　=makes　　　　　[대리·대용] ~ 대신, ~을 위해

find the customer's unique strengths. Then they build a personal brand by

using the customer's personality, knowledge, and skills. To get this job, you
전치사 뒤에 동명사 by -ing: ~함으로써　　　　　　　　to부정사의 부사적 용법(목적)

need to have great communication skills.
　　need의 목적어

구문해설 • unique: 유일(무이)한, 독특한 • knowledge: 지식 • skill: 기술

개인 브랜드 상담가

개인 브랜드 상담가는 한 개인의 브랜드를 그들의 고객들을 위해 만든다. 그들은 고객의 독특한 장점을 찾는다. 그러고 나서 그들은 고객의 개성, 지식 그리고 기술을 사용하여 개인 브랜드를 만든다. 이 직업을 갖기 위해서 당신은 훌륭한 의사소통 기술을 갖출 필요가 있다.

Do It Yourself A

B: Hey, Mandy. What are you looking at?
　　　　　　　　　　　look at ~을 보다

G: Hey, Edward. Look! Some volunteers are needed for the school festival.
　　　　　　　　　　자원봉사자가 학교 축제에 필요한 것이므로 수동태(be+p.p)를 사용한다.

B: Really? I want to help out. You know I'm good at drawing pictures. I think
　　　　want는 to동사원형을 목적어로 받는다　접속사 that 생략 (know와 I'm 사이)

　I can do something for the festival.

G: I think you can help out at the cartoon event.
　　　　　　　　　　도와주다

B: Right! Why don't we apply together?
　'Why don't we ~?': 상대방에게 제안하는 표현

G: Well, I am not good at drawing pictures. But I'm good at playing board games.

B: You can help out at the game event then.

G: Okay. Let's go and apply to become volunteers.
　　　　　　go와 apply가 and로 연결되어 있는 병렬구조이다.

구문해설 • volunteer: 자원 봉사자 • help out: 도와주다, 거들다 • be good at: ~을 잘하다
• cartoon: 만화 • apply: 지원하다, 신청하다

B: 안녕, Mandy. 무엇을 보고 있니?

G: 안녕, Edward. 봐! 자원 봉사자들이 학교 축제에서 필요하대.

B: 정말? 나 돕고 싶어. 너도 알다시피 내가 그림을 잘 그리잖아. 내 생각엔 내가 축제에서 어떤 것을 할 수 있을 것 같아.

G: 나는 네가 만화 행사에서 도움이 될 수 있을 거라고 생각해.

B: 맞아! 우리 함께 지원해 보는 게 어때?

G: 음, 나는 그림을 잘 그리지 못해. 하지만, 나는 보드게임을 잘해.

B: 그러면 너는 게임 행사에서 도울 수 있겠다.

G: 좋아. 우리 가서 함께 자원 봉사자에 지원하자.

Words & Expressions

01 다음 짝지어진 단어의 관계가 같도록 빈칸에 알맞은 말을 쓰시오.

> design : designer – consult : _____

02 밑줄 친 부분과 의미가 가장 가까운 것을 고르시오.

> They work together as a team.

① lead   ② enforce   ③ allow
④ apply   ⑤ collaborate

03 빈칸에 들어갈 알맞은 말을 〈보기〉에서 골라 쓰시오. (형태 변화 가능)

> ┤ 보기 ├
> allow   apply   decorate   float

(1) Will you help me _____ the Christmas tree?
(2) Nobody is _____ to smoke here.
(3) I'm very happy to _____ for the overseas volunteer program.
(4) They will _____ if you drop them in the water.

04 다음 영영풀이에 해당하는 단어를 고르시오.

> a way between two places

① route   ② street   ③ travel
④ destination   ⑤ chance

Conversation

[05~07] 다음 대화를 읽고 물음에 답하시오.

B: Hey, Mandy. ①What are you looking at?
G: Hey, Edward. Look! ②Some volunteers are needed for the school festival.
B: Really? I want to help out. You know I'm good at drawing pictures. ③I think I can do something for the festival.
G: I think you can help out at the cartoon event.
B: Right! ④Why don't we apply together?
G: Well, ⑤I am good at drawing pictures. But I'm good at playing board games.
B: You can help out at the game event then.
G: Okay. Let's go and apply to become volunteers.

05 위 대화의 ①~⑤ 중 흐름상 어색한 부분을 고르시오.

①   ②   ③   ④   ⑤

06 다음 영영풀이에 해당하는 단어를 대화에서 찾아 쓰시오.

> to give someone papers that say you want to do something

➡ _____

07 위 대화의 내용과 일치하지 않는 것은?

① They will apply for volunteer work.
② They want to help out at the same event for the school festival.
③ The boy can draw pictures well.
④ The girl is looking at something about the school festival.
⑤ The girl is good at playing board games.

[08~09] 다음 대화를 읽고 물음에 답하시오.

B: I want to be a scientist. (A)_____

W: You need to study science. And (B)문제 해결 능력을 개발할 필요가 있어요.

08 빈칸 (A)에 들어갈 수 <u>없는</u> 것을 고르시오.

① What do I need to do?
② What do I want to do?
③ What do you suggest?
④ What should I do to be a scientist?
⑤ How can I be a scientist?

09 주어진 단어를 이용하여 밑줄 친 (B)의 우리말을 영작하시오.

➡ _____

(solve, develop, need, skills)

[10~12] 다음 대화를 읽고 물음에 답하시오.

B: Jessica, what are you going to do for the school talent show?

G: I didn't decide yet. (①) (A)_____

B: You're good at dancing, aren't you? (②)

G: Not really. (③) But I think I'm good at (B)_____. I like singing very much. (④)

B: Really? (⑤) Why don't you (C)_____ for us?

G: Sure, I'd love to.

10 위 대화의 ①~⑤ 중 주어진 문장이 들어갈 알맞은 곳은?

Actually, I'm planning to play rock music with my band.

①　　　②　　　③　　　④　　　⑤

11 빈칸 (A)에 들어갈 수 있는 말을 <u>모두</u> 고르시오.

① Do you know how to dance?
② What are you planning to do?
③ What am I good at?
④ What are you able to do?
⑤ What can I do well?

12 빈칸 (B)와 (C)에 sing을 알맞게 채우시오.

➡ (B) _____ (C) _____

Grammar

13 다음 중 어법상 올바른 것은?

① We expect you to winning the singing contest.
② The son asked his mom give him more pocket money.
③ I want Juhee coming to my birthday party.
④ He ordered us finished the project by Monday.
⑤ Good health enabled him to carry out the plan.

14 다음 중 어법상 <u>어색한</u> 것은?

① If you know Mr. Lee, please introduce me to him.
② If the weather is fine, take a trip somewhere.
③ If you will miss it, you'll regret it.
④ You must not drink if you drive.
⑤ Let's go for a picnic if it doesn't rain.

15 주어진 어구를 바르게 배열하여 문장을 완성하시오.

(1) the pool, a shower, you, you, can't, don't, go, take, first, if, into

➡ _____

(2) if, you, you, an upcycling designer, art, be, learn, become, want, should, creative, and, to, about

➡ _____

_____

(3) the grandfather, his grandson, this weekend, him, wanted, visit, to

➡ _____

_____

(4) I, me, him, tomorrow, asked, call, back, to

➡ _____

(5) a, I, me, you, favor, do, need, to

➡ _____

16 다음 문장의 밑줄 친 부분과 쓰임이 같은 것은?

> • <u>If</u> you want to help me, please give me a rope, too.

① Would you please check <u>if</u> I filled out this card right?

② <u>If</u> you take a taxi, you can get there in ten minutes.

③ Some people wonder <u>if</u> another writer just used his name.

④ The police weren't sure <u>if</u> he could catch a thief.

⑤ <u>If</u> he were here, he would be very pleased by your words.

17 다음 그림을 보고 주어진 어휘를 이용하여 빈칸을 알맞게 채우시오.

➡ The teacher told them _____ again. If they fight again, they _____. (fight, punish)

18 다음 빈칸에 들어갈 수 <u>없는</u> 것을 고르시오.

> • Daniel _____ his son to study science harder.

① advised ② wanted ③ got

④ had ⑤ encouraged

19 주어진 표현을 이용하여 문장을 완성하시오.

(1) You won't be late for school _____ _____. (the bus, miss, unless)

(2) You will be in trouble _____. (a lie, tell, if)

20 If를 사용하여 한 문장으로 연결하시오.

> • Go to Europe.
> • You can see many old structures.

➡ _____

Reading

[21~23] 다음 글을 읽고 물음에 답하시오.

Look at the pictures above. Do ⓐthese ideas surprise you? You can see that our lives will be very different in the future. As our lives change, many new jobs will appear. What kind of job do you want? What will your future life be ⓑlike? The following people looked ahead and chose jobs that will be important in the future. Let's read about their jobs!

21 위 글의 밑줄 친 ⓐthese ideas에 해당되지 않는 것을 고르시오.

① Self-driving cars will be offered for sale in the 2020s.
② In the 2030s, people will be able to make robots do everything for them.
③ In the 2030s, almost everything will be printed out by 3D printers in every home.
④ People will go on space trips in the 2050s.
⑤ People will live in space in the 2050s.

22 위 글의 밑줄 친 ⓑlike와 문법적 쓰임이 다른 것을 모두 고르시오.

① He just looks like his father.
② How did you like the book?
③ She's wearing a dress like yours.
④ They sell various things of like shape.
⑤ The boy was like a son to me.

23 위 글의 뒤에 올 내용으로 가장 알맞은 것을 고르시오.

① 미래에 달라질 삶의 모습에 대한 소개
② 미래의 사람들이 선호할 직업 소개
③ 미래에 중요하게 될 직업을 선택한 사람들과 그들의 직업
④ 미래에 사라질 직업 소개
⑤ 미래에도 꾸준히 인기 있는 직업들 소개

[24~25] 다음 글을 읽고 물음에 답하시오.

Do you see the flower pot that Sujin made? ⓐIt was made from old street flags. She is an ___(A)___ designer. She works with waste materials to make new products. Her products show people that old materials can be useful in new ways. ___(A)___ can reduce the amount of waste in the future. To become an ___(A)___ designer, you should be creative and learn about art.

24 주어진 영영풀이를 참고하여 빈칸 (A)에 철자 u로 시작하는 단어를 쓰시오. (대·소문자 무시)

the process of transforming by-products, waste materials, useless or unwanted products into new materials or products of better quality and environmental value

➡ _____

25 위 글의 밑줄 친 ⓐ를 능동태로 고치시오.

➡ _____

[26~27] 다음 글을 읽고 물음에 답하시오.

ⓐHave you ever heard of 3D modelers? Taeho, a 3D modeler, works for a company that makes artificial hands and legs. Taeho uses special software to print out new hands and legs. They are made specially for patients. If you are good at computer programming and art, you can be a 3D modeler. Taeho wants more people to use 3D printed products in the future.

26 다음 중 3D 모형 제작자가 될 수 있는 사람을 고르시오.

> 보람: I'm good at computer programming and art.
> 정호: I always want to help handicapped people but my computer programming is not good yet.
> 이슬: I'm good at computer programming but I don't like art.
> 창수: I have an excellent problem-solving skills.
> 민규: I'm not good at computer programming but I like art.

① 보람   ② 정호   ③ 이슬
④ 창수   ⑤ 민규

27 위 글의 밑줄 친 문장 ⓐ의 현재완료와 용법이 같은 것을 모두 고르시오.

① She has gone to New York.
② Tom has just eaten breakfast.
③ How many times have you met her?
④ How long have they known each other?
⑤ I have visited Paris before.

[28~30] 다음 글을 읽고 물음에 답하시오.

Jihye is a big data specialist. She works on many projects. ⓐ , last year, she made bus routes. To find the best night routes, she needed to collect smartphone use data and taxi use patterns from late-night travelers. Then she analyzed this information to create the most useful routes. Now Jihye is working with an online shopping mall. She is collecting data from customers to find out the best styles for them. She knows big data allows us to learn more about our daily lives. If you want to become a big data specialist, you should develop your math and problem-solving skills!

Think about yourself and prepare for your future. If you keep looking ahead and dreaming big, your future will be bright.

28 위 글의 빈칸 ⓐ에 들어갈 알맞은 말을 고르시오.

① Therefore   ② For example
③ However   ④ In addition
⑤ Moreover

29 What is Jihye doing as a big data specialist now? Fill in the blanks with the suitable words.

➡ Now she is _____ _____ from customers of an online shopping mall _____ _____ _____ the best styles for them.

30 본문의 내용과 일치하도록 다음 빈칸 (A)와 (B)에 알맞은 단어를 쓰시오.

> According to Jihye, (A)_____ _____ allows us to learn more about (B)_____ _____ _____ .

출제율 90%

01 다음 짝지어진 두 단어의 관계가 같도록 빈칸에 알맞은 단어를 쓰시오.

analysis : analyze – _____ : advise

출제율 100%

02 다음 빈칸에 공통으로 들어갈 말로 알맞은 것을 쓰시오.

- I'd like to help _____ if I can.
- Could you please print _____ this document for me?

출제율 95%

03 다음 중 밑줄 친 부분의 뜻풀이가 바르지 <u>않은</u> 것은?

① These <u>artificial</u> roses are quite lifelike. (인조의)
② Scientists have sent people out into <u>space</u>. (공간)
③ Terry suggested many <u>kinds</u> of movies. (종류)
④ She always gets <u>creative</u> ideas from children. (창조적인)
⑤ One of my <u>strengths</u> is that I never give up. (장점)

출제율 85%

04 대화의 순서를 올바르게 배열하시오.

(A) You're good at dancing, aren't you?
(B) I didn't decide yet. What am I good at?
(C) Jessica, what are you going to do for the school talent show?
(D) Not really. But I think I'm good at singing. I like singing very much.

➡ _____

출제율 90%

05 다음 영영풀이에 해당하는 단어를 쓰시오.

to stay up on water

➡ _____

[06~08] 다음 대화를 읽고 물음에 답하시오.

G: Jason, I read your paper. It was so (A)[amazing / amazed]!
B: Thank you for saying that. (①) I'm trying hard to improve my writing skills. I want to be a writer someday.
G: Really? (②) I want to write well like you. What do I need to do?
B: You need to read a lot of books. (③)
G: What else do I need to do?
B: Well, I write almost every day. (④) Why don't you (B)[to start / start] keeping a diary?
G: Thank you for your advice. (⑤) I'll start today.

출제율 100%

06 위 대화의 ①~⑤ 중 주어진 문장이 들어갈 알맞은 곳은?

Reading makes your writing better.

①   ②   ③   ④   ⑤

출제율 90%

07 괄호 (A)와 (B)에서 적절한 것을 고르시오.

➡ (A) _____ (B) _____

출제율 85%

08 다음 영영풀이에 해당하는 단어를 대화에서 찾아 쓰시오.

to make something better

➡ _____

09 다음 짝지어진 대화 중 <u>어색한</u> 것은? (출제율 95%)

① A: What do I need to do to become a painter?
　B: Well, I need to study art history.

② A: Do you know how to do magic tricks?
　B: No, I have no idea about it.

③ A: What do you suggest to get better grades?
　B: I think you should take good notes in class.

④ A: How can I get better from this cold?
　B: You need to drink a lot of water.

⑤ A: What do I need to do not to be late?
　B: You should sleep early.

[10~12] 다음 대화를 읽고 물음에 답하시오.

G: Hello, Mr. Watson! Thank you for doing this interview. (①)

M: Sure, no problem.

G: This interview is for students (A)[what / which / who] want to be food stylists. (②)

M: Sure. You may see pictures of food in books or on TV. (③) A food stylist (B)[decorates / has / likes] food to look good for pictures or movies.

G: I want to be a food stylist like you. What do I need to do?

M: (④) You need to learn about many kinds of food.

G: What else do I need to do?

M: You need to study art, too. (⑤) Creativity is important.

G: All right! Thank you for your time, Mr. Watson.

10 위 대화의 ①~⑤ 중 주어진 문장이 들어갈 알맞은 곳은? (출제율 90%)

> Can you tell me about your job?

①　　②　　③　　④　　⑤

11 괄호 (A)와 (B)에서 적절한 것을 고르시오. (출제율 90%)

➡ (A) ＿＿＿＿＿＿ (B) ＿＿＿＿＿＿

12 위 대화의 내용으로 대답할 수 <u>없는</u> 질문을 고르시오. (출제율 100%)

① What does the girl want to be in the future?

② What does the girl need to do to become a food stylist?

③ What is the most important thing to become a food stylist?

④ What does a food stylist do?

⑤ What does the man do?

13 다음 중 어법상 바르지 <u>않은</u> 것은? (출제율 95%)

> She ①knows big data ②allows us ③ learn ④more about our daily ⑤lives.

14 다음 중 어법상 바른 것은? (출제율 100%)

① The father told his daughter did her homework.

② I want Seri watching the movie with us.

③ Because something happens tomorrow, call me immediately.

④ I'll do it after I finish here.

⑤ I didn't expect you get home so fast.

15 다음 문장에서 어법상 잘못된 것을 고치시오.

(1) The teacher requested her go back to her seat.

➡ _____

(2) His dad won't let him to do it again in the future.

➡ _____

[16~18] 다음 글을 읽고 물음에 답하시오.

Do you see the flower pot that Sujin made? It was made from (A)[new / old] street flags. She is an upcycling designer. She works with (B)[useful / waste] materials to make new products. Her products show people that old materials can be (C)[useful / useless] in new ways. Upcycling can reduce the amount of waste in the future. To become an upcycling designer, you should be creative and learn about art.

16 위 글의 괄호 (A)~(C)에서 문맥상 알맞은 낱말을 골라 쓰시오.

➡ (A)_____ (B)_____ (C)_____

17 본문의 내용을 참고하여 다음 빈칸 (A)와 (B)에 알맞은 단어를 쓰시오.

> We can say that upcycling is good for protecting environment because it can (A)_____ the amount of (B)_____ .

18 위 글의 내용과 일치하지 <u>않는</u> 것은?

① 수진은 화분을 만들었다.
② 수진은 업사이클링 디자이너이다.
③ 수진의 제품들은 낡은 재료를 새로운 방식으로 만든 것들이다.
④ 업사이클링으로 인해 미래에는 쓰레기의 종류가 늘어날 것이다.
⑤ 업사이클링 디자이너가 되려면 당신은 창의적이어야 하며 미술을 배워야 한다.

[19~21] 다음 글을 읽고 물음에 답하시오.

2020s • Self-driving cars will be on the market.
2030s • People will have robots __ⓐ__ do everything for them.
　　• 3D printers in every home will print out almost everything.
2050s • People will take space trips.
　　• People will live under the sea or in floating cities.

Look at the pictures above. Do these ideas surprise you? You can see __ⓑ__ our lives will be very different in the future. As our lives change, many new jobs will ©appear. What kind of job do you want? What will your future life be like? The following people looked ahead and chose jobs that will be important in the future. Let's read about their jobs!

19 위 글의 빈칸 ⓐ와 ⓑ에 공통으로 들어갈 알맞은 단어를 고르시오.

① which　　② what　　③ while
④ that　　⑤ as

20 위 글의 밑줄 친 ©appear와 바꿔 쓸 수 <u>없는</u> 말을 고르시오.

① show up　　② emerge
③ come along　　④ turn up
⑤ encounter

21 How will our lives be different in the 2020s? Fill in the blanks with the suitable words.

➡ _____ _____ will be sold in the 2020s.

[22~23] 다음 글을 읽고 물음에 답하시오.

Have you ever heard of 3D modelers? Taeho, a 3D modeler, works for a company that makes artificial hands and legs. Taeho uses special software to print out new hands and legs. ⓐThey are made specially for patients. If you are good at computer programming and art, you can be a 3D modeler. Taeho wants more people to use 3D printed products in the future.

22 위 글의 밑줄 친 ⓐThey가 가리키는 것을 본문에서 찾아 쓰시오.

➡ _____

23 위 글을 읽고 대답할 수 없는 질문은?

① What is Taeho's job?
② Where does Taeho work?
③ What does Taeho make at the company?
④ Who does Taeho work with?
⑤ What do you need to do well to become a 3D modeler?

[24~26] 다음 글을 읽고 물음에 답하시오.

Jihye is a big data specialist. She works on many projects. For example, last year, she made bus routes. To find the best night routes, she needed to collect smartphone use data and taxi use patterns from late-night travelers. Then she analyzed this information to create the most useful routes. Now Jihye is working with an online shopping mall. She is collecting data from customers to find out the best styles for them. She knows big data allows us ⓐto learn more about our daily lives. If you want to become a big data specialist, you should develop your math and problem-solving skills!

Think about yourself and prepare for your future. If you keep looking ahead and dreaming big, your future will be bright.

24 위 글에 나온 big data 수집의 예 두 가지를 우리말로 쓰시오.

➡ (1) _____
(2) _____
_____

25 아래 〈보기〉에서 위 글의 밑줄 친 ⓐto learn과 to부정사의 용법이 다른 것의 개수를 고르시오. (2개)

┌─ 보기 ─┐
① She has a few friends to play with.
② I found it difficult to do so.
③ My goal is to become a great physicist.
④ She was sorry to hear that.
⑤ I told her to do it next.
└──────┘

① 1개 ② 2개 ③ 3개 ④ 4개 ⑤ 5개

26 If you want to make your future bright, what do you need to do? Answer in English in a full sentence. (9 words)

➡ _____
_____

[01~02] 다음 대화를 읽고 물음에 답하시오.

> B: Jessica, what are you (A)going to do for the school talent show?
> G: I didn't decide yet. (B)_____
> B: You're good at dancing, aren't you?
> G: Not really. But I think I'm good at singing. I like singing very much.
> B: Really? Actually, I'm planning to play rock music with my band. Why don't you sing for us?
> G: Sure, I'd love to.

01 밑줄 친 (A)와 바꿔 쓸 수 있는 말을 대화에서 찾아 쓰시오.

➡ _____

02 빈칸 (B)에 들어갈 말을 주어진 단어를 이용하여 완성하시오.

➡ _____ (good, at)

03 다음 대화의 ①~⑤ 중 어색한 곳을 골라 바르게 고치시오.

> A: ①What are you good at?
> B: ②I'm good at took care of people.
> A: Then how about becoming a nurse?
> B: That sounds good. ③What do I need to do to become a nurse?
> A: ④You need to learn about the human body.
> B: ⑤What skills do I need to develop?
> A: You need to develop your communication skills.

➡ _____
_____

04 다음 빈칸을 알맞은 말로 채워 같은 뜻을 갖는 문장으로 바꾸어 쓰시오.

(1) Mary told her son that he should clean his room for himself.
➡ Mary asked _____ .

(2) The doctor told him that he should stop smoking to live a life without pain.
➡ The doctor warned _____
_____ .

(3) We hope that John will pass the entrance exam.
➡ We expect _____ .

05 다음 문장에서 어법상 어색한 부분을 찾아 바르게 고쳐 다시 쓰시오.

(1) What do you want me doing for you?
➡ _____

(2) Can you ask my prince comes to this tower?
➡ _____

(3) If you want to save us throw a rope down to us.
➡ _____

(4) If Seri will watch the movie with us, I will buy her some popcorn.
➡ _____

06 다음 우리말에 맞게 빈칸에 알맞은 말을 쓰시오.

> • _____ you want, I _____ there.
> 네가 원하지 않으면, 나는 거기 안 갈 거야.

Look at the pictures above. Do these ideas surprise you? You can see that our lives will be very different in the future. As our lives change, many new jobs will appear. What kind of job do you want? ⓐ미래의 당신 삶은 어떤 모습일까요? The following people looked ahead and chose jobs that will be important in the future. Let's read about their jobs!

07 위 글의 밑줄 친 ⓐ의 우리말에 맞게 한 단어를 보충하여, 주어진 어휘를 알맞게 배열하시오.

> future / be / will / life / what / your / ?

➡ _____

08 In the 2040s, will it be possible for you to take a space trip? Answer in English. (3 words)

➡ _____

09 다음 빈칸에 알맞은 단어를 넣어 위 글의 요지를 완성하시오.

> In the future, our lives will not be the same as those of today. As our lives change, there will be many _____ _____.

Jihye is a big data specialist. She works on many projects. For example, last year, she made bus routes. To find the best night routes, she needed to (A)[collect / correct] smartphone use data and taxi use patterns from late-night travelers. Then she analyzed ⓐthis information to create the most useful routes. Now Jihye is working with an online shopping mall. She is collecting data from customers to find out the best styles for them. She knows big data allows us to learn more about our (B)[daily / dairy] lives. If you want to become a big data specialist, you should develop your math and problem-solving skills!

Think about (C)[you / yourself] and prepare for your future. If you keep looking ahead and dreaming big, your future will be bright.

10 위 글의 괄호 (A)~(C)에서 문맥이나 어법상 알맞은 낱말을 골라 쓰시오.

➡ (A)_____ (B)_____ (C)_____

11 위 글의 밑줄 친 ⓐthis information이 가리키는 것을 본문에서 찾아 쓰시오.

➡ _____

_____

12 다음 빈칸 (A)와 (B)에 알맞은 단어를 넣어 지혜의 직업에 대한 소개를 완성하시오.

> Her Job: She is (A)_____.
> To Get the Job: You should develop your (B)_____.

01 다음 그림의 상황을 보고, 조언을 구하고 답하는 대화를 주어진 단어를 이용하여 완성하시오.

A: Can I ask you something?
B: Sure. What is it?
A: _____ a good cook? (need)
B: _____
A: _____ (need)
B: You should try to make new dishes.

02 다음 기대 사항과 일치하도록 expect를 이용하여 어법에 맞게 쓰시오.

Mom's expectations
(1) me: get good grades
(2) my sister: become a scientist
(3) my dad: do not smoke

(1) _____
(2) _____
(3) _____

03 다음 내용을 바탕으로 20년 뒤 자신의 직업에 관해 강연할 원고를 작성하시오.

1. What is your job and where do you work?
   I am a computer programmer and work at a software company.
2. What do you usually do at work?
   I develop new software for computers.
3. Who do you work with?
   I work with people from different countries.
4. Why did you choose your job?
   I chose this job because I am interested in math and science.
5. What did you do to get this job?
   I studied computer science and developed my problem-solving skills.

Hello, everyone. My name is Soin Kim. I'm excited to tell you about my job. I am (A)_____, and I work at a software company. I develop (B)_____ for computers there. I work with many people (C)_____. I chose this job because I am interested in (D)_____. To become a computer programmer, I studied (E)_____ and developed my problem-solving skills. If you have a dream, work hard for it. Then it will come true someday.

단원별 모의고사

[01~02] 다음 빈칸에 알맞은 단어를 고르시오.

01

There was a large _____ of information.

① average　　　　② number
③ amount　　　　④ order
⑤ much

02 우리말에 맞게 주어진 단어를 이용하여 빈칸을 채우시오.

(1) The team project needs everyone's
_____. (collaborate) (그 팀 프로젝트
는 모든 사람들의 협동을 필요로 한다.)

(2) _____ is the key to success.
(creative) (창의력은 성공의 비결이다.)

03 다음 우리말과 일치하도록 빈칸을 채우시오. (주어진 철자
로 시작할 것)

(1) 해가 하늘에 나타났다.
➡ The sun a_____ in the sky.

(2) 그녀는 그 일자리에 지원했다.
➡ She a_____ for the job.

(3) 나는 나의 담임선생님께 상담을 받았다.
➡ I received some c_____ from my
homeroom teacher.

(4) 지금은 미래를 내다봐야 할 시기이다.
➡ Now is the time to l_____
a_____.

04 다음 영영풀이에 해당하는 단어를 고르시오.

a natural ability to do something well

① career　　② knowledge　　③ talent
④ job　　　⑤ artificial

[05~07] 다음 대화를 읽고 물음에 답하시오.

G: Hello, Mr. Watson! Thank you for doing
this interview.
M: Sure, no problem.
G: This interview is for students who want to
be food stylists. (A)_____
M: Sure. You may see pictures of food in
books or on TV. A food stylist decorates
food to look good for pictures or movies.
G: I want to be a food stylist like you.
(B)_____
M: 많은 종류의 음식에 대해 배워야 해요. (need)
G: (C)_____
M: You need to study art, too. Creativity is
important.
G: All right! Thank you for your time, Mr. Watson.

05 위 대화의 빈칸 (A)~(C)에 알맞은 말을 〈보기〉에서 골라 순서
대로 배열한 것은?

┤ 보기 ├
ⓐ What else do I need to do?
ⓑ What do I need to do?
ⓒ Can you tell me about your job?

① ⓐ - ⓒ - ⓑ　　　　② ⓑ - ⓐ - ⓒ
③ ⓑ - ⓒ - ⓐ　　　　④ ⓒ - ⓐ - ⓑ
⑤ ⓒ - ⓑ - ⓐ

06 다음 영영풀이에 해당하는 단어를 대화에서 찾아 쓰시오.

the ability to think of or create something
new

➡ _____

07 밑줄 친 우리말을 주어진 단어를 이용하여 영작하시오.

➡ _____

[08~10] 다음 대화를 읽고 물음에 답하시오.

A: What are you good (A)_____?

B: I'm good at taking care (B)_____ people.

A: Then how (C)_____ becoming a nurse?

B: That sounds good. What do I need to do to become a nurse?

A: You need to learn (D)_____ the human body.

B: (do, skills, develop, what, to, I, need)?

A: You need to develop your communication skills.

8 빈칸 (A)~(D)에 들어갈 알맞은 말을 〈보기〉에서 골라 쓰시오. (중복 가능)

┌─ 보기 ─┐
about   at   from   of   to
└────────┘

➡ (A)_____   (B)_____
  (C)_____   (D)_____

9 다음 영영풀이에 해당하는 단어를 대화에서 찾아 쓰시오.

┌──────────────────────────────┐
to grow or become more advanced
└──────────────────────────────┘

➡ _____

10 괄호 안의 단어를 알맞게 배열하여 영작하시오.

➡ _____

[11~12] 다음 대화를 읽고 물음에 답하시오.

B: Hey, Mandy. What are you ⓐ_____ at?

G: Hey, Edward. Look! Some volunteers ⓑ_____ for the school festival.

B: Really? I want ⓒ_____ out. You know I'm good at ⓓ_____ pictures. I think I can do something for the festival.

G: I think you can help out at the cartoon event.

B: Right!

G: Well, 나는 그림을 잘 그리지 못해. But I'm good at playing board games.

B: You can help out at the game event then.

G: Okay. Let's go and ⓔ_____ to become volunteers.

11 빈칸 ⓐ~ⓔ에 들어갈 말로 올바르게 짝지어진 것을 모두 고르시오.

① ⓐ looked
② ⓑ need
③ ⓒ to help
④ ⓓ drawing
⑤ ⓔ to apply

12 밑줄 친 우리말을 주어진 말을 이용해 영작하시오. (good, draw)

➡ _____

13 다음 중 밑줄 친 부분의 쓰임이 바르지 못한 것은?

① I want you to listen to your father.
② You can persuade him do it again.
③ What made you think about it?
④ I need you to help me.
⑤ She advised me not to do it.

14 다음 빈칸에 들어갈 말로 어법상 적절한 것을 모두 고르시오.

┌──────────────────────────────┐
_____ you get enough sleep, you will feel tired.
└──────────────────────────────┘

① Unless   ② Until   ③ As
④ When   ⑤ Because

15 다음 상황에 알맞은 말을 어법에 맞게 빈칸에 쓰시오.

(1) Jack was very disappointed. Then, Paul told him that he could win the contest.
→ Paul encouraged Jack _____ _____ the contest.

(2) Today Mike was late for work. His boss said to him, "Don't be late again."
→ His boss ordered Mike _____ _____ _____ again.

16 어법상 어색한 것을 고쳐 문장을 다시 쓰시오.

(1) The mother wanted her son cleans his room.
➡ _____

(2) I expect Juho exercising more.
➡ _____

(3) The doctor advised me stop eating junk food.
➡ _____

(4) Unless you show us your hand, we will open the door.
➡ _____

(5) If you won't sleep enough, you will be very tired.
➡ _____

17 괄호 안에 주어진 동사를 어법에 맞게 빈칸에 쓰시오.

(1) The boy told the woman _____ first. (go)

(2) If it _____ tomorrow, I will stay home. (rain)

[18~20] 다음 글을 읽고 물음에 답하시오.

Jihye is a big data specialist. She works on many projects. (①) For example, last year, she made bus routes. (②) To find the best night routes, she needed to collect smartphone use data and taxi use patterns from late-night travelers. (③) Now Jihye is working with an online shopping mall. (④) She is collecting data from customers to find out the best styles for them. (⑤) She knows big data allows us to learn more about our daily lives. If you want to become a big data specialist, you should develop your math and problem-solving skills!

Think about yourself and prepare for your future. ⓐ만약 당신이 계속 앞을 내다보고 꿈을 크게 꾼다면, your future will be bright.

18 위 글의 흐름으로 보아, 주어진 문장이 들어가기에 가장 적절한 곳은?

> Then she analyzed this information to create the most useful routes.

① ② ③ ④ ⑤

19 위 글의 밑줄 친 ⓐ의 우리말에 맞게 주어진 어휘를 이용하여 8 단어로 영작하시오.

> keep, ahead, big

➡ _____

20 위 글의 내용과 일치하지 않는 것은?

① 지혜는 빅데이터 전문가이다.
② 지혜는 작년에 버스 노선을 만들었다.
③ 현재 지혜는 온라인 쇼핑몰과 작업하고 있다.
④ 지혜는 빅데이터가 미래에 관하여 더 많이 알게 해 준다는 것을 알고 있다.
⑤ 빅데이터 전문가가 되고 싶다면, 수학과 문제 해결 능력을 계발해야 한다.

단원별 모의고사

[21~22] 다음 글을 읽고 물음에 답하시오.

Do you see the flower pot that Sujin made? It was made from old street flags. She is an upcycling designer. She works with waste materials to make new products. Her products show people that old materials can be useful in new ways. Upcycling can reduce the amount of ⓐwaste in the future. To become an upcycling designer, you should be ___(A)___ and learn about art.

21 위 글의 빈칸 (A)에 create를 알맞은 형태로 쓰시오.

➡ _____

22 위 글의 밑줄 친 ⓐwaste와 같은 의미로 쓰인 것을 고르시오.

① Don't waste your energy on useless things.
② The cause of pollution is industrial waste.
③ You should not waste a good opportunity.
④ It's a waste of time to do such a thing.
⑤ Waste water is pumped from the factory into a nearby river.

[23~25] 다음 글을 읽고 물음에 답하시오.

2020s • Self-driving cars will be on the market.
2030s • People will have robots that do everything for them.
   • 3D printers in every home will print out almost everything.
2050s • People will take space trips.
   • People will live under the sea or in floating cities.

Look at the pictures above. Do these ideas surprise you? You can see that our lives will be very different in the future. As our lives change, many new jobs will appear. What kind of job do you want? What will your future life be like? The following people looked ahead and chose jobs ⓐthat will be important in the future. Let's read about ⓑtheir jobs!

23 위 글의 밑줄 친 ⓐthat과 문법적 쓰임이 같은 것을 모두 고르시오.

① He is the greatest novelist that has ever lived.
② It's true that we were a little late.
③ There was no hope that she would recover her health.
④ The watch that you gave me keeps perfect time.
⑤ She said that the story was true.

24 위 글의 밑줄 친 ⓑtheir가 가리키는 것을 본문에서 찾아 쓰시오.

➡ _____

25 위 글을 읽고 대답할 수 없는 질문은?

① What will happen in the 2020s?
② How will our lives be different in the 2030s?
③ When will people be able to live in floating cities?
④ What will our lives be like in the 2060s?
⑤ Why will many new jobs appear in the future?

Lesson

8

Who Is Happy?

Words & Expressions

교과서

Key Words

□ **anywhere**[énihwɛər] 부 어느 곳이나, 어디든

□ **appearance**[əpíərəns] 명 외모

□ **beauty**[bjúːti] 명 아름다움

□ **brightly**[bráitli] 부 밝게

□ **cage**[keidʒ] 명 우리, 새장

□ **chase**[tʃeis] 동 ~를 뒤쫓다, 추적하다

□ **colorful**[kʌ́lərfəl] 형 색채가 다양한, 형형색색의

□ **crow**[krou] 명 까마귀

□ **director**[diréktər] 명 감독

□ **edit**[édit] 동 편집하다

□ **explain**[ikspléin] 동 설명하다

□ **express**[iksprés] 동 표현하다, 나타내다

□ **feather**[féðər] 명 (새의) 털, 깃털

□ **fly**[flai] 동 날다 (**fly–flew–flown**)

□ **forest**[fɔ́ːrist] 명 숲

□ **gorgeous**[gɔ́ːrdʒəs] 형 매력적인, 멋진

□ **happiness**[hǽpinis] 명 행복, 만족

□ **impressive**[imprésiv] 형 (사물·사람이) 인상적인, 인상 깊은

□ **lake**[leik] 명 호수, 연못

□ **parrot**[pǽrət] 명 앵무새

□ **peacock**[píːkàk] 명 공작(새)

□ **praise**[preiz] 동 칭송하다, 칭찬하다

□ **predict**[pridíkt] 동 예언하다, 예측하다

□ **shine**[ʃain] 동 빛나다 (**shine–shone–shone**)

□ **shiny**[ʃáini] 형 빛나는, 반짝거리는

□ **so**[sou] 부 너무나, 대단히, 그렇게

□ **swan**[swɑn] 명 백조

□ **thought**[θɔːt] 명 생각, 사고

□ **unlike**[ənláik] 전 ~와 다른, ~와 달리

□ **until**[əntíl] 접 ~할 때까지

□ **zoo**[zuː] 명 동물원

Key Expressions

□ **around the world** 세계 곳곳에

□ **be free to 동사원형** 자유롭게 ~하다

□ **be proud of** ~을 자랑으로 여기다

□ **be stuck in** ~에 (갇혀) 있다

□ **because of** ~ 때문에

□ **chase ~ away** ~을 쫓아내다

□ **find out** 알게 되다, 발견하다

□ **go back to** ~로 돌아가다

□ **must+동사원형** ~임에 틀림없다(강한 추측)

□ **on the other hand** 반면에

□ **once upon a time** 옛날 옛적에 (= **a long time ago**)

□ **one day** 어느 날

□ **think of** ~을 생각하다

□ **think to oneself** 조용히 생각하다, 마음속으로 생각하다

Word Power

※ 부사 **so**의 여러 가지 뜻

□ 너무나, 대단히

Why didn't you call? We were so worried. (너는 왜 전화를 걸지 않았니? 우리는 매우 걱정했어.)

□ 너무 ~해서 …하다(**so** 형용사/부사 **that**절)

Everything happened so quickly that I didn't have time to think. (모든 것이 너무 빨리 일어나서 생각할 시간이 없었다.)

□ (이미 언급된 것을 다시 가리키는 말로) 그렇게 (주로 **hope so/think so/say so**)

A: Will I need my umbrella? (내가 우산이 필요할까?)

B: I don't think so. (그렇게 생각 안 해요.)

※ **because**와 **because of**의 차이

□ **because**와 **because of**는 둘 다 '~ 때문에'라는 뜻으로 이유를 나타낸다. **because**는 접속사로서 뒤에 주어와 동사로 이루어진 절이 오고, **because of** 뒤에는 명사나 동명사가 온다.

● **I'm tired because of the work.** (나는 그 일 때문에 피곤하다.)

● **Because it rained, I stayed at home.** (비가 왔기 때문에 나는 집에 있었다.)

English Dictionary

□ **anywhere** 어느 곳이나, 어디든
→ at any place
어디에서나

□ **bright** 밝은
→ being filled with light
빛으로 가득 찬

□ **cage** 우리, 새장
→ a box made to hold animals
동물을 가두기 위해 만들어진 상자

□ **director** 감독
→ a person in charge of something
어떤 것을 책임지는 사람

□ **edit** 편집하다
→ to change, correct, or improve a text
본문을 바꾸거나, 고치거나, 개선하다

□ **explain** 설명하다
→ to make something easy to understand
어떤 것을 이해하기 쉽게 만들다

□ **express** 표현하다, 나타내다
→ to talk or write about something
무언가에 대해 쓰거나 말하다

□ **feather** (새의) 털, 깃털
→ a light and soft thing that covers a bird's body
새의 몸통을 덮고 있는 가볍고 부드러운 것

□ **gorgeous** 매력적인, 멋진
→ very attractive
매우 매력적인

□ **happiness** 행복, 만족
→ the state of being happy
행복한 상태

□ **predict** 예언하다, 예측하다
→ to say what will happen in the future
미래에 무엇이 일어날지 말하다

□ **shine** 빛나다
→ to give off light
빛을 방출하다

□ **unlike** ~와 다른, ~와 달리
→ different from
~와 다른

□ **until** ~할 때까지
→ up to a certain time
특정한 시간까지

Reading

Who Is Happy?

Once upon a time, there was a crow who lived in a forest. The crow was very happy with his life. He always looked at himself in the water. He thought no one was more beautiful than he was.

Then one day, the crow saw a swan on the lake. "The swan is so white," he thought, "but I am so black. I have never seen such a white bird before. His beauty shines so brightly. The swan must be the happiest bird in the world." He went to the swan and expressed his thoughts. "Actually," the swan said, "I thought that I was the happiest bird. But then I saw a parrot. Now I think the parrot is the happiest bird in the world." The crow asked why he thought so. The swan answered, "The parrot has colorful feathers. He is more beautiful than I am. He must be proud of his appearance."

The crow then flew to the parrot and said, "The swan said you are the happiest bird because you have colorful feathers." The parrot explained, "I lived a very happy life until I saw a peacock. My feathers are colorful, but the peacock's feathers are colorful, big, and gorgeous. So he is loved by everyone."

once upon a time: 옛날 옛적에
shine: 빛나다 (shine—shone—shone)
brightly: 밝게
express: 표현하다
feather: 깃털
be proud of: ~을 자랑으로 여기다
explain: 설명하다
until: ~할 때까지
gorgeous: 매력적인, 멋진

 확인문제

- 다음 문장이 본문의 내용과 일치하면 T, 일치하지 않으면 F를 쓰시오.

1 The crow thought no one was more beautiful than he was before he saw a swan.

2 The swan is proud of his appearance.

3 The parrot's feathers are colorful, big, and gorgeous.

4 Everyone loves the peacock.

The crow then visited the peacock at the zoo. There were a lot of [=many] people around the peacock, and they praised him for his beauty. The crow thought the peacock must be the happiest bird in the world. After all the people left, the crow started to talk to the peacock. "Peacock, you are so beautiful. Many people come to see you every day. On the other hand, when people see me, they chase me away. I think you are the happiest bird in the world."

The peacock said, "I may be the most beautiful bird, but I'm not happy. Because of my beauty, I am stuck in this zoo. Unlike me, you aren't kept in a cage. I want to be like you because you can go anywhere."

After the crow talked to the peacock, he started to think about who the happiest bird was. The crow thought to himself, "The peacock's feathers are impressive, but he is stuck in a cage. I don't have colorful feathers, but I'm free to fly anywhere." The crow went back to the forest. He looked at himself in the water again and saw the happiest bird in the world.

on the other hand 반면에
chase ~ away: ~을 쫓아내다
be stuck in: ~에 (갇혀) 있다
unlike: ~와 달리
cage: 우리, 새장
think to oneself: 조용히 생각하다, 마음속으로 생각하다
impressive: (사물·사람이) 인상적인, 인상 깊은

 확인문제

● 다음 문장이 본문의 내용과 일치하면 T, 일치하지 않으면 F를 쓰시오.

1 There were a lot of people around the peacock at the zoo. ☐

2 The peacock said he was the happiest bird in the world. ☐

3 Because of his beauty, the peacock was stuck in this zoo. ☐

4 The crow wanted to be like the peacock. ☐

5 The crow thought to himself that the peacock's feathers were impressive. ☐

6 The crow had colorful feathers and was free to fly anywhere. ☐

● 우리말을 참고하여 빈칸에 알맞은 말을 쓰시오.

1 _____ Is Happy?

2 _____ _____ _____ _____, there was a crow who lived in a forest.

3 The crow was very _____ _____ his life.

4 He always _____ _____ _____ in the water.

5 He thought no one was _____ _____ _____ he was.

6 Then one day, the crow saw a swan _____ _____ _____ .

7 "The swan is _____ _____," he thought, "but I am _____ _____ .

8 I have never seen _____ _____ _____ _____ before.

9 His beauty _____ _____ _____ .

10 The swan _____ _____ the happiest bird in the world."

11 He went to the swan and expressed _____ _____ .

12 "_____," the swan said, "I thought that I was the happiest bird.

13 But _____ I saw a parrot.

14 Now I think the parrot is _____ _____ _____ in the world."

15 The crow asked _____ _____ _____ _____ .

16 The swan answered, "The parrot has _____ _____ .

17 He is _____ _____ _____ I am.

18 He _____ _____ _____ his appearance."

19 The crow then _____ to the parrot and said, "The swan said you are the happiest bird _____ you have colorful feathers."

1	누가 행복한가?
2	옛날 옛적에 숲에 사는 까마귀 한 마리가 있었다.
3	그 까마귀는 그의 삶에 매우 행복했다.
4	그는 항상 자신의 모습을 물에 비춰 보았다.
5	그는 자신보다 더 아름다운 새는 없다고 생각했다.
6	그러던 어느 날 까마귀는 호수에서 백조를 보았다.
7	"백조는 정말 하얗구나." 그는 생각했다. "그런데 나는 너무 까매.
8	나는 저렇게 하얀 새를 전에 본 적이 없어.
9	그의 아름다움은 정말 환하게 빛나는구나.
10	백조가 세상에서 가장 행복한 새인 것이 틀림없어."
11	그는 백조에게 가서 그의 생각을 표현했다.
12	"사실은." 백조가 말했다. "나는 내가 가장 행복한 새라고 생각했어.
13	하지만 곧 앵무새를 보았지.
14	이제 난 앵무새가 세상에서 가장 행복한 새라고 생각해."
15	까마귀는 그가 왜 그렇게 생각하는지 물었다.
16	백조는 대답했다. "앵무새는 형형색색의 깃털을 가졌거든.
17	그는 나보다 더 아름다워.
18	그는 틀림없이 자신의 외모를 자랑스러워할 거야."
19	까마귀는 그 다음에 앵무새에게 날아가서 말했다. "백조가 말하기를 당신이 형형색색의 깃털을 가졌기 때문에 가장 행복한 새래요."

20 The parrot _____, "I lived a very happy life _____ I saw a peacock.

21 My feathers are colorful, but _____ _____ _____ are colorful, big, and _____.

22 So he _____ _____ _____ everyone."

23 The crow then visited the peacock _____ _____ _____.

24 There were a lot of people around the peacock, and they _____ him _____ his beauty.

25 The crow thought the peacock _____ _____ the happiest bird in the world.

26 After all the people left, the crow _____ _____ _____ to the peacock.

27 "Peacock, you are _____ _____.

28 Many people _____ _____ _____ you every day.

29 _____ _____ _____ _____, when people see me, they _____ _____ _____.

30 I think you are the happiest bird _____ _____ _____."

31 The peacock said, "I may be _____ _____ bird, but I'm not happy.

32 _____ _____ my beauty, I _____ _____ this zoo.

33 _____ me, you aren't kept in a cage.

34 I want to _____ _____ you because you can go anywhere."

35 After the crow talked to the peacock, he started to think about _____ _____ _____ _____ _____.

36 The crow _____ _____ _____, "The peacock's feathers are impressive, but he is stuck in a cage.

37 I don't have colorful feathers, but I'm _____ _____ _____ anywhere."

38 The crow _____ _____ _____ the forest.

39 He _____ _____ _____ in the water again and saw the happiest bird in the world.

---

20 앵무새는 설명했다. "나는 공작새를 보기 전까지는 매우 행복한 삶을 살았어.

21 내 깃털은 색이 다채롭지만, 공작새의 깃털은 색이 다채로운데다 크고 화려하기까지 하거든.

22 그래서 그는 모든 사람에게 사랑받지."

23 까마귀는 그래서 동물원의 공작새에게 갔다.

24 공작새 주변에는 많은 사람이 있었고, 그들은 그의 아름다움을 칭송했다.

25 까마귀는 공작새가 세상에서 가장 행복한 새가 틀림없다고 생각했다.

26 모든 사람이 떠난 후, 까마귀는 공작새에게 말을 걸기 시작했다.

27 "공작새님, 당신은 참 아름다워요.

28 매일 많은 사람이 당신을 보러 와요.

29 반면에 사람들은 저를 보면, 저를 쫓아내요.

30 나는 당신이 세상에서 가장 행복한 새라고 생각해요."

31 공작새는 말했다. "내가 가장 아름다운 새일지는 모르지만 나는 행복하지 않아.

32 나의 아름다움 때문에 내가 이 동물원에 갇혀 있거든.

33 나와 달리 너는 우리에 갇혀 있지 않잖아.

34 너는 어디든 갈 수 있으니 나는 너처럼 되고 싶어."

35 까마귀는 공작새와 대화한 후에, 누가 가장 행복한 새인지 생각하기 시작했다.

36 까마귀는 조용히 생각했다. "공작새의 깃털은 인상적이지만 그는 우리에 갇혀 있어.

37 나는 형형색색의 깃털은 없지만, 어디든 자유롭게 날아갈 수 있어."

38 까마귀는 숲으로 돌아갔다.

39 그는 물에 비친 자신을 다시 보았고 세상에서 가장 행복한 새를 보았다.

● 우리말을 참고하여 본문을 영작하시오.

1 ▶ 누가 행복한가?
➡ _____

2 ▶ 옛날 옛적에 숲에 사는 까마귀 한 마리가 있었다.
➡ _____

3 ▶ 그 까마귀는 그의 삶에 매우 행복했다.
➡ _____

4 ▶ 그는 항상 자신의 모습을 물에 비춰 보았다.
➡ _____

5 ▶ 그는 자신보다 더 아름다운 새는 없다고 생각했다.
➡ _____

6 ▶ 그러던 어느 날 까마귀는 호수에서 백조를 보았다.
➡ _____

7 ▶ "백조는 정말 하얗구나." 그는 생각했다. "그런데 나는 너무 까매.
➡ _____

8 ▶ 나는 저렇게 하얀 새를 전에 본 적이 없어.
➡ _____

9 ▶ 그의 아름다움은 정말 환하게 빛나는구나.
➡ _____

10 ▶ 백조가 세상에서 가장 행복한 새인 것이 틀림없어."
➡ _____

11 ▶ 그는 백조에게 가서 그의 생각을 표현했다.
➡ _____

12 ▶ "사실은," 백조가 말했다. "나는 내가 가장 행복한 새라고 생각했어.
➡ _____

13 ▶ 하지만 곧 앵무새를 보았지.
➡ _____

14 ▶ 이제 난 앵무새가 세상에서 가장 행복한 새라고 생각해."
➡ _____

15 ▶ 까마귀는 그가 왜 그렇게 생각하는지 물었다.
➡ _____

16 ▶ 백조는 대답했다. "앵무새는 형형색색의 깃털을 가졌거든.
➡ _____

17 ▶ 그는 나보다 더 아름다워.
➡ _____

18 ▶ 그는 틀림없이 자신이 외모를 자랑스러워할 거야."
➡ _____

19 ▶ 까마귀는 그 다음에 앵무새에게 날아가서 말했다. "백조가 말하기를 당신이 형형색색의 깃털을 가졌기 때문에 가장 행복한 새래요."
➡ _____

20 ▶ 앵무새는 설명했다. "나는 공작새를 보기 전까지는 매우 행복한 삶을 살았어.
➡ _____

21 내 깃털은 색이 다채롭지만, 공작새의 깃털은 색이 다채로운 데다 크고 화려하기까지 하거든.

➡ _____

22 그래서 그는 모든 사람에게 사랑받지."

➡ _____

23 까마귀는 그래서 동물원의 공작새에게 갔다.

➡ _____

24 공작새 주변에는 많은 사람이 있었고, 그들은 그의 아름다움을 칭송했다.

➡ _____

25 까마귀는 공작새가 세상에서 가장 행복한 새가 틀림없다고 생각했다.

➡ _____

26 모든 사람이 떠난 후, 까마귀는 공작새에게 말을 걸기 시작했다.

➡ _____

27 "공작새님, 당신은 참 아름다워요.

➡ _____

28 매일 많은 사람이 당신을 보러 와요.

➡ _____

29 반면에 사람들은 저를 보면, 저를 쫓아내요.

➡ _____

30 나는 당신이 세상에서 가장 행복한 새라고 생각해요."

➡ _____

31 공작새는 말했다. "내가 가장 아름다운 새일지는 모르지만 나는 행복하지 않아.

➡ _____

32 나의 아름다움 때문에 내가 이 동물원에 갇혀 있거든.

➡ _____

33 나와 달리 너는 우리에 갇혀 있지 않잖아.

➡ _____

34 너는 어디든 갈 수 있으니 나는 너처럼 되고 싶어."

➡ _____

35 까마귀는 공작새와 대화한 후에, 누가 가장 행복한 새인지 생각하기 시작했다.

➡ _____

36 까마귀는 조용히 생각했다. "공작새의 깃털은 인상적이지만 그는 우리에 갇혀 있어.

➡ _____

37 나는 형형색색의 깃털은 없지만, 어디든 자유롭게 날아갈 수 있어."

➡ _____

38 까마귀는 숲으로 돌아갔다.

➡ _____

39 그는 물에 비친 자신을 다시 보았고 세상에서 가장 행복한 새를 보았다.

➡ _____

01 주어진 단어를 이용해 우리말 해석에 맞게 빈칸을 완성하시오.

(1) We want our children to have the best possible chance of _____. (happy)
(우리는 우리 아이들이 가장 행복할 수 있는 기회를 가지기를 원한다.)

(2) The concept of _____ changes according to the times. (beautiful)
(아름다움의 개념은 시대에 따라 변한다.)

02 그림을 보고 빈칸을 채우시오. (주어진 철자가 있으면 그 철자로 시작할 것)

➡ The dog _____ s_____ _____ the fence.

03 다음 주어진 우리말에 맞게 빈칸을 채우시오. (철자가 주어진 경우 그 철지로 시작할 것)

(1) 그 배우의 외모는 매년 바뀌었다.
➡ The actor's a_____ changed each year.

(2) 새는 정기적으로 깃털이 빠진다.
➡ Birds lose their _____ regularly.

(3) 어둠 속에서 달이 빛난다.
➡ The moon _____ in the dark.

(4) 그 문제에 대해 당신의 생각은 어떠한가?
➡ What are your t_____ on the matter?

04 밑줄 친 부분과 의미가 가장 가까운 단어를 주어진 철자로 시작하여 쓰시오.

You look attractive today! What have you done?

➡ g_____

05 다음 빈칸에 알맞은 단어를 〈보기〉에서 골라 쓰시오.

┌─ 보기 ┐
away   for   from   of
└────────┘

(1) I chased _____ all the mosquitoes.
(2) I am really proud _____ you.

[06~07] 다음 빈칸에 공통으로 들어갈 말을 쓰시오.

06
• I have never thought _____ becoming an actor.
• He stayed home from work because _____ the flu.

07
• I'm _____ tired because I worked all night.
• I'm _____ hungry that I can't concentrate anymore.
• The movie was a little sad. Don't you think _____?

08

나는 언제든 자유롭게 오고 가기를 원한다.
(go, to, want, anytime, I, and, be, at, free, to, come)

➡ _____

09

나는 세계여행을 하고 싶다.
(world, like, around, travel, the, I'd, to)

➡ _____

[10~11] 다음 영영풀이에 해당하는 단어를 주어진 철자로 시작하여 쓰시오.

10

d_____ : a person in charge of something

11

c_____ : a box made to hold animals

12 다음 두 문장을 하나의 문장으로 바꿔 쓰시오.

(1) The crow thought. + Was the swan really white?

➡ _____

(2) The man asks. + Whose is this bag?

➡ _____

(3) The peacock didn't know. + Why did people chase him away?

➡ _____
_____

(4) Do you think? + When did the crow visit the peacock?

➡ _____

[13~16] 다음 두 문장을 관계대명사를 이용하여 한 문장으로 연결하여 쓰시오.

13

• There was a beautiful princess.
• The princess lived in a forest.

➡ _____
_____

14

• *Naruto* is an animation.
• My brother loves watching it.

➡ _____
_____

15

• That is the house.
• Mariel lives in the house.

➡ _____
_____

16

• Gabriel saw a boy and his dog.
• They were playing together in the park.

➡ _____
_____

[17~18] 다음 문장에서 어법상 어색한 것을 찾아 바르게 고치시오.

17

> I am such black. I have never seen so a white bird before.

_____

18 중요

> Erase your name on the envelope before you throw away it.

_____ ➡ _____

[19~20] 다음 문장을 어법에 맞게 고쳐 쓰시오.

19

> She looked at her in the mirror to straighten her own dress.

➡ _____

_____

20

> He has to be stupid to ask such things.

➡ _____

[21~23] 다음 글을 읽고 물음에 답하시오.

Then one day, the crow saw a swan on the lake. "The swan is so white," he thought, "but I am so black. ⓐ나는 저렇게 하얀 새를 전에 본 적이 없어. His beauty shines so brightly. ⓑThe swan must be the happiest bird in the world." He went to the swan and expressed his thoughts. "Actually," the swan said, "I thought that I was the happiest bird. But then I saw a parrot. Now I think the parrot is the happiest bird in the world." The crow asked why he thought ⓒso. The swan answered, "The parrot has colorful feathers. He is more beautiful than I am. He must be proud of his appearance."

21 중요 위 글의 밑줄 친 ⓐ의 우리말에 맞게 한 단어를 보충하여, 주어진 어휘를 알맞게 배열하시오.

> white / seen / such / have / I / bird / never / a

➡ _____

22 위 글의 밑줄 친 ⓑ를 다음과 같이 바꿔 쓸 때 빈칸에 들어갈 알맞은 말을 쓰시오.

> I am _____ that the swan is the happiest bird in the world.

23 중요 위 글의 밑줄 친 ⓒso가 가리키는 내용을 본문에서 찾아 그대로 쓰시오.

➡ _____

Once upon a time, there was a crow ⓐwho lived in a forest. The crow was very happy with his life. ⓑHe always looked at him in the water. He thought no one was __(A)__ beautiful __(B)__ he was.

24 다음과 같은 뜻이 되도록 위 글의 빈칸 (A)와 (B)에 알맞은 단어를 쓰시오.

he was the most beautiful of all

➡ _____

25 위 글의 밑줄 친 ⓐwho와 바꿔 쓸 수 있는 단어를 쓰시오.

➡ _____

26 위 글의 밑줄 친 ⓑ에서 어법상 틀린 부분을 찾아 고치시오.

➡ _____

The crow then __ⓐ__ to the parrot and said, "The swan said you are the happiest bird because you have colorful feathers." The parrot explained, "ⓑI lived a very happy life until I saw a peacock. My feathers are colorful, but the peacock's feathers are colorful, big, and gorgeous. So ⓒhe is loved by everyone."

27 위 글의 빈칸 ⓐ에 fly를 알맞은 형태로 쓰시오.

➡ _____

28 위 글의 밑줄 친 ⓑ를 다음과 같이 바꿔 쓸 때 빈칸에 들어갈 알맞은 말을 쓰시오.

➡ I lived very _____.

29 위 글의 밑줄 친 ⓒ를 능동태로 고치시오.

➡ _____

[30~32] 다음 글을 읽고 물음에 답하시오.

The crow then visited the peacock at the zoo. There were a lot of people around the peacock, and they praised him for his beauty. The crow thought the peacock must be the happiest bird in the world. After all the people left, the crow started to talk to the peacock. "Peacock, you are so beautiful. Many people come to see you every day. ⓐ On the other hand, when people see me, they chase away me. I think you are the happiest bird in the world." The peacock said, "I may be the most beautiful bird, but I'm not happy. (A) _____ _____ my beauty, I am stuck in this zoo. Unlike me, you aren't kept in a cage. I want to be like you (B)_____ you can go anywhere."

30 위 글의 빈칸 (A)와 (B)에 들어갈 알맞은 말을 쓰시오.

➡ (A) _____ (B) _____

31 위 글의 밑줄 친 ⓐ에서 어법상 틀린 부분을 찾아 고치시오.

➡ _____

32 the crow와 the peacock의 삶의 좋은 면과 애환을 각각 우리말로 쓰시오.

- the crow의 삶의 좋은 면: _____
- the crow의 애환: _____
- the peacock의 삶의 좋은 면: _____
  _____
- the peacock의 애환: _____

[33~35] 다음 글을 읽고 물음에 답하시오.

Then one day, the crow saw a swan on the lake. "The swan is (A)[so / such] white," he thought, "but I am so black. I have never seen (B)[so / such] a white bird before. His beauty shines so brightly. The swan must be the happiest bird in the world." He went to the swan and expressed ⓐhis thoughts. "Actually," the swan said, "I thought that I was the happiest bird. But then I saw a parrot. Now I think the parrot is the happiest bird in the world." The crow asked why he thought so. The swan answered, "The parrot has colorful (C)[feathers / features]. He is more beautiful than I am. He must be proud of his appearance."

33 위 글의 괄호 (A)~(C)에서 문맥이나 어법상 알맞은 낱말을 골라 쓰시오.

➡ (A) _____ (B) _____ (C) _____

34 위 글의 밑줄 친 ⓐhis thoughts가 가리키는 것을 본문에서 찾아 쓰시오.

➡ _____

35 본문의 내용과 일치하도록 다음 빈칸 (A)~(C)에 알맞은 단어를 쓰시오.

The crow with (A)_____ feathers said that the swan's beauty shone brightly because of his (B)_____ feathers, but the swan thought that a parrot was more beautiful than he was because of a parrot's (C)_____ feathers.

After the crow talked to the peacock, ⓐhe started to think about who the happiest bird was. ⓑ까마귀는 조용히 생각했다, "The peacock's feathers are impressive, but he is stuck in a cage. I don't have colorful feathers, but I'm free to fly anywhere." The crow went back to the forest. ⓒHe looked at himself in the water again and saw the unhappiest bird in the world.

36 위 글의 밑줄 친 ⓐ를 다음과 같이 바꿔 쓸 때 빈칸에 들어갈 알맞은 말을 쓰시오.

➡ he started _____ about who the happiest bird was

37 위 글의 밑줄 친 ⓑ의 우리말에 맞게 재귀대명사를 이용하여 5 단어로 영작하시오.

➡ _____

38 위 글의 밑줄 친 ⓒ에서 흐름상 어색한 부분을 찾아 고치시오.

➡ _____

The crow then visited the peacock at the zoo. There were a lot of people around the peacock, and they praised him for his beauty. The crow thought the peacock must be the happiest bird in the world. After all the people left, the crow started to talk to the peacock. "Peacock, you are so beautiful. Many people come to see you every day. On the other hand, when people see me, they chase me away. I think you are the happiest bird in the world." The peacock said, "ⓐI may be the most beautiful bird, but I'm not happy. Because of my beauty, I am _____(A) in this zoo. Unlike me, you aren't kept in a cage. I want to be like you because you can go anywhere."

39 위 글의 빈칸 (A)에 stick을 알맞은 형태로 쓰시오.

➡ _____

40 위 글의 밑줄 친 ⓐ를 Though로 시작하여 고치시오.

➡ _____

41 본문의 내용과 일치하도록 다음 빈칸 (A)~(D)에 알맞은 단어를 쓰시오.

The crow was (A)_____ away by people but he wasn't kept in a cage and could go (B)_____. On the other hand, the peacock might be the (C)_____ _____ bird, but he was kept in the zoo because he was (D)_____.

[01~03] 다음 빈칸에 알맞은 단어를 고르시오.

01 출제율 90%

On the one hand, we love children, but _____, we don't want to spend too much time on them.

① unless   ② at last
③ therefore   ④ although
⑤ on the other hand

02 출제율 95%

You _____ be hungry after all that walking.

① have to   ② must   ③ can't
④ need not   ⑤ won't

03 출제율 90%

We looked for the puppy but couldn't find it _____.

① another   ② anytime
③ anybody   ④ anywhere
⑤ where

04 출제율 100%

다음 문장의 빈칸에 알맞은 것을 〈보기〉에서 찾아 쓰시오. (형태 변화 가능)

┌─ 보기 ─┐
explain   fly   predict   shine

(1) The sun was _____ on the water.
(2) Some animals have the ability to _____ earthquakes.
(3) The mother bird will feed her chicks until they are able to _____.
(4) Let me _____ what I mean.

05 출제율 90%

다음 중 밑줄 친 부분의 뜻풀이가 바르지 않은 것은?

① My cat loves to chase a ball. (뒤쫓다)
② It's difficult to tell the twins by their appearance. (외모)
③ Jane was praised by her teacher. (야단치다)
④ Look at the colorful flowers in the picture. (형형색색의)
⑤ Elon told me impressive success stories. (인상적인)

06 출제율 85%

밑줄 친 부분과 의미가 가장 가까운 단어를 주어진 철자로 시작하여 쓰시오.

(1) A long time ago, there was a traveler.
  ➡ O_____ (4 단어)
(2) You can buy clothes like these at any place.
  ➡ a_____

07 출제율 95%

주어진 단어를 이용하여 빈칸을 완성하시오.

I can't bear the _____(think) of waking up at 5 a.m.

08 출제율 85%

주어진 영영풀이의 어휘를 빈칸에 써 넣으시오.

being filled with light

Kate went into a _____ room.

09 다음 주어진 우리말에 맞게 빈칸을 채우시오.

(1) James가 그 쇼의 음악 감독이다.
➡ James is the musical _____ of the show.

(2) 건강은 행복의 요건 중 하나이다.
➡ Good health is a factor of _____.

(3) 우리는 비가 그치기 전까지 밖에 나갈 수 없다.
➡ We can't go outside _____ the rain stops.

(4) 그 경기의 규칙을 설명해 주시겠어요?
➡ Can you _____ the rules of the game?

(5) 우리는 감정을 표현할 필요가 있다.
➡ We need to _____ our feelings.

10 다음 빈칸에 알맞은 말이 순서대로 바르게 배열된 것은?

• I studied hard yesterday because (A)_____ my English test.
• I'm trying to find (B)_____ what that is.
• My cat chases (C)_____ any dog that comes into the garden.

	(A)	(B)	(C)
①	at	out	away
②	at	in	for
③	of	for	away
④	of	out	away
⑤	of	in	for

11 다음 우리말에 맞게 주어진 단어를 바르게 배열하시오.

(1) 그는 다른 사람과 다르다.
(unlike, other, he, any, is)
➡ _____

(2) 그 공원은 풍경이 매력적이다.
(park, scenery, the, some, gorgeous, has)
➡ _____

(3) 올 여름은 무더울 것으로 예측된다.
(this, it's, be, that, hot, predicted, summer, will)
➡ _____

(4) 이 기사는 편집될 필요가 있다.
(this, be, article, edited, needs, to)
➡ _____

[12~13] 다음 영영풀이에 해당하는 단어를 주어진 철자로 시작하여 쓰시오.

12

to talk or write about something

➡ e_____

13

to give off light

➡ s_____

14 다음 우리말을 괄호 안에 주어진 어휘를 이용하여 영작하시오.

(1) 그는 영국에 두 번 가 본 적이 있다. (be, 6 단어)
➡ _____

(2) 우리는 차가운 물로 우리를 식혀야 한다. (cool, cold, should, with, 8 단어)
➡ _____

(3) 축구 경기는 영국인들에 의해 만들어졌다. (the English, the game of football, invent, 9 단어)
➡ _____
_____

15 출제율 90%

다음 문장과 같은 뜻의 문장을 고르시오.

> No student in his class is stronger than William.

① William is as strong as other students in his class.
② All the students in his class is stronger than William.
③ William is stronger than all the other students in his class.
④ Other students in his class is as strong as William.
⑤ William isn't stronger than other students in his class.

16 출제율 95%

다음 중 두 문장을 잘못 고쳐 쓴 것은?

① He was loved by a lot of people because he was honest.
→ A lot of people loved him because he was honest.
② The crow visited the peacock at the zoo.
→ The peacock at the zoo was visited by the crow.
③ The crow saw the happiest bird in the world.
→ The happiest bird in the world was seen by the crow.
④ They made Peter solve the puzzle by the next morning.
→ Peter was made solve the puzzle by the next morning by them.
⑤ My teacher advised me to study math harder.
→ I was advised to study math harder by my teacher.

17 출제율 100%

다음 두 문장을 한 문장으로 바꿔 쓰시오.

(1) The parrot was not sure. Who was the happiest bird?
➡ _____

(2) He saw a swan on the lake. The swan was so white.
➡ _____

(3) The peacock's feathers are gorgeous. So he is loved by everyone.
➡ _____

(4) Shirley went to Paris. She is in Paris now.
➡ _____

18 출제율 90%

〈보기〉의 밑줄 친 that과 용법이 다른 하나는?

> 보기
> Now I think that the parrot is the happiest bird in the world.

① Sometimes they forget that Koreans don't tip.
② The crow thought that the peacock's feathers were impressive.
③ I didn't know that so many people speak English.
④ She thinks that Frank told a lie.
⑤ Tom Sawyer has many friends that help him.

19 다음 문장을 어법에 맞게 고쳐 쓰시오. [출제율 90%]

(1) An interesting toy was bought to my little sister by Mom.

➡ _____

_____

(2) Sean lost the toy with that he used to play.

➡ _____

_____

(3) We have known each other since a long time.

➡ _____

(4) Patricia will ask you what did you do last night.

➡ _____

(5) Don't put off it until tomorrow when you can do it today.

➡ _____

(6) Any other country uses more oil than the U.S. does.

➡ _____

[20~22] 다음 글을 읽고 물음에 답하시오.

ⓐOnce upon a time, there was a crow who lived in a forest. The crow was very happy with his life. He always looked at himself in the water. He thought ⓑno one was more beautiful than he was.

20 위 글의 종류로 알맞은 것을 고르시오. [출제율 100%]

① review ② book report
③ essay ④ fable
⑤ summary

21 위 글의 밑줄 친 ⓐ와 바꿔 쓸 수 없는 말을 고르시오. [출제율 95%]

① A long time ago
② Once in a while
③ Long, long time ago
④ A long while ago
⑤ Long ago

22 위 글의 밑줄 친 ⓑ와 의미가 다른 문장을 고르시오. [출제율 90%]

① no one was as beautiful as he was
② he was the most beautiful of all
③ he was not so beautiful as others
④ no one was so beautiful as he was
⑤ he was more beautiful than anyone else

[23~25] 다음 글을 읽고 물음에 답하시오.

Then one day, the crow saw a swan on the lake. "The swan is so white," he thought, "but I am so black. I have never seen such a white bird before. His beauty shines so brightly. The swan ⓐmust be the happiest bird in the world." He went to the swan and expressed his thoughts. "Actually," the swan said, "I thought that I was the happiest bird. But then I saw a parrot. Now I think the parrot is the happiest bird in the world." The crow asked why he thought so. The swan answered, "The parrot has colorful feathers. He is more beautiful than I am. He must be proud of his (A) ."

23 위 글의 빈칸 (A)에 들어갈 알맞은 말을 고르시오. [출제율 95%]

① voice ② cleverness
③ appearance ④ popularity
⑤ personality

24 위 글의 밑줄 친 ⓐmust와 같은 의미로 쓰인 것을 모두 고르시오.

① You must be hungry after all that walking.
② All students must keep quiet in the library.
③ You must be careful when you cross the street.
④ He must be at home. I see his car in his garage.
⑤ This must be done before tonight.

25 위 글을 읽고 대답할 수 없는 질문은?

① What did the crow think when he saw the swan?
② Why did the crow think that the swan was the happiest bird?
③ What did the swan think about himself before he saw a parrot?
④ Why did the swan think the parrot was the happiest bird?
⑤ Who did the swan think was the ugliest bird in the world?

[26~28] 다음 글을 읽고 물음에 답하시오.

The crow then visited the peacock at the zoo. There were a lot of people around the peacock, and they (A)[blamed / praised] him for his beauty. The crow thought the peacock must be the happiest bird in the world. After all the people left, the crow started to talk to the peacock. "Peacock, you are so beautiful. Many people come to see you every day. On the other hand, when people see me, they chase me away. I think you are the happiest bird in the world."

The peacock said, "I ⓐmay be the most beautiful bird, but I'm not happy. Because of my beauty, I am stuck in this zoo. (B)[Like / Unlike] me, you aren't kept in a cage. I want to be (C)[like / unlike] you because you can go anywhere."

26 위 글의 괄호 (A)~(C)에서 문맥이나 어법상 알맞은 낱말을 골라 쓰시오.

➡ (A) _____ (B) _____ (C) _____

27 아래 〈보기〉에서 위 글의 밑줄 친 ⓐmay와 문법적 쓰임이 같은 것의 개수를 고르시오.

┌─ 보기 ─┐
① You may come in if you wish.
② With the sky like this, it may rain at any moment.
③ He works hard so that he may succeed.
④ You may not smoke here.
⑤ May you live long!

① 1개　② 2개　③ 3개　④ 4개　⑤ 5개

28 다음 중 위 글의 내용을 올바르게 이해하지 못한 사람을 고르시오.

지민: The crow went to the zoo to visit the peacock.
아람: The peacock was praised for his beauty.
이슬: When the crow saw people, he chased after them.
우주: The peacock said that maybe he was the most beautiful bird but that he was not happy.
보배: The peacock wanted to be like the crow because he could go anywhere.

① 지민　② 아람　③ 이슬
④ 우주　⑤ 보배

[29~31] 다음 글을 읽고 물음에 답하시오.

Then one day, the crow saw a swan on the lake. "The swan is so white," he thought, "but I am so black. I have never seen such a white bird before. His beauty shines so brightly. The swan must be the happiest bird in the world." He went to the swan and expressed his thoughts. "ⓐ Actually," the swan said, "I thought that I was the happiest bird. But then I saw a parrot. Now I think the parrot is the happiest bird in the world." (A)＿＿＿＿＿＿＿＿ The swan answered, "The parrot has colorful feathers. He is more beautiful than I am. He must be proud of his appearance."

✏️ 출제율 85%
29 위 글의 빈칸 (A)에 다음 두 문장을 한 문장으로 쓰시오.

> • The crow asked.
> • Why did he think so?

➡ ＿＿＿＿＿＿＿＿＿＿＿＿＿＿＿

✏️ 출제율 90%
30 위 글의 밑줄 친 ⓐActually와 바꿔 쓸 수 있는 말을 모두 고르시오.

① In fact   ② Exactly
③ Immediately   ④ Certainly
⑤ As a matter of fact

✏️ 출제율 100%
31 위 글의 내용과 일치하지 않는 것은?

① The crow has never seen such a white bird as the swan before.
② The crow thinks that the swan is the happiest bird in the world.
③ In the past, the swan thought he was the happiest bird.
④ The swan thinks the parrot is more beautiful than he is.
⑤ The crow is sure that the swan is proud of his appearance.

[32~34] 다음 글을 읽고 물음에 답하시오.

After the crow talked to the peacock, he started to think about who the happiest bird was. The crow thought to himself, "The peacock's feathers are impressive, but he is stuck in a cage. I don't have colorful feathers, but I'm free ⓐto fly anywhere." The crow went back to the forest. He looked at himself in the water again and saw the happiest bird in the world.

✏️ 출제율 90%
32 위 글의 밑줄 친 ⓐto fly와 to부정사의 용법이 다른 것을 고르시오.

① The water in this well is not good to drink.
② Are you ready to start?
③ This book is difficult to read.
④ I studied hard to pass the test.
⑤ The river is too dangerous to swim in.

✏️ 출제율 95%
33 위 글의 교훈으로 알맞은 것을 고르시오. (2개)

① Birds of a feather flock together.
② Don't compare yourself with others.
③ Where there is a will, there is a way.
④ Those with least wisdom or knowledge are always the most talkative.
⑤ You should be satisfied with what you have.

✏️ 출제율 90%
34 다음 문장에서 위 글의 내용과 다른 부분을 찾아서 고치시오.

> Finally the crow thought that the peacock was the happiest bird in the world.

➡ ＿＿＿＿＿＿＿＿＿＿＿＿＿＿＿

[35~37] 다음 글을 읽고 물음에 답하시오.

The crow then flew to the parrot and said, "The swan said you are the happiest bird because you have colorful feathers." The parrot explained, "ⓐI lived a very happy life while I saw a peacock. My feathers are colorful, but the peacock's feathers are colorful, big, and gorgeous. ⓑ그래서 그는 모든 사람에게 사랑받지."

✎ 출제율 95%

35 위 글의 밑줄 친 ⓐ에서 흐름상 어색한 부분을 찾아 고치시오.

➡ _____

✎ 출제율 90%

36 주어진 영영풀이에 해당하는 단어를 위 글에서 찾아 쓰시오.

very beautiful; very attractive

➡ _____

✎ 출제율 90%

37 위 글의 밑줄 친 ⓑ의 우리말에 맞게 주어진 어휘를 이용하여 6 단어로 영작하시오.

So, everyone

➡ _____

[38~40] 다음 글을 읽고 물음에 답하시오.

The crow then visited the peacock at the zoo. There were a lot of people around the peacock, and they praised him for his beauty. The crow thought ⓐ공작새가 세상에서 가장 행복한 새가 틀림없다. After all the people left, the crow started to talk to the peacock. "Peacock, ①you are so beautiful. Many people come to see you every day. __(A)__ , when people see me, they chase me away. ②I think you are the happiest bird in the world." The peacock said, "③I may be the most beautiful bird, but I'm not happy. Because of my beauty, ④I am stuck in this zoo. Unlike me, you aren't kept in a cage. ⑤I want to be like you because you can go anywhere."

✎ 출제율 95%

38 위 글의 빈칸 (A)에 들어갈 알맞은 말을 고르시오.

① Therefore   ② In addition
③ In other words   ④ For example
⑤ On the other hand

✎ 출제율 90%

39 위 글의 밑줄 친 ⓐ의 우리말에 맞게 주어진 어휘를 이용하여 10 단어로 영작하시오.

must

➡ _____

✎ 출제율 100%

40 밑줄 친 ①~⑤ 중에서 가리키는 대상이 나머지 넷과 다른 것은?

①   ②   ③   ④   ⑤

[41~43] 다음 글을 읽고 물음에 답하시오.

The crow then flew to the parrot and said, "The swan said you are the happiest bird because you have colorful feathers." The parrot explained, "ⓐI lived a very happy life until I saw a peacock. My feathers are colorful, but the peacock's feathers are colorful, big, and gorgeous. So he is loved by everyone."

✎ 출제율 85%

41 What did the parrot think about his feathers and the peacock's feathers after he saw a peacock? Fill in the blanks with the suitable words.

➡ He thought that though his feathers were _____, the peacock's feathers were not only colorful but also _____ and _____.

42 위 글의 밑줄 친 ⓐ와 목적어의 쓰임이 <u>다른</u> 것을 <u>모두</u> 고르시오.

① She smiled a bright smile.
② He killed himself.
③ He dreamed a strange dream.
④ He died a miserable death.
⑤ He absented himself from the meeting yesterday.

43 위 글의 내용으로 보아 대답할 수 <u>없는</u> 것을 고르시오.

① Why did the crow fly to the parrot?
② What did the swan say about the parrot?
③ Did the parrot live happily even after he met a peacock?
④ Which is happier, a parrot or a peacock?
⑤ Why is the peacock loved by everyone?

[44~46] 다음 글을 읽고 물음에 답하시오.

The crow then visited the peacock ⓐat the zoo. There were a lot of people ⓑaround the peacock, and they praised him ⓒto his beauty. The crow thought the peacock must be the happiest bird in the world. After all the people left, the crow started to talk to the peacock. "Peacock, you are so beautiful. Many people come to see you every day. (①) On the other hand, when people see me, they chase me away. (②) I think you are the happiest bird ⓓin the world." (③) The peacock said, "I may be the most beautiful bird, but I'm not happy. (④) Because of my beauty, I am stuck ⓔin this zoo. (⑤) I want to be like you because you can go anywhere."

44 위 글의 흐름으로 보아, 주어진 문장이 들어가기에 가장 적절한 곳은?

| Unlike me, you aren't kept in a cage. |

①　　　②　　　③　　　④　　　⑤

45 위 글의 밑줄 친 전치사 ⓐ~ⓔ 중 어법상 <u>틀린</u> 것을 찾아 고치시오.

➡ _____ 번, _____

46 위 글의 내용과 일치하지 <u>않는</u> 것은?

① 공작새 주변에는 많은 사람이 있었다.
② 까마귀는 공작새가 세상에서 가장 행복한 새가 틀림없다고 생각했다.
③ 공작새는 자신이 가장 행복한 새일지는 모르지만 아름답지 않다고 말했다.
④ 공작새는 동물원에 갇혀 있지만 까마귀는 우리에 갇혀 있지 않다.
⑤ 공작새는 어디든 갈 수 있는 까마귀처럼 되고 싶다고 했다.

MEMO

중간 + 기말
plus
적중100
영어 기출문제집

영어 중 **2**

능률 | 김성곤

Best Collection

내용문의 중등영어발전소 적중100 편집부 TEL 070-7707-0457

INSIGHT
on the textbook

교과서 파헤치기

영어 기출 문제집

적중 100 plus
2학기 전과정

영어 중 2

능률 | 김성곤

INSIGHT
on the textbook
교과서 파헤치기

※ 다음 영어를 우리말로 쓰시오.

01	accident	22	luckily
02	fame	23	serve
03	beauty	24	nursing home
04	moment	25	volunteer
05	spirit	26	homeless
06	collect	27	praise
07	elderly	28	mission
08	survive	29	raise
09	respect	30	honor
10	following	31	turning point
11	goodwill ambassador	32	saying
12	statue	33	favor
13	realize	34	support
14	blind	35	all the time
15	international	36	fall down
16	alive	37	hand out
17	worldwide	38	pass away
18	feed	39	thanks to
19	item	40	clean up
20	medicine	41	give a hand
21	donate	42	search for
		43	take care of

※ 다음 우리말을 영어로 쓰시오.

01 존경하다

02 눈 먼, 장님의

03 속담, 격언

04 (음식을) 제공하다

05 세계적인

06 아름다움, 미(美)

07 임무, 사명

08 순간, 잠깐

09 친선 대사

10 호의, 친절

11 (그) 다음의

12 조각상

13 열다, 개최하다

14 사고

15 들어 올리다, (자금을) 모으다

16 나이가 지긋한

17 깨닫다, 알아차리다

18 모으다, 수집하다

19 양로원

20 마음, 정신, 영혼

21 명성

22 예우하다, 존중하다

23 살아 있는, 존속하는

24 전환점

25 지지하다, 원조하다

26 칭찬하다

27 운이 좋게도, 다행스럽게도

28 풀, 잔디

29 약

30 살아남다, 생존하다

31 기부하다

32 집 없는, 노숙자의

33 자원봉사의, 자원 봉사자

34 먹이를 주다

35 사망하다

36 넘어지다

37 ~을 돌보다

38 나누어 주다

39 ~ 덕분에

40 ~을 돕다

41 어려움에 처한

42 ~을 치우다, 청소하다

43 늘, 내내

※ 다음 영영풀이에 알맞은 단어를 <보기>에서 골라 쓴 후, 우리말 뜻을 쓰시오.

1 _____ : the state of being famous: _____

2 _____ : not able to see anything: _____

3 _____ : a sudden event that causes damage: _____

4 _____ : to put things together in one place: _____

5 _____ : to say nice things about someone: _____

6 _____ : to suddenly know something: _____

7 _____ : to provide with assistance: _____

8 _____ : to admire or look up to somebody: _____

9 _____ : to give something to help people: _____

10 _____ : a time when a huge change takes place: _____

11 _____ : to treat someone with respect: _____

12 _____ : a special task to be accomplished: _____

13 _____ : a sculpture of a person made from stone or metal: _____

14 _____ : to continue to live after something bad happens: _____

15 _____ : someone who is willing to do a job without getting paid: _____

16 _____ : a place where people who are too old or sick to take care of themselves live:

_____

보기			
statue	fame	turning point	support
blind	nursing home	praise	volunteer
mission	collect	respect	realize
accident	survive	honor	donate

※ 다음 우리말과 일치하도록 빈칸에 알맞은 말을 쓰시오.

Listen & Talk 1 A

B: Mia, _____ you _____ _____ _____ these books?

G: Sure. _____ _____ you _____ _____ do with them?

B: I'm _____ _____ _____ them to a children's library.

B: Mia, 이 책들 옮기는 거 도와줄 수 있어?
G: 그럼. 너 이 책으로 뭐 할 거야?
B: 나는 이 책을 어린이 도서관에 기부할 거야.

Listen & Talk 1 B

B: Hey, Minji! What's _____ _____ your leg?

G: I _____ _____ last week.

B: Really? What _____?

G: I was in _____ _____ _____ _____ a train. But I _____ _____ in the street.

B: Oh, that's _____! _____ _____ anything I _____ _____ for you?

G: Well, _____ _____ _____ _____ _____ _____ this bag?

B: Sure.

B: 민지야! 너 다리에 무슨 문제가 있니?
G: 지난주에 부러졌어.
B: 그래? 무슨 일이야?
G: 기차를 타려고 서두르고 있었어. 그런데 길에 넘어졌어.
B: 오, 정말 끔찍하다! 내가 너를 위해 해줄 게 있니?
G: 음, 이 가방을 드는 걸 도와줄 수 있니?
B: 그럼.

Listen & Talk 1 C

B1: Wow! These dogs are so dirty. Jay, _____ _____ _____ me _____ _____?

B2: Allen, I'm sorry, _____ I _____. I have _____ _____ the cats now. _____ _____ _____ _____ Nicky?

B1: Okay! Nicky, can I _____ _____ _____ _____ _____?

G: Sure, Allen. _____ is it?

B1: _____ _____ _____ me _____ these dogs?

G: Sure. But I _____ _____ _____ _____ these dogs first. After that, I will help you.

B1: All right! _____ _____.

B1: 와! 이 개들 정말 더럽다. Jay, 이 개들 씻기는 거 도와줄 수 있니?
B2: Allen, 미안한데 못할 거 같아. 지금 이 고양이들에게 밥 줘야 해. Nicky한테 물어보는 게 어때?
B1: 알겠어! Nicky, 나 좀 도와줄 수 있니?
G: 물론이지, Allen. 뭔데?
B1: 이 개들 씻기는 거 도와줄 수 있니?
G: 그럼. 근데 나 이 개들 산책 먼저 시켜야 해. 끝나고 나서 도와줄게.
B1: 그래! 고마워.

Listen & Talk 2 A

G: _____ _____ _____ _____ _____ activities can we do?

B: Why _____ _____ _____ _____ our town's streets?

G: All _____! _____ do it.

G: 우리 어떤 종류의 봉사 활동을 할 수 있을까?
B: 우리 동네 길거리를 청소하는 게 어때?
G: 좋아! 그러자.

Listen & talk 2 B

G: Good morning, students! _____ _____ _____, there _____ a big fire in Mapletown. _____ _____ _____ _____ _____ money and help the people there? Come to our special event _____ the school grounds _____ _____ 3! Please _____ _____ _____ and _____ them. We will sell your items. Then, we will _____ _____ _____ _____ _____ Mapletown. Please _____ _____ to people _____ _____.

Listen & Talk 2 C

B1: Next Wednesday is Volunteer Day. We _____ _____ the park last time. What are _____ _____ _____ do this time?

G: Why _____ _____ _____ a _____ _____ and _____ _____ _____?

B2: That's not a _____ _____. But I want _____ _____ _____ _____. _____ _____ a party for the people there?

G: That's a good idea. _____ can we do at the party?

B1: We _____ _____ some food.

B2: And _____ _____ _____ some music? I can play the piano.

G: And I _____ _____ _____ _____ _____.

B1: It _____ _____ a good plan.

Do It Yourself A

G1: We have a class activity day next Friday. What do you _____ _____ _____ _____ _____?

B: _____ _____ we do some _____ _____? We can _____ _____ and _____ our community _____.

G1: That _____ _____, but choosing a good place _____ not easy.

B: We need someone _____ _____ _____ _____ _____.

G1: I know Sumin _____ _____ a lot. Sumin, can you _____ _____ some good places?

G2: Sure. I _____ _____ _____ information on the internet. Why _____ _____ _____ the volunteering website for teens?

B: That's a _____ _____.

G: 좋은 아침입니다, 학생 여러분! 아시다시피, Mapletown에 큰 화재가 있었습니다. 우리 돈을 모금해서 그 곳 사람들을 도와주는 게 어떨까요? 5월 3일 학교 운동장에서 열리는 특별 행사에 오세요! 물품들을 가져와서 그것들을 기부해 주세요. 우리는 여러분의 물품들을 팔 것입니다. 그리고, 모든 돈을 Mapletown에 기부할 것입니다. 어려운 사람들에게 도움을 줍시다.

B1: 다음 주 수요일이 봉사 활동 날이네. 우리 저번에는 공원을 청소했지. 이번엔 뭘 할까?

G: 양로원 가서 청소하는 건 어때?

B2: 나쁜 생각은 아니야. 근데 좀 재미있는 걸 하고 싶어. 거기 계신 분들을 위해 파티를 여는 게 어떨까?

G: 좋은 생각이야. 우리가 파티에서 뭘 할 수 있지?

B1: 음식을 대접할 수 있지.

B2: 그리고 연주를 하는 게 어때? 나 피아노 칠 수 있어.

G: 나는 첼로를 켤 수 있어.

B1: 아주 좋은 계획 같아.

G1: 우리 다음 주 금요일에 학급 활동이 있어. 그 날 어떤 것을 하고 싶니?

B: 우리 자원 봉사 활동들을 해 보는 게 어때? 우리가 다른 사람들을 도울 수 있고, 우리의 지역 사회를 더 좋게 만들 수 있어.

G1: 그거 좋다, 하지만 좋은 장소를 고르는 건 쉽지 않아.

B: 우리는 봉사 활동을 많이 해본 사람이 필요해.

G1: 나는 수민이가 봉사 활동을 많이 한 것을 알고 있어. 수민아, 우리가 좋은 장소들을 찾는 것을 도와주겠니?

G2: 물론. 나는 주로 인터넷에서 정보를 찾아. 십대들을 위한 자원 봉사 웹사이트를 확인해 보는 게 어떠니?

B: 좋은 생각이다.

※ 다음 우리말에 맞도록 대화를 영어로 쓰시오.

해석

Listen & Talk 1 A

B: _____

G: _____

B: _____

B: Mia, 이 책들 옮기는 거 도와줄 수 있어?
G: 그럼. 너 이 책으로 뭐 할 거야?
B: 나는 이 책을 어린이 도서관에 기부할 거야.

Listen & Talk 1 B

B: _____

G: _____

B: _____

G: _____

B: _____

G: _____

B: _____

B: 민지야! 너 다리에 무슨 문제가 있니?
G: 지난주에 부러졌어.
B: 그래? 무슨 일이야?
G: 기차를 타려고 서두르고 있었어. 그런데 길에 넘어졌어.
B: 오, 정말 끔찍하다! 내가 너를 위해 해줄 게 있니?
G: 음, 이 가방을 드는 걸 도와줄 수 있니?
B: 그럼.

Listen & Talk 1 C

B1: _____

B2: _____

_____

B1: _____

G: _____

B1: _____

G: _____

B1: _____

B1: 와! 이 개들 정말 더럽다. Jay, 이 개들 씻기는 거 도와줄 수 있니?
B2: Allen, 미안한데 못할 거 같아. 지금 이 고양이들에게 밥 줘야 해. Nicky한테 물어보는 게 어때?
B1: 알겠어! Nicky, 나 좀 도와줄 수 있니?
G: 물론이지, Allen. 뭔데?
B1: 이 개들 씻기는 거 도와줄 수 있니?
G: 그럼. 근데 나 이 개들 산책 먼저 시켜야 해. 끝나고 나서 도와줄게.
B1: 그래! 고마워.

Listen & Talk 2 A

G: _____

B: _____

G: _____

G: 우리 어떤 종류의 봉사 활동을 할 수 있을까?
B: 우리 동네 길거리를 청소하는 게 어때?
G: 좋아! 그러자.

Listen & talk 2 B

G: _____

_____

_____

_____

_____

G: 좋은 아침입니다, 학생 여러분! 아시다시피, Mapletown에 큰 화재가 있었습니다. 우리 돈을 모금해서 그 곳 사람들을 도와주는 게 어떨까요? 5월 3일 학교 운동장에서 열리는 특별 행사에 오세요! 물품들을 가져와서 그것들을 기부해 주세요. 우리는 여러분의 물품들을 팔 것입니다. 그리고, 모든 돈을 Mapletown에 기부할 것입니다. 어려운 사람들에게 도움을 줍시다.

Listen & Talk 2 C

B1: _____

_____

G: _____

B2: _____

_____

G: _____

B1: _____

B2: _____

G: _____

B1: _____

B1: 다음 주 수요일이 봉사 활동 날이네. 우리 저번에는 공원을 청소했지. 이번엔 뭘 할까?
G: 양로원 가서 청소하는 건 어때?
B2: 나쁜 생각은 아니야. 근데 좀 재미있는 걸 하고 싶어. 거기 계신 분들을 위해 파티를 여는 게 어떨까?
G: 좋은 생각이야. 우리가 파티에서 뭘 할 수 있지?
B1: 음식을 대접할 수 있지.
B2: 그리고 연주를 하는 게 어때? 나 피아노 칠 수 있어.
G: 나는 첼로를 켤 수 있어.
B1: 아주 좋은 계획 같아.

Do It Yourself A

G1: _____

B: _____

_____

G1: _____

B: _____

G1: _____

_____

G2: _____

_____

B: _____

G1: 우리 다음 주 금요일에 학급 활동이 있어. 그 날 어떤 것을 하고 싶니?
B: 우리 자원 봉사 활동들을 해 보는 게 어때? 우리가 다른 사람들을 도울 수 있고, 우리의 지역 사회를 더 좋게 만들 수 있어.
G1: 그거 좋다, 하지만 좋은 장소를 고르는 건 쉽지 않아.
B: 우리는 봉사 활동을 많이 해본 사람이 필요해.
G1: 나는 수민이가 봉사 활동을 많이 한 것을 알고 있어. 수민아, 우리가 좋은 장소들을 찾는 것을 도와주겠니?
G2: 물론. 나는 주로 인터넷에서 정보를 찾아. 십대들을 위한 자원 봉사 웹사이트를 확인해 보는 게 어떠니?
B: 좋은 생각이다.

※ 다음 우리말과 일치하도록 빈칸에 알맞은 것을 골라 쓰시오.

1 The _____ of _____
A. Audrey   B. Spirit

2 _____ World War II, a _____ girl and her mother _____ hungry and sick.
A. little   B. during   C. were

3 The only food _____ they could _____ _____ grass.
A. that   B. was   C. find

4 The little girl _____ all the _____.
A. scared   B. felt   C. time

5 _____, the girl survived, _____ _____ the help of others.
A. to   B. luckily   C. thanks

6 One of the _____ that _____ her _____ UNICEF.
A. helped   B. was   C. groups

7 _____, the girl _____ a _____ movie star.
A. worldwide   B. became   C. later

8 _____ _____ was Audrey Hepburn.
A. name   B. her

9 _____ she grew _____, Hepburn became a symbol of _____.
A. beauty   B. up   C. when

10 She was very popular _____ _____ her hit movies, _____ _____ *My Fair Lady* and *Roman Holiday*.
A. of   B. as   C. such   D. because

11 The little black dress _____ she _____ in a movie is famous _____ today.
A. wore   B. even   C. which

12 Many people _____ _____ her _____.
A. style   B. love   C. still

13 The autumn of 1987 was a _____ _____ in Hepburn's _____.
A. life   B. point   C. turning

14 She _____ to an _____ music _____ in Macau.
A. went   B. festival   C. international

15 Many people _____ _____ at the festival, and the money _____ to UNICEF.
A. money   B. went   C. donated

---

1 오드리의 정신

2 제2차 세계 대전 동안, 한 어린 소녀와 그녀의 어머니는 굶주리고 아팠다.

3 그들이 찾을 수 있었던 유일한 음식은 풀뿐이었다.

4 어린 소녀는 내내 겁에 질려 있었다.

5 다행히도, 소녀는 다른 사람들의 도움 덕분에 살아남았다.

6 그녀를 도왔던 단체 중 하나는 유니세프(국제 연합 아동 기금)였다.

7 후에, 소녀는 세계적인 영화배우가 되었다.

8 그녀의 이름은 오드리 헵번이었다.

9 그녀가 자랐을 때, 헵번은 아름다움의 상징이 되었다.

10 그녀는 〈마이 페어 레이디〉와 〈로마의 휴일〉과 같은 흥행 영화들로 인해 매우 인기가 있었다.

11 그녀가 영화에서 입었던 아담한 검은 드레스는 심지어 오늘날까지도 유명하다.

12 많은 사람이 여전히 그녀의 스타일을 사랑한다.

13 1987년 가을은 헵번의 인생 전환점이었다.

14 그녀는 마카오의 한 국제 음악 축제에 갔다.

15 많은 사람이 축제에서 돈을 기부했고, 그 돈은 유니세프로 보내졌다.

16 _____ _____ her fame, UNICEF collected _____ money _____ ever before.

    A. than   B. to   C. more   D. thanks

17 Hepburn _____ that her _____ could help _____, so she became a UNICEF Goodwill Ambassador.

    A. realized   B. others   C. fame

18 First, Hepburn _____ _____ Ethiopia _____ 1988.

    A. to   B. in   C. went

19 _____, she _____ food _____ hungry children.

    A. brought   B. to   C. there

20 She was _____ _____ their _____ were very difficult.

    A. lives   B. because   C. shocked

21 _____ that, she _____ in _____ countries.

    A. after   B. other   C. volunteered

22 In 1990, she _____ Vietnam to _____ _____ medicine and _____ clean drinking water programs.

    A. out   B. visited   C. support   D. hand

23 Her last trip was _____ Somalia in 1992, and she _____ _____ the _____ year.

    A. away   B. to   C. following   D. passed

24 Many people _____ her _____ and style, but Hepburn's _____ was her _____.

    A. beauty   B. heart   C. real   D. praised

25 _____ _____ her, UNICEF made a _____, *The Spirit of Audrey*.

    A. honor   B. statue   C. to

26 People who _____ her _____ her mission _____.

    A. alive   B. keep   C. respect

27 Her _____ _____ shows her _____.

    A. saying   B. favorite   C. mission

28 _____ *you* _____ *older,* _____ *you have two hands.*

    A. remember   B. get   C. as

29 _____ *is for helping* _____, *and the* _____ *is for helping* _____.

    A. other   B. one   C. others   D. yourself

---

16 그녀의 명성 덕분에, 유니세프는 어느 때보다도 더 많은 돈을 모았다.

17 헵번은 자신의 명성이 다른 사람들을 도울 수 있다는 것을 깨닫고, 유니세프 친선 대사가 되었다.

18 먼저, 헵번은 1988년에 에티오피아로 갔다.

19 그곳에서, 그녀는 굶주린 아이들에게 음식을 가져다주었다.

20 그녀는 그들의 삶이 매우 어려웠기 때문에 충격을 받았다.

21 그 후, 그녀는 다른 나라들에서도 봉사하였다.

22 1990년, 그녀는 의약품을 나눠 주고 깨끗한 식수 프로그램을 지원하기 위하여 베트남을 방문하였다.

23 그녀의 마지막 여행은 1992년 소말리아에 간 것이었으며, 이듬해 그녀는 사망하였다.

24 많은 사람이 그녀의 아름다움과 스타일을 칭송했지만, 헵번의 진정한 아름다움은 그녀의 마음이었다.

25 그녀를 기리기 위해, 유니세프는 '오드리의 정신'이라는 동상을 만들었다.

26 그녀를 존경하는 사람들이 그녀의 사명을 이어 나가고 있다.

27 그녀가 가장 좋아했던 구절은 그녀의 사명을 보여 준다.

28 나이가 들어갈수록, 당신에게 손이 두 개가 있다는 것을 기억하라.

29 한 손은 자신을 돕기 위한 것이고, 다른 한 손은 타인을 돕기 위한 것이다.

※ 다음 우리말과 일치하도록 빈칸에 알맞은 말을 쓰시오.

1 The _____ _____ _____

2 _____ World War II, a _____ girl and her mother _____ _____ and _____.

3 _____ _____ food _____ they could find _____ grass.

4 The little girl _____ _____ _____ _____ _____.

5 _____, the girl survived, _____ _____ the help of _____.

6 _____ _____ _____ _____ _____ _____ helped her _____ UNICEF.

7 Later, the girl became _____ _____ _____ _____.

8 _____ _____ _____ Audrey Hepburn.

9 When she _____ _____, Hepburn became _____ _____ _____ _____.

10 She was very popular _____ _____ her hit movies, _____ _____ *My Fair Lady* and *Roman Holiday*.

11 The little black dress _____ _____ _____ in a movie _____ _____ even today.

12 Many people _____ _____ _____ _____.

13 The autumn of 1987 was _____ _____ _____ in Hepburn's life.

14 She went to _____ _____ _____ _____ in Macau.

15 Many people _____ _____ at the festival, and the money went _____ _____.

1 오드리의 정신

2 제2차 세계 대전 동안, 한 어린 소녀와 그녀의 어머니는 굶주리고 아팠다.

3 그들이 찾을 수 있었던 유일한 음식은 풀뿐이었다.

4 어린 소녀는 내내 겁에 질려 있었다.

5 다행히도, 소녀는 다른 사람들의 도움 덕분에 살아남았다.

6 그녀를 도왔던 단체 중 하나는 유니세프(국제 연합 아동 기금)였다.

7 후에, 소녀는 세계적인 영화배우가 되었다.

8 그녀의 이름은 오드리 헵번이었다.

9 그녀가 자랐을 때, 헵번은 아름다움의 상징이 되었다.

10 그녀는 〈마이 페어 레이디〉와 〈로마의 휴일〉과 같은 흥행 영화들로 인해 매우 인기가 있었다.

11 그녀가 영화에서 입었던 아담한 검은 드레스는 심지어 오늘날까지도 유명하다.

12 많은 사람이 여전히 그녀의 스타일을 사랑한다.

13 1987년 가을은 헵번의 인생 전환점이었다.

14 그녀는 마카오의 한 국제 음악 축제에 갔다.

15 많은 사람이 축제에서 돈을 기부했고, 그 돈은 유니세프로 보내졌다.

16 _____ _____ her fame, UNICEF _____ _____ money _____ ever before.

17 Hepburn _____ _____ her fame could _____ _____, so she became _____ _____ _____ _____.

18 First, Hepburn _____ _____ _____ in 1988.

19 There, she _____ food _____ _____ _____.

20 She _____ _____ _____ their _____ were very difficult.

21 After that, she _____ _____ _____ _____.

22 In 1990, she visited Vietnam _____ _____ _____ _____ and _____ clean drinking water programs.

23 Her last trip was _____ Somalia in 1992, and she _____ _____ the _____ _____.

24 Many people _____ her beauty and style, but Hepburn's _____ _____ _____ _____ _____.

25 _____ _____ her, UNICEF _____ _____ _____, *The Spirit of Audrey.*

26 People _____ _____ her _____ her mission _____.

27 Her _____ _____ shows _____ _____.

28 _____ *you* _____ _____, *remember you have two hands.*

29 _____ *is for helping* _____, *and* _____ _____ *is for helping* _____.

16 그녀의 명성 덕분에, 유니세프는 어느 때보다도 더 많은 돈을 모았다.

17 헵번은 자신의 명성이 다른 사람들을 도울 수 있다는 것을 깨닫고, 유니세프 친선 대사가 되었다.

18 먼저, 헵번은 1988년에 에티오피아로 갔다.

19 그곳에서, 그녀는 굶주린 아이들에게 음식을 가져다주었다.

20 그녀는 그들의 삶이 매우 어려웠기 때문에 충격을 받았다.

21 그 후, 그녀는 다른 나라들에서도 봉사하였다.

22 1990년, 그녀는 의약품을 나눠 주고 깨끗한 식수 프로그램을 지원하기 위하여 베트남을 방문하였다.

23 그녀의 마지막 여행은 1992년 소말리아에 간 것이었으며, 이듬해 그녀는 사망하였다.

24 많은 사람이 그녀의 아름다움과 스타일을 칭송했지만, 헵번의 진정한 아름다움은 그녀의 마음이었다.

25 그녀를 기리기 위해, 유니세프는 '오드리의 정신'이라는 동상을 만들었다.

26 그녀를 존경하는 사람들이 그녀의 사명을 이어 나가고 있다.

27 그녀가 가장 좋아했던 구절은 그녀의 사명을 보여 준다.

28 나이가 들어갈수록, 당신에게 손이 두 개가 있다는 것을 기억하라.

29 한 손은 자신을 돕기 위한 것이고, 다른 한 손은 타인을 돕기 위한 것이다.

※ 다음 문장을 우리말로 쓰시오.

1 The Spirit of Audrey

➡ _____

2 During World War II, a little girl and her mother were hungry and sick.

➡ _____

3 The only food that they could find was grass.

➡ _____

4 The little girl felt scared all the time.

➡ _____

5 Luckily, the girl survived, thanks to the help of others.

➡ _____

6 One of the groups that helped her was UNICEF.

➡ _____

7 Later, the girl became a worldwide movie star.

➡ _____

8 Her name was Audrey Hepburn.

➡ _____

9 When she grew up, Hepburn became a symbol of beauty.

➡ _____

10 She was very popular because of her hit movies, such as *My Fair Lady* and *Roman Holiday*.

➡ _____

11 The little black dress which she wore in a movie is famous even today.

➡ _____

12 Many people still love her style.

➡ _____

13 The autumn of 1987 was a turning point in Hepburn's life.

➡ _____

14 She went to an international music festival in Macau.

➡ _____

15 Many people donated money at the festival, and the money went to UNICEF.

➡ _____

16 Thanks to her fame, UNICEF collected more money than ever before.

➡ _____

17 Hepburn realized that her fame could help others, so she became a UNICEF Goodwill Ambassador.

➡ _____

18 First, Hepburn went to Ethiopia in 1988.

➡ _____

19 There, she brought food to hungry children.

➡ _____

20 She was shocked because their lives were very difficult.

➡ _____

21 After that, she volunteered in other countries.

➡ _____

22 In 1990, she visited Vietnam to hand out medicine and support clean drinking water programs.

➡ _____

23 Her last trip was to Somalia in 1992, and she passed away the following year.

➡ _____

24 Many people praised her beauty and style, but Hepburn's real beauty was her heart.

➡ _____

25 To honor her, UNICEF made a statue, *The Spirit of Audrey*.

➡ _____

26 People who respect her keep her mission alive.

➡ _____

27 Her favorite saying shows her mission.

➡ _____

28 *As you get older, remember you have two hands.*

➡ _____

29 *One is for helping yourself, and the other is for helping others.*

➡ _____

※ 다음 괄호 안의 단어들을 우리말에 맞도록 바르게 배열하시오.

1 (Spirit / The / Audrey / of)
➡ _____

2 (World / II, / During / War / little / a / girl / and / mother / her / were / sick. / and / hungry)
➡ _____

3 (only / the / that / food / they / find / could / grass. / was)
➡ _____

4 (little / the / girl / scared / felt / time. / the / all)
➡ _____

5 (the / luckily / girl / survived, / to / thanks / the / of / others. / help)
➡ _____

6 (of / one / groups / the / helped / that / UNICEF. / was / her)
➡ _____

7 (the / later, / girl / became / worldwide / a / star. / movie)
➡ _____

8 (name / her / Hepburn. / Audrey / was)
➡ _____

9 (she / when / up, / grew / became / Hepburn / symbol / a / beauty. / of)
➡ _____

10 (was / she / popular / very / of / because / her / movies, / hit / as / such / *Lady* / *Fair* / *My* / and / *Holiday*. / *Roman*)
➡ _____

11 (little / the / dress / black / she / which / wore / a / in / movie / is / today. / even / famous)
➡ _____

12 (people / many / love / still / style. / her)
➡ _____

13 (autumn / the / 1987 / of / was / turning / a / point / life. / Hepburn's / in)
➡ _____

14 (went / she / to / international / an / festival / music / Macau. / in)
➡ _____

15 (people / many / money / donated / the / at / festival, / and / money / the / UNICEF. / to / went)
➡ _____

---

1 오드리의 정신

2 제2차 세계 대전 동안, 한 어린 소녀와 그녀의 어머니는 굶주리고 아팠다.

3 그들이 찾을 수 있었던 유일한 음식은 풀뿐이었다.

4 어린 소녀는 내내 겁에 질려 있었다.

5 다행히도, 소녀는 다른 사람들의 도움 덕분에 살아남았다.

6 그녀를 도왔던 단체 중 하나는 유니세프(국제 연합 아동 기금)였다.

7 후에, 소녀는 세계적인 영화배우가 되었다.

8 그녀의 이름은 오드리 헵번이었다.

9 그녀가 자랐을 때, 헵번은 아름다움의 상징이 되었다.

10 그녀는 〈마이 페어 레이디〉와 〈로마의 휴일〉과 같은 흥행 영화들로 인해 매우 인기가 있었다.

11 그녀가 영화에서 입었던 아담한 검은 드레스는 심지어 오늘날까지도 유명하다.

12 많은 사람이 여전히 그녀의 스타일을 사랑한다.

13 1987년 가을은 헵번의 인생 전환점이었다.

14 그녀는 마카오의 한 국제 음악 축제에 갔다.

15 많은 사람이 축제에서 돈을 기부했고, 그 돈은 유니세프로 보내졌다.

16 (to / thanks / fame, / her / UNICEF / more / collected / money / ever / before. / than)

➡ _____

17 (realized / Hepburn / that / fame / her / help / could / others, / she / so / became / UNICEF / a / Ambassador. / Goodwill)

➡ _____

18 (Hepburn / first, / to / went / 1988 / in / Ethiopia)

➡ _____

19 (she / there, / brought / to / food / children. / hungry)

➡ _____

20 (was / she / because / shocked / lives / their / difficult. / very / were)

➡ _____

21 (that, / after / volunteered / she / countries. / other / in)

➡ _____

22 (1990, / in / visited / she / Vietnam / hand / to / medicine / out / and / clean / support / drinking / programs. / water)

➡ _____

23 (last / her / trip / to / was / Somalia / 1992, / in / she / and / away / passed / year. / following / the)

➡ _____

24 (people / many / her / praised / beauty / and / style, / but / real / Hepburn's / beauty / heart. / her / was)

➡ _____

25 (honor / to / her, / made / UNICEF / statue, / a / of / Spirit / Audrey. / The)

➡ _____

26 (who / people / her / respect / keep / alive. / mission / her)

➡ _____

27 (favorite / her / shows / mission. / her / saying)

➡ _____

28 (you / as / older, / get / you / remember / hands. / two / have)

➡ _____

29 (is / one / helping / for / yourself, / the / and / other / for / is / others. / helping)

➡ _____

16 그녀의 명성 덕분에, 유니세프는 어느 때보다도 더 많은 돈을 모았다.

17 헵번은 자신의 명성이 다른 사람들을 도울 수 있다는 것을 깨닫고, 유니세프 친선 대사가 되었다.

18 먼저, 헵번은 1988년에 에티오피아로 갔다.

19 그곳에서, 그녀는 굶주린 아이들에게 음식을 가져다주었다.

20 그녀는 그들의 삶이 매우 어려웠기 때문에 충격을 받았다.

21 그 후, 그녀는 다른 나라들에서도 봉사하였다.

22 1990년, 그녀는 의약품을 나눠 주고 깨끗한 식수 프로그램을 지원하기 위하여 베트남을 방문하였다.

23 그녀의 마지막 여행은 1992년 소말리아에 간 것이었으며, 이듬해 그녀는 사망하였다.

24 많은 사람이 그녀의 아름다움과 스타일을 칭송했지만, 헵번의 진정한 아름다움은 그녀의 마음이었다.

25 그녀를 기리기 위해, 유니세프는 '오드리의 정신'이라는 동상을 만들었다.

26 그녀를 존경하는 사람들이 그녀의 사명을 이어 나가고 있다.

27 그녀가 가장 좋아했던 구절은 그녀의 사명을 보여 준다.

28 나이가 들어갈수록, 당신에게 손이 두 개가 있다는 것을 기억하라.

29 한 손은 자신을 돕기 위한 것이고, 다른 한 손은 타인을 돕기 위한 것이다.

※ 다음 우리말을 영어로 쓰시오.

1 오드리의 정신

➡ _____

2 제2차 세계 대전 동안, 한 어린 소녀와 그녀의 어머니는 굶주리고 아팠다.

➡ _____

3 그들이 찾을 수 있었던 유일한 음식은 풀뿐이었다.

➡ _____

4 어린 소녀는 내내 겁에 질려 있었다.

➡ _____

5 다행히도, 소녀는 다른 사람들의 도움 덕분에 살아남았다.

➡ _____

6 그녀를 도왔던 단체 중 하나는 유니세프(국제 연합 아동 기금)였다.

➡ _____

7 후에, 소녀는 세계적인 영화배우가 되었다.

➡ _____

8 그녀의 이름은 오드리 헵번이었다.

➡ _____

9 그녀가 자랐을 때, 헵번은 아름다움의 상징이 되었다.

➡ _____

10 그녀는 〈마이 페어 레이디〉와 〈로마의 휴일〉과 같은 흥행 영화들로 인해 매우 인기가 있었다.

➡ _____

11 그녀가 영화에서 입었던 아담한 검은 드레스는 심지어 오늘날까지도 유명하다.

➡ _____

12 많은 사람이 여전히 그녀의 스타일을 사랑한다.

➡ _____

13 1987년 가을은 헵번의 인생 전환점이었다.

➡ _____

14 그녀는 마카오의 한 국제 음악 축제에 갔다.

➡ _____

15 많은 사람이 축제에서 돈을 기부했고, 그 돈은 유니세프로 보내졌다.

➡ _____

16 그녀의 명성 덕분에, 유니세프는 어느 때보다도 더 많은 돈을 모았다.

➡ _____

17 헵번은 자신의 명성이 다른 사람들을 도울 수 있다는 것을 깨닫고, 유니세프 친선 대사가 되었다.

➡ _____

18 먼저, 헵번은 1988년에 에티오피아로 갔다.

➡ _____

19 그곳에서, 그녀는 굶주린 아이들에게 음식을 가져다주었다.

➡ _____

20 그녀는 그들의 삶이 매우 어려웠기 때문에 충격을 받았다.

➡ _____

21 그 후, 그녀는 다른 나라들에서도 봉사하였다.

➡ _____

22 1990년, 그녀는 의약품을 나눠 주고 깨끗한 식수 프로그램을 지원하기 위하여 베트남을 방문하였다.

➡ _____

23 그녀의 마지막 여행은 1992년 소말리아에 간 것이었으며, 이듬해 그녀는 사망하였다.

➡ _____

24 많은 사람이 그녀의 아름다움과 스타일을 칭송했지만, 헵번의 진정한 아름다움은 그녀의 마음이었다.

➡ _____

25 그녀를 기리기 위해, 유니세프는 '오드리의 정신'이라는 동상을 만들었다.

➡ _____

26 그녀를 존경하는 사람들이 그녀의 사명을 이어 나가고 있다.

➡ _____

27 그녀가 가장 좋아했던 구절은 그녀의 사명을 보여 준다.

➡ _____

28 나이가 들어갈수록, 당신에게 손이 두 개가 있다는 것을 기억하라.

➡ _____

29 한 손은 자신을 돕기 위한 것이고, 다른 한 손은 타인을 돕기 위한 것이다.

➡ _____

※ 다음 우리말과 일치하도록 빈칸에 알맞은 말을 쓰시오.

Presentation Time

1. Lee Taeseok was _____ _____ _____.

2. He was a _____ and _____ a doctor.

3. He _____ hospitals and schools _____ the people of Tonj.

4. He _____ _____ _____ them and _____ _____.

5. _____ this person, I learned _____ I _____ _____ people _____ _____.

1. 이태석은 위대한 사람이었다.
2. 그는 성직자이고 또한 의사였다.
3. 그는 톤즈의 사람들을 위해 병원과 학교를 세웠다.
4. 그는 그들을 돌보고 수업을 했다.
5. 이 사람으로부터, 나는 어려움에 처한 사람들을 도와야 한다고 배웠다.

After You Read B

1. Reporter: _____ was your life _____ World War II?

2. Can you _____ _____ _____ it?

3. Audrey: It was _____. My family and I _____ _____ and _____.

4. We _____ _____ _____ the help of _____.

5. Reporter: How did you _____ _____ _____ for UNICEF?

6. Audrey: In 1987, a musical festival in Macau _____ _____ _____.

7. I learned _____ my fame _____ _____ _____ _____.

8. Reporter: _____ _____, what _____ you _____?

9. Audrey: I _____ _____ _____ in Africa and Asia and _____ _____.

1. 리포터: 제2차 세계 대전 동안 당신의 삶은 어땠습니까?
2. 그것에 대해 말해주실 수 있나요?
3. 오드리: 끔찍했어요. 제 가족과 저는 굶주리고 아팠어요.
4. 우리는 다른 사람들의 도움 덕분에 살아남았어요.
5. 리포터: 당신은 어떻게 유니세프를 위해 일하게 되었나요?
6. 오드리: 1987년에, 마카오의 한 음악 축제가 제 삶을 바꿨어요.
7. 저는 제 명성이 다른 사람들을 도울 수 있다는 것을 알게 되었어요.
8. 리포터: 그 다음에, 무엇을 했나요?
9. 오드리: 아프리카와 아시아의 몇몇 나라들을 방문해서 그곳에서 자원 봉사를 했어요.

Culture Link

1. _____ _____ Program

2. This is a _____ _____ _____ audiobooks for _____ people.

3. It _____ _____ in 1931 in the United States.

4. You just read books and _____ _____ _____.

5. These audiobooks _____ _____ to blind people _____ _____.

1. 말하는 책 프로그램
2. 이것은 시각장애인을 위한 오디오북을 만드는 프로그램이다.
3. 이것은 1931년 미국에서 시작되었다.
4. 당신은 책을 읽고 당신의 목소리를 녹음하기만 하면 된다.
5. 이러한 오디오북들은 시각장애인들에게 무료로 주어진다.

※ 다음 우리말을 영어로 쓰시오.

Presentation Time

1. 이태석은 위대한 사람이었다.
➡ _____

2. 그는 성직자이고 또한 의사였다.
➡ _____

3. 그는 톤즈의 사람들을 위해 병원과 학교를 세웠다.
➡ _____

4. 그는 그들을 돌보고 수업을 했다.
➡ _____

5. 이 사람으로부터, 나는 어려움에 처한 사람들을 도와야 한다고 배웠다.
➡ _____

After You Read B

1. 리포터: 제2차 세계 대전 동안 당신의 삶은 어땠습니까?
➡ _____

2. 그것에 대해 말해주실 수 있나요?
➡ _____

3. 오드리: 끔찍했어요. 제 가족과 저는 굶주리고 아팠어요.
➡ _____

4. 우리는 다른 사람들의 도움 덕분에 살아남았어요.
➡ _____

5. 리포터: 당신은 어떻게 유니세프를 위해 일하게 되었나요?
➡ _____

6. 오드리: 1987년에, 마카오의 한 음악 축제가 제 삶을 바꿨어요.
➡ _____

7. 저는 제 명성이 다른 사람들을 도울 수 있다는 것을 알게 되었어요.
➡ _____

8. 리포터: 그 다음에, 무엇을 했나요?
➡ _____

9. 오드리: 아프리카와 아시아의 몇몇 나라들을 방문해서 그곳에서 자원 봉사를 했어요.
➡ _____

Culture Link

1. 말하는 책 프로그램
➡ _____

2. 이것은 시각장애인을 위한 오디오북을 만드는 프로그램이다.
➡ _____

3. 이것은 1931년 미국에서 시작되었다.
➡ _____

4. 당신은 책을 읽고 당신의 목소리를 녹음하기만 하면 된다.
➡ _____

5. 이러한 오디오북들은 시각장애인들에게 무료로 주어진다.
➡ _____

※ 다음 영어를 우리말로 쓰시오.

01 presentation _____

02 view _____

03 relax _____

04 awesome _____

05 stop _____

06 comic book _____

07 condition _____

08 field trip _____

09 amazing _____

10 art museum _____

11 history _____

12 purpose _____

13 amusement park _____

14 foreign _____

15 street food _____

16 hike _____

17 straight _____

18 holiday _____

19 international _____

20 village _____

21 art show _____

22 historical _____

23 site _____

24 natural _____

25 painting _____

26 goods _____

27 plan _____

28 rafting _____

29 autumn _____

30 rough _____

31 scenery _____

32 university _____

33 museum _____

34 visit _____

35 at the same time _____

36 on foot _____

37 be able to 동사원형 _____

38 get off _____

39 no longer _____

40 a variety of _____

41 focus on _____

42 in front of _____

43 by bus _____

※ 다음 우리말을 영어로 쓰시오.

01 만화책

02 풍경, 경치

03 국제적인

04 똑바로, 일직선으로

05 상태, 상황

06 발표

07 박물관

08 놀라운, 멋진

09 미술관

10 전망

11 정거장, (여행 중) 머무른 곳

12 거친, 파도가 심한

13 견학 여행, 현장 학습

14 도보 여행하다

15 휴식을 취하다, 느긋이 쉬다

16 역사

17 마을

18 외국의

19 대학교

20 목적, 목표

21 가을

22 방문하다, 찾아가다

23 역사적인, 역사상의

24 장소

25 휴가, 공휴일, 휴일

26 놀이공원

27 길거리 음식

28 상품, 물건

29 미술 전시회

30 자연의

31 래프팅, 급류 타기

32 매우 멋진

33 그림

34 계획하다; 계획

35 (~에) 집중하다, 초점을 맞추다

36 걸어서, 도보로

37 내리다, 하차하다

38 여러 가지의, 다양한

39 버스로

40 ~ 앞에서

41 더 이상 ~하지 않는

42 ~할 수 있다

43 동시에, 한꺼번에

※ 다음 영영풀이에 알맞은 단어를 <보기>에서 골라 쓴 후, 우리말 뜻을 쓰시오.

1　_____ : the state of something: _____

2　_____ : wonderful or impressive: _____

3　_____ : products for sale: _____

4　_____ : a beautiful view of nature: _____

5　_____ : a place that has many games and rides: _____

6　_____ : the season after summer and before winter: _____

7　_____ : not to do anything: _____

8　_____ : a large sports field: _____

9　_____ : from another country: _____

10　_____ : events that have happened in the past: _____

11　_____ : the reason why something is used or done: _____

12　_____ : having a bumpy surface: _____

13　_____ : traveling down a river in a small, flat boat: _____

14　_____ : a place where one stops during a trip: _____

15　_____ : a visit made by students and teachers to learn about something:
_____

16　_____ : a building where historical or artistic objects are displayed: _____

foreign	awesome	stadium	history
goods	purpose	scenery	stop
field trip	relax	autumn	condition
rough	museum	rafting	amusement park

※ 다음 우리말과 일치하도록 빈칸에 알맞은 말을 쓰시오.

Listen & Talk 1 A

B: _____ _____ _____ going to do _____ _____?

G: I'm _____ _____ _____ to Jeju-do.

B: _____ are _____ _____ _____ there?

G: _____ _____ _____ go hiking on Hallasan.

Listen & Talk 1 B

B: We _____ a long holiday _____ month. Do you _____ _____ plans?

G: I'm _____ to visit my grandparents in Jeonju.

B: Oh, really? That's nice. _____ are you _____ _____ do _____ them?

G: _____ _____ to go to Hanok Village _____ _____. How _____ you? What are your _____ _____ the holiday?

B: I'm _____ to _____ _____ and _____.

G: That's also a _____ _____!

Listen & Talk 1 C

B: Hi, Nuri. _____ is your class going for the _____ _____ tomorrow?

G: Hello, Mike. _____ _____ _____ _____ the art museum.

B: Sounds _____. What are you _____ _____ _____ there?

G: There _____ three art shows _____ _____. _____ _____ Vincent van Gogh's paintings. _____ is your class _____?

B: _____ _____ _____ _____ the _____ park. I'm _____ _____ a roller coaster!

G: That _____ _____. Have a _____ _____!

Listen & Talk 2 A

G: _____ do you _____ _____ _____?

B: I go to school _____ _____.

G: _____ does it _____ _____ _____ there?

B: _____ 15 minutes.

Listen & Talk 2 B

B: Wow, these _____ are so _____. _____ did you _____ them?

G: At Riverside Park. There _____ _____ _____ flowers. You _____ go there!

B: I want _____. _____ do I _____ there _____ our school?

G: _____ _____ bus number 135 and _____ _____ at the Riverside Stadium stop. You can _____ the park _____ _____ _____ the bus stop.

B: How _____ does it _____ _____ _____ there?

G: It _____ 30 _____.

B: Thanks. I'll go there _____ _____.

Listen & Talk 2 C

B: Excuse me. _____ _____ _____ _____ _____ _____ _____ Hanguk University from here?

W: You can _____ _____ _____ _____ _____ _____ _____ _____.

B: _____ _____ does it _____ _____ _____ _____ there?

W: It takes five minutes _____ bus and 20 minutes _____ _____.

B: Oh, then I _____ _____ there. _____ _____ me _____ _____ _____ there?

W: _____ _____ for two blocks, and then _____ left. You will see Hanguk University _____ _____ _____.

B: _____ straight _____ two blocks and _____ _____. Thank you!

Do It Yourself A

G: _____ are you _____ _____ _____ _____ _____ weekend?

B: I'm planning _____ _____ _____ a baseball game in Daegu.

G: _____ _____ going _____ _____ the All-Star Game?

B: Yes. It _____ be fun. Also, _____ _____ _____ my friend there.

G: Nice. _____ _____ does it take _____ _____ there?

B: It takes _____ express train.

G: Wow, it's _____ _____ _____ I thought. I hope you a _____!

B: Thank you.

남: 와, 이 사진들 너무 예쁘다. 어디서 찍었어?

여: Riverside Park에서. 꽃이 많았어. 넌 거기 꼭 가 봐야 해!

남: 나도 가고 싶어. 학교에서 거기까지 어떻게 가니?

여: 135번 버스를 타고 Riverside Stadium 정류장에서 내리면 돼. 버스 정류장 앞에 공원이 보일 거야.

남: 거기까지 가는 데 얼마나 걸려?

여: 30분 걸려.

남: 고마워. 다음 주말에 그곳에 가야겠다.

남: 실례합니다. 여기서 한국 대학교까지 어떻게 가나요?

여: 버스 타고 가거나 걸어서 갈 수 있어요.

남: 거기까지 가는 데 얼마나 걸리나요?

여: 버스 타면 5분 걸리고, 걸어서는 20분 걸려요.

남: 아, 그러면 걸어서 갈래요. 어떻게 가는지 말해 줄 수 있나요?

여: 2블록 직진한 다음에 좌회전하세요. 그러면 오른쪽에 한국 대학교가 보일 거예요.

남: 2블록 직진해서 좌회전이요. 감사합니다!

여: 이번 주말에 너는 무엇을 할 계획이니?

남: 나는 대구에 야구 경기를 보러 갈 계획이야.

여: 올 스타 경기를 보러 갈 예정이야?

남: 응. 재미있을 거야. 또한, 그곳에서 내 친구를 만날 계획이야.

여: 좋다. 거기까지 가는 데 얼마나 걸리니?

남: 급행열차로 1시간 40분이 걸려.

여: 와, 내가 생각한 것보다 훨씬 더 빠르다. 즐거운 여행이 되길 바랄게.

남: 고마워.

※ 다음 우리말에 맞도록 대화를 영어로 쓰시오.

Listen & Talk 1 A

B: _____

G: _____

B: _____

G: _____

남: 너 이번 주말에 뭐 할 거야?
여: 제주도에 갈 거야.
남: 거기서 뭐 할 계획이야?
여: 한라산에 올라갈 계획이야.

Listen & Talk 1 B

B: _____

G: _____

B: _____

G: _____

B: _____

G: _____

남: 우리 이번 달에 긴 휴가가 있어. 무슨 계획이라도 있니?
여: 나는 전주에 있는 나의 조부모님을 방문할 예정이야.
남: 아, 그래? 좋다. 그분들과 어떤 것을 할 계획이야?
여: 그분들과 한옥 마을에 갈 계획이야. 너는 어때? 휴가 때 무슨 계획 있어?
남: 나는 집에 머물면서 쉴 거야.
여: 그것도 좋은 아이디어다!

Listen & Talk 1 C

B: _____

G: _____

B: _____

G: _____

B: _____

G: _____

남: 안녕, 누리야. 너희 반은 내일 현장 학습으로 어디 가니?
여: 안녕, 마이크. 우리는 미술관에 갈 거야.
남: 재미있겠다. 너 거기서 뭐 볼 계획이니?
여: 지금 3개의 전시회가 있어. 나는 빈센트 반 고흐의 그림을 볼 거야. 너희 반은 어디로 가니?
남: 우리는 놀이동산에 갈 거야. 롤러 코스터를 타게 되어 신나!
여: 재미있겠다. 좋은 여행하길 바라!

Listen & Talk 2 A

G: _____

B: _____

G: _____

B: _____

여: 너 학교에 어떻게 가니?
남: 버스 타고 가.
여: 거기까지 가는 데 얼마나 걸려?
남: 15분 걸려.

Listen & Talk 2 B

B: _____

G: _____

B: _____

G: _____
_____

B: _____

G: _____

B: _____

남: 와, 이 사진들 너무 예쁘다. 어디서 찍었어?

여: Riverside Park에서. 꽃이 많았어. 넌 거기 꼭 가 봐야 해!

남: 나도 가고 싶어. 학교에서 거기까지 어떻게 가니?

여: 135번 버스를 타고 Riverside Stadium 정류장에서 내리면 돼. 버스 정류장 앞에 공원이 보일 거야.

남: 거기까지 가는 데 얼마나 걸려?

여: 30분 걸려.

남: 고마워. 다음 주말에 그곳에 가야겠다.

Listen & Talk 2 C

B: _____

W: _____

B: _____

W: _____

B: _____

W: _____
_____

B: _____

남: 실례합니다. 여기서 한국 대학교까지 어떻게 가나요?

여: 버스 타고 가거나 걸어서 갈 수 있어요.

남: 거기까지 가는 데 얼마나 걸리나요?

여: 버스 타면 5분 걸리고, 걸어서는 20분 걸려요.

남: 아, 그러면 걸어서 갈래요. 어떻게 가는지 말해 줄 수 있나요?

여: 2블록 직진한 다음에 좌회전하세요. 그러면 오른쪽에 한국 대학교가 보일 거예요.

남: 2블록 직진해서 좌회전이요. 감사합니다!

Do It Yourself A

G: _____

B: _____

G: _____

B: _____

G: _____

B: _____

G: _____

B: _____

여: 이번 주말에 너는 무엇을 할 계획이니?

남: 나는 대구에 야구 경기를 보러 갈 계획이야.

여: 올 스타 경기를 보러 갈 예정이야?

남: 응. 재미있을 거야. 또한, 그곳에서 내 친구를 만날 계획이야.

여: 좋다. 거기까지 가는 데 얼마나 걸리니?

남: 급행열차로 1시간 40분이 걸려.

여: 와, 내가 생각한 것보다 훨씬 더 빠르다. 즐거운 여행이 되길 바랄게.

남: 고마워.

※ 다음 우리말과 일치하도록 빈칸에 알맞은 것을 골라 쓰시오.

1 The _____ _____ of the _____ Trip
  A. Field   B. Moment   C. Best

2 Teacher: Good morning, everyone! _____ were your field _____ last week? Please _____ _____ about them!
  A. how   B. tell   C. trips   D. us

3 Busan, _____ _____
  A. Heaven   B. Market

4 Do you like _____ _____?
  A. markets   B. traditional

5 _____ _____ to Gukje Market _____ Busan.
  A. go   B. in   C. then

6 It is _____ of the _____ _____ _____ in Busan.
  A. most   B. one   C. markets   D. famous

7 Do you know _____ it is _____ _____?
  A. for   B. what   C. famous

8 It is famous for _____ a _____ _____ goods from _____ countries.
  A. different   B. variety   C. selling   D. of

9 It was _____ to see _____ the _____ _____ there.
  A. international   B. interesting   C. goods   D. all

10 We also ate many _____ _____ street food, _____ _____ *Gimbap*, fish cake, and *Hotteok*.
  A. kinds   B. as   C. of   D. such

11 _____ we _____ _____ Bosu-dong Book Street.
  A. walked   B. then   C. to

12 _____ _____ there sell _____ _____.
  A. used   B. many   C. bookstores   D. books

13 We were really _____ _____ we _____ some old comic books!
  A. found   B. excited   C. because

14 It was _____ to _____ in a café and _____ them.
  A. relax   B. nice   C. read

15 Gangwon-do, _____ of _____
  A. Beauty   B. Full   C. Natural

16 There is no _____ _____ Gangwon-do for beautiful _____.
  A. nature   B. like   C. place

17 _____, we _____ _____ Baengnyong Cave.
  A. went   B. to   C. first

18 This 1.8-kilometer-long _____ is still _____ good _____.
  A. condition   B. in   C. cave

19 It was so _____ to see its _____ _____.
  A. beauty   B. amazing   C. natural

1 수학여행에서의 가장 좋았던 순간

2 교사: 안녕하세요, 여러분! 지난 주 수학여행은 어땠나요? 얘기해 봅시다!

3 부산, 시장 천국

4 전통 시장을 좋아하세요?

5 그렇다면 부산에 있는 국제시장으로 가세요.

6 그곳은 부산에서 가장 유명한 시장 중 하나입니다.

7 그곳이 무엇으로 유명한지 아세요?

8 그 시장은 여러 나라에서 온 다양한 제품들을 파는 것으로 유명합니다.

9 그곳에서 세계 곳곳의 제품들을 모두 볼 수 있어서 흥미로웠습니다.

10 우리는 또한 김밥, 어묵 그리고 호떡과 같은 여러 종류의 길거리 음식을 먹었습니다.

11 그러고 나서 우리는 보수동 책방 거리로 걸어갔습니다.

12 그곳의 많은 서점에서는 중고 책을 팝니다.

13 우리는 몇 권의 오래된 만화책을 발견해서 정말 신이 났습니다!

14 카페에서 휴식을 취하며 그 책들을 읽는 것이 좋았습니다.

15 강원도, 자연의 아름다움으로 가득한 곳

16 아름다운 자연에 관한 한 강원도만 한 곳이 없습니다.

17 우선, 우리는 백룡동굴로 갔습니다.

18 이 1.8킬로미터 길이의 동굴은 여전히 잘 보존된 상태입니다.

19 그곳의 자연의 아름다움을 보는 것은 매우 놀라웠습니다.

20 _____ the end of our cave tour, the guide _____ _____ the lights in the cave for a _____.

  A. off   B. minute   C. turned   D. near

21 Everything _____ very dark, so we were _____ to _____ the sounds there.

  A. able   B. became   C. focus   D. on

22 It was the _____ _____ _____ of the tour!

  A. experience B. most   C. amazing

23 _____ _____ _____ was Donggang.

  A. stop   B. next   C. our

24 We _____ _____ !

  A. rafting   B. went

25 It was _____ to ride on the _____ water and enjoy the _____ at the _____ time.

  A. rough   B. exciting   C. same   D. view

26 Incheon, A _____ _____ _____

  A. Firsts   B. of   C. City

27 Do you know _____ the _____ train station in Korea _____ ?

  A. is   B. first   C. where

28 _____ _____ the first _Jajangmyeon_?

  A. about   B. how

29 The _____ _____ Incheon!

  A. answer   B. is

30 This _____ has _____ of Korea's _____.

  A. firsts   B. many   C. place

31 _____ _____ there, we _____ to Incheon Station.

  A. get   B. went   C. to

32 The Jajangmyeon Museum is _____ _____ the _____.

  A. station   B. to   C. next

33 We _____ the _____ of _Jajangmyeon_ there.

  A. history   B. learned   C. about

34 Later, we _____ Jayu Park, the first _____ park in Korea.

  A. around   B. Western-style C. walked

35 The _____ _____ the park was _____ !

  A. from   B. awesome   C. view

36 It was _____ to see the _____ _____ of this city from the park.

  A. great   B. sites   C. historical

37 Teacher: Wow, these _____ _____ _____ !

  A. great   B. sound   C. places

38 You _____ have _____ a wonderful job _____ your _____ !

  A. presentations B. done   C. on   D. all

20 동굴 관광의 끝 무렵, 안내인이 동굴 안의 불을 잠시 껐습니다.

21 모든 것이 매우 어두워져서, 우리는 그곳의 소리에 집중할 수 있었습니다.

22 그것은 여행에서 가장 경이로운 경험이었습니다!

23 우리의 다음 여행지는 동강이었습니다.

24 우리는 래프팅을 하러 갔습니다!

25 급류를 타면서 동시에 경치를 즐기는 것은 흥미진진했습니다.

26 인천, '최초의 것'들의 도시

27 한국 최초의 기차역이 어디인지 아세요?

28 첫 번째 자장면은요?

29 그 답은 인천입니다!

30 이곳에는 한국의 최초의 것들이 많이 있습니다.

31 그곳으로 가기 위하여, 우리는 인천역으로 갔습니다.

32 자장면 박물관은 역 옆에 있습니다.

33 우리는 그곳에서 자장면의 역사에 대하여 배웠습니다.

34 다음에는, 한국 최초의 서구식 공원인 자유 공원을 거닐었습니다.

35 공원에서 바라본 경치는 정말 멋있었습니다!

36 공원에서 이 도시의 역사적인 장소들을 바라보는 것은 아주 좋았습니다.

37 교사: 와, 이 장소들은 멋지게 들리네요!

38 여러분 모두 발표를 훌륭하게 잘했어요!

※ 다음 우리말과 일치하도록 빈칸에 알맞은 말을 쓰시오.

1 _____ _____ _____ of the _____ _____

2 Teacher: Good morning, everyone! _____ _____ your field trips _____ _____? _____ _____ _____ about them!

3 Busan, _____ _____

4 Do you like _____ _____?

5 _____ _____ _____ Gukje Market in Busan.

6 It is _____ _____ _____ _____ _____ _____ in Busan.

7 Do you know _____ _____ _____ _____ _____ _____?

8 It _____ _____ _____ selling _____ _____ _____ from different countries.

9 _____ was interesting _____ _____ _____ _____ _____ there.

10 We _____ _____ _____ _____ _____ _____ street food, _____ _____ Gimbap, fish cake, and Hotteok.

11 _____ we _____ _____ Bosu-dong Book Street.

12 Many bookstores there _____ _____ _____.

13 We were _____ _____ _____ we _____ some old comic books!

14 It was nice _____ _____ in a café and _____ them.

15 Gangwon-do, _____ _____

16 There is _____ _____ _____ Gangwon-do for _____ _____.

17 _____, we _____ _____ Baengnyong Cave.

18 This 1.8-kilometer-long cave is still _____ _____.

19 It was _____ _____ to see its _____ _____.

1 수학여행에서의 가장 좋았던 순간

2 교사: 안녕하세요, 여러분! 지난 주 수학여행은 어땠나요? 얘기해 봅시다!

3 부산, 시장 천국

4 전통 시장을 좋아하세요?

5 그렇다면 부산에 있는 국제시장으로 가세요.

6 그곳은 부산에서 가장 유명한 시장 중 하나입니다.

7 그곳이 무엇으로 유명한지 아세요?

8 그 시장은 여러 나라에서 온 다양한 제품들을 파는 것으로 유명합니다.

9 그곳에서 세계 곳곳의 제품들을 모두 볼 수 있어서 흥미로웠습니다.

10 우리는 또한 김밥, 어묵 그리고 호떡과 같은 여러 종류의 길거리 음식을 먹었습니다.

11 그러고 나서 우리는 보수동 책방 거리로 걸어갔습니다.

12 그곳의 많은 서점에서는 중고 책을 팝니다.

13 우리는 몇 권의 오래된 만화책을 발견해서 정말 신이 났습니다!

14 카페에서 휴식을 취하며 그 책들을 읽는 것이 좋았습니다.

15 강원도, 자연의 아름다움으로 가득한 곳

16 아름다운 자연에 관한 한 강원도만 한 곳이 없습니다.

17 우신, 우리는 백룡동굴로 갔습니다.

18 이 1.8킬로미터 길이의 동굴은 여전히 잘 보존된 상태입니다.

19 그곳의 자연의 아름다움을 보는 것은 매우 놀라웠습니다.

20 Near the end of our _____ _____, the guide _____
_____ the lights in the cave _____ _____ _____.

21 Everything became very dark, so we _____ _____ _____
_____ _____ the sounds there.

22 It was _____ _____ _____ _____ of the tour!

23 _____ _____ _____ was Donggang.

24 We _____ _____!

25 It was _____ _____ _____ on the rough water and enjoy
the view _____ _____ _____ _____.

26 Incheon, A City of _____

27 Do you know _____ the first train station in Korea _____ ?

28 _____ _____ the first *Jajangmyeon*?

29 _____ _____ is Incheon!

30 This place has _____ _____ _____ _____ _____.

31 _____ _____ _____ , we _____ to Incheon Station.

32 The Jajangmyeon Museum is _____ _____ the station.

33 We learned about _____ _____ _____ _____ there.

34 Later, we walked around Jayu Park, _____ _____ _____
_____ in Korea.

35 The _____ _____ the park was _____!

36 It was great _____ _____ _____ _____ _____ of
this city from the park.

37 Teacher: Wow, these places _____ _____!

38 You all have done a wonderful job _____ _____ _____!

---

20 동굴 관광의 끝 무렵, 안내인이 동굴 안의 불을 잠시 껐습니다.

21 모든 것이 매우 어두워져서, 우리는 그곳의 소리에 집중할 수 있었습니다.

22 그것은 여행에서 가장 경이로운 경험이었습니다!

23 우리의 다음 여행지는 동강이었습니다.

24 우리는 래프팅을 하러 갔습니다!

25 급류를 타면서 동시에 경치를 즐기는 것은 흥미진진했습니다.

26 인천, '최초의 것'들의 도시

27 한국 최초의 기차역이 어디인지 아세요?

28 첫 번째 자장면은요?

29 그 답은 인천입니다!

30 이곳에는 한국의 최초의 것들이 많이 있습니다.

31 그곳으로 가기 위하여, 우리는 인천역으로 갔습니다.

32 자장면 박물관은 역 옆에 있습니다.

33 우리는 그곳에서 자장면의 역사에 대하여 배웠습니다.

34 다음에는, 한국 최초의 서구식 공원인 자유 공원을 거닐었습니다.

35 공원에서 바라본 경치는 정말 멋있었습니다!

36 공원에서 이 도시의 역사적인 장소들을 바라보는 것은 아주 좋았습니다.

37 교사: 와, 이 장소들은 멋지게 들리네요!

38 여러분 모두 발표를 훌륭하게 잘했어요!

※ 다음 문장을 우리말로 쓰시오.

1 ▶ The Best Moment of the Field Trip
➡ _____

2 ▶ Teacher: Good morning, everyone! How were your field trips last week? Please tell us about them!
➡ _____

3 ▶ Busan, Market Heaven
➡ _____

4 ▶ Do you like traditional markets?
➡ _____

5 ▶ Then go to Gukje Market in Busan.
➡ _____

6 ▶ It is one of the most famous markets in Busan.
➡ _____

7 ▶ Do you know what it is famous for?
➡ _____

8 ▶ It is famous for selling a variety of goods from different countries.
➡ _____

9 ▶ It was interesting to see all the international goods there.
➡ _____

10 ▶ We also ate many kinds of street food, such as *Gimbap*, fish cake, and *Hotteok*.
➡ _____

11 ▶ Then we walked to Bosu-dong Book Street.
➡ _____

12 ▶ Many bookstores there sell used books.
➡ _____

13 ▶ We were really excited because we found some old comic books!
➡ _____

14 ▶ It was nice to relax in a café and read them.
➡ _____

15 ▶ Gangwon-do, Full of Natural Beauty
➡ _____

16 ▶ There is no place like Gangwon-do for beautiful nature.
➡ _____

17 ▶ First, we went to Baengnyong Cave.
➡ _____

18 ▶ This 1.8-kilometer-long cave is still in good condition.
➡ _____

19 ▶ It was so amazing to see its natural beauty.
➡ _____

20 ▶ Near the end of our cave tour, the guide turned off the lights in the cave for a minute.

➡ _____

21 ▶ Everything became very dark, so we were able to focus on the sounds there.

➡ _____

22 ▶ It was the most amazing experience of the tour!

➡ _____

23 ▶ Our next stop was Donggang.

➡ _____

24 ▶ We went rafting!

➡ _____

25 ▶ It was exciting to ride on the rough water and enjoy the view at the same time.

➡ _____

26 ▶ Incheon, A City of Firsts

➡ _____

27 ▶ Do you know where the first train station in Korea is?

➡ _____

28 ▶ How about the first *Jajangmyeon*?

➡ _____

29 ▶ The answer is Incheon!

➡ _____

30 ▶ This place has many of Korea's firsts.

➡ _____

31 ▶ To get there, we went to Incheon Station.

➡ _____

32 ▶ The Jajangmyeon Museum is next to the station.

➡ _____

33 ▶ We learned about the history of *Jajangmyeon* there.

➡ _____

34 ▶ Later, we walked around Jayu Park, the first Western-style park in Korea.

➡ _____

35 ▶ The view from the park was awesome!

➡ _____

36 ▶ It was great to see the historical sites of this city from the park.

➡ _____

37 ▶ Teacher: Wow, these places sound great!

➡ _____

38 ▶ You all have done a wonderful job on your presentations!

➡ _____

※ 다음 괄호 안의 단어들을 우리말에 맞도록 바르게 배열하시오.

1 (Best / of / Moment / The / Trip / Field / the)
➡ _____

2 (Teacher: / morning, / good / everyone! // were / how / field / your / week? / last / trips // tell / please / about / us / them!)
➡ _____

3 (Busan, / Heaven / Market)
➡ _____

4 (like / you / do / markets? / traditional)
➡ _____

5 (go / then / Gukje / to / Busan. / in / Market)
➡ _____

6 (is / it / of / one / the / famous / most / Busan. / in / markets)
➡ _____

7 (know / you / do / it / what / for? / famous / is)
➡ _____

8 (is / it / for / famous / selling / variety / a / goods / of / countries. / different / from)
➡ _____

9 (was / it / to / interesting / see / the / all / there. / goods / international)
➡ _____

10 (also / we / many / ate / kinds / of / food, / street / as / such / *Gimbap*, / cake, / fish / *Hotteok*. / and)
➡ _____

11 (we / then / to / walked / Book / Street. / Bosu-dong)
➡ _____

12 (bookstores / many / sell / there / books. / used)
➡ _____

13 (were / we / excited / really / we / because / some / found / books! / comic / old)
➡ _____

14 (was / it / to / nice / in / relax / a / café / and / them. / read)
➡ _____

15 (Full / Gangwon-do, / Beauty / Natural / of)
➡ _____

16 (is / there / place / no / Gangwon-do / like / nature. / beautiful / for)
➡ _____

17 (we / first, / to / went / Cave. / Baengnyong)
➡ _____

18 (1.8-kilometer-long / is / this / cave / in / still / condition. / good)
➡ _____

19 (was / it / amazing / so / see / to / its / beauty. / natural)
➡

1 수학여행에서의 가장 좋았던 순간

2 교사: 안녕하세요, 여러분! 지난 주 수학여행은 어땠나요? 얘기해 봅시다!

3 부산, 시장 천국

4 전통 시장을 좋아하세요?

5 그렇다면 부산에 있는 국제시장으로 가세요.

6 그곳은 부산에서 가장 유명한 시장 중 하나입니다.

7 그곳이 무엇으로 유명한지 아세요?

8 그 시장은 여러 나라에서 온 다양한 제품들을 파는 것으로 유명합니다.

9 그곳에서 세계 곳곳의 제품들을 모두 볼 수 있어서 흥미로웠습니다.

10 우리는 또한 김밥, 어묵 그리고 호떡과 같은 여러 종류의 길거리 음식을 먹었습니다.

11 그러고 나서 우리는 보수동 책방 거리로 걸어갔습니다.

12 그곳의 많은 서점에서는 중고 책을 팝니다.

13 우리는 몇 권의 오래된 만화책을 발견해서 정말 신이 났습니다!

14 카페에서 휴식을 취하며 그 책들을 읽는 것이 좋았습니다.

15 강원도, 자연의 아름다움으로 가득한 곳

16 아름다운 자연에 관한 한 강원도만 한 곳이 없습니다.

17 우선, 우리는 백룡동굴로 갔습니다.

18 이 1.8킬로미터 길이의 동굴은 여전히 잘 보존된 상태입니다.

19 그곳의 자연의 아름다움을 보는 것은 매우 놀라웠습니다.

20 (the / near / end / our / of / tour, / cave / guide / the / off / turned / lights / the / the / in / cave / minute. / a / for)
➡ _____

21 (became / everythiing / dark, / very / we / so / able / were / to / on / focus / the / there. / sounds)
➡ _____

22 (was / is / most / the / amazing / of / experience / tour! / the)
➡ _____

23 (next / our / was / Donggang. / stop)
➡ _____

24 (went / rafting! / we)
➡ _____

25 (was / it / to / exciting / on / ride / rough / the / and / water / enjoy / view / the / at / time. / same / the)
➡ _____

26 (A / Incheon, / of / City / Firsts)
➡ _____

27 (you / do / where / know / first / the / station / train / is? / Korea / in)
➡ _____

28 (about / how / first / the / *Jajangmyeon*?)
➡ _____

29 (answer / the / Incheon! / is)
➡ _____

30 (place / this / many / has / firsts. / Korea's / of)
➡ _____

31 (get / to / there, / went / we / Incheon / to / Station.)
➡ _____

32 (Jajangmyeon / The / Museum / next / is / station. / the / to)
➡ _____

33 (learned / we / the / about / of / history / there. / *Jajangmyeon*)
➡ _____

34 (we / later, / around / walked / Park, / Jayu / first / the / park / Western-style / Korea. / in)
➡ _____

35 (view / the / from / park / the / awesome! / was)
➡ _____

36 (was / it / to / great / see / historical / the / sites / this / of / city / from / park. / the)
➡ _____

37 (Teacher: / these / wow, / places / great! / sound)
➡ _____

38 (all / you / done / have / wonderful / a / job / presentations! / your)
➡ _____

20 동굴 관광의 끝 무렵, 안내인이 동굴 안의 불을 잠시 껐습니다.

21 모든 것이 매우 어두워져서, 우리는 그곳의 소리에 집중할 수 있었습니다.

22 그것은 여행에서 가장 경이로운 경험이었습니다!

23 우리의 다음 여행지는 동강이었습니다.

24 우리는 래프팅을 하러 갔습니다!

25 급류를 타면서 동시에 경치를 즐기는 것은 흥미진진했습니다.

26 인천, '최초의 것'들의 도시

27 한국 최초의 기차역이 어디인지 아세요?

28 첫 번째 자장면은요?

29 그 답은 인천입니다!

30 이곳에는 한국의 최초의 것들이 많이 있습니다.

31 그곳으로 가기 위하여, 우리는 인천역으로 갔습니다.

32 자장면 박물관은 역 옆에 있습니다.

33 우리는 그곳에서 자장면의 역사에 대하여 배웠습니다.

34 다음에는, 한국 최초의 서구식 공원인 자유 공원을 거닐었습니다.

35 공원에서 바라본 경치는 정말 멋있었습니다!

36 공원에서 이 도시의 역사적인 장소들을 바라보는 것은 아주 좋았습니다.

37 교사: 와, 이 장소들은 멋지게 들리네요!

38 여러분 모두 발표를 훌륭하게 잘했어요!

※ 다음 우리말을 영어로 쓰시오.

1 수학여행에서의 가장 좋았던 순간

➡ _____

2 교사: 안녕하세요, 여러분! 지난주 수학여행은 어땠나요? 얘기해 봅시다!

➡ _____

3 부산, 시장 천국

➡ _____

4 전통 시장을 좋아하세요?

➡ _____

5 그렇다면 부산에 있는 국제시장으로 가세요.

➡ _____

6 그곳은 부산에서 가장 유명한 시장 중 하나입니다.

➡ _____

7 그곳이 무엇으로 유명한지 아세요?

➡ _____

8 그 시장은 여러 나라에서 온 다양한 제품들을 파는 것으로 유명합니다.

➡ _____

9 그곳에서 세계 곳곳의 제품들을 모두 볼 수 있어서 흥미로웠습니다.

➡ _____

10 우리는 또한 김밥, 어묵 그리고 호떡과 같은 여러 종류의 길거리 음식을 먹었습니다

➡ _____

11 그러고 나서 우리는 보수동 책방 거리로 걸어갔습니다.

➡ _____

12 그곳의 많은 서점에서는 중고 책을 팝니다.

➡ _____

13 우리는 몇 권의 오래된 만화책을 발견해서 정말 신이 났습니다!

➡ _____

14 카페에서 휴식을 취하며 그 책들을 읽는 것이 좋았습니다.

➡ _____

15 강원도, 자연의 아름다움으로 가득한 곳

➡ _____

16 아름다운 자연에 관한 한 강원도만 한 곳이 없습니다.

➡ _____

17 우선, 우리는 백룡동굴로 갔습니다.

➡ _____

18 이 1.8킬로미터 길이의 동굴은 여전히 잘 보존된 상태입니다.

➡ _____

19 그곳의 자연의 아름다움을 보는 것은 매우 놀라웠습니다.

➡ _____

20 동굴 관광의 끝 무렵, 안내인이 동굴 안의 불을 잠시 껐습니다.

➡ _____

21 모든 것이 매우 어두워져서, 우리는 그곳의 소리에 집중할 수 있었습니다.

➡ _____

22 그것은 여행에서 가장 경이로운 경험이었습니다!

➡ _____

23 우리의 다음 여행지는 동강이었습니다.

➡ _____

24 우리는 래프팅을 하러 갔습니다!

➡ _____

25 급류를 타면서 동시에 경치를 즐기는 것은 흥미진진했습니다.

➡ _____

26 인천, '최초의 것'들의 도시

➡ _____

27 한국 최초의 기차역이 어디인지 아세요?

➡ _____

28 첫 번째 자장면은요?

➡ _____

29 그 답은 인천입니다!

➡ _____

30 이곳에는 한국의 최초의 것들이 많이 있습니다.

➡ _____

31 그곳으로 가기 위하여, 우리는 인천역으로 갔습니다.

➡ _____

32 자장면 박물관은 역 옆에 있습니다.

➡ _____

33 우리는 그곳에서 자장면의 역사에 대하여 배웠습니다.

➡ _____

34 다음에는, 한국 최초의 서구식 공원인 자유 공원을 거닐었습니다.

➡ _____

35 공원에서 바라본 경치는 정말 멋있었습니다!

➡ _____

36 공원에서 이 도시의 역사적인 장소들을 바라보는 것은 아주 좋았습니다.

➡ _____

37 교사: 와, 이곳들은 멋지게 들리네요!

➡ _____

38 여러분 모두 발표를 훌륭하게 잘했어요!

➡ _____

※ 다음 우리말과 일치하도록 빈칸에 알맞은 말을 쓰시오.

After You Read D

1. I _____ _____ Hang-dong, Seoul.

2. _____ _____ an old _____.

3. It is _____ _____ _____.

4. You can walk there and _____ _____ _____ beautiful _____.

1. 나는 서울의 항동에 산다.
2. 오래된 철도가 있다.
3. 이것은 더 이상 사용되지 않는다.
4. 너는 그 철길을 걸을 수 있고 예쁜 풍경 사진을 찍을 수도 있다.

Think & Write Step 3

1. _____ _____ in Naejangsan

2. _____ _____, I _____ _____ Naejangsan _____ my family.

3. I _____ a cable car _____ _____ _____ _____ the mountain.

4. _____, I _____ _____ the top.

5. _____ _____ _____, I saw beautiful _____ _____. I _____ many _____.

6. _____ was _____ and _____ _____ _____ beautiful autumn leaves.

1. 내장산에서의 가을 산행
2. 지난 가을, 나는 가족과 함께 내장산에 갔다.
3. 나는 산의 중간까지 케이블 카를 타고 갔다.
4. 그리고 나서, 나는 정상까지 하이킹을 갔다.
5. 정상에서, 나는 아름다운 가을 경치를 보았다. 나는 많은 사진을 찍었다.
6. 아름다운 가을 나뭇잎을 보는 것은 놀랍고 흥미진진했다.

Culture Link

1. _____ Trip

2. Some people _____ _____ in nature _____ _____ the environment.

3. They think _____ is important _____ _____ _____.

4. _____ Trip

5. Some people _____ _____ _____ for _____ _____.

6. They travel _____ _____ _____ _____.

7. They help _____ _____ or wild animals _____ their trips.

8. _____

9. _____ _____ _____, people visit _____ _____ and _____ history.

10. _____ this trip, people _____ _____ the _____ of people _____ _____ _____.

1. 생태 여행
2. 몇몇 사람들은 자연 속에서 환경을 해치지 않고 여행을 합니다.
3. 그들은 자연을 보호하는 것이 중요하다고 생각합니다.
4. 자원봉사 여행
5. 몇몇 사람들은 특별한 목적을 위해 여행을 갑니다.
6. 그들은 자원봉사를 하기 위해 여행합니다.
7. 그들은 그들의 여행 중에 지역 사회와 야생 동물들을 돕습니다.
8. 역사 여행
9. 이 여행에서 사람들은 역사적인 유적들을 방문하고 역사에 대해 배웁니다.
10. 이 여행 동안 사람들은 과거의 사람들의 삶을 이해할 수 있습니다.

※ 다음 우리말을 영어로 쓰시오.

After You Read D

1. 나는 서울의 항동에 산다.
   ➡ _____

2. 오래된 철도가 있다.
   ➡ _____

3. 이것은 더 이상 사용되지 않는다.
   ➡ _____

4. 너는 그 철길을 걸을 수 있고 예쁜 풍경 사진을 찍을 수도 있다.
   ➡ _____

Think & Write Step 3

1. 내장산에서의 가을 산행
   ➡ _____

2. 지난 가을, 나는 가족과 함께 내장산에 갔다.
   ➡ _____

3. 나는 산의 중간까지 케이블 카를 타고 갔다.
   ➡ _____

4. 그러고 나서, 나는 정상까지 하이킹을 갔다.
   ➡ _____

5. 정상에서, 나는 아름다운 가을 경치를 보았다. 나는 많은 사진을 찍었다.
   ➡ _____

6. 아름다운 가을 나뭇잎을 보는 것은 놀랍고 흥미진진했다.
   ➡ _____

Culture Link

1. 생태 여행
   ➡ _____

2. 몇몇 사람들은 자연 속에서 환경을 해치지 않고 여행을 합니다.
   ➡ _____

3. 그들은 자연을 보호하는 것이 중요하다고 생각합니다.
   ➡ _____

4. 자원봉사 여행
   ➡ _____

5. 몇몇 사람들은 특별한 목적을 위해 여행을 갑니다.
   ➡ _____

6. 그들은 자원봉사를 하기 위해 여행합니다.
   ➡ _____

7. 그들은 그들의 여행 중에 지역 사회와 야생 동물들을 돕습니다.
   ➡ _____

8. 역사 여행
   ➡ _____

9. 이 여행에서 사람들은 역사적인 유적들을 방문하고 역사에 대해 배웁니다.
   ➡ _____

10. 이 여행 동안 사람들은 과거의 사람들의 삶을 이해할 수 있습니다.
    ➡ _____

※ 다음 영어를 우리말로 쓰시오.

01 amount _____

02 career _____

03 collaboration _____

04 self-driving car _____

05 collect _____

06 appear _____

07 consultant _____

08 develop _____

09 emotion _____

10 analyze _____

11 float _____

12 counseling _____

13 artificial _____

14 improve _____

15 interpreter _____

16 strength _____

17 late-night _____

18 apply _____

19 talent _____

20 patient _____

21 waste material _____

22 specialist _____

23 collaborate _____

24 route _____

25 decorate _____

26 creativity _____

27 reduce _____

28 space _____

29 customer _____

30 problem-solving _____

31 following _____

32 upcycle _____

33 reviewer _____

34 creative _____

35 first of all _____

36 take care of _____

37 look ahead _____

38 be good at _____

39 what else _____

40 come true _____

41 fill out _____

42 keep a diary _____

43 print out _____

※ 다음 우리말을 영어로 쓰시오.

01 충고, 조언

02 진로, 직업

03 기능, 기술

04 줄이다, 감소시키다

05 (타고난) 재능, 재주

06 (책, 영화 등의) 논평가

07 상담

08 전문가

09 협력하다

10 지원하다, 신청하다

11 꾸미다, 장식하다

12 통역사

13 분석하다

14 감정

15 상담가

16 인공적인, 인조의

17 (물 위에) 뜨다, 떠다니다

18 힘, 강점, 장점

19 공동 작업, 협동

20 다음에 나오는[언급되는]

21 개선하다, 향상시키다

22 심야의

23 창의적인

24 환자

25 양, 총액

26 문제 해결의

27 허락하다

28 이유, 원인

29 손님, 고객

30 경로, 노선

31 발달시키다, 발전하다

32 나타나다, 보이기 시작하다

33 창의력, 독창력

34 우주, 공간

35 일기를 쓰다

36 (앞일을) 내다보다, 예견하다

37 출력하다

38 ~을 돌보다

39 그 외에, 그 밖에

40 (서식 등을) 작성하다

41 이루어지다, 실현되다

42 ~을 잘하다

43 무엇보다도

※ 다음 영영풀이에 알맞은 단어를 <보기>에서 골라 쓴 후, 우리말 뜻을 쓰시오.

1 _____ : late at night: _____

2 _____ : to study in detail: _____

3 _____ : a way between two places: _____

4 _____ : to make something better: _____

5 _____ : a person who has a special skill: _____

6 _____ : a person who receives medical care: _____

7 _____ : to stay up on water: _____

8 _____ : not natural; created by humans: _____

9 _____ : an advantageous quality or ability: _____

10 _____ : advice that is given to someone to help them with their problems:
_____

11 _____ : a natural ability to do something well: _____

12 _____ : the ability to think of or create something new: _____

13 _____ : to grow or become more advanced: _____

14 _____ : a job that requires special skills or training: _____

15 _____ : to give someone papers that say you want to do something:
_____

16 _____ : a person who writes opinions about the quality of a book, movie, or
product: _____

<보기>

artificial	late-night	analyze	improve
route	reviewer	strength	develop
creativity	apply	career	counseling
float	patient	specialist	talent

※ 다음 우리말과 일치하도록 빈칸에 알맞은 말을 쓰시오.

Listen & Talk 1 A

G: _____ _____ basketball.

B: Well… I'm _____ _____ _____ playing basketball. Are you?

G: Yes, I think I am. _____ _____ _____ _____ _____ _____?

B: I'm _____ _____ _____ soccer.

G: Okay, then _____ _____ soccer.

Listen & Talk 1 B

B: Jessica, what _____ you _____ _____ _____ _____ for the school talent show?

G: I didn't _____ yet. _____ _____ I _____ _____ _____?

B: You're _____ _____ _____, _____ you?

G: Not really. But I think I'm _____ _____ _____. I like _____ very much.

B: Really? Actually, I'm _____ _____ _____ rock music with my band. _____ _____ _____ _____ sing for us?

G: Sure, I'd _____ _____.

Listen & Talk 1 C

B: Mom, I _____ _____ _____ _____ this form for tomorrow's _____ _____ program. Could you help me?

W: Sure. Let me see. You already _____ your dream job _____ hobby.

B: Yes, I want to _____ a _____ _____, and my hobby is _____ sports games. But _____ my _____ is hard. _____ _____ _____ _____ at?

W: Well, I think you have _____ of strengths. _____ _____ all, you _____ _____ playing baseball, _____ _____?

B: Oh, yes. _____ _____ _____ _____ _____ _____.

W: And you have many _____ _____.

B: You're right. I also _____ well with _____ _____. And I'm good _____ _____ _____ people.

W: Right! _____ _____ _____ _____ so many things.

B: _____, Mom.

해석

G: 우리 농구하자.
B: 음... 나는 농구를 잘하지 못해. 너는 잘하니?
G: 응, 내 생각에 나는 잘하는 것 같아. 넌 어떤 것을 잘해?
B: 나는 축구를 잘해.
G: 그래, 그러면 축구를 하자.

B: Jessica, 학교 재능 발표회에서 뭐 할 거야?
G: 아직 결정 안 했어. 나 어떤 것을 잘하지?
B: 너 춤 잘 추잖아, 그렇지 않니?
G: 사실은 그렇지 않아. 하지만 내 생각에는 나는 노래를 잘해. 나는 노래하는 것을 매우 좋아해.
B: 정말? 사실 나 우리 밴드와 록 음악을 연주할 계획이야. 우리를 위해 노래해 주는 게 어때?
G: 그래, 좋아.

B: 엄마, 저 내일 있을 진로 상담 프로그램을 준비하기 위해 이 양식을 작성해야 해요. 저 좀 도와주시겠어요?
W: 물론이지. 어디 보자. 이미 하고 싶은 직업과 취미는 적었구나.
B: 네. 저는 체육 선생님이 되고 싶어요. 제 취미는 스포츠 경기 보는 거예요. 하지만, 제 강점을 적는 것은 어려워요. 저는 무엇을 잘하죠?
W: 음, 나는 네게 많은 강점이 있다고 생각해. 무엇보다도 너는 야구를 잘하잖니, 그렇지 않니?
B: 아, 맞아요. 저는 야구를 잘해요.
W: 그리고 너는 다른 강점들도 가지고 있단다.
B: 맞아요. 저는 다른 사람들과 협업을 잘해요. 그리고 사람들의 이야기를 잘 들어 줘요.
W: 그렇지! 너는 아주 많은 것들을 잘한단다.
B: 감사해요, 엄마.

Listen & Talk 2 A

B: I _____ _____ _____ a scientist. _____ do I _____

_____ _____?

W: You _____ _____ study science. And you need to _____

your _____ _____.

B: 저는 과학자가 되고 싶어요. 저는 어떤 것을 해야 할까요?
W: 과학 공부를 해야 돼요. 그리고 문제 해결 능력을 개발할 필요가 있어요.

Listen & Talk 2 B

G: Jason, I read your paper. It was so _____!

B: _____ you _____ that. I'm _____ hard

__ _____ my _____ _____. I want to be a _____ someday.

G: Really? I _____ to write well _____ you. _____ _____

_____ need _____ do?

B: You need to read _____ _____ _____ books. _____

_____ _____ _____ _____.

G: What _____ do I _____ do?

B: Well, I write almost _____ _____. Why _____ you start

_____ a diary?

G: _____ you _____ your _____. I'll start today.

G: Jason, 나 너의 글을 읽었어. 아주 놀라웠어!
B: 그렇게 말해 줘서 고마워. 나는 내 글쓰기 기량을 발전시키려고 노력하고 있어. 언젠가 작가가 되고 싶어.
G: 정말? 나도 너처럼 글을 잘 쓰고 싶어. 뭘 해야 하니?
B: 책을 많이 읽어야 해. 독서가 네 글쓰기를 더 좋게 만들거든.
G: 다른 건 또 뭘 해야 할까?
B: 음, 나는 거의 매일 글을 쓰고 있어. 일기 쓰기를 시작하는 건 어때?
G: 조언 고마워. 오늘부터 시작할게.

Listen & Talk 2 C

G: Hello, Mr. Watson! _____ you _____ doing this interview.

M: Sure, no _____.

G: This interview is for students _____ _____ _____ _____

_____ stylists. Can you tell me _____ _____ _____?

M: Sure. You may see pictures of food in books or on TV. A food stylist

_____ food _____ _____ good for pictures or movies.

G: I want _____ _____ _____ _____ _____ _____ like you.

_____ do I _____ to do?

M: You _____ _____ _____ about many _____ of food.

G: _____ _____ do I _____ _____?

M: You need to study art, _____. _____ is important.

G: All right! _____ you _____ your time, Mr. Watson.

G: 안녕하세요, Watson 씨! 오늘 인터뷰 감사해요.
M: 네, 문제 없어요.
G: 이 인터뷰는 푸드 스타일리스트가 되고 싶어 하는 학생들을 위한 것이에요. 당신의 직업에 대해 말씀해 주시겠어요?
M: 그럼요. 아마 여러분은 책이나 TV에서 음식 사진을 보셨을 겁니다. 푸드 스타일리스트는 사진이나 영화에서 음식이 맛있어 보이도록 장식하는 일을 합니다.
G: 저도 Watson 씨와 같은 푸드 스타일리스트가 되고 싶어요. 뭘 해야 하나요?
M: 많은 종류의 음식에 대해 배워야 해요.
G: 다른 건 뭘 해야 하죠?
M: 미술 공부도 해야 해요. 창의력이 중요하거든요.
G: 알겠습니다! 시간 내 주셔서 감사합니다, Watson 씨.

※ 다음 우리말에 맞도록 대화를 영어로 쓰시오.

 해석

Listen & Talk 1 A

G: _____

B: _____

G: _____

B: _____

G: _____

G: 우리 농구하자.
B: 음... 나는 농구를 잘하지 못해. 너는 잘하니?
G: 응, 내 생각에 나는 잘하는 것 같아. 넌 어떤 것을 잘해?
B: 나는 축구를 잘해.
G: 그래, 그러면 축구를 하자.

Listen & Talk 1 B

B: _____

G: _____

B: _____

G: _____

B: _____

G: _____

B: Jessica, 학교 재능 발표회에서 뭐 할 거야?
G: 아직 결정 안 했어. 나 어떤 것을 잘 하지?
B: 너 춤 잘 추잖아, 그렇지 않니?
G: 사실은 그렇지 않아. 하지만 내 생각 에는 나는 노래를 잘해. 나는 노래하는 것을 매우 좋아해.
B: 정말? 사실 나 우리 밴드와 록 음악을 연주할 계획이야. 우리를 위해 노래해 주는 게 어때?
G: 그래, 좋아.

Listen & Talk 1 C

B: _____

W: _____

B: _____

W: _____

B: _____

W: _____

B: _____

W: _____

B: _____

B: 엄마, 저 내일 있을 진로 상담 프로그 램을 준비하기 위해 이 양식을 작성해 야 해요. 저 좀 도와주시겠어요?
W: 물론이지. 어디 보자. 이미 하고 싶은 직업과 취미는 적었구나.
B: 네. 저는 체육 선생님이 되고 싶어요. 제 취미는 스포츠 경기 보는 거예요. 하지만, 제 강점을 적는 것은 어려워 요. 저는 무엇을 잘하죠?
W: 음, 나는 네게 많은 강점이 있다고 생 각해. 무엇보다도 너는 야구를 잘하잖 니, 그렇지 않니?
B: 아, 맞아요. 저는 야구를 잘해요.
W: 그리고 너는 다른 강점들도 가지고 있단다.
B: 맞아요. 저는 다른 사람들과 협업을 잘해요. 그리고 사람들의 이야기를 잘 들어 줘요.
W: 그렇지! 너는 아주 많은 것들을 잘한 단다.
B: 감사해요, 엄마.

Listen & Talk 2 A

B: _____

W: _____

B: 저는 과학자가 되고 싶어요. 저는 어떤 것을 해야 할까요?

W: 과학 공부를 해야 돼요. 그리고 문제 해결 능력을 개발할 필요가 있어요.

Listen & Talk 2 B

G: _____

B: _____

_____

G: _____

B: _____

G: _____

B: _____

G: _____

G: Jason, 나 너의 글을 읽었어. 아주 놀라웠어!

B: 그렇게 말해 줘서 고마워. 나는 내 글쓰기 기량을 발전시키려고 노력하고 있어. 언젠가 작가가 되고 싶어.

G: 정말? 나도 너처럼 글을 잘 쓰고 싶어. 뭘 해야 하니?

B: 책을 많이 읽어야 해. 독서가 네 글쓰기를 더 좋게 만들거든.

G: 다른 건 또 뭘 해야 할까?

B: 음, 나는 거의 매일 글을 쓰고 있어. 일기 쓰기를 시작하는 건 어때?

G: 조언 고마워. 오늘부터 시작할게.

Listen & Talk 2 C

G: _____

M: _____

G: _____

M: _____

G: _____

M: _____

G: _____

M: _____

G: _____

G: 안녕하세요, Watson 씨! 오늘 인터뷰 감사해요.

M: 네, 문제 없어요.

G: 이 인터뷰는 푸드 스타일리스트가 되고 싶어 하는 학생들을 위한 것이에요. 당신의 직업에 대해 말씀해 주시겠어요?

M: 그럼요. 아마 여러분은 책이나 TV에서 음식 사진을 보셨을 겁니다. 푸드 스타일리스트는 사진이나 영화에서 음식이 맛있어 보이도록 장식하는 일을 합니다.

G: 저도 Watson 씨와 같은 푸드 스타일리스트가 되고 싶어요. 뭘 해야 하나요?

M: 많은 종류의 음식에 대해 배워야 해요.

G: 다른 건 뭘 해야 하죠?

M: 미술 공부도 해야 해요. 창의력이 중요하거든요.

G: 알겠습니다! 시간 내 주셔서 감사합니다, Watson 씨.

※ 다음 우리말과 일치하도록 빈칸에 알맞은 것을 골라 쓰시오.

1 _____ the _____
A. Future   B. of   C. Jobs

2 2020s: Self-driving cars will _____ _____ the _____.
A. market   B. on   C. be

3 2030s: People will have _____ _____ do _____ for them.
A. that   B. everything   C. robots

4 2030s: 3D printers in _____ home will _____ _____ everything.
A. almost   B. print   C. every   D. out

5 2050s: People will _____ _____ _____.
A. trips   B. space   C. take

6 2050s: People will live _____ the sea or in _____ _____.
A. floating   B. under   C. cities

7 _____ _____ the pictures _____.
A. at   B. above   C. look

8 _____ these _____ _____ you?
A. ideas   B. surprise   C. do

9 You can see that our _____ will be very _____ in the _____.
A. different   B. lives   C. future

10 _____ our lives _____, many new jobs will _____.
A. appear   B. as   C. change

11 _____ of _____ do you want?
A. kind   B. job   C. what

12 What _____ your future life _____ _____?
A. like   B. be   C. will

13 The _____ people _____ _____ and _____ jobs that will be important in the future.
A. chose   B. ahead   C. following   D. looked

14 _____ _____ about _____ jobs!
A. read   B. their   C. let's

15 Do you see the flower _____ _____ Sujin _____?
A. made   B. that   C. pot

16 It was _____ _____ old street _____.
A. made   B. flags   C. from

17 She is an _____ _____.
A. designer   B. upcycling

18 She works with _____ _____ to make new _____.
A. waste   B. products   C. materials

19 Her products show people _____ old materials can be _____ _____ new _____.
A. ways   B. useful   C. in   D. that

20 _____ can _____ the amount of _____ in the future.
A. waste   B. upcycling   C. reduce

21 To _____ an upcycling designer, you should be _____ and _____ about art.
A. creative   B. become   C. learn

---

1 미래의 직업

2 2020년대: 자율주행차들이 시장에 나올 것이다.

3 2030년대: 사람들은 그들을 위하여 모든 것을 하는 로봇을 갖게 될 것이다.

4 2030년대: 모든 가정의 3D 프린터가 거의 모든 것을 출력해 낼 것이다.

5 2050년대: 사람들은 우주여행을 할 것이다.

6 2050년대: 사람들은 바다 밑이나 수상 도시에서 살 것이다.

7 위의 그림들을 보세요.

8 이 생각들이 놀랍습니까?

9 당신은 미래에 우리의 삶이 매우 달라질 것을 볼 수 있습니다.

10 우리의 삶이 변화함에 따라 새로운 직업들이 많이 생겨날 것입니다.

11 당신은 어떤 직업을 원하세요?

12 미래의 당신 삶은 어떤 모습일까요?

13 다음의 사람들은 앞을 내다보고 미래에 중요하게 될 직업을 선택하였습니다.

14 그들의 직업에 관하여 읽어 봅시다!

15 수진이 만든 화분이 보이시나요?

16 이것은 거리의 낡은 깃발들로 만들어졌습니다.

17 그녀는 업사이클링 디자이너입니다.

18 그녀는 새로운 제품을 만들기 위해 폐기물을 가지고 작업합니다.

19 그녀의 제품들은 낡은 재료가 새로운 방식으로 유용해질 수 있다는 것을 사람들에게 보여줍니다.

20 업사이클링은 미래에 쓰레기의 양을 줄일 수 있습니다.

21 업사이클링 디자이너가 되려면 당신은 창의적이어야 하며 미술을 배워야 합니다.

22 _____ you _____ _____ of 3D modelers?

A. heard   B. ever   C. have

23 Taeho, a 3D modeler, _____ _____ a company that _____ hands and legs.

A. artificial   B. works   C. makes   D. for

24 Taeho uses _____ _____ to _____ _____ new hands and legs.

A. out   B. special   C. print   D. software

25 They are _____ _____ for _____.

A. patients   B. specially   C. made

26 If you are _____ _____ computer programming and art, you can be a 3D _____.

A. at   B. good   C. modeler

27 Taeho wants more people to _____ 3D _____ products in the _____.

A. printed   B. use   C. future

28 Jihye is a _____ _____ _____.

A. data   B. big   C. specialist

29 She _____ _____ many _____.

A. on   B. works   C. projects

30 _____ _____, _____ year, she made bus _____.

A. routes   B. last   C. example   D. for

31 To find the best night routes, she needed to _____ smartphone use data and taxi _____ patterns from _____ _____.

A. collect   B. late-night   C. use   D. travelers

32 Then she _____ this information to _____ the most _____ routes.

A. useful   B. analyzed   C. create

33 Now Jihye is _____ _____ an _____ shopping mall.

A. with   B. online   C. working

34 She is _____ data _____ customers to _____ _____ the best styles for them.

A. find   B. collecting   C. out   D. from

35 She knows big data _____ us to _____ more about our _____ lives.

A. daily   B. learn   C. allows

36 If you want to become a big data _____, you should _____ your math and _____ skills!

A. develop   B. problem-solving   C. specialist

37 _____ about _____ and _____ your future.

A. yourself   B. for   C. think   D. prepare

38 If you _____ _____ and _____ big, your future will be bright.

A. keep   B. ahead   C. dreaming   D. looking

---

22 3D 모형 제작자에 관하여 들어 본 적이 있으신가요?

23 3D 모형 제작자인 태호는 인공 손과 다리를 만드는 회사에서 일합니다.

24 태호는 새 손과 다리를 출력하기 위하여 특별한 소프트웨어를 사용합니다.

25 그것들은 환자를 위하여 특별히 제작됩니다.

26 만약 당신이 컴퓨터 프로그래밍이나 미술을 잘한다면, 3D 모형 제작자가 될 수 있습니다.

27 태호는 미래에 더 많은 사람들이 3D 프린터로 출력된 제품들을 사용하기를 원합니다.

28 지혜는 빅데이터 전문가입니다.

29 그녀는 많은 프로젝트에서 일합니다.

30 예를 들어, 작년에 그녀는 버스 노선을 만들었습니다.

31 최적의 심야 노선을 찾기 위하여, 그녀는 심야에 이동하는 사람들의 스마트폰 이용 정보와 택시 이용 패턴을 수집할 필요가 있었습니다.

32 그런 다음 그녀는 그 정보를 분석하여 가장 유용한 노선을 만들었습니다.

33 현재 지혜는 온라인 쇼핑몰과 작업하고 있습니다.

34 그녀는 소비자들에게 맞는 최적의 스타일을 찾기 위하여 그들로부터 데이터를 수집하고 있습니다.

35 그녀는 빅데이터가 우리에게 일상생활에 관하여 더 많이 알게 해 준다는 것을 알고 있습니다.

36 만약 당신이 빅데이터 전문가가 되고 싶다면, 수학과 문제 해결 능력을 계발해야 합니다!

37 자신에 대하여 생각해 보고 미래를 준비하세요.

38 만약 당신이 계속 앞을 내다보고 꿈을 크게 꾼다면, 당신의 미래는 밝을 것입니다.

※ 다음 우리말과 일치하도록 빈칸에 알맞은 말을 쓰시오.

1 Jobs _____ _____ _____

2 2020s: _____ cars will _____ _____ _____ _____.

3 2030s: People will have robots _____ do _____ for them.

4 2030s: 3D printers in every home _____ _____ _____ _____.

5 2050s: People will _____ _____ _____.

6 2050s: People will live _____ _____ _____ or _____ _____ _____.

7 _____ _____ the pictures _____.

8 Do _____ ideas _____ you?

9 You can see that _____ _____ will be very different _____ _____ _____.

10 _____ our lives _____, many new jobs _____ _____.

11 _____ _____ _____ _____ do you want?

12 _____ _____ your future life _____ _____?

13 _____ _____ people _____ _____ and _____ _____ that will _____ _____ in the future.

14 _____ _____ about their jobs!

15 Do you see the _____ _____ _____ _____ _____ _____ _____?

16 It _____ _____ _____ old street _____.

17 She is an _____ _____.

18 She works with _____ _____ to make new _____.

19 Her products show people that old materials _____ _____ _____ _____ _____.

20 Upcycling can _____ _____ _____ _____ _____ in the future.

21 _____ _____ an _____ _____, you should be _____ and learn about art.

1 미래의 직업

2 2020년대: 자율주행차들이 시장에 나올 것이다.

3 2030년대: 사람들은 그들을 위하여 모든 것을 하는 로봇을 갖게 될 것이다.

4 2030년대: 모든 가정의 3D 프린터가 거의 모든 것을 출력해 낼 것이다.

5 2050년대: 사람들은 우주여행을 할 것이다.

6 2050년대: 사람들은 바다 밑이나 수상 도시에서 살 것이다.

7 위의 그림들을 보세요.

8 이 생각들이 놀랍습니까?

9 당신은 미래에 우리의 삶이 매우 달라질 것을 볼 수 있습니다.

10 우리의 삶이 변화함에 따라 새로운 직업들이 많이 생겨날 것입니다.

11 당신은 어떤 직업을 원하세요?

12 미래의 당신 삶은 어떤 모습일까요?

13 다음의 사람들은 앞을 내다보고 미래에 중요하게 될 직업을 선택하였습니다.

14 그들의 직업에 관하여 읽어 봅시다!

15 수진이 만든 화분이 보이시나요?

16 이것은 거리의 낡은 깃발들로 만들어졌습니다.

17 그녀는 업사이클링 디자이너입니다.

18 그녀는 새로운 제품을 만들기 위해 폐기물을 가지고 작업합니다.

19 그녀의 제품들은 낡은 재료가 새로운 방식으로 유용해질 수 있다는 것을 사람들에게 보여줍니다.

20 업사이클링은 미래에 쓰레기의 양을 줄일 수 있습니다.

21 업사이클링 디자이너가 되려면 당신은 창의적이어야 하며 미술을 배워야 합니다.

22 _____ _____ _____ _____ of 3D _____?

23 Taeho, a 3D modeler, _____ _____ a company _____ _____ _____ hands and legs.

24 Taeho uses _____ _____ to print out new hands and legs.

25 They are made _____ _____ _____.

26 If you _____ _____ _____ computer programming and art, you can _____ _____ _____ _____ _____.

27 Taeho _____ more people _____ _____ 3D printed products _____ _____ _____.

28 Jihye is a _____ _____ _____.

29 She _____ _____ many projects.

30 _____ _____, last year, she made _____ _____.

31 To find the best night routes, she needed to collect smartphone use data and _____ _____ from _____ _____.

32 Then she _____ this information _____ _____ the most _____ _____.

33 Now Jihye is _____ _____ an online shopping mall.

34 She is _____ _____ _____ customers to _____ _____ the best styles for them.

35 She knows big data _____ _____ _____ _____ more about _____ _____ _____.

36 If you want to become a big data _____, you should _____ your math and _____ _____!

37 _____ about _____ and _____ _____ your future.

38 If you _____ _____ ahead and _____ big, your future will _____ _____.

22 3D 모형 제작자에 관하여 들어 본 적이 있으신가요?

23 3D 모형 제작자인 태호는 인공 손과 다리를 만드는 회사에서 일합니다.

24 태호는 새 손과 다리를 출력하기 위하여 특별한 소프트웨어를 사용합니다.

25 그것들은 환자를 위하여 특별히 제작됩니다.

26 만약 당신이 컴퓨터 프로그래밍이나 미술을 잘한다면, 3D 모형 제작자가 될 수 있습니다.

27 태호는 미래에 더 많은 사람들이 3D 프린터로 출력된 제품들을 사용하기를 원합니다.

28 지혜는 빅데이터 전문가입니다.

29 그녀는 많은 프로젝트에서 일합니다.

30 예를 들어, 작년에 그녀는 버스 노선을 만들었습니다.

31 최적의 심야 노선을 찾기 위하여, 그녀는 심야에 이동하는 사람들의 스마트폰 이용 정보와 택시 이용 패턴을 수집할 필요가 있었습니다.

32 그런 다음 그녀는 그 정보를 분석하여 가장 유용한 노선을 만들었습니다.

33 현재 지혜는 온라인 쇼핑몰과 작업하고 있습니다.

34 그녀는 소비자들에게 맞는 최적의 스타일을 찾기 위하여 그들로부터 데이터를 수집하고 있습니다.

35 그녀는 빅데이터가 우리에게 일상생활에 관하여 더 많이 알게 해 준다는 것을 알고 있습니다.

36 만약 당신이 빅데이터 전문가가 되고 싶다면, 수학과 문제 해결 능력을 계발해야 합니다!

37 자신에 대하여 생각해 보고 미래를 준비하세요.

38 만약 당신이 계속 앞을 내다보고 꿈을 크게 꾼다면, 당신의 미래는 밝을 것입니다.

※ 다음 문장을 우리말로 쓰시오.

1 Jobs of the Future

➡ _____

2 2020s: Self-driving cars will be on the market.

➡ _____

3 2030s: People will have robots that do everything for them.

➡ _____

4 2030s: 3D printers in every home will print out almost everything.

➡ _____

5 2050s: People will take space trips.

➡ _____

6 2050s: People will live under the sea or in floating cities.

➡ _____

7 Look at the pictures above.

➡ _____

8 Do these ideas surprise you?

➡ _____

9 You can see that our lives will be very different in the future.

➡ _____

10 As our lives change, many new jobs will appear.

➡ _____

11 What kind of job do you want?

➡ _____

12 What will your future life be like?

➡ _____

13 The following people looked ahead and chose jobs that will be important in the future.

➡ _____

14 Let's read about their jobs!

➡ _____

15 Do you see the flower pot that Sujin made?

➡ _____

16 It was made from old street flags.

➡ _____

17 She is an upcycling designer.

➡ _____

18 She works with waste materials to make new products.
➡ _____

19 Her products show people that old materials can be useful in new ways.
➡ _____

20 Upcycling can reduce the amount of waste in the future.
➡ _____

21 To become an upcycling designer, you should be creative and learn about art.
➡ _____

22 Have you ever heard of 3D modelers?
➡ _____

23 Taeho, a 3D modeler, works for a company that makes artificial hands and legs.
➡ _____

24 Taeho uses special software to print out new hands and legs.
➡ _____

25 They are made specially for patients.
➡ _____

26 If you are good at computer programming and art, you can be a 3D modeler.
➡ _____

27 Taeho wants more people to use 3D printed products in the future.
➡ _____

28 Jihye is a big data specialist.
➡ _____

29 She works on many projects.
➡ _____

30 For example, last year, she made bus routes.
➡ _____

31 To find the best night routes, she needed to collect smartphone use data and taxi use patterns from late-night travelers.
➡ _____

32 Then she analyzed this information to create the most useful routes.
➡ _____

33 Now Jihye is working with an online shopping mall.
➡ _____

34 She is collecting data from customers to find out the best styles for them.
➡ _____

35 She knows big data allows us to learn more about our daily lives.
➡ _____

36 If you want to become a big data specialist, you should develop your math and problem-solving skills!
➡ _____

37 Think about yourself and prepare for your future.
➡ _____

38 If you keep looking ahead and dreaming big, your future will be bright.
➡ _____

※ 다음 괄호 안의 단어들을 우리말에 맞도록 바르게 배열하시오.

1 (of / Future / the / Jobs)
➡ _____

2 (2020s: / cars / self-driving / be / will / the / market. / on)
➡ _____

3 (2030s: / will / people / robots / have / do / that / for / everything / them.)
➡ _____

4 (2030s: / printers / 3D / every / in / will / home / out / print / everything. / almost)
➡ _____

5 (2050s: / will / people / space / take / trips.)
➡ _____

6 (2050s: / people / live / will / the / under / sea / or / in / cities. / floating)
➡ _____

7 (at / look / above. / pictures / the)
➡ _____

8 (these / do / surprise / you? / ideas)
➡ _____

9 (can / you / see / lives / our / that / will / be / different / very / future. / the / in)
➡ _____

10 (our / as / change, / lives / new / many / jobs / appear. / will)
➡ _____

11 (kind / what / job / of / do / want? / you)
➡ _____

12 (will / what / future / your / like? / be / life)
➡ _____

13 (following / the / looked / people / ahead / and / jobs / chose / will / that / be / in / important / the / future.)
➡ _____

14 (read / let's / their / jobs! / about)
➡ _____

15 (you / do / see / flower / the / pot / made? / Sujin / that)
➡ _____

16 (was / it / from / made / street / flags. / old)
➡ _____

17 (is / she / designer. / upcycling / an)
➡ _____

18 (works / she / waste / with / to / materials / make / products. / new)
➡ _____

19 (products / her / people / show / old / that / materials / be / can / useful / ways. / new / in)
➡ _____

20 (can / upcycling / reduce / amount / the / waste / of / future. / the / in)
➡ _____

21 (become / to / upcycling / an / designer, / should / you / creative / be / and / about / learn / art.)
➡ _____

1 미래의 직업

2 2020년대: 자율주행차들이 시장에 나올 것이다.

3 2030년대: 사람들은 그들을 위하여 모든 것을 하는 로봇을 갖게 될 것이다.

4 2030년대: 모든 가정의 3D 프린터가 거의 모든 것을 출력해 낼 것이다.

5 2050년대: 사람들은 우주여행을 할 것이다.

6 2050년대: 사람들은 바다 밑이나 수상 도시에서 살 것이다.

7 위의 그림들을 보세요.

8 이 생각들이 놀랍습니까?

9 당신은 미래에 우리의 삶이 매우 달라질 것을 볼 수 있습니다.

10 우리의 삶이 변화함에 따라 새로운 직업들이 많이 생겨날 것입니다.

11 당신은 어떤 직업을 원하세요?

12 미래의 당신 삶은 어떤 모습일까요?

13 다음의 사람들은 앞을 내다보고 미래에 중요하게 될 직업을 선택하였습니다.

14 그들의 직업에 관하여 읽어 봅시다!

15 수진이 만든 화분이 보이시나요?

16 이것은 거리의 낡은 깃발들로 만들어졌습니다.

17 그녀는 업사이클링 디자이너입니다.

18 그녀는 새로운 제품을 만들기 위해 폐기물을 가지고 작업합니다.

19 그녀의 제품들은 낡은 재료가 새로운 방식으로 유용해질 수 있다는 것을 사람들에게 보여줍니다.

20 업사이클링은 미래에 쓰레기의 양을 줄일 수 있습니다.

21 업사이클링 디자이너가 되려면 당신은 창의적이어야 하며 미술을 배워야 합니다.

22 (you / have / ever / heard / 3D / modelers? / of)
➡ _____

23 (a / Taeho, / modeler, / 3D / for / works / company / a / makes / that / hands / legs. / and / artificial)
➡ _____

24 (uses / Taeho / software / special / print / to / out / hands / new / legs. / and)
➡ _____

25 (are / they / specially / made / patients. / for)
➡ _____

26 (you / if / good / are / at / programming / computer / and / art, / can / you / be / a / modeler. / 3D)
➡ _____

27 (wants / Taeho / people / more / use / to / printed / 3D / products / future. / the / in)
➡ _____

28 (a / Jihye / is / big / specialist. / data)
➡ _____

29 (works / she / many / on / projects.)
➡ _____

30 (example, / for / year, / last / made / she / routes. / bus)
➡ _____

31 (find / to / best / the / routes, / night / needed / she / collect / to / use / smartphone / data / and / use / taxi / from / patterns / travelers. / late-night)
➡ _____
_____

32 (she / then / analyzed / information / this / create / to / most / the / routes. / useful)
➡ _____

33 (now / Jihye / working / is / with / online / an / mall. / shopping)
➡ _____

34 (is / she / collecting / from / data / customers / find / to / out / best / the / for / styles / them.)
➡ _____

35 (knows / she / data / big / us / allows / learn / to / about / more / lives. / daily / our)
➡ _____

36 (you / if / become / to / want / a / data / big / specialist, / should / you / your / develop / math / and / skills! / problem-solving)
➡ _____

37 (about / think / yourself / and / for / prepare / future. / your)
➡ _____

38 (you / if / keep / ahead / looking / and / big, / dreaming / future / your / will / bright. / be)
➡ _____

22 3D 모형 제작자에 관하여 들어 본 적이 있으신가요?

23 3D 모형 제작자인 태호는 인공 손과 다리를 만드는 회사에서 일합니다.

24 태호는 새 손과 다리를 출력하기 위하여 특별한 소프트웨어를 사용합니다.

25 그것들은 환자를 위하여 특별히 제작됩니다.

26 만약 당신이 컴퓨터 프로그래밍이나 미술을 잘한다면, 3D 모형 제작자가 될 수 있습니다.

27 태호는 미래에 더 많은 사람들이 3D 프린터로 출력된 제품들을 사용하기를 원합니다.

28 지혜는 빅데이터 전문가입니다.

29 그녀는 많은 프로젝트에서 일합니다.

30 예를 들어, 작년에 그녀는 버스 노선을 만들었습니다.

31 최적의 심야 노선을 찾기 위하여, 그녀는 심야에 이동하는 사람들의 스마트폰 이용 정보와 택시 이용 패턴을 수집할 필요가 있었습니다.

32 그런 다음 그녀는 그 정보를 분석하여 가장 유용한 노선을 만들었습니다.

33 현재 지혜는 온라인 쇼핑몰과 작업하고 있습니다.

34 그녀는 소비자들에게 맞는 최적의 스타일을 찾기 위하여 그들로부터 데이터를 수집하고 있습니다.

35 그녀는 빅데이터가 우리에게 일상생활에 관하여 더 많이 알게 해 준다는 것을 알고 있습니다.

36 만약 당신이 빅데이터 전문가가 되고 싶다면, 수학과 문제 해결 능력을 계발해야 합니다!

37 자신에 대하여 생각해 보고 미래를 준비하세요.

38 만약 당신이 계속 앞을 내다보고 꿈을 크게 꾼다면, 당신의 미래는 밝을 것입니다.

※ 다음 우리말을 영어로 쓰시오.

1 미래의 직업

➡ _____

2 2020년대: 자율주행차들이 시장에 나올 것이다.

➡ _____

3 2030년대: 사람들은 그들을 위하여 모든 것을 하는 로봇을 갖게 될 것이다.

➡ _____

4 2030년대: 모든 가정의 3D 프린터가 거의 모든 것을 출력해 낼 것이다.

➡ _____

5 2050년대: 사람들은 우주여행을 할 것이다.

➡ _____

6 2050년대: 사람들은 바다 밑이나 수상 도시에서 살 것이다.

➡ _____

7 위의 그림들을 보세요.

➡ _____

8 이 생각들이 놀랍습니까?

➡ _____

9 당신은 미래에 우리의 삶이 매우 달라질 것을 볼 수 있습니다.

➡ _____

10 우리의 삶이 변화함에 따라 새로운 직업들이 많이 생겨날 것입니다.

➡ _____

11 당신은 어떤 직업을 원하세요?

➡ _____

12 미래의 당신 삶은 어떤 모습일까요?

➡ _____

13 다음의 사람들은 앞을 내다보고 미래에 중요하게 될 직업을 선택하였습니다.

➡ _____

14 그들의 직업에 관하여 읽어 봅시다!

➡ _____

15 수진이 만든 화분이 보이시나요?

➡ _____

16 이것은 거리의 낡은 깃발들로 만들어진 것입니다.

➡ _____

17 그녀는 업사이클링 디자이너입니다.

➡ _____

18 그녀는 새로운 제품을 만들기 위해 폐기물을 가지고 작업합니다.
➡ _____

19 그녀의 제품들은 낡은 재료가 새로운 방식으로 유용해질 수 있다는 것을 사람들에게 보여줍니다.
➡ _____

20 업사이클링은 미래에 쓰레기의 양을 줄일 수 있습니다.
➡ _____

21 업사이클링 디자이너가 되려면 당신은 창의적이어야 하며 미술을 배워야 합니다.
➡ _____

22 3D 모형 제작자에 관하여 들어 본 적이 있으신가요?
➡ _____

23 3D 모형 제작자인 태호는 인공 손과 다리를 만드는 회사에서 일합니다.
➡ _____

24 태호는 새 손과 다리를 출력하기 위하여 특별한 소프트웨어를 사용합니다.
➡ _____

25 그것들은 환자를 위하여 특별히 제작됩니다.
➡ _____

26 만약 당신이 컴퓨터 프로그래밍이나 미술을 잘한다면, 3D 모형 제작자가 될 수 있습니다.
➡ _____

27 태호는 미래에 더 많은 사람들이 3D 프린터로 출력된 제품들을 사용하기를 원합니다.
➡ _____

28 지혜는 빅데이터 전문가입니다.
➡ _____

29 그녀는 많은 프로젝트에서 일합니다.
➡ _____

30 예를 들어, 작년에 그녀는 버스 노선을 만들었습니다.
➡ _____

31 최적의 심야 노선을 찾기 위하여, 그녀는 심야에 이동하는 사람들의 스마트폰 이용 정보와 택시 이용 패턴을 수집할 필요가 있었습니다.
➡ _____

32 그런 다음 그녀는 그 정보를 분석하여 가장 유용한 노선을 만들었습니다.
➡ _____

33 현재 지혜는 온라인 쇼핑몰과 작업하고 있습니다.
➡ _____

34 그녀는 소비자들에게 맞는 최적의 스타일을 찾기 위하여 그들로부터 데이터를 수집하고 있습니다.
➡ _____

35 그녀는 빅데이터가 우리에게 일상생활에 관하여 더 많이 알게 해 준다는 것을 알고 있습니다.
➡ _____

36 만약 당신이 빅데이터 전문가가 되고 싶다면, 수학과 문제 해결 능력을 계발해야 합니다!
➡ _____

37 자신에 대하여 생각해 보고 미래를 준비하세요.
➡ _____

38 만약 당신이 계속 앞을 내다보고 꿈을 크게 꾼다면, 당신의 미래는 밝을 것입니다.
➡ _____

※ 다음 우리말과 일치하도록 빈칸에 알맞은 말을 쓰시오.

After You Read D

1. Taehun Kim is a movie _____. He _____ _____ about new movies.

2. He _____ this job _____ he loves _____ _____.

3. _____ _____ this job, he read many books to _____ his _____ _____.

4. He also watched _____ _____ _____ of movies.

Culture Link

1. _____ Brand _____

2. A personal brand consultant _____ a personal brand for _____ _____.

3. They find the customer's _____ _____.

4. Then they build a personal brand _____ _____ the customer's _____, _____, and _____.

5. _____ _____ this job, you _____ _____ have great _____ _____.

Do It Yourself A

1. B: Hey, Mandy. What are you _____ _____?

2. G: Hey, Edward. Look! Some volunteers _____ _____ for the school festival.

3. B: Really? I want to _____ _____. You know I'm _____ _____ _____ pictures. I think I can do something for the festival.

4. G: I think you can _____ _____ at the cartoon event.

5. B: Right! _____ _____ _____ _____ together?

6. G: Well, I am _____ _____ _____ drawing pictures. But I'm _____ _____ _____ board games.

7. B: You can _____ _____ at the game event then.

8. G: Okay. _____ go and _____ _____ _____ volunteers.

1. 김태훈은 영화 비평가이다. 그는 새로운 영화에 대한 기사를 쓴다.
2. 그는 영화 보는 것을 매우 좋아하기 때문에 이 직업을 선택했다.
3. 이 직업을 얻기 위해 그는 글쓰기 기술을 향상시키려고 많은 책들을 읽었다.
4. 그는 또한 많은 다른 유형의 영화들을 보았다.

1. 개인 브랜드 상담가
2. 개인 브랜드 상담가는 한 개인의 브랜드를 그들의 고객들을 위해 만든다.
3. 그들은 고객의 독특한 장점을 찾는다.
4. 그러고 나서 그들은 고객의 개성, 지식 그리고 기술을 사용하여 개인 브랜드를 만든다.
5. 이 직업을 갖기 위해서 당신은 훌륭한 의사소통 기술을 갖출 필요가 있다.

1. B: Mandy. 무엇을 보고 있니?
2. G: Edward. 봐! 자원봉사자들이 학교 축제에서 필요하대.
3. B: 정말? 나 돕고 싶다. 너도 알다시피 내가 그림을 잘 그리잖아. 내 생각엔 내가 축제에서 어떤 것을 할 수 있을 것 같아.
4. G: 나는 네가 만화 행사에서 도움이 될 수 있을 거로 생각해.
5. B: 맞아! 우리 함께 지원해 보는 게 어때?
6. G: 음, 나는 그림을 잘 그리지 못해. 하지만, 나는 보드게임을 잘해.
7. B: 그러면 너는 게임 행사에서 도울 수 있겠다.
8. G: 좋아. 우리 가서 함께 자원봉사자에 지원하자.

※ 다음 우리말을 영어로 쓰시오.

After You Read D

1. 김태훈은 영화 비평가이다. 그는 새로운 영화에 대한 기사를 쓴다.
➡ _____

2. 그는 영화 보는 것을 매우 좋아하기 때문에 이 직업을 선택했다.
➡ _____

3. 이 직업을 얻기 위해 그는 글쓰기 기술을 향상시키려고 많은 책들을 읽었다.
➡ _____

4. 그는 또한 많은 다른 유형의 영화들을 보았다.
➡ _____

Culture Link

1. 개인 브랜드 상담가
➡ _____

2. 개인 브랜드 상담가는 한 개인의 브랜드를 그들의 고객들을 위해 만든다.
➡ _____

3. 그들은 고객의 독특한 장점을 찾는다.
➡ _____

4. 그리고 나서 그들은 고객의 개성, 지식, 그리고 기술을 사용하여 개인 브랜드를 만든다.
➡ _____

5. 이 직업을 갖기 위해서 당신은 훌륭한 의사소통 기술을 갖출 필요가 있다.
➡ _____

Do It Yourself A

1. B: Mandy. 무엇을 보고 있니?
➡ _____

2. G: Edward. 봐! 자원봉사자들이 학교 축제에서 필요하대.
➡ _____

3. B: 정말? 나 돕고 싶어. 너도 알다시피 내가 그림을 잘 그리잖아. 내 생각엔 내가 축제에서 어떤 것을 할 수 있을 것 같아.
➡ _____
_____

4. G: 나는 네가 만화 행사에서 도움이 될 수 있을 거로 생각해.
➡ _____

5. B: 맞아! 우리 함께 지원해 보는 게 어때?
➡ _____

6. G: 음, 나는 그림을 잘 그리지 못해. 하지만, 나는 보드게임을 잘해.
➡ _____

7. B: 그러면 너는 게임 행사에서 도울 수 있겠다.
➡ _____

8. G: 좋아. 우리 가서 함께 자원봉사자에 지원하자.
➡ _____

※ 다음 영어를 우리말로 쓰시오.

01 beauty	_____
02 chase	_____
03 fly	_____
04 until	_____
05 shiny	_____
06 explain	_____
07 anywhere	_____
08 praise	_____
09 appearance	_____
10 colorful	_____
11 forest	_____
12 express	_____
13 gorgeous	_____
14 director	_____
15 predict	_____
16 happiness	_____
17 impressive	_____
18 parrot	_____
19 brightly	_____
20 feather	_____
21 edit	_____
22 shine	_____

23 cage	_____
24 peacock	_____
25 swan	_____
26 thought	_____
27 unlike	_____
28 zoo	_____
29 lake	_____
30 crow	_____
31 so	_____
32 think to oneself	_____
33 be stuck in	_____
34 on the other hand	_____
35 chase ~ away	_____
36 be free to 동사원형	_____
37 once upon a time	_____
38 be proud of	_____
39 around the world	_____
40 because of	_____
41 find out	_____
42 go back to	_____
43 must+동사원형	_____
44 one day	_____

※ 다음 우리말을 영어로 쓰시오.

01 우리, 새장

02 빛나다

03 ~와 다른, ~와 달리

04 어느 곳이나, 어디든

05 까마귀

06 감독

07 설명하다

08 (새의) 털, 깃털

09 빛나는, 반짝거리는

10 공작(새)

11 백조

12 숲

13 동물원

14 칭송하다, 칭찬하다

15 밝게

16 ~할 때까지

17 날다

18 외모

19 매력적인, 멋진

20 편집하다

21 행복, 만족

22 표현하다, 나타내다

23 (사물·사람이) 인상적인

24 호수, 연못

25 앵무새

26 ~를 뒤쫓다, 추적하다

27 색채가 다양한, 형형색색의

28 아름다움

29 예언하다, 예측하다

30 너무나, 대단히, 그렇게

31 생각, 사고

32 반면에

33 ~로 돌아가다

34 세계 곳곳에

35 ~을 자랑으로 여기다

36 옛날 옛적에

37 ~에 (갇혀) 있다

38 마음속으로 생각하다

39 ~ 때문에

40 ~을 쫓아내다

41 알게 되다, 발견하다

42 어느 날

43 ~을 생각하다

44 자유롭게 ~하다

※ 다음 영영풀이에 알맞은 단어를 <보기>에서 골라 쓴 후, 우리말 뜻을 쓰시오.

1 _____ : very attractive: _____

2 _____ : to give off light: _____

3 _____ : different from: _____

4 _____ : at any place: _____

5 _____ : being filled with light: _____

6 _____ : a box made to hold animals: _____

7 _____ : up to a certain time: _____

8 _____ : a person in charge of something: _____

9 _____ : to change, correct, or improve a text: _____

10 _____ : to talk or write about something: _____

11 _____ : the state of being happy: _____

12 _____ : to make something easy to understand: _____

13 _____ : a large bird that is usually white and has a long thin neck: _____

14 _____ : a large area of land that is thickly covered with trees: _____

15 _____ : a light and soft thing that covers a bird's body: _____

16 _____ : to say what will happen in the future: _____

보기

anywhere	gorgeous	edit	explain
cage	unlike	bright	director
until	forest	predict	swan
happiness	feather	shine	express

※ 다음 우리말과 일치하도록 빈칸에 알맞은 것을 골라 쓰시오.

1 _____ Is _____?
A. Happy   B. Who

2 _____ upon a _____, there was a crow who lived in a _____.
A. time   B. forest   C. once

3 The _____ was very happy _____ his _____.
A. with   B. crow   C. life

4 He always _____ _____ _____ in the water.
A. at   B. looked   C. himself

5 He _____ no one was _____ beautiful _____ he was.
A. than   B. more   C. thought

6 Then _____ day, the crow saw a _____ on the _____.
A. swan   B. one   C. lake

7 "The swan is _____ white," he _____, "but I am so _____.
A. black   B. so   C. thought

8 I have never _____ _____ a white bird _____.
A. such   B. seen   C. before

9 His _____ shines _____ _____.
A. brightly   B. beauty   C. so

10 The swan _____ _____ the _____ bird in the world."
A. happiest   B. be   C. must

11 He _____ to the swan and _____ his _____.
A. expressed   B. went   C. thoughts

12 "_____," the swan said, "I _____ that I was the _____ _____.
A. bird   B. actually   C. happiest   D. thought

13 But _____ I _____ a parrot.
A. saw   B. then

14 Now I think the _____ is the happiest _____ in the _____."
A. world   B. parrot   C. bird

15 The crow _____ _____ he _____ so.
A. why   B. asked   C. thought

16 The _____ answered, "The parrot has _____ _____.
A. colorful   B. swan   C. feathers

17 He is _____ _____ _____ I am.
A. beautiful   B. than   C. more

18 He _____ be _____ of his _____."
A. proud   B. must   C. appearance

19 The crow then _____ to the parrot and said, "The swan said you are the _____ bird _____ you have colorful _____."
A. because   B. flew   C. feathers   D. happiest

20 The parrot _____, "I lived a very happy life _____ I saw a _____.
A. until   B. explained   C. peacock

21 My feathers are _____, but the peacock's _____ are colorful, big, and _____.
A. colorful   B. gorgeous   C. feathers

---

1 누가 행복한가?

2 옛날 옛적에 숲에 사는 까마귀 한 마리가 있었다.

3 그 까마귀는 그의 삶에 매우 행복했다.

4 그는 항상 자신의 모습을 물에 비춰 보았다.

5 그는 자신보다 더 아름다운 새는 없다고 생각했다.

6 그러던 어느 날 까마귀는 호수에서 백조를 보았다.

7 "백조는 정말 하얗구나." 그는 생각했다. "그런데 나는 너무 까매.

8 나는 저렇게 하얀 새를 전에 본 적이 없어.

9 그의 아름다움은 정말 환하게 빛나는구나.

10 백조가 세상에서 가장 행복한 새인 것이 틀림없어."

11 그는 백조에게 가서 그의 생각을 표현했다.

12 "사실은," 백조가 말했다. "나는 내가 가장 행복한 새라고 생각했어.

13 하지만 곧 앵무새를 보았지.

14 이제 난 앵무새가 세상에서 가장 행복한 새라고 생각해."

15 까마귀는 그가 왜 그렇게 생각하는지 물었다.

16 백조는 대답했다. "앵무새는 형형색색의 깃털을 가졌거든.

17 그는 나보다 더 아름다워.

18 그는 틀림없이 자신의 외모를 자랑스러워할 거야."

19 까마귀는 그 다음에 앵무새에게 날아가서 말했다. "백조가 말하기를 당신이 형형색색의 깃털을 가졌기 때문에 가장 행복한 새래요."

20 앵무새는 설명했다. "나는 공작새를 보기 전까지는 매우 행복한 삶을 살았어.

21 내 깃털은 색이 다채롭지만, 공작새의 깃털은 색이 다채로운 데다 크고 화려하기까지 하거든.

22 _____ he is _____ _____ everyone."
A. by   B. so   C. loved

23 The _____ then visited the _____ at the _____.
A. peacock   B. crow   C. zoo

24 There were a _____ of people _____ the peacock, and they _____ him for his _____.
A. around   B. beauty   C. lot   D. praised

25 The crow _____ the peacock _____ _____ the happiest bird in the world.
A. be   B. thought   C. must

26 _____ all the people _____, the crow _____ to talk to the peacock.
A. left   B. started   C. after

27 "Peacock, you are _____ _____.
A. beautiful   B. so

28 _____ people come to see you _____ _____.
A. every   B. many   C. day

29 _____ the other _____, when people see me, they _____ me _____.
A. hand   B. away   C. on   D. chase

30 I think you are the _____ _____ in the _____."
A. world   B. bird   C. happiest

31 The peacock said, "I _____ be the _____ _____ bird, but I'm not _____.
A. most   B. may   C. happy   D. beautiful

32 _____ _____ my beauty, I am _____ in this zoo.
A. of   B. stuck   C. because

33 _____ me, you aren't _____ in a _____.
A. kept   B. unlike   C. cage

34 I want to be _____ you _____ you can go _____."
A. anywhere   B. because   C. like

35 After the crow _____ to the peacock, he _____ to _____ about who the happiest bird _____.
A. was   B. started   C. talked   D. think

36 The crow thought to _____, "The peacock's feathers are _____, but he is _____ in a cage.
A. himself   B. stuck   C. impressive

37 I don't have _____ feathers, but I'm _____ to _____ anywhere."
A. free   B. colorful   C. fly

38 The crow _____ _____ _____ the forest.
A. back   B. to   C. went

39 He _____ _____ _____ in the water again and _____ the happiest bird in the world.
A. himself   B. saw   C. at   D. looked

---

22 그래서 그는 모든 사람에게 사랑받지."

23 까마귀는 그래서 동물원의 공작새에게 갔다.

24 공작새 주변에는 많은 사람이 있었고, 그들은 그의 아름다움을 칭송했다.

25 까마귀는 공작새가 세상에서 가장 행복한 새가 틀림없다고 생각했다.

26 모든 사람이 떠난 후, 까마귀는 공작새에게 말을 걸기 시작했다.

27 "공작새님, 당신은 참 아름다워요.

28 매일 많은 사람이 당신을 보러 와요.

29 반면에 사람들은 저를 보면, 저를 쫓아내요.

30 나는 당신이 세상에서 가장 행복한 새라고 생각해요."

31 공작새는 말했다. "내가 가장 아름다운 새일지는 모르지만 나는 행복하지 않아.

32 나의 아름다움 때문에 내가 이 동물원에 갇혀 있거든.

33 나와 달리 너는 우리에 갇혀 있지 않잖아.

34 너는 어디든 갈 수 있으니 나는 너처럼 되고 싶어."

35 까마귀는 공작새와 대화한 후에, 누가 가장 행복한 새인지 생각하기 시작했다.

36 까마귀는 조용히 생각했다. "공작새의 깃털은 인상적이지만 그는 우리에 갇혀 있어.

37 나는 형형색색의 깃털은 없지만, 어디든 자유롭게 날아갈 수 있어."

38 까마귀는 숲으로 돌아갔다.

39 그는 물에 비친 자신을 다시 보았고 세상에서 가장 행복한 새를 보았다.

※ 다음 우리말과 일치하도록 빈칸에 알맞은 말을 쓰시오.

1 _____ Is _____?

2 _____ _____ _____ _____, there was a crow who _____ in a _____.

3 The crow was very _____ _____ _____ _____.

4 He _____ _____ _____ _____ in the water.

5 He _____ no one was _____ _____ _____ he was.

6 Then one day, the crow saw a swan _____ _____ _____.

7 "The swan is _____ _____," he thought, "but I am _____ _____.

8 I have never seen _____ _____ _____ _____ before.

9 His _____ _____ _____ _____.

10 The swan _____ _____ the _____ bird in the world."

11 He went to the swan and _____ _____ _____.

12 "_____," the swan said, "I thought that I was the happiest bird.

13 But _____ I _____ a parrot.

14 Now I think the parrot is _____ _____ _____ in the world."

15 The crow _____ _____ _____ _____ _____ _____.

16 The swan answered, "The parrot has _____ _____.

17 He is _____ _____ _____ I am.

18 He _____ _____ his _____."

19 The crow then _____ to the parrot and said, "The swan said you are the happiest bird _____ you have _____ _____."

1 누가 행복한가?

2 옛날 옛적에 숲에 사는 까마귀 한 마리가 있었다.

3 그 까마귀는 그의 삶에 매우 행복했다.

4 그는 항상 자신의 모습을 물에 비춰 보았다.

5 그는 자신보다 더 아름다운 새는 없다고 생각했다.

6 그러던 어느 날 까마귀는 호수에서 백조를 보았다.

7 "백조는 정말 하얗구나." 그는 생각했다. "그런데 나는 너무 까매.

8 나는 저렇게 하얀 새를 전에 본 적이 없어.

9 그의 아름다움은 정말 환하게 빛나는구나.

10 백조가 세상에서 가장 행복한 새인 것이 틀림없어."

11 그는 백조에게 가서 그의 생각을 표현했다.

12 "사실은." 백조가 말했다. "나는 내가 가장 행복한 새라고 생각했어.

13 하지만 곧 앵무새를 보았지.

14 이제 난 앵무새가 세상에서 가장 행복한 새라고 생각해."

15 까마귀는 그가 왜 그렇게 생각하는지 물었다.

16 백조는 대답했다. "앵무새는 형형색색의 깃털을 가졌거든.

17 그는 나보다 더 아름다워.

18 그는 틀림없이 자신의 외모를 자랑스러워할 거야."

19 까마귀는 그 다음에 앵무새에게 날아가서 말했다. "백조가 말하기를 당신이 형형색색의 깃털을 가졌기 때문에 가장 행복한 새래요."

20 The parrot _____, "I _____ a very happy _____ _____ I saw a peacock.

21 My feathers are colorful, but _____ _____ are _____, _____, and _____.

22 So he _____ _____ _____ _____."

23 The crow then visited the peacock _____ _____ _____.

24 There were a lot of people _____ the peacock, and they _____ him _____ his _____.

25 The crow thought the peacock _____ _____ the happiest bird in the world.

26 _____ all the people _____, the crow _____ _____ to the peacock.

27 "Peacock, you are _____ _____.

28 Many people _____ _____ _____ you every day.

29 _____ _____ _____ _____, when people see me, they _____ _____ _____.

30 I think you are the happiest bird _____ _____ _____."

31 The peacock said, "I may be _____ _____ _____ bird, but I'm _____ _____.

32 _____ _____ my beauty, I _____ _____ _____ this zoo.

33 _____ me, you _____ _____ in a cage.

34 I want to _____ _____ you because you can go anywhere."

35 After the crow talked to the peacock, he started to _____ _____ _____ _____ _____ _____ _____.

36 The crow _____ _____ _____, "The peacock's feathers are _____, but he _____ _____ in a cage.

37 I don't have colorful feathers, but I'm _____ _____ _____ _____."

38 The crow _____ _____ _____ the forest.

39 He _____ _____ _____ in the water again and saw the happiest bird in the world.

20 앵무새는 설명했다. "나는 공작새를 보기 전까지는 매우 행복한 삶을 살았어.

21 내 깃털은 색이 다채롭지만, 공작새의 깃털은 색이 다채로운데다 크고 화려하기까지 하거든.

22 그래서 그는 모든 사람에게 사랑받지."

23 까마귀는 그래서 동물원의 공작새에게 갔다.

24 공작새 주변에는 많은 사람이 있었고, 그들은 그의 아름다움을 칭송했다.

25 까마귀는 공작새가 세상에서 가장 행복한 새가 틀림없다고 생각했다.

26 모든 사람이 떠난 후, 까마귀는 공작새에게 말을 걸기 시작했다.

27 "공작새님, 당신은 참 아름다워요.

28 매일 많은 사람이 당신을 보러 와요.

29 반면에 사람들은 저를 보면, 저를 쫓아내요.

30 나는 당신이 세상에서 가장 행복한 새라고 생각해요."

31 공작새는 말했다. "내가 가장 아름다운 새일지는 모르지만 나는 행복하지 않아.

32 나의 아름다움 때문에 내가 이 동물원에 갇혀 있거든.

33 나와 달리 너는 우리에 갇혀 있지 않잖아.

34 너는 어디든 갈 수 있으니 나는 너처럼 되고 싶어."

35 까마귀는 공작새와 대화한 후에, 누가 가장 행복한 새인지 생각하기 시작했다.

36 까마귀는 조용히 생각했다. "공작새의 깃털은 인상적이지만 그는 우리에 갇혀 있어.

37 나는 형형색색의 깃털은 없지만, 어디든 자유롭게 날아갈 수 있어."

38 까마귀는 숲으로 돌아갔다.

39 그는 물에 비친 자신을 다시 보았고 세상에서 가장 행복한 새를 보았다.

※ 다음 문장을 우리말로 쓰시오.

1 ▶ Who Is Happy?
➡ _____

2 ▶ Once upon a time, there was a crow who lived in a forest.
➡ _____

3 ▶ The crow was very happy with his life.
➡ _____

4 ▶ He always looked at himself in the water.
➡ _____

5 ▶ He thought no one was more beautiful than he was.
➡ _____

6 ▶ Then one day, the crow saw a swan on the lake.
➡ _____

7 ▶ "The swan is so white," he thought, "but I am so black.
➡ _____

8 ▶ I have never seen such a white bird before.
➡ _____

9 ▶ His beauty shines so brightly.
➡ _____

10 ▶ The swan must be the happiest bird in the world."
➡ _____

11 ▶ He went to the swan and expressed his thoughts.
➡ _____

12 ▶ "Actually," the swan said, "I thought that I was the happiest bird.
➡ _____

13 ▶ But then I saw a parrot.
➡ _____

14 ▶ Now I think the parrot is the happiest bird in the world."
➡ _____

15 ▶ The crow asked why he thought so.
➡ _____

16 ▶ The swan answered, "The parrot has colorful feathers.
➡ _____

17 ▶ He is more beautiful than I am.
➡ _____

18 ▶ He must be proud of his appearance."
➡ _____

19 ▶ The crow then flew to the parrot and said, "The swan said you are the happiest bird because you have colorful feathers."
➡ _____

20 The parrot explained, "I lived a very happy life until I saw a peacock.
➡ _____

21 My feathers are colorful, but the peacock's feathers are colorful, big, and gorgeous.
➡ _____

22 So he is loved by everyone."
➡ _____

23 The crow then visited the peacock at the zoo.
➡ _____

24 There were a lot of people around the peacock, and they praised him for his beauty.
➡ _____

25 The crow thought the peacock must be the happiest bird in the world.
➡ _____

26 After all the people left, the crow started to talk to the peacock.
➡ _____

27 "Peacock, you are so beautiful.
➡ _____

28 Many people come to see you every day.
➡ _____

29 On the other hand, when people see me, they chase me away.
➡ _____

30 I think you are the happiest bird in the world."
➡ _____

31 The peacock said, "I may be the most beautiful bird, but I'm not happy.
➡ _____

32 Because of my beauty, I am stuck in this zoo.
➡ _____

33 Unlike me, you aren't kept in a cage.
➡ _____

34 I want to be like you because you can go anywhere."
➡ _____

35 After the crow talked to the peacock, he started to think about who the happiest bird was.
➡ _____

36 The crow thought to himself, "The peacock's feathers are impressive, but he is stuck in a cage.
➡ _____

37 I don't have colorful feathers, but I'm free to fly anywhere."
➡ _____

38 The crow went back to the forest.
➡ _____

39 He looked at himself in the water again and saw the happiest bird in the world.
➡ _____

※ 다음 괄호 안의 단어들을 우리말에 맞도록 바르게 배열하시오.

1 (Happy? / Is / Who)
➡ _____

2 (upon / once / time, / a / was / there / crow / a / lived / who / in / forest. / a)
➡ _____

3 (crow / the / was / happy / very / with / life. / his)
➡ _____

4 (always / he / looked / himself / at / in / water. / the)
➡ _____

5 (thought / he / one / no / was / beautiful / more / he / than / was.)
➡ _____

6 (one / then / day, / crow / the / saw / swan / a / lake. / the / on)
➡ _____

7 ("the / is / swan / white," / so / thought, / he / "but / am / I / black. / so)
➡ _____

8 (I / never / have / seen / such / bird / a / before. / white)
➡ _____

9 (beauty / his / so / shines / brightly.)
➡ _____

10 (swan / the / must / be / happiest / the / bird / in / world." / the)
➡ _____

11 (went / he / the / to / swan / and / his / expressed / thoughts.)
➡ _____

12 ("actually," / the / said, / swan / "I / that / thought / was / I / the / bird. / happiest)
➡ _____

13 (then / I / but / saw / parrot. / a)
➡ _____

14 (I / now / think / parrot / the / is / happiest / the / bird / world." / the / in)
➡ _____

15 (crow / the / asked / he / why / so. / thought)
➡ _____

16 (swan / the / answered, / "the / has / parrot / feathers. / colorful)
➡ _____

17 (is / he / beautiful / more / I / than / am.)
➡ _____

18 (must / he / proud / be / his / of / appearance.")
➡ _____

19 (the / then / crow / to / flew / the / and / parrot / said, / "the / said / swan / are / you / the / bird / happiest / you / because / colorful / have / feather.")
➡ _____

20 (parrot / the / explained, / "I / a / lived / life / happy / very / until / saw / I / peacock. / a)
➡ _____

21 (feathers / my / colorful, / are / the / but / feathers / peacock's / colorful, / are / and / gorgeous. / big,)
➡ _____

1 누가 행복한가?

2 옛날 옛적에 숲에 사는 까마귀 한 마리가 있었다.

3 그 까마귀는 그의 삶에 매우 행복했다.

4 그는 항상 자신의 모습을 물에 비춰 보았다.

5 그는 자신보다 더 아름다운 새는 없다고 생각했다.

6 그러던 어느 날 까마귀는 호수에서 백조를 보았다.

7 "백조는 정말 하얗구나." 그는 생각했다. "그런데 나는 너무 까매.

8 나는 저렇게 하얀 새를 전에 본 적이 없어.

9 그의 아름다움은 정말 환하게 빛나는구나.

10 백조가 세상에서 가장 행복한 새인 것이 틀림없어."

11 그는 백조에게 가서 그의 생각을 표현했다.

12 "사실은," 백조가 말했다. "나는 내가 가장 행복한 새라고 생각했어.

13 하지만 곧 앵무새를 보았지.

14 이제 난 앵무새가 세상에서 가장 행복한 새라고 생각해."

15 까마귀는 그가 왜 그렇게 생각하는지 물었다.

16 백조는 대답했다. "앵무새는 형형색색의 깃털을 가졌거든.

17 그는 나보다 더 아름다워.

18 그는 틀림없이 자신의 외모를 자랑스러워할 거야."

19 까마귀는 그 다음에 앵무새에게 날아가서 말했다. "백조가 말하기를 당신이 형형색색의 깃털을 가졌기 때문에 가장 행복한 새래요."

20 앵무새는 설명했다. "나는 공작새를 보기 전까지는 매우 행복한 삶을 살았어.

21 내 깃털은 색이 다채롭지만, 공작새의 깃털은 색이 다채로운데다 크고 화려하기까지 하거든.

22 (he / so / loved / is / everyone." / by)
➡ _____

23 (crow / the / visited / then / the / at / zoo. / peacock / the)
➡ _____

24 (were / there / lot / a / of / around / people / the / peacock, / they / and / praised / for / him / beauty. / his)
➡ _____

25 (the / thought / crow / the / must / peacock / be / happiest / the / bird / world. / the / in)
➡ _____

26 (all / after / people / the / left, / crow / the / to / started / talk / the / to / peacock.)
➡ _____

27 ("peacock, / are / you / beautiful. / so)
➡ _____

28 (people / many / to / come / see / every / you / day.)
➡ _____

29 (the / on / hand, / other / people / when / me, / see / they / away. / me / chase)
➡ _____

30 (you / think / I / are / happiest / the / bird / the / world." / in)
➡ _____

31 (peacock / the / said, / "I / be / may / most / the / bird, / beautiful / but / not / happy. / I'm)
➡ _____

32 (of / because / beauty, / my / am / I / stuck / in / zoo. / this)
➡ _____

33 (me, / unlike / aren't / you / in / kept / cage. / a)
➡ _____

34 (want / I / be / to / like / because / you / can / you / anywhere." / go)
➡ _____

35 (the / after / crow / to / talked / the / peacock, / started / he / think / to / who / about / happiest / the / was. / bird)
➡ _____

36 (crow / the / to / thought / himself, / "the / feathers / peacock's / are / impressive, / he / but / stuck / is / a / in / cage.)
➡ _____

37 (don't / I / have / feathers, / colorful / I'm / but / to / free / anywhere." / fly)
➡ _____

38 (crow / the / back / went / the / forest. / to)
➡ _____

39 (he / at / looked / himself / the / in / water / and / again / saw / happiest / the / bird / in / word. / the)
➡ _____

22 그래서 그는 모든 사람에게 사랑받지."

23 까마귀는 그래서 동물원의 공작새에게 갔다.

24 공작새 주변에는 많은 사람이 있었고, 그들은 그의 아름다움을 칭송했다.

25 까마귀는 공작새가 세상에서 가장 행복한 새가 틀림없다고 생각했다.

26 모든 사람이 떠난 후, 까마귀는 공작새에게 말을 걸기 시작했다.

27 "공작새님, 당신은 참 아름다워요.

28 매일 많은 사람이 당신을 보러와요.

29 반면에 사람들은 저를 보면, 저를 쫓아내요.

30 나는 당신이 세상에서 가장 행복한 새라고 생각해요."

31 공작새는 말했다. "내가 가장 아름다운 새일지는 모르지만 나는 행복하지 않아.

32 나의 아름다움 때문에 내가 이 동물원에 갇혀 있거든.

33 나와 달리 너는 우리에 갇혀 있지 않잖아.

34 너는 어디든 갈 수 있으니 나는 너처럼 되고 싶어."

35 까마귀는 공작새와 대화한 후에, 누가 가장 행복한 새인지 생각하기 시작했다.

36 까마귀는 조용히 생각했다. "공작새의 깃털은 인상적이지만 그는 우리에 갇혀 있어.

37 나는 형형색색의 깃털은 없지만, 어디든 자유롭게 날아갈 수 있어."

38 까마귀는 숲으로 돌아갔다.

39 그는 물에 비친 자신을 다시 보았고 세상에서 가장 행복한 새를 보았다.

※ 다음 우리말을 영어로 쓰시오.

1 누가 행복한가?
➡ _____

2 옛날 옛적에 숲에 사는 까마귀 한 마리가 있었다.
➡ _____

3 그 까마귀는 그의 삶에 매우 행복했다.
➡ _____

4 그는 항상 자신의 모습을 물에 비춰 보았다.
➡ _____

5 그는 자신보다 더 아름다운 새는 없다고 생각했다.
➡ _____

6 그러던 어느 날 까마귀는 호수에서 백조를 보았다.
➡ _____

7 "백조는 정말 하얗구나." 그는 생각했다. "그런데 나는 너무 까매.
➡ _____

8 나는 저렇게 하얀 새를 전에 본 적이 없어.
➡ _____

9 그의 아름다움은 정말 환하게 빛나는구나.
➡ _____

10 백조가 세상에서 가장 행복한 새인 것이 틀림없어."
➡ _____

11 그는 백조에게 가서 그의 생각을 표현했다.
➡ _____

12 "사실은," 백조가 말했다. "나는 내가 가장 행복한 새라고 생각했어.
➡ _____

13 하지만 곧 앵무새를 보았지.
➡ _____

14 이제 난 앵무새가 세상에서 가장 행복한 새라고 생각해."
➡ _____

15 까마귀는 그가 왜 그렇게 생각하는지 물었다.
➡ _____

16 백조는 대답했다. "앵무새는 형형색색의 깃털을 가졌거든.
➡ _____

17 그는 나보다 더 아름다워.
➡ _____

18 그는 틀림없이 자신의 외모를 자랑스러워할 거야."
➡ _____

19 까마귀는 그 다음에 앵무새에게 날아가서 말했다. "백조가 말하기를 당신이 형형색색의 깃털을 가졌기 때문에 가장 행복한 새래요."
➡ _____

20 앵무새는 설명했다. "나는 공작새를 보기 전까지는 매우 행복한 삶을 살았어.
➡ _____

21 내 깃털은 색이 다채롭지만, 공작새의 깃털은 색이 다채로운 데다 크고 화려하기까지 하거든.

➡ _____

22 그래서 그는 모든 사람에게 사랑받지."

➡ _____

23 까마귀는 그래서 동물원의 공작새에게 갔다.

➡ _____

24 공작새 주변에는 많은 사람이 있었고, 그들은 그의 아름다움을 칭송했다.

➡ _____

25 까마귀는 공작새가 세상에서 가장 행복한 새가 틀림없다고 생각했다.

➡ _____

26 모든 사람이 떠난 후, 까마귀는 공작새에게 말을 걸기 시작했다.

➡ _____

27 "공작새님, 당신은 참 아름다워요.

➡ _____

28 매일 많은 사람이 당신을 보러 와요.

➡ _____

29 반면에 사람들은 저를 보면, 저를 쫓아내요.

➡ _____

30 나는 당신이 세상에서 가장 행복한 새라고 생각해요."

➡ _____

31 공작새는 말했다. "내가 가장 아름다운 새일지는 모르지만 나는 행복하지 않아.

➡ _____

32 나의 아름다움 때문에 내가 이 동물원에 갇혀 있거든.

➡ _____

33 나와 달리 너는 우리에 갇혀 있지 않잖아.

➡ _____

34 너는 어디든 갈 수 있으니 나는 너처럼 되고 싶어."

➡ _____

35 까마귀는 공작새와 대화한 후에, 누가 가장 행복한 새인지 생각하기 시작했다.

➡ _____

36 까마귀는 조용히 생각했다. "공작새의 깃털은 인상적이지만 그는 우리에 갇혀 있어.

➡ _____

37 나는 형형색색의 깃털은 없지만, 어디든 자유롭게 날아갈 수 있어."

➡ _____

38 까마귀는 숲으로 돌아갔다.

➡ _____

39 그는 물에 비친 자신을 다시 보았고 세상에서 가장 행복한 새를 보았다.

➡ _____

MEMO

적중100 plus

2학기 전과정

영어 기출 문제집

영어 기출 문제집

적중100 plus
2학기 전과정

2학기
정답 및 해설

능률 | 김성곤

중 2

적중100

Lesson 5

Give a Helping Hand

시험대비 실력평가 p.08

01 ④　02 ①　03 ①　04 ③
05 ②　06 ③　07 ⑤　08 ①
09 ③

01 ④ lucky(운이 좋은) 이외의 단어들은 사람의 성격을 묘사할 때 사용할 수 있는 단어이다. ① creative: 창의적인 ② generous: 관대한 ③ lively: 쾌활한 ⑤ passionate: 열정적인

02 feed: 먹이를 주다

03 carry: 나르다, 운반하다

04 item: 항목, 물품 goods: 상품, 물품

05 die: 죽다 pass away: 죽다, 사망하다

06 all over the world: 전 세계에 worldwide: 세계적인; 세계적으로 ① nationally: 전국적으로 ② internationally: 국제적으로 ④ global: 세계적인 ⑤ variously: 여러 가지로

07 raise money: 돈을 모금하다

08 turning point: 전환점 / 큰 변화가 발생하는 때

09 moment: 순간, 잠깐 / 시간 상의 특정한 시점

서술형 시험대비 p.09

01 (a)live
02 (s)pirit
03 in
04 gave
05 (1) take　(2) broke　(3) handed　(4) search
06 (1) I feel better thanks to your advice.
　(2) She passed away last month.
　(3) The government planned to support the elderly.
　(4) He gained both wealth and fame.
07 (1) (b)lind　(2) (s)urvive　(3) (h)onor

01 둘은 반의어 관계이다. luckily: 운이 좋게도 unluckily: 불행히도 alive: 살아 있는 dead: 죽은

02 soul: 영혼, 넋, 정신, 마음 spirit: 마음, 정신

03 be in a hurry: 급하다 in need: 어려움에 처한

04 give: 주다 give a hand: 돕다

05 (1) take care of: ~을 돌보다 (2) break one's arm: 팔이 부러지다 (3) hand out: 나누어 주다 (4) search for: ~을 찾다

06 (1) thanks to ~: ~ 덕분에 (2) pass away: 사망하다 (3) support: 지지하다, 원조하다 (4) fame: 명성

07 (1) blind: 눈 먼, 장님의 / 어떤 것도 볼 수 없는 (2) survive: 살아남다, 생존하다 / 나쁜 일이 일어난 후에 계속 살다 (3) honor: 예우하다, 존중하다 / 존경심을 가지고 누군가를 대하다

교과서 Conversation

핵심 Check p.10~11

1 favor / No problem
2 Can you help me to wash the dishes
3 Why don't we have some ice cream?
　What about having some ice cream?
　Let's have some ice cream.
4 Why don't we go to the movies tomorrow
5 How about playing soccer after school

교과서 대화문 익히기

Check(√) True or False p.12

1 F　2 T　3 T　4 T

교과서 확인학습 p.14~15

Listen & Talk 1 A
can, help me / What are, going / going to donate

Listen & Talk 1 B
with / broke it / a hurry, fell down / Is there, can do / can you help

Listen & Talk 1 C
can you help, wash them / but, to feed, don't you / ask you a favor / Can you help /have to

Listen & Talk 2 A
kinds of volunteer / don't we clean up

Listen & Talk 2 B
As, was, don't we raise, at, on, bring, donate, give a hand, need

Listen & Talk 2 C

cleaned up, we going to / don't we visit, it up / to do, hold / What / serve / about playing / like

Do It Yourself A

to do / don't, volunteer activities, make / is / who has volunteered / has volunteered, help us find / search for, don't we check

---

시험대비 기본평가   p.16

01 ②   02 ⑤   03 ③   04 ②

01 특정 행동을 같이 하자고 제안할 때는 'Why don't we ~?'로 시작하는 표현을 쓴다. 'How about ~?'이나 'What about ~?' 'Let's 동사원형 ~.' 등의 표현도 쓸 수 있는데 'Why don't you+동사 ~?'는 함께 하자는 것은 아니고 상대방에게만 권유하는 것이다.

02 ⑤는 '내가 도와줄까요?'의 의미이고, 나머지 보기들은 상대방에게 도움을 요청하는 말이다.

03 상대방에게 도움을 요청할 때는 'Can you help me ~?'로 시작하는 문장으로 표현할 수 있다. 이 때 can 대신 will을 쓸 수 있으며 would나 could를 써서 'Could you help me ~?'나 'Would you help me ~?'라고 말하면 공손하고 정중한 느낌을 준다.

04 what kinds of ~: 어떤 종류의 volunteer: 자원봉사의; 자원봉사자 / 어떤 종류의 봉사 활동을 할 수 있느냐는 질문을 했으므로, 구체적인 봉사 활동의 예시를 들며 같이 하자고 제안하는 것이 어울린다.

시험대비 실력평가   p.17~18

01 ①, ③   02 ③   03 ③   04 ④

05 ②   06 Can you help me buy a train ticket?

07 ③   08 give   09 bring your items and donate them   10 ④   11 ④   12 And how about playing some music?   13 ②

01 help는 5형식 동사로 '~이 …하는 것을 돕다'의 의미로 사용된다. 목적격 보어로 to부정사와 동사원형을 쓸 수 있다.

02 (B) be going to 동사원형: ~할 것이다 (C) these books를 받는 인칭대명사가 와야 하므로, 복수형 them이 어울린다.

03 fall down: 넘어지다 / 기차를 타려고 서두르다가 길에 넘어졌다는 말이 연결되어야 자연스럽다.

04 ① 어떻게 남자아이가 여자아이를 도울 것인가? ② 언제 여자아이가 다쳤는가? ③ 왜 여자 아이가 서둘렀는가? ④ 그들은 어디를 갈 것인가? ⑤ 여자아이는 무엇을 부러뜨렸는가?

---

05 ② 도와준다는 말에 내가 할 수 없다고 말하는 것은 어색하다. Can I give you a hand? → Can you give me a hand?

06 help 목적어 (to) 동사원형: ~가 …하는 것을 돕다

07 as: (접) ~과 같이, ~하는 대로 as you know: 아시다시피

08 give: 주다 give a hand: ~을 돕다

09 item: 항목, 물품 donate: 기부하다

10 ① 특별 행사의 목적 ② 특별 행사가 어디서 열리는지 ③ 특별 행사가 언제 열리는지 ④ 어떤 품목을 기부할 수 없는지 ⑤ 특별 행사에서 모금한 돈이 어디로 주어지는지

11 양로원에서 청소를 하자고 제안하자 좀 더 재미있는 걸 하고 싶다고 이야기했으므로 ③은 답이 되지 않는다. 빈칸 (A) 다음 문장에서 여자아이가 'What can we do at the party?(우리가 파티에서 뭘 할 수 있지?)'라고 말했으므로 파티를 열자고 제안한 것을 추리할 수 있다.

12 How about (동)명사: ~하는 게 어떨까?

13 ① 여자아이는 무슨 악기를 연주할 수 있는가? ② 어떤 음식을 양로원에 있는 사람들에게 대접할 것인가? ③ 언제가 봉사 활동의 날인가? ④ 그들은 봉사활동을 위해 어디로 갈 것인가? ⑤ 양로원에서 그들은 무엇을 할 것인가?

서술형 시험대비   p.19

01 (D) → (B) → (A) → (C)

02 (A) → (C) → (B) → (D)

03 ④ which has volunteered a lot → who[that] has volunteered a lot

04 can you help us find some good places?

05 do

06 of

01 다리에 무슨 문제가 있는지 묻는 질문에 (D) 지난주에 부러졌다고 대답한다. (B) 어떻게 된 일인지 질문하자 (A) 기차를 타려고 서두르다가 길에 넘어졌다고 답한다. (C) 이에, 정말 끔찍하다고 말한다.

02 봉사 활동의 날에 무엇을 할 건지 묻는 질문에 (A) 양로원에 가서 청소를 하자고 제안한다. (C) 이 제안에 나쁜 생각은 아니지만 좀 재미있는 걸 하고 싶다고 말하며 파티를 여는 것을 제안하고 (B) 좋은 생각이라고 답하며, 파티에서 무엇을 할 수 있는지 질문하자 (D) 음식을 대접할 수 있다고 대답한다.

03 선행사인 수민이는 사람이므로 주격 관계대명사 who나 that이 적절하다.

04 Can you help 목적어 (to) 동사원형 ~?: 목적어가 ~하는 것을 도와주겠니?

05 do volunteer work: 자원 봉사를 하다

06 take care of: ~을 돌보다 short: 짧은 / tail: 꼬리

핵심 Check   p.20~21

1 (1) whom   (2) which

2 (1) sleeping   (2) exciting   (3) written   (4) excited

시험대비 기본평가   p.22

01 ①, ②, ③

02 ④

03 (1) who → which[that]

   (2) which → who[whom/that]

   (3) exciting → excited

04 The chicken salad which my mom made is very delicious.

01 선행사가 The only food로 사물이며 find의 목적어 역할을 할 수 있는 목적격 관계대명사 that이나 which가 적절하다.

02 감정을 나타내는 타동사의 과거분사는 '~한 감정을 느끼는'이라는 의미로, 주로 사람을 주어로 하며, 현재분사는 주로 사물을 주어로 하여 '~한 감정을 유발하는'의 의미를 나타낸다.

03 (1) 선행사가 동물이므로 who를 which나 that으로 고쳐야 한다. (2) 선행사가 사람이므로 which를 who나 whom 또는 that으로 고쳐야 한다. (3) 사람이 주어이며 '신나는 감정을 느끼는' 것이므로 과거분사가 적절하다.

04 '우리 엄마가 만든'을 관계대명사절로 하여 '치킨 샐러드'를 수식하는 구조로 쓴다. 선행사가 사물이므로 목적격 관계대명사로 which를 쓴다.

시험대비 실력평가   p.23~25

01 ②   02 ③   03 ③

04 There is a dress in the box (which[that]) Alex sent (to) me.

05 (1) that   (2) who   (3) whom   (4) interested

   (5) interesting

06 ④   07 ①   08 ②

09 (1) scared (2) embarrassing (3) shocked 10 ③, ⑤

11 (1) who (2) that (3) which is   12 ④

13 (1) Audrey Hepburn is a person who[whom/that] my partner respects a lot.

   (2) This is the ID which[that] the spy used before.

   (3) The letter which[that] you sent to me last week made me happy.

   (4) Do you remember the girl who[whom/that] I met at the party?

   (5) I like the music to which I often listen. 또는 I like the music which[that] I often listen to.

   (6) Do you know the girl to whom Ann is talking? / Do you know the girl who[whom/that] Ann is talking to?

14 ③   15 ④

16 (1) She was shocked because their lives were very difficult.

   (2) I can't forget the tiger which I saw on safari.

   (3) Are you satisfied with your job as a tour guide?

17 (1) amazed   (2) amazing

01 <보기>와 나머지는 목적격 관계대명사이지만 ②번은 주격 관계대명사이다.

02 모두 목적격으로 사용된 관계대명사 that이 들어갈 수 있지만 ③번은 소유격 관계대명사 whose가 들어가야 한다.

03 감정을 나타내는 타동사의 과거분사는 '~한 감정을 느끼는'이라는 의미로, 주로 사람을 주어로 한다.

04 'Alex가 나에게 보낸 박스'에서 목적격 관계대명사를 이용하여 '박스'를 'Alex가 나에게 보낸'이 수식하는 구조로 만들어 준다.

05 (1) 선행사가 사물이므로 that, (2) 선행사가 사람이므로 who, (3) 전치사 with가 있으므로 that은 쓸 수 없다. (4) 내가 흥미를 갖게 되는 '수동'의 의미이므로 과거분사 interested가 적절하다. (5) the game이 흥미롭게 만들어 주는 '능동'의 의미이므로 현재분사가 적절하다.

06 아이들이 놀라게 되는 것이므로 '능동'의 frightening이 아니라 '수동'의 의미를 나타내는 frightened가 되어야 한다.

07 ① 목적격 관계대명사는 생략될 수 있다. ②, ④ 관계대명사의 선행사가 사람이면 who, whom이나 that을 쓰고 사물이면 which나 that을 쓴다. ③ 관계대명사가 접속사와 대명사의 역할을 하므로 목적어로 쓴 it을 삭제해야 한다. ⑤ 전치사가 관계대명사 앞에 올 경우에는 관계대명사 that을 쓸 수 없으며, 관계대명사를 생략하지 않는다.

08 ②번은 접속사이지만 나머지는 모두 관계대명사이다.

09 감정을 나타내는 타동사의 과거분사는 '~한 감정을 느끼는'이라는 의미로, 주로 사람을 주어로 하며, 현재분사는 주로 사물을 주어로 하여 '~한 감정을 유발하는'의 의미를 나타낸다.

10 선행사가 사물이므로 which나 that을 이용하고 목적격이므로 목적어로 쓰인 it은 쓰지 말아야 한다. 또한 목적격 관계대명사는 생략될 수 있다.

11 목적격 관계대명사와 '주격 관계대명사+be동사'는 생략할 수 있다.

12 Everyone feels depressed at some time or another. 사람이 주어로 우울해지는 것이므로 과거분사가 적절하다. some time or another: 이런저런 때에, 언젠가

13 목적격 관계대명사는 선행사가 사람이면 who나 whom, that

을, 사람이나 동물이면 which나 that을 쓴다. 일반적으로 목적격 관계대명사는 생략될 수 있다. 목적격 관계대명사가 전치사의 목적어인 경우 전치사는 관계대명사절의 끝에 오거나 관계대명사 앞에 올 수 있다. 전치사가 관계대명사절의 끝에 올 경우에는 관계대명사를 생략할 수 있다. 전치사가 관계대명사 앞에 올 경우에는 관계대명사 that을 쓸 수 없으며, 관계대명사를 생략하지 않는다.

14 감정을 나타내는 타동사의 현재분사는 주로 사물을 주어로 하여 '~한 감정을 유발하는'의 의미를 나타낸다. 의미상 영어가 나를 '신나게 하는' 것이 아니라 '지루하게 만드는' 것이 자연스러우므로 boring이 적절하다.

15 관계대명사 that은 전치사 다음에는 쓸 수 없다. that → whom

16 (1) '충격을 받은'은 '수동'의 뜻이므로 과거분사를 쓴다. (2) '사파리에서 보았던 호랑이'를 '사파리에서 보았던'이 호랑이를 수식하는 관계대명사절로 수식하도록 한다. (3) be satisfied with: ~에 만족하다

17 감정을 나타내는 타동사가 '어떤 감정을 느끼게 하면' 주로 사물을 주어로 하여 현재분사를 쓰고, '어떤 감정을 느끼면' 주로 사람을 주어로 하여 과거분사를 쓴다.

서술형 시험대비 p.26~27

01 Playing, excited

02 (1) I didn't know you were interested in Latin dance.
   (2) Emma was disappointed at her test score.
   (3) I think these highway signs are very confusing.
   (4) No one knows that I am worried about such a thing.
   (5) For me he was not boring, so I was not bored.

03 that → which

04 (1) Jayu Park is a park which[that] my grandfather often visits.
   (2) *Tom and Jerry* is a cartoon which[that] my little sister often watches.
   (3) That is the girl who[whom/that] I saw this morning.
   (4) The girl who[whom/that] I wanted to meet did not participate in the meeting.
   (5) The woman who[whom/that] Mom is talking to is Ms. Larson. 또는 The woman to whom Mom is talking is Ms. Larson.
   (6) Mariel took pictures of Ben and his car that were on the crime scene.

05 (1) King Sejong is a person who/whom/that my brother respects a lot.
   (2) This is the bridge which/that they built about 20 years ago.
   (3) The girl talked to a boy whom she met at the

party.
   (4) I don't like the movie which I saw yesterday.
   (5) There are many subjects about which people feel little interest. 또는 There are many subjects (that/which) people feel little interest about.

06 (1) I felt very tired all day because I didn't sleep well last night.
   (2) I was scared to be left home alone.
   (3) Watching a baseball game makes me bored.

07 (1) *The Smurfs* is a cartoon.
   (2) Let me introduce my friend.
   (3) Laura was looking for the key all day long.
   (4) I cannot speak about it for the reason.

08 (1) He put me in a very embarrassing situation.
   (2) My mom was surprised at the news.
   (3) It was shocking that he lied to me.
   (4) We were all excited because my brother made a goal in the soccer game.

01 주어로 동명사 Playing을 쓰고 '내가 신이 나게 되는' 것이므로 과거분사 excited를 쓴다.

02 (1)~(4) 감정을 나타내는 타동사의 과거분사는 '~한 감정을 느끼는'이라는 의미로, 주로 사람을 주어로 하며, 현재분사는 주로 사물을 주어로 하여 '~한 감정을 유발하는'의 의미를 나타낸다. (5) 주어가 사람일 때도 현재분사를 쓸 수 있다. '나에게 그가 따분하게 만들지 않아서 내가 따분하지 않았다'는 의미이다.

03 관계대명사 that은 전치사와 함께 쓰이지 않는다.

04 (1), (2) 선행사가 사물이므로 관계대명사 which나 that, (3), (4) 선행사가 사람이므로 관계대명사 who, whom이나 that, (5) 목적격 관계대명사가 전치사의 목적어인 경우 전치사는 관계대명사절의 끝에 오거나 관계대명사 앞에 올 수 있으며 전치사가 관계대명사절의 끝에 올 경우에는 관계대명사를 생략할 수 있다. 전치사가 관계대명사 앞에 올 경우에는 관계대명사 that을 쓸 수 없다. (6) 선행사가 '사람+사물'이므로 관계대명사 that을 써야 한다. 목적격 관계대명사는 생략될 수 있다. crime scene: 범죄 현장

05 (1) 선행사가 사람이므로 who, whom이나 that, (2) 선행사가 사물이므로 which나 that, (3) 관계대명사가 접속사와 대명사의 역할을 하므로 him을 삭제해야 한다. (4) 관계대명사가 접속사와 대명사의 역할을 하므로 it을 삭제해야 한다. (5) 전치사가 관계대명사 앞에 올 경우에는 관계대명사 that을 쓸 수 없으며, 관계대명사를 생략하지 않는다.

06 감정을 나타내는 타동사의 과거분사는 '~한 감정을 느끼는'이라는 의미로, 주로 사람을 주어로 하며, 현재분사는 주로 사물을 주어로 하여 '~한 감정을 유발하는'의 의미를 나타낸다.

07 목적격 관계대명사는 접속사와 목적어 역할을 하며 선행사가

사람이면 who나 whom, that, 사물이나 동물이면 which나 that을 쓴다. 목적격 관계대명사절에는 동사 뒤에 목적어가 없다는 것에 주의한다.

08 (1), (3) '난처하게 만드는 상황', '충격을 주는'의 뜻이 자연스러우므로 현재분사, (2), (4) '놀라게 되는', '신나게 되는'이 자연스러우므로 과거분사가 적절하다.

교과서 Reading

확인문제 p.28

1 T 2 F 3 F 4 T

확인문제 p.29

1 F 2 T 3 F 4 T

확인문제 p.29

1 T 2 F 3 F 4 T 5 T 6 F

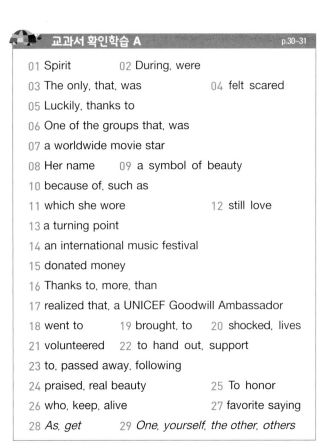

교과서 확인학습 A p.30~31

01 Spirit
02 During, were
03 The only, that, was
04 felt scared
05 Luckily, thanks to
06 One of the groups that, was
07 a worldwide movie star
08 Her name
09 a symbol of beauty
10 because of, such as
11 which she wore
12 still love
13 a turning point
14 an international music festival
15 donated money
16 Thanks to, more, than
17 realized that, a UNICEF Goodwill Ambassador
18 went to
19 brought, to
20 shocked, lives
21 volunteered
22 to hand out, support
23 to, passed away, following
24 praised, real beauty
25 To honor
26 who, keep, alive
27 favorite saying
28 *As, get*
29 *One, yourself, the other, others*

교과서 확인학습 B p.32~33

1 The Spirit of Audrey
2 During World War II, a little girl and her mother were hungry and sick.
3 The only food that they could find was grass.
4 The little girl felt scared all the time.
5 Luckily, the girl survived, thanks to the help of others.
6 One of the groups that helped her was UNICEF.
7 Later, the girl became a worldwide movie star.
8 Her name was Audrey Hepburn.
9 When she grew up, Hepburn became a symbol of beauty.
10 She was very popular because of her hit movies, such as *My Fair Lady and Roman Holiday.*
11 The little black dress which she wore in a movie is famous even today.
12 Many people still love her style.
13 The autumn of 1987 was a turning point in Hepburn's life.
14 She went to an international music festival in Macau.
15 Many people donated money at the festival, and the money went to UNICEF.
16 Thanks to her fame, UNICEF collected more money than ever before.
17 Hepburn realized that her fame could help others, so she became a UNICEF Goodwill Ambassador.
18 First, Hepburn went to Ethiopia in 1988.
19 There, she brought food to hungry children.
20 She was shocked because their lives were very difficult.
21 After that, she volunteered in other countries.
22 In 1990, she visited Vietnam to hand out medicine and support clean drinking water programs.
23 Her last trip was to Somalia in 1992, and she passed away the following year.
24 Many people praised her beauty and style, but Hepburn's real beauty was her heart.
25 To honor her, UNICEF made a statue, *The Spirit of Audrey.*
26 People who respect her keep her mission alive.
27 Her favorite saying shows her mission.
28 *As you get older, remember you have two hands.*
29 *One is for helping yourself, and the other is for helping others.*

01 (A) During (B)was (C)was		02 a little	
girl and her mother		03 ③	04 Later
05 like	06 fame	07 ①, ⑤	08 ③
09 ③	10 ②	11 ⑤	12 ②
13 ①	14 was → were		
15 before → after		16 ③	17 ②, ④
18 ③	19 ⑤	20 ②, ④	21 ②
22 ③	23 ②	24 ④, ⑤	
25 It made a statue, *The Spirit of Audrey.*			

01 (A) during+ 특정 기간을 나타내는 명사, while+주어+동사 (B) 주어 The only food를 서술하는 동사를 써야 하므로 was가 적절하다. that they could find는 주어를 수식하는 관계대명사절이다. (C) 문장의 주어는 groups가 아니라 One이므로 was가 적절하다.

02 '한 어린 소녀와 그녀의 어머니'를 가리킨다.

03 ⓑ: ~ 덕분에, ~ 때문에, ①, ②, ④, ⑤: ~ 때문에, ③ ~ 대신에

04 late: 늦은; 늦게 / later 나중에

05 such as = like: ~와 같은

06 famous의 명사 'fame'을 쓰는 것이 적절하다.

07 ⓒ와 ①, ⑤번은 접속사, 나머지는 다 관계대명사이다

08 ③ 1987년 가을은 헵번의 인생 '전환점'이었다.

09 주어진 문장의 that에 주목한다. ③번 앞 문장의 내용을 받고 있으므로 ③번이 적절하다.

10 ⓐ와 ①, ②, ④: 동명사, ③, ⑤: 현재분사

11 위 글은 ⑤ '전기'이다. ① (신문·잡지의) 기사, ③ 독후감, ④ 수필

12 ② 헵번은 에티오피아에서 '굶주린 아이들에게 음식을 가져다주었다.'

13 ① how: 어떻게, 어떠하게, ⓐ 제2차 세계 대전 중에 당신의 삶은 '어땠나요?' ⓒ '어떻게' 유니세프를 위해 일하기 시작했나요?

14 주어가 My family and I이기 때문에 were로 고치는 것이 적절하다.

15 1987년 마카오의 한 음악 축제가 오드리의 인생을 바꾼 것이기 때문에, 1987년 '이후에' 아프리카와 아시아의 몇 나라들을 방문해서 봉사했다고 고치는 것이 적절하다.

16 ⓐ bring A to B: B에게 A를 가져다주다, to Somalia: 소말리아에[로] ⓒ for helping: 돕기 위한

17 ⓑ 부사적 용법(목적), ① 부사적 용법(결과), ③ 부사적 용법(원인), ⑤ 부사적 용법(목적), ② 명사적 용법, ④ 형용사적 용법

18 ③ 헵번이 배우로서의 성공 여부는 본문에 언급되어 있지 않다.

19 ⑤ 유니세프가 '오드리의 정신'이라는 동상을 어디에 만들었는지는 대답할 수 없다. ① In 1988. ② She brought food to them. ③ To hand out medicine and support clean drinking water programs. ④ In 1992.

20 ② 실제로, ④ 적어도, ⓐ와 나머지: 마침내

21 ① 의지가 강한, ② 이기적인, ③ 다정한, ④ 자선을 베푸는, 궁핍한 사람들을 돕는, ⑤ 관대한

22 ③ 글쓴이의 엄마가 언제 행복하게 느끼는지는 알 수 없다. ① The writer's mom. ② She smiles a lot and tries to see the good in everything. ④ She had a serious car accident. She was in the hospital for six months. ⑤ Because she always helps people in need and she donates money and does volunteer work.

23 오드리 헵번이 방문한 국가와 그곳에서 한 활동을 소개함으로써 필자는 '헵번의 진정한 아름다움이 그녀의 마음이었음을' 설명하고 있다.

24 ⓐ와 ④, ⑤번은 동명사이다. 명사를 수식하더라도 목적이나 용도를 나타낼 때는 동명사이다. drinking water: 식수, be fond of: ~을 좋아하다, 나머지는 다 현재분사

25 그녀를 기리기 위해, 유니세프는 '오드리의 정신'이라는 동상을 만들었다.

01 World War Two 또는 the second World War
02 that
03 (A) the help   (B) movie star
04 (A) music festival   (B) UNICEF Goodwill Ambassador
05 donated   06 (A)Thanks to (B)collected (C)than
07 As[Because]
08 (A)shocked   (B)keep   (C) *the other*
09 (A) volunteered   (B)her heart
10 ⓐ died ⓑ *become* 또는 *grow*
11 your life during World War Ⅱ
12 others
13 (A)help   (B)help

01 로마 숫자를 포함하고 있는 단어를 영어로 읽을 때 '단어+기수' 또는 'the+서수+단어'로 읽는다. 단, Elizabeth Ⅱ는 Elizabeth the second로 읽는다.

02 선행사에 수식어 the only가 있을 때에는 보통 관계대명사 that을 사용한다.

03 오드리 헵번은 다른 사람들의 '도움' 덕분에 제2차 세계 대전에서 살아남았고 후에 세계적인 '영화배우'가 되었다.

04 매우 인기 있는 여배우였던 헵번은 1987년 가을에 마카오의 한국제 '음악 축제'에 갔다. 그 때 그녀는 자신의 명성이 다른 사람들을 도울 수 있다는 것을 깨닫고, '유니세프 친선 대사'가 되었다.

7

05 donate: 기부하다, 자선단체에 주다 / 과거시제로 쓰는 것이 적절하다.

06 (A) 그녀의 명성 '덕분에'라고 해야 하므로 Thanks to가 적절하다. in spite of: ~에도 불구하고, (B) 더 많은 돈을 '모았다'고 해야 하므로 collected가 적절하다. correct: 바로잡다, 정정하다, (C) 어느 때'보다도' 더 많은 돈이라고 해야 하므로 than이 적절하다. then: 그때, 그 다음에

07 'so' 대신에, 이유를 나타내는 접속사 'As[Because, Since]'를 맨 앞에 쓰는 것이 적절하다.

08 (A) 그녀가 '충격을 받은' 것이기 때문에 shocked가 적절하다. (B) 주어가 복수(People)이므로 동사는 keep이 적절하다. (C) 두 개의 손 중에 다른 한 손을 가리키므로 the other가 적절하다. the other: 둘 중 나머지 하나, another 셋 이상 중에서 두 번째 것을 가리킨다.

09 헵번이 많은 나라들을 방문하고 그곳에서 '봉사한' 것으로 판단하건대, 헵번의 진정한 아름다움은 '그녀의 마음'이었다. judging from ~으로 판단하건대[미루어 보아]

10 ⓐ pass away 죽다, ⓑ get[become, grow]+형용사의 비교급: 점점 ~해지다

11 '제2차 세계 대전 동안 당신의 삶'을 가리킨다.

12 other people은 others로 바꿔 쓸 수 있다.

13 제2차 세계 대전 동안, Audrey의 가족과 Audrey는 굶주리고 아팠고 다른 사람들의 '도움' 덕분에 살아남았다. 1987년 마카오의 한 음악 축제 이후, Audrey는 자신의 명성이 다른 사람들을 '도울 수 있다'는 것을 알게 되었고, 유니세프를 위해 일하기 시작했다.

영역별 핵심문제
p.41~45

01 ③　　**02** (1) (m)oment　(2) (p)raised
(3) (r)ealized　(4) (c)ollecting　　**03** ④
04 (1) hold　(2) fell　(3) clean　(4) raise
05 can you help me wash them?
06 (A) Why, (B) What　　**07** ③
08 Shall we raise money and help the people there?
Let's raise money and help the people there.
09 ⑤
10 can you help me (to) move these books?
11 donate　　**12** ②
13 Doing[To do] yoga makes me relaxed.
14 ③　　　**15** ④　　　**16** ②, ③　　　**17** ③, ⑤
18 (1) interesting, bored　(2) tired
19 (1) The man (who/whom) I saw at the café was
Park Jisung.
(2) I love the dog (which) my grandmother adopted.
(3) Jason didn't know about the party, so he was
really surprised.

---

(4) We were so shocked when we heard about the
accident.　　　**20** which　　**21** ②
22 People who[that] respect her keep her mission
alive.　　**23** ⑤
24 (1) 에티오피아(1988년), (2) 베트남(1990년), (3) 소말리아
(1992년)　　**25** (A) terrible (B)changed (C)what
26 working　　**27** ④
28 helped young students with math homework
29 are → is

01 ① homeless: 집 없는, 노숙자의 ② elderly: 나이가 지긋한 ③ worldwide: 세계적인 ④ international: 국제적인 ⑤ following: (그) 다음의

02 (1) moment: 순간, 잠깐 (2) praise: 칭찬하다 (3) realize: 깨닫다, 알아차리다 (4) collect: 모으다, 수집하다

03 fame: 명성 / 유명한 상태

04 (1) hold a party: 파티를 열다 (2) fall down: 넘어지다 (3) clean up: ~을 치우다, ~을 청소하다 (4) raise money: 돈을 모금하다

05 Can you help 목적어 (to) 동사원형 ~?: 목적어가 ~하는 것을 도와주겠니?

06 Why don't you ~?: ~하지 그래? What: 무엇

07 남자아이 1이 'Can you help me wash these dogs?(이 개들 씻기는 거 도와줄 수 있니?)'라는 묻는 질문에 'Sure. But I have to walk these dogs first. After that, I will help you.(그럼. 근데 나 이 개들 산책 먼저 시켜야 해. 끝나고 나서 도와줄게.)'라고 대답했으므로, 개 산책을 시킬 것이다.

08 특정 행동을 제안할 때는 'Why don't we ~?'로 시작하는 표현을 쓴다. 'Shall we ~?', 'Let's ~' 등의 표현도 쓸 수 있다.

09 ① 어떻게 어려움에 처한 사람들을 위해 돈을 모금할 것인가? ② 어디서 특별 행사가 열리는가? ③ 언제 특별 행사가 열리는가? ④ 어디서 큰 불이 있었는가? ⑤ 언제 Mapletown에서 큰 불이 있었는가?

10 Can you help 목적어 (to) 동사원형 ~?: 목적어가 ~하는 것을 도와주겠니?

11 donate: 기부하다 / 사람들을 돕기 위해 무언가를 주다

12 오늘 오후에 무엇을 하기를 원하는지 묻는 질문에, 테니스를 같이 치자고 제안하는 것이 적절하다. Why don't we ~?: ~하는 게 어떨까?

13 내가 느긋해지는 것이므로 relaxed로 써야 한다.

14 감정을 나타내는 타동사의 과거분사는 '~한 감정을 느끼는'이라는 의미로, 주로 사람을 주어로 하며, 현재분사는 주로 사물을 주어로 하여 '~한 감정을 유발하는'의 의미를 나타낸다.

15 ④ Susan is the woman (who/whom/that) I helped on the street.

16 ① The little girl felt scared all the time. ④ Riding

a roller coaster makes me excited. ⑤ It was very exciting, and I became interested in hockey!

17 ③, ⑤번은 주격 관계대명사이고, 나머지는 모두 목적격 관계대명사이다. run into: ~을 우연히 만나다

18 감정을 나타내는 타동사의 과거분사는 '~한 감정을 느끼는'이라는 의미로, 주로 사람을 주어로 하며, 현재분사는 주로 사물을 주어로 하여 '~한 감정을 유발하는'의 의미를 나타낸다.

19 (1), (2) 관계대명사의 선행사가 사람이면 who, whom이나 that을, 사물이면 which나 that을 사용한다. (3), (4) 감정을 나타내는 타동사의 과거분사는 '~한 감정을 느끼는'이라는 의미로, 주로 사람을 주어로 한다.

20 목적격 관계대명사 which를 생략할 수 있다.

21 ② 많은 사람이 '여전히 그녀의 스타일을 사랑한다.'

22 주격 관계대명사 'who'나 'that'을 보충하면 된다.

23 ⓑ와 ⑤번은 (비례) ~함에 따라, ~할수록, As you get older: 나이가 들어갈수록, ① 같은 정도로, 마찬가지로, ② ~처럼, ~하는 대로, ③ ~할 때, ④ ~이므로, ~이기 때문에

24 에티오피아(1988년) → 베트남(1990년) → 소말리아(1992년) 순서로 방문했다.

25 (A) 제2차 세계 대전 동안 나의 삶은 '끔찍했다'고 해야 하므로 terrible이 적절하다. terrific: 아주 좋은, 멋진, 훌륭한, (B) 마카오의 한 음악 축제가 인생을 '바꿨다'고 해야 하므로 changed가 적절하다. exchange: 교환하다, (C) 당신은 '무엇을' 했습니까?'라고 해야 하므로 what이 적절하다. how를 쓰면 do 다음에 목적어를 써야 한다.

26 begin은 목적어로 to부정사와 동명사를 둘 다 쓸 수 있다.

27 ④ 마카오의 음악 축제에 Audrey가 참가한 이유는 알 수 없다. ① It was terrible. ② Thanks to the help of others. ③ In 1987, a musical festival in Macau changed her life and she learned that her fame could help other people. ⑤ Some countries in Africa and Asia.

28 앞 문장의 내용을 가리킨다.

29 주어가 동명사 helping이므로 단수로 취급해야 하고, helping 이하는 일반적인 사실을 나타내기 때문에 현재시제로 써야 하므로 is로 고치는 것이 적절하다.

단원별 예상문제
p.46~49

01 favor   02 ④   03 What   04 ②, ⑤
05 ③   06 ⑤   07 ①   08 ⑤
09 nursing home   10 ②   11 ③
12 Why don't we check the volunteering website for teens?
13 (1) This is the cell phone (which/that) I broke yesterday.
   (2) The speed at which everything moved felt strange.

---

   (3) The girl who I met the other day was very pretty.
   (4) I was very worried about his health.

14 (1) excited   (2) interested

15 ②번, excited → scared 또는 frightened   16 ③, ⑤

17 (A)because of (B)is (C)turning   18 ④

19 she realized (that) her fame could help others.

20 volunteered   21 helping others

22 *you → yourself*

23 We survived thanks to the help of others.

24 in some countries in Africa and Asia   25 ⑤

01 주어진 보기는 명사와 형용사의 관계이다. beauty: 아름다움, 미(美) beautiful: 아름다운 favor: 호의, 친절 favorable: 호의적인

02 friendly: 친절한 gentle: 온화한 curious: 호기심 많은 polite: 공손한 careful: 주의깊은 outgoing: 외향적인 patient: 끈기 있는

03 What kinds of ~: 어떤 종류의 What about 동명사 ~?: ~하는 게 어떨까?

04 thanks to: ~ 덕분에 because of: ~ 때문에 due to: ~ 때문에, ~ 덕분에

05 (B) 책을 옮기는 것을 도와줄 수 있느냐는 질문에 (C) 도와줄 수 있다고 대답하며 책으로 뭘 할지 질문하자 (A) 어린이 도서관에 기부할 거라고 대답한다.

06 (C) 어린이 병원에서 봉사 활동을 할 것을 제안하자 (B) 좋다고 대답하며, 거기서 뭘 할 수 있는지 질문한다. (A) 아픈 아이들을 위해 음악을 연주할 수 있다고 대답한다.

07 저번에 봉사 활동으로 공원을 청소했으므로 이번에는 무엇을 할지 묻는 질문이 연결되는 것이 자연스럽다. 또한 주어진 문장에 대해 양로원에 가서 청소하는 것을 제안하는 내용이 나오는 ① 이 적절하다.

08 ⓐ visit ⓑ clean it up ⓒ to do ⓓ something fun ⓔ hold

09 nursing home: 양로원 / 너무 나이 들거나 병이 들어서 스스로를 돌볼 수 없는 사람들이 사는 장소

10 주어진 문장은 봉사활동에 대한 부가적 설명으로, 봉사활동을 제안하는 말에 이어 나오는 것이 적절하다.

11 do volunteer work: 자원 봉사를 하다

12 Why don't we ~?: ~하는 게 어떠니? check: 확인하다

13 (1) 선행사가 사물이므로 which나 that, (2) 전치사가 관계대명사 앞에 올 경우에는 관계대명사 that을 쓸 수 없으며, 관계대명사를 생략하지 않는다. (3) 관계대명사가 접속사와 대명사의 역할을 하므로 목적어 her를 삭제해야 한다. (4) 감정을 나타내는 타동사의 과거분사는 '~한 감정을 느끼는'이라는 의미로, 주로 사람을 주어로 한다.

14 (1) excite는 타동사로 '흥분시키다'라는 의미이다. 경기가 나를

흥분시키고 나는 흥분되는 것이므로 game을 주어로 할 때는 현재분사가, 나를 주어로 할 때는 과거분사가 적절하다. (2) 야구가 지루하다고 생각하는 것이므로 관심이 없다고 쓸 수 있다.

15 제2차 세계 대전 동안, 어린 소녀는 굶주리고 아팠기 때문에 내내 '겁에 질려 있었다.'로 고쳐야 한다. frightened: 겁먹은, 무서워하는

16 ③, ⑤번은 접속사, ⓐ와 나머지는 관계대명사이다.

17 (A) 뒤에 명사가 나오므로 because of가 적절하다. because of+명사나 동명사, because+주어+동사, (B) 주어 The little black dress를 서술하는 동사를 써야 하므로 is가 적절하다. which she wore in a movie는 주어를 수식하는 관계대명사절이다. (C) 인생의 '전환점'이라고 해야 하므로 turning이 적절하다. turning point: 전환점

18 주어진 문장의 UNICEF collected more money than ever before에 주목한다. ④번 앞 문장의 내용에 이어지는 말이므로 ④번이 적절하다.

19 헵번은 '자신의 명성이 다른 사람들을 도울 수 있다는 것을 깨닫고', 유니세프 친선 대사가 되었다.

20 volunteer: (어떤 일을 하겠다고) 자원[자진]하다 / 자원 봉사로 하다, 어떤 일을 하도록 강요받지 않고 해주다 / 과거시제로 쓰는 것이 적절하다.

21 '타인을 돕는 것'을 가리킨다.

22 자기 자신을 돕는 것으로 주어와 목적

23 survive: 살아남다, 생존하다, thanks to: ~ 덕택에, ~ 때문에

24 '아프리카와 아시아의 몇몇 나라들'을 가리킨다.

25 Audrey는 아프리카와 아시아의 몇몇 나라들에서 봉사하였다.

서술형 실전문제 p.50~51

01 ⓐ with ⓑ in ⓒ to ⓓ down

02 Is there anything (that) I can do for you?

03 (A) Why don't we raise money and help the people there?
   (B) Please give a hand to people in need.

04 (1) I told you about her.
   (2) I made it for my family.
   (3) The food was delicious.
   (4) You ate dinner with her last Sunday.

05 (1) disappointed   (2) excited

06 because she was a UNICEF Goodwill Ambassador
   → because of her hit movies, such as *My Fair Lady* and *Roman Holiday*

07 The little black dress which she wore in a movie is famous even today.

08 a turning point

09 (A)shocked   (B)last   (C)alive

10 ②번, from Somalia → to Somalia

11 She passed away in 1993.

01 ⓐ What's wrong with ~?: ~에 무슨 문제가 있는 겁니까? ⓑ be in a hurry: 서두르다 ⓒ to부정사의 부사적 용법 중 목적(~하기 위해서) ⓓ fall down: 넘어지다

02 there is ~: ~가 있다 for: ~을 위해

03 (A) Why don't we ~?: ~하는 게 어떨까? raise money: 돈을 모금하다 (B) give a hand: ~을 돕다 in need: 어려움에 처한

04 목적격 관계대명사는 선행사가 사람이면 who나 whom, that을, 사람이 아니면 which나 that을 쓴다. 목적격 관계대명사는 생략될 수 있다. 목적격 관계대명사가 전치사의 목적어인 경우 전치사는 관계대명사절의 끝에 오거나 관계대명사 앞에 올 수 있으며 끝에 올 경우에는 관계대명사를 생략할 수 있다. 앞에 올 경우에는 관계대명사 that을 쓸 수 없으며, 관계대명사를 생략하지 않는다.

05 (1) disappoint는 타동사로 '실망시키다'라는 의미이다. 결과가 Nick을 실망시키고 Nick은 실망이 되는 것이므로 the result를 주어로 할 때는 현재분사가, Nick을 주어로 할 때는 과거분사가 적절하다. (2) Alita가 신난다고 생각하는 것이므로 Alita에 대해 신이 났다고 쓸 수 있다. 보통 과거분사는 사람을 주어로 하며 현재분사는 사물을 주어로 한다.

06 헵번은 '<마이 페어 레이디>와 <로마의 휴일>과 같은 흥행 영화들로 인해' 매우 인기가 있었다.

07 'even'을 보충하면 된다.

08 헵번의 인생에서 '전환점'이 된 행사는 1987년 가을에 열린 마카오의 한 국제 음악 축제였다.

09 (A) 그들의 삶이 매우 어려웠기 때문에 '충격을 받았다'고 해야 하므로 shocked가 적절하다. pleased: 기쁜, (B) 그녀의 '마지막' 여행이라고 해야 하므로 last가 적절하다. last: 마지막의, latest: 최근의, (C) 목적격보어로 쓰였고 뒤에 명사가 없기 때문에 alive가 적절하다. alive: 살아 있는, 존속하는(명사 앞에는 안 씀), live: 살아 있는(주로 명사 앞에 씀)

10 그녀의 마지막 여행은 1992년 '소말리아에' 간 것이었다고 해야 하므로 to Somalia로 고쳐야 한다.

11 그녀의 마지막 여행은 1992년 소말리아에 간 것이었으며, 이듬해 그녀는 사망하였다고 했으므로 1993년에 사망하였다.

창의사고력 서술형 문제 p.52

01 Why don't we / How about meeting at 1? / I'm afraid I can't. / What about meeting / Let's
[모범답안]
02 my mom / the good / car accident / in need / big hero

01 What[How] about 동명사 ~?: ~하는 게 어떨까? Why don't we ~?: ~하는 게 어떨까? I'm afraid I can't.: 유감이지만 할 수 없어.

01 ⑤ 02 ③

03 (1) honor (2) broke, accident (3) mission
   (4) statue (5) survived

04 all the time

05 ⓒ am → was ⓔ terrific → terrible

06 can you help me (to) carry this bag?

07 ③ 08 Can you help me (to) solve a math problem[math problems]?

09 ⑤

10 We need someone who has volunteered a lot.

11 for 12 ② 13 ④

14 (1) relaxed (2) interesting

15 ①, ③, ④

16 (1) The book (which/that) she was reading is missing.
  (2) The man (who/whom/that) I was having lunch with was Yoojin. 또는 The man with whom I was having lunch was Yoojin.
  (3) We were amazed at the beautiful scenery.
  (4) Dan is not a funny guy, but I'm not bored when I am with him.

17 ⑤ 18 thanks to Hepburn's fame 19 ③

20 hungry children 21 ⑤ 22 ②

23 ④

24 She was in the hospital for six months. 25 ③

---

01 collect: 모으다, 수집하다

02 hold: 열다, 개최하다

03 (1) honor: 존경하다, 존중하다 (2) break one's leg: 다리가 부러지다 accident: 사고 (3) mission: 임무, 사명 (4) statue: 조각상 (5) survive: 살아남다, 생존하다

04 always: 항상 all the time: 늘, 내내

05 'What happened?'는 과거에 무슨 일이 있었는지 질문하는 것이므로 과거시제로 써야 맞다. terrific: 멋진 terrible: 끔찍한

06 Can you help 목적어 (to) 동사원형 ~?: 목적어가 ~하는 것을 도와주겠니?

07 ⓐ can you help ⓑ move these books ⓒ Sure / Of course ⓓ What are you going ⓔ I'm going to

08 Can you help 목적어 (to) 동사원형 ~?: 목적어가 ~하는 것을 도와주겠니? solve a problem: 문제를 풀다 math: 수학

09 are → is / 동명사 주어는 단수 취급한다.

10 need: 필요하다 volunteer: 자원봉사를 하다 a lot: 많이

11 search for: ~을 찾다 for: ~을 위한

12 ② 수민이가 아니라 다른 여자아이의 생각이다.

13 관계대명사가 접속사와 대명사의 역할을 하므로 bought 다음에 목적어로 쓴 it을 삭제해야 한다.

14 영화를 보는 것이 '긴장이 풀어지도록 하는' 것이므로 과거분사, 게임이 '재미있게 해주는' 것이므로 현재분사를 쓴다.

15 선행사가 사람이므로 목적격 관계대명사로 who나 whom 또는 that을 써야 한다.

16 (1) 목적격 관계대명사를 이용하여 '그녀가 읽고 있던' 이 '책'을 수식하는 구조로 쓴다. (2) '내가 함께 점심을 먹고 있던'이 '남자'를 수식하는 구조로 쓴다. 목적격 관계대명사가 전치사 with의 목적어 역할을 한다. 목적격 관계대명사는 생략될 수 있다. (3), (4) 감정을 나타내는 타동사의 과거분사는 '~한 감정을 느끼는'이라는 의미로, 주로 사람을 주어로 한다.

17 ⑤ Someone was following me, and I felt scared. crocodile: 악어

18 '헵번의 명성 덕분에', 유니세프는 어느 때보다도 더 많은 돈을 모을 수 있었다.

19 이 글은 '헵번의 명성과 그녀의 인생 전환점'에 관한 글이다.

20 에티오피아의 '굶주린 아이들'의 삶을 가리킨다.

21 ⓑ 선행사 People을 수식하는 주격 관계대명사, ⑤ 선행사 Anyone을 수식하는 주격 관계대명사 나머지는 다 의문대명사 (누구)

22 다른 한 손은 '타인'을 돕기 위한 것이라고 하는 것이 적절하다.

23 위 글은 필자가 존경하는 영웅에 대한 이야기이므로 제목으로는 '나의 작지만 거대한 영웅'이 적절하다.

24 글쓴이의 엄마는 '6개월' 동안 병원에 있었다.

25 ③ 그녀는 자동차 사고에서 '회복했다.'

The Best Trip of Your Life

시험대비 실력평가
p.60

01 ③ 02 ③ 03 (1) scenery
(2) condition (3) autumn (5) amusement park
04 (a)wesome 05 (p)urpose 06 ④
07 ③ 08 ③ 09 ⑤

01 item: 물품 goods: 상품, 물건
02 a variety of: 여러 가지의, 다양한
03 (1) scenery: 풍경, 경치 / 나는 이 해변을 추천한다. 그것은 가장 아름다운 풍경을 가지고 있다. (2) condition: 상태, 상황 / 그 차는 상태가 좋다. (3) autumn: 가을 / 가을에 잎은 빨갛게 변한다. (4) amusement park: 놀이공원 / 그들은 놀이공원에서 재미있게 놀고 있다.
04 awesome: 매우 멋진 / 멋지거나 인상적인
05 purpose: 목적, 목표 / 어떤 것이 사용되거나 행해지는 이유
06 take: (얼마의 시간이) 걸리다
07 get to: (장소·위치에) 도착하다 / 우리는 곧 공항에 도착할 것이다.
08 rough: 거친, 파도가 심한 / 그 보트는 거친 파도를 헤치며 항해했다.

서술형 시험대비
p.61

01 goods
02 (p)laces
03 (1) Eugene's violin is old but still in good condition.
(2) The restaurant features a variety of desserts.
(3) You have to focus on your studies.
(4) I visited a foreign country last month.
04 (1) amazing (2) natural
05 get
06 how
07 (1) comic books (2) plans (3) block (4) cafe

01 goods: 상품, 물건 / 판매를 위한 물품 / 그들은 영국으로부터 비싼 상품들을 수입했다.
02 site: 장소 place: 장소, 곳 / 그 도시에는 중요한 역사적 장소들이 많다.
03 (1) condition: 상태, 상황 (2) a variety of: 여러 가지의, 다양한 (3) focus on: (~에) 집중하다, 초점을 맞추다 (4) foreign: 외국의 visit: 방문하다, 찾아가다

04 (1) amaze: 놀라게 하다 amazing: 놀라운, 멋진 (2) nature: 자연 natural: 자연의
05 get off: 내리다, 하차하다 get on: 타다, 승차하다
06 Can you tell me how to get ~?: ~에 어떻게 가는지 말해줄 수 있나요? How long does it take to go to ~?:~까지 가는데 얼마나 걸리나요?
07 (1) comic book: 만화책 (2) plan: 계획 (3) block: 블록, 구역 (4) cafe: 카페, 커피숍

교과서 Conversation

핵심 Check
p.62~63

1 What are you, to do / I'm planning to do / What are you / going to see a movie
2 What are you planning to do this weekend? / I'm planning to visit my grandparents in Seoul.
3 (1) (C) → (A) → (B) → (D)
(2) (D) → (B) → (C) → (A) → (E)
4 How long does it take? / It takes 30 minutes by bus.

교과서 대화문 익히기

Check(√) True or False
p.64

1 T 2 F 3 F 4 T

교과서 확인학습
p.66~67

Listen & Talk 1 A

What are you, this / going, go / What, you, do / I'm planning to

Listen & Talk 1 B

have, this, have any / (g)oing / What, (p)lanning to, with / I'm (p)lanning, with them, about, plans for / (g)oing, stay, relax

Listen & Talk 1 C

Where, field trip / We are going to / (i)nteresting, (p)lanning to see / are, I'm (p)lanning to see, Where /

We are going to, amusement, excited

Listen & Talk 2 A
How, get / by / How long, take, get / It takes

Listen & Talk 2 B
pictures, beautiful, Where, take / were, of, should / to, How, get, from / Get on, off, see, front / long, take / takes / next weekend

Listen & Talk 2 C
How do I get to / go there by bus or on foot / How long, take / by, on foot / Can you tell, how to get / Go, turn, on / Go, for, turn left

Do It Yourself A
What, (p)lanning to do this / to go to / Are you, to see / will, I'm, to visit / How long / an hour and 40 minutes by / much, than, have

시험대비 기본평가   p.68

01 ②, ⑤   02 ④   03 ③   04 ③

01 What are you going to 동사원형 ~?: 너는 무엇을 할 거니? What are you planning to 동사원형 ~?: 너는 뭐 할 계획이니? be going to 동사원형: ~할 예정이다

02 특정 장소까지의 소요 시간을 물을 때는 'How long does it take to get ~?'이라고 묻는다. 시간이 얼마 걸린다는 표현이 나와야 한다. It takes (about) 시간: ~ (정도) 걸려.

03 계획을 대답할 때 'I'm going to 동사원형 ~.', 'I'm thinking of (동)명사 ~.', 'I'm planning to 동사원형 ~.' 또는 'I will 동사원형'을 사용하여 말할 수 있다.

04 ③번은 현재진행형을 사용해서 휴가 동안 무엇을 하고 있는 중인지 묻고 있는 질문이다. 이외의 문장들은 계획을 묻고 있는 것들이다.

시험대비 실력평가   p.69~70

01 ①   02 go there   03 ④   04 ④
05 ④   06 ④   07 ①   08 ②, ⑤
09 ④   10 have   11 ⑤
12 I'm going to stay home and relax.

01 주어진 문장은 '(사진을) 어디서 찍었어?'란 의미이므로, 사진들이 예쁘다고 말한 이후에 질문하고, 여자아이가 Riverside Park에서 찍었다고 대답하는 것이 어울린다. 그러므로 ①이 적절하다.

02 여자아이의 'You should go there.(넌 거기 꼭 가 봐야 해.)'라는 말에 'I want to.'라고 대답하고 있으므로 '나도 거기 가 보고 싶

다.'라는 말을 줄여서 쓴 것임을 알 수 있다.

03 ④ this weekend → next weekend 남자아이는 다음 주말에 Riverside Park에 갈 것이다.

04 ④ 소요 시간을 물어보는 질문에 거리를 말하는 것은 어색하다. How long does it take to get ~?: ~에 가는 데 얼마나 걸려?

05 (C) 학교에 어떻게 가는지 질문하자 (B) 버스를 타고 간다고 대답한다. (A) 거기(학교)까지 가는 데 얼마나 걸리는지 소요 시간을 묻자, (D) 15분 걸린다고 대답한다.

06 주어진 문장은 '거기(한국 대학교)에 어떻게 가는지 말해 줄 수 있나요?'란 뜻으로 다음에 버스를 타거나, 걸어서 갈 수 있다고 가는 방법을 안내해 주는 말이 나오는 ④번이 적절하다.

07 How do I get to 장소: ~에 어떻게 가나요? How long does it take to get ~?: ~까지 가는 데 얼마나 걸리나요?

08 ① 사진을 찍다 ③ 가져가다 ④ (버스를) 타다 ② 시간이 그렇게 많이 걸리지 않아요. ⑤ 그것을 준비하려면 많은 시간이 걸릴 것이다.

09 휴가 동안 여자아이의 계획은 조부모님을 방문해 한옥 마을에 갈 계획이라고 말하고, 이에 남자 아이는 휴가 때 무슨 계획이 있는지 질문해야 '나는 집에 머물면서 쉴 거야.'로 대답할 수 있으므로 ④번이 적절하다.

10 have a holiday: 휴가를 보내다 Do you have any plans?: 무슨 계획이라도 있니?

11 빈칸 다음에 남자아이가 'What are you planning to do with them?(그분들과 어떤 것을 할 계획이야?)'으로 말한 것으로 보아 여자아이는 them이라고 지칭할 만한 대상과 같이 무엇을 할 예정이다.

12 be going to 동사원형: ~할 예정이다 relax: 휴식을 취하다, 느긋이 쉬다

서술형 시험대비   p.71

01 to do
02 she is going to do this weekend, is going to go to, is planning to go hiking
03 (D) → (B) → (A) → (C)
04 (1) I will watch a soccer game.
   (2) I am going to watch a soccer game.
   (3) I am thinking of watching a soccer game.
05 (A) interesting (B) excited
06 What are you planning to see there?

01 be going to 동사원형: ~할 예정이다 be planning to 동사원형: ~할 계획이다 do: 하다

02 be going to 동사원형: ~할 예정이다 this weekend: 이번 주말에 여자아이는 제주도에 가서 한라산에 하이킹을 갈 계획을 가지고 있다.

03 어디 갈 것인지 묻는 질문에 → (D) 바르셀로나에 갈 것이라고
대답한다. → (B) 거기(바르셀로나)까지 가는 데 얼마나 걸리는
지 소요시간을 묻고 → (A) 비행기를 타고 14시간이 걸린다고
대답한다. → (C) 그곳에서의 계획을 묻자 축구 경기를 볼 계획
이라고 대답한다.

04 계획을 대답할 때 'I'm going to 동사원형 ~.', 'I'm thinking
of (동)명사 ~.', 'I'm planning to 동사원형 ~.' 또는 'I will
동사원형'을 사용하여 말할 수 있다. be going to 동사원형: ~
할 예정이다 be planning to 동사원형: ~할 계획이다 'I'm
thinking of ~': 나는 ~을 할까 생각 중이다

05 감정을 나타내는 동사의 경우 현재분사는 '~하게 하는'의 뜻으
로 감정을 유발하는 대상에 쓰이고, 과거분사는 '~하게 된'의 뜻
으로 감정을 느끼는 대상에 쓰인다. (A)는 '미술관에 가는 것이
재미있겠다'라는 의미이므로 현재분사형, (B)는 남자아이가 롤
러코스터 탈 생각으로 신나는 감정을 느끼는 것이므로 과거분사
형을 쓴다.

06 be planning to 동사원형: ~할 계획이다 there: 거기에서

교과서
Grammar

핵심 Check   p.72~73

1 (1) it safe to   (2) It, to   (3) important not to
2 (1) what you bought   (2) if[whether] you like
  (3) Who do you think will

시험대비 기본평가   p.74

01 ②   02 ③   03 ⑤
04 (1) It was nice to relax in a café and read the
      books.
   (2) Do you know where the first train station in
      Korea is?

01 간접의문문은 '의문사+주어+동사'의 형태로 다른 문장 안에서
주어, 목적어, 보어 역할을 한다.

02 ③번은 거리를 나타내는 비인칭 주어이고, 나머지는 모두 가주
어이다.

03 간접의문문은 '의문사+주어+동사'의 어순이다. It으로 받고 있
으므로 단수가 적절하다.

04 (1) 가주어 it과 진주어로 to부정사를 이용하여 문장을 배열한
다. (2) 간접의문문의 어순(의문사+주어+동사)에 주의하여 배
열한다.

시험대비 실력평가   p.75~77

01 ②   02 ③   03 (1) It (2) to win
  (3) stand (4) she left (5) he is (6) if
04 ④   05 ⑤
06 It is not difficult to use the Internet in Korea.
07 ④   08 ⑤   09 ④   10 ③
11 ①   12 ②   13 ⑤   14 ②
15 (1) To ride[Riding] a motorcycle without a helmet
      is dangerous. 또는 It is dangerous to ride a
      motorcycle without a helmet.
   (2) It is great to make good friends in your life.
   (3) It is not easy to keep a diary in English every
      day.
   (4) It is important to learn the history of your
      country.
   (5) The girl is asking where the nearest bus stop
      is.
   (6) Do you know if[whether] the leaves will turn
      yellow in autumn?
   (7) Will you tell me when you met her?
16 ④   17 ⑤   18 ①
19 why you couldn't[didn't]

01 가주어로는 that이 아니라 it을 쓴다.

02 간접의문문의 어순은 '의문사+주어+동사'의 형태임에 유의한다.

03 (1) 가주어로는 that이 아니라 it을 쓴다. (2), (3) 진주어로 to
부정사가 적절하다. (4), (5) 간접의문문의 어순은 '의문사+주
어+동사'이다. (6) 간접의문문에서 의문사가 없는 경우에는 의
문사 대신에 if나 whether를 쓴다.

04 ④번은 인칭대명사로 '그것'이라고 해석하지만 나머지는 모두
가주어로 쓰인 it이다. bill: 계산서

05 간접의문문의 어순은 '의문사+주어+동사'의 형태임에 유의한다.

06 '한국에서 인터넷을 사용하는 것(to use the Internet in Korea)'
을 진주어로 하고 가주어 It을 이용하여 'It ~ to ...' 형식으로 쓴
다.

07 ④ 의문사가 없는 간접의문문의 어순은 'if[whether]+주어+동사'
이며 if는 or not과 붙여 쓰지 않는다.

08 가주어로 it이 나와야 하며 진주어로 동명사가 나와야 한다.

09 진주어로 to부정사가 나와야 한다.

10 ⓐ to help로 진주어 ⓒ 의문사가 없으므로 if he will come
ⓓ 의미상의 주어로 'for+목적격'이 나와 있으므로 진주어로 to
부정사를 써야 한다. the elderly: 어르신들

11 간접의문문의 어순은 '의문사+주어+동사'이며 의문사가 없는 경우
는 'if[whether]+주어+동사'로 쓴다.

12 ②번에는 Mastering 혹은 To master로 주어가 되도록 해야
하지만 나머지는 모두 가주어 It을 쓴다.

13 간접의문문의 어순은 '의문사+주어+동사'이다.

14 ② It was foolish of her to think so. to부정사가 진주어가 되도록 한다. Greek: 그리스어, 그리스 사람

15 (1) to부정사나 동명사가 주어가 되도록 하거나 가주어 it을 사용하고 진주어로 to부정사를 쓴다. (2), (4) 진주어로 to부정사를 쓴다. (3) 가주어로는 this가 아니라 it을 쓴다. (5), (6), (7) 간접의문문의 어순은 '의문사+주어+동사'이며 의문사가 없는 경우는 'if[whether]+주어+동사'로 쓴다.

16 의문사가 없는 간접의문문은 'if[whether]+주어+동사'로 쓴다.

17 가주어 it을 이용하여 바꿔 쓰는 것으로 to부정사를 진주어로 쓴다.

18 ①번은 진주어로 쓰인 명사적 용법이지만 나머지는 모두 to부정사의 부사적 용법으로 쓰였다.

19 이유를 답하고 있으므로 'why+주어+동사'를 쓰면 된다.

서술형 시험대비
p.78~79

01 (1) Tell me what you want for Christmas.
(2) She asked me how much sugar is there in the coke.
(3) Do you know where Greece is on the map?
(4) I wonder if[whether] he is a singer.
(5) I have no idea if[whether] he will join us soon.
(6) Where do you think your soul goes after you die?

02 (1) It is dangerous to climb that high mountain.
(2) It is not safe to walk on this road as it is very slippery.
(3) It is very smart of him to teach himself.

03 (1) what it is (2) where it is

04 (1) It was exciting to ride on the rough water and enjoy the view at the same time.
(2) It is no good trying to excuse yourself.
(3) It is wise not to take the car out during rush hours.
(4) It is no use continuing the search.
(5) It is highly regrettable for Laura to marry such a man.

05 (1) How long does it take to reach the top?
(2) Was the thief a man or a woman?
(3) What is the secret of his success?

06 (1) It is hard to read your handwriting.
(2) It is very dangerous to swim in this river.
(3) It is very easy to read and write Hangeul.
(4) It is impossible for me to run 1,000 meters in three minutes.
(5) It is unbelievable that she passed the exam.

07 (1) It is dangerous to cross this street at night.
(2) It is important not to give up.
(3) It was believed that Mike told a lie to his friends.
(4) The doctor will ask you what you ate for breakfast.
(5) Please let us know if[whether] you are able to attend.
(6) What do you suppose they are thinking?

08 (1) It was so amazing to see its natural beauty.
(2) It was necessary to take small risks.
(3) Daniel told us how he became a singer.
(4) It is doubtful whether he will come or not.

01 간접의문문의 어순은 '의문사+주어+동사'이며 의문사가 없는 경우는 'if[whether]+주어+동사'로 쓴다. think 동사가 주절에 있을 경우 간접의문문의 의문사를 문장 맨 앞에 놓는다.

02 (1) It을 가주어로 하고 진주어 to climb의 목적어로 that high mountain을 쓴다. (2) 전치사 on의 목적어로 this road를 쓴다. (3) to teach의 주어가 he이므로 of him으로 의미상의 주어를 나타내야 한다.

03 간접의문문의 어순은 '의문사+주어+동사'이며 (1)에는 무엇인지를 묻는 표현이, (2)에는 장소를 묻는 표현이 들어가는 것이 적절하다.

04 문장의 주어로 쓰인 to부정사를 뒤로 보내고 대신 주어 자리에 가주어 it을 쓴다. (5)번의 경우 For Laura는 to부정사의 의미상의 주어이다.

05 간접의문문의 어순은 '의문사+주어+동사'이며 의문사가 없는 경우는 'if[whether]+주어+동사'로 쓴다. (3)에서 believe 동사가 주절에 있을 경우 간접의문문의 의문사를 문장 맨 앞으로 배치한다.

06 (1)~(4) 문장의 주어로 쓰인 to부정사를 뒤로 보내고 대신 주어 자리에 가주어 it을 쓴다. (5) to부정사뿐만 아니라 주어로 쓰인 that절의 경우에도 긴 that절을 뒤로 보내고 주어 자리에 가주어 it을 쓴다. (4)번의 경우 For me는 to부정사의 의미상의 주어이다.

07 (1) 가주어로 it이 나와야 하며 진주어로 to부정사가 나와야 한다. (2) to부정사의 부정은 to부정사 앞에 not을 쓴다. (3) that절이 진주어인 경우이며 이때도 가주어로는 that이 아니라 it을 쓴다. (4), (5), (6) 간접의문문의 어순은 '의문사+주어+동사'이며 의문사가 없는 경우는 'if[whether]+주어+동사'로 쓴다. suppose 동사가 주절에 있을 경우 간접의문문의 의문사를 문장 맨 앞으로 배치한다.

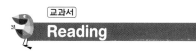

Reading

확인문제   p.80

1 T   2 F   3 F   4 T

확인문제   p.81

1 T   2 F   3 F   4 T   5 T   6 F

교과서 확인학습 A   p.82~83

01 The Best Moment
02 How were, Please tell us
03 Market Heaven
04 traditional markets   05 Then
06 one of the most famous markets
07 what it is famous for
08 a variety of
09 all the international goods
10 many kinds of, such as   11 Then
12 used books   13 really excited
14 to relax   15 Full of Natural Beauty
16 no place like   17 First
18 in good condition   19 so amazing
20 turned off, for a minute   21 focus on
22 the most amazing experience
23 Our next stop   24 went rafting
25 at the same time   26 Firsts
27 where, is   28 How about   29 The answer
30 Korea's firsts   31 To get there   32 next to
33 the history of *Jajangmyeon*
34 the first Western-style park
35 from, awesome
36 the historical sites   37 sound great
38 on your presentations

교과서 확인학습 B   p.84~85

1 The Best Moment of the Field Trip
2 Teacher: Good morning, everyone! How were your field trips last week? Please tell us about them!
3 Busan, Market Heaven
4 Do you like traditional markets?
5 Then go to Gukje Market in Busan.
6 It is one of the most famous markets in Busan.
7 Do you know what it is famous for?
8 It is famous for selling a variety of goods from different countries.
9 It was interesting to see all the international goods there.
10 We also ate many kinds of street food, such as *Gimbap*, fish cake, and *Hotteok*.
11 Then we walked to Bosu-dong Book Street.
12 Many bookstores there sell used books.
13 We were really excited because we found some old comic books!
14 It was nice to relax in a café and read them.
15 Gangwon-do, Full of Natural Beauty
16 There is no place like Gangwon-do for beautiful nature.
17 First, we went to Baengnyong Cave.
18 This 1.8-kilometer-long cave is still in good condition.
19 It was so amazing to see its natural beauty.
20 Near the end of our cave tour, the guide turned off the lights in the cave for a minute.
21 Everything became very dark, so we were able to focus on the sounds there.
22 It was the most amazing experience of the tour!
23 Our next stop was Donggang.
24 We went rafting!
25 It was exciting to ride on the rough water and enjoy the view at the same time.
26 Incheon, A City of Firsts
27 Do you know where the first train station in Korea is?
28 How about the first *Jajangmyeon*?
29 The answer is Incheon!
30 This place has many of Korea's firsts.
31 To get there, we went to Incheon Station.
32 The Jajangmyeon Museum is next to the station.
33 We learned about the history of *Jajangmyeon* there.
34 Later, we walked around Jayu Park, the first Western-style park in Korea.
35 The view from the park was awesome!
36 It was great to see the historical sites of this city from the park.
37 Teacher: Wow, these places sound great!
38 You all have done a wonderful job on your presentations!

01 ②   02 ①   03 ③, ④

04 What about

05 This place has many of Korea's firsts.

06 at the Jajangmyeon Museum   07 ②, ④

08 ②번, good → goods   09 ①, ④, ⑤

10 Gukje Market / Bosu-dong Book Street   11 ③

12 stop   13 ⑤

14 (A) Natural (B) off (C) rough   15 ②, ④

16 ①   17 Near the end of our cave tour, the guide turned off the lights in the cave for a minute. Everything became very dark, so we were able to focus on the sounds there.   18 ②

19 They learned about the history of *Jajangmyeon*.

20 (A) Incheon Station, (B) the Jajangmyeon Museum, (C) Jayu Park

21 ⓐ your field trips last week / ⓒ some old comic books

22 like   23 ⑤

24 People no longer use it.

25 ③, ⑤   26 ②

01 부산의 재래시장인 국제시장을 중점적으로 소개하는 글이므로 제목으로는 '부산, 시장 천국'이 적절하다.

02 주어진 문장의 Then에 주목한다. ①번 앞 문장에 대한 긍정의 답을 가정하는 것이므로 ①번이 적절하다.

03 ⓐ와 ③, ④번: 가주어, ①, ⑤: 비인칭 주어, ② 가목적어

04 How about ~? = What about ~?: ~은 어때?

05 Korea's firsts: 한국의 최초의 것들

06 '자장면 박물관'을 가리킨다.

07 ⓓ와 ②, ④: 명사적 용법, ①, ⑤: 부사적 용법, ③ 형용사적 용법

08 그 시장은 여러 나라에서 온 다양한 '상품'들을 파는 것으로 유명하다고 해야 하므로, 'good'이 아니라 'goods'가 적절하다. goods: 상품, 제품, good: 선(善) 도움, 소용

09 ⓐ와 ②, ③번: 동명사, ①, ④, ⑤: 현재분사

10 '국제시장,' ⓒ '보수동 책방 거리'를 가리킨다.

11 '아름다운 자연'에 관한 한 강원도만 한 곳이 없다고 하는 것이 적절하다. ② 다양한 유적지, ④ 인공적인 구조물, ⑤ 전통적인 공연들

12 stop: (여행 도중에) 머무르기, 체재, 들르기

13 백룡동굴에서 동강까지 얼마나 먼지는 대답할 수 없다. ① They went to Baengnyong Cave first. ② It is 1.8 kilometers long. ③ He[She] turned off the lights in the cave for a minute. ④ They went to Donggang.

14 (A) '자연'의 아름다움으로 가득한 곳이라고 해야 하므로 Natural이 적절하다. artificial: 인공[인조]의, (B) 동굴 안의 불을 잠시 '껐다'고 해야 하므로 off가 적절하다. turn off: (전기·가스·수도 등을) 끄다, (C) '급류'라고 해야 하므로 rough가

적절하다. rough water: 격랑, 거친 물결, tough: 힘든, 어려운, (신체적으로) 억센[튼튼한]

15 가주어 자리에 to부정사나 동명사를 주어로 하여 고치는 것이 적절하다.

16 급류를 타면서 동시에 경치를 즐기는 것은 흥미진진했다고 했기 때문에, 학생들은 '만족한' 심경이었다고 하는 것이 적절하다. ② 놀란, ③ 지루한, ④ 실망한, ⑤ 속상한, 마음이 상한

17 동굴 관광의 끝 무렵, 안내인이 동굴 안의 불을 잠시 끄자 모든 것이 매우 어두워서, 학생들은 그곳의 소리에 집중 할 수 있었다. 그것은 여행에서 가장 경이로운 경험이었다.

18 한국 최초의 기차역이 인천에 있고 첫 번째 자장면의 경우도 인천이라고 했고 한국 최초의 서구식 공원이 인천의 자유 공원이라고 했으므로, 한국의 '최초의 것들'이 많이 있다고 하는 것이 적절하다. ① 뜻밖의[놀라운] 일[소식], ③ 자원, ④ 발명, ⑤ 전통

19 '자장면의 역사'에 대하여 배웠다.

20 학생들은 '인천역', '자장면 박물관', '자유 공원'과 같은 한국의 최초의 것들과 관련이 있는 장소들에 갔다. be related to: …와 관계가 있다

21 ⓐ '지난주 수학여행' ⓒ '몇 권의 오래된 만화책들'을 가리킨다.

22 such as = like: …와 같은

23 중고 책을 파는 곳은 '보수동 책방 거리'이다.

24 People를 주어로 하여 고치는 것이 적절하다.

25 no longer = no more = not ~ any longer = not ~ any more: 더 이상 …아닌[하지 않는]

26 take pictures of: ~을 사진을 찍다

01 If you like traditional markets,

02 It is one of the most famous markets in Busan.

03 (A) interesting (B) used (C) excited

04 where

05 There are many of Korea's firsts in this place.

06 (1) 한국 최초의 기차역 (2) 한국 최초의 자장면
(3) 한국 최초의 서구식 공원인 자유 공원

07 We can see the historical sites of this city from the park.

08 the most famous market → one of the most famous markets

09 (1) 세계 곳곳에서 온 상품들을 보았다.
(2) 김밥, 어묵 그리고 호떡과 같은 여러 종류의 길거리 음식을 먹었다.

10 used books

11 best

12 rafting

13 It was exciting to ride on the rough water and enjoy the view at the same time.

14 (A) see (B) the sounds

17

01 Then(그렇다면)은 '전통 시장을 좋아하면'이라는 뜻이다.

02 one of the 복수명사: ~ 중의 하나

03 (A) 감정을 나타내는 동사가 사물을 수식할 때는 보통 현재분사로 쓰므로 interesting이 적절하다. (B) '중고책'이라고 해야 하므로 used가 적절하다. (C) 감정을 나타내는 동사가 사람을 수식할 때는 보통 과거분사로 쓰므로 excited가 적절하다.

04 '첫 번째 자장면은요?'라는 말은 '한국 최초의 자장면이 어디에서 소개되었는지 아세요?'와 같은 뜻이다.

05 There are로 시작하여 고치는 것이 적절하다.

06 인천에는 '한국 최초의 기차역', '자장면', '자유 공원'과 같이 '한국의 최초의 것들'이 많이 있다.

07 공원에서 이 도시의 역사적인 장소들을 볼 수 있다.

08 국제시장은 부산에서 '가장 유명한 시장 중 하나'이다.

09 (1) 그곳에서 세계 곳곳에서 온 상품들을 모두 볼 수 있어서 흥미로웠다고 했다. (2) 우리는 또한 김밥, 어묵 그리고 호떡과 같은 여러 종류의 길거리 음식을 먹었다고 했다.

10 보수동 책방 거리의 많은 서점들은 '중고 책'을 파는 것으로 유명하다.

11 '아름다운 자연에 관한 한 강원도만 한 곳이 없다.'는 말은 아름다운 자연에 관한 한 강원도가 '제일 좋은' 장소라는 뜻이다.

12 go ~ing: ~하러 가다

13 'on'을 보충하면 된다.

14 안내인이 불을 껐을 때 모든 것이 매우 어두워져서 학생들은 동굴의 자연의 아름다움을 '볼 수' 없게 되었고, 그들은 그곳의 '소리'에만 집중할 수 있었다.

영역별 핵심문제
p.93~97

01 ③　　02 ④　　03 have　　04 ④

05 ④　　06 ②　　07 ⑤　　08 going

09 It takes an hour and 40 minutes by express train.

10 ⑤　　11 relax　　12 ③

13 for you to pay attention to your teacher in class

14 ⑤　　15 ④　　16 ⑤

17 (1) Nobody knows. Why did Lauren leave the office early?

(2) It is difficult to understand. What does the teacher say?

(3) Steve didn't tell me. When did the movie begin?

(4) Do you think? What is the most typical Korean dish?

(5) Mariel wants to know. Is Kate going to meet Asako?

(6) They wonder. Can they borrow a few books today?

18 (1) I'll tell you where he has been since last Monday.

(2) I'd like to know if[whether] you met her.

(3) Where do you think I can find some fruit?

19 (1) It is abnormal to have the heart on the right side.

(2) It is hard to grab fish with your bare hands.

(3) I don't know where the girl lives.

(4) Could you tell me when the next train comes?

20 ①

21 After we (also) ate many kinds of street food, such as *Gimbap*, fish cake, and *Hotteok*

22 ④　　　　　　23 ②

24 ③

25 (A) Later (B) awesome (C) presentations

26 ④　　　　　　27 ②

28 산의 중간까지 케이블 카를 타고 간 다음, 정상까지 걸어서 갔다.

29 amazed, excited

01 ③의 get은 '얻다'의 의미로 사용되었다. 이외의 보기들은 '(장소·위치에) 도착하다'의 의미로 사용되었다. ① 너는 가능한 한 빨리 그곳에 도착해야 한다. ② 캐나다에 도착하자마자 너에게 편지를 보낼 것이다. ③ 너는 도서관에서 정보를 얻을 수 있다. ④ 택시를 타면, 그곳에 10분이면 도착할 수 있어요. ⑤ 아무래도 제시간에 학교에 도착하기는 틀린 것 같아요.

02 at the same time: 동시에, 한꺼번에

03 Do you have any plans?: 무슨 계획이라도 있니? Have a good trip.: 좋은 여행하길 바라.

04 ① rough: 거친 ② natural: 자연의 ③ Western-style: 서양풍의, 서양식의 ④ foreign: 외국의 ⑤ awesome: 매우 멋진

05 How long does it take to get ~?: ~까지 가는 데 얼마나 걸리나요?(소요 시간 묻기)

06 What are you planning to 동사원형 ~?: 뭐 할 계획이야? be going to 동사원형: ~할 예정이다

07 주어진 문장은 '내가 생각한 것보다 훨씬 더 빠르다.'의 의미인데, 대구까지 가는 것에 대해 고속 열차로 1시간 40분 걸린다는 말에 대해 말한 것으로 볼 수 있다.

08 be going to 동사원형: ~할 예정이다 be planning to 동사원형: ~할 계획이다

09 It takes 시간: (시간이) ~ 걸린다 hour: 시간 minute: 분

10 ⑤ 남자아이가 친구와 같이 올스타 경기를 보러 간다고는 언급하지 않았다. 남자아이는 올스타 경기를 보고, 또한 친구를 만날 계획을 가지고 있다.

11 relax: 휴식을 취하다, 느긋이 쉬다 / 아무것도 하지 않다

12 ③ 휴가가 얼마나 긴지는 언급되어 있지 않았다. ① 그들은 무엇에 대해서 이야기하고 있는가? ② 여자아이의 조부모님은 어디에 사는가? ③ 휴가는 얼마나 긴가? ④ 여자아이는 그녀의 조부모님과 어디를 갈 계획인가? ⑤ 남자 아이의 휴가 계획은 무엇인가?

13 '~해야 한다'는 의미를 가주어 it을 이용하여 '~할 필요가 있다'라고 쓰려면 진주어로 to부정사를 이용한다. 이때 의미상의 주어를 빠뜨리지 않도록 주의한다.

14 의문사가 없는 간접의문문의 어순은 'if[whether]+주어+동사'이지만 if를 쓸 경우 or not을 바로 붙여 쓰지 않는다.

15 ④번은 강조 용법으로 쓰인 it이고 나머지는 모두 가주어로 쓰인 it이다.

16 'It ~ to부정사' 구문을 이용하고 to부정사의 의미상 주어는 'for+목적격'을 쓰지만, 사람의 태도나 성질에 관한 형용사가 올 경우 'of+목적격'을 쓴다.

17 간접의문문의 어순은 '의문사+주어+동사'이며 의문사가 없는 경우는 'if[whether]+주어+동사'로 쓴다. think 동사가 주절에 있을 경우 간접의문문의 의문사를 문장 맨 앞으로 배치한다.

18 간접의문문의 어순은 '의문사+주어+동사'이며 의문사가 없는 경우는 'if[whether]+주어+동사'로 쓴다. think 동사가 주절에 있을 경우 간접의문문의 의문사를 문장 맨 앞으로 배치한다.

19 (1), (2) 'It ~ to부정사'의 가주어·진주어 구문을 이용한다.
(3), (4) 간접의문문의 어순은 '의문사+주어+동사'이다.

20 ⓐ, ⓑ, ⓒ는 Gukje Market, ⓓ는 to see all the international goods there, ⓔ는 to relax in a café and read them을 가리킨다.

21 Then(그러고 나서)은 '우리가 김밥, 어묵 그리고 호떡과 같은 여러 종류의 길거리 음식을 먹은 뒤에'라는 뜻이다.

22 ④번 다음 문장의 It에 주목한다. 주어진 문장의 내용을 받고 있으므로 ④번이 적절하다.

23 ⓐ for: (관련) …에 관해서(는), …의 점에서는, for beautiful nature: 아름다운 자연에 관한 한, ⓑ be in good condition: 상태가 좋다

24 동굴은 여전히 잘 보존된 상태이다.

25 (A) '나중에'라고 해야 하므로 Later가 적절하다. later: (지금 이야기 중인 시간보다) 후에[뒤에], latter: 후자의, (나열된 것들 중에서) 마지막의, (B) 경치는 정말 '멋있었다'고 해야 하므로 awesome이 적절하다. awesome: 경탄할 만한, 엄청난, awful: 끔찍한, 지독한, (C) '발표'를 훌륭하게 잘했다고 해야 하므로 presentations가 적절하다. presentation: 발표, preparation: 준비

26 부사적 용법(목적)의 to 부정사: in order to 동사원형 = so as to 동사원형 = in order that ~ may[can] = so that ~ may[can]

27 ② 누가 한국에서 첫 번째 자장면을 만들었는지는 대답할 수 없다. ① In Incheon. ③ At the Jajangmyeon Museum. ④ It is Jayu Park. ⑤ It was awesome.

28 산의 중간까지는 케이블 카를 타고 간 다음에, 정상까지 하이킹을 했다고 했다.

29 감정을 나타내는 동사의 경우 과거분사는 '~하게 된'의 뜻으로 보통 감정을 느끼는 대상에 쓰인다.

단원별 예상문제 p.98~101

01 (c)ondition 02 am able to 03 on foot 04 take
05 ④ 06 stadium
07 ⓐ of, ⓑ from, ⓒ off, ⓓ in, ⓔ of 08 ①, ⑤
09 How long does it take to get there? 10 ①
11 (A) by, (B) on 12 ④ 13 ④
14 (1) Do you know who that tall guy over there is?
　(2) Tell me who made this chocolate cake.
　(3) I wonder if[whether] Marianne got married.
　(4) Where do you think Snow White is?
15 |모범답안| It is easy for him to do dunk shot.
16 ③ 17 was → were 18 ③
19 ④ 20 ①
21 (A) 1.8-kilometer-long (B) rafting
　(C) at the same time
22 very dark, focus on
23 (1) 남자 형제들과 수영을 했다.
　(2) 해변에서 게를 잡았다.
　(3) 아름다운 일몰을 보았다.
24 awful → awesome

01 주어진 보기는 동의어 관계이다. amazing: 놀라운, 멋진 incredible: 믿을 수 없는 condition: 상태, 상황 state: 상태

02 be able to 동사원형: ~을 할 수 있다

03 on foot: 걸어서, 도보로

04 take: (얼마의 시간이) 걸리다 / 내 컴퓨터로 자료를 다운 받으려면 시간이 오래 걸릴 것이다. take a field trip: 현장 학습을 하다 / 우리 현장 학습 간다는 얘기 들었니?

05 긴 연휴에 대한 계획을 물으니 → (C) 전주에 있는 조부모님을 방문할 계획이라고 대답한다. → 이어서 (B) 그분들과 어떤 것을 할 계획인지 묻자 → (D) 한옥 마을에 갈 것이라고 대답하며, 상대방의 연휴 때 계획을 질문한다. → (E) 집에서 머물면서 쉴 거라는 대답에 → (A) 좋은 생각이라고 말한다.

06 stadium: 경기장, 스타디움 / 규모가 큰 운동 경기장

07 lots of: 많은 from: ~로부터 get off: 내리다, 하차하다 in front of: ~ 앞에서

08 (A)stop과 ②, ③, ④ 정류장, 정거장 ① 중단하다 ⑤ 멈추다

09 How long does it take to get ~?: ~에 가는 데 얼마나 걸리나요?

10 How do I get from Hanguk University to here? → How do I get to Hanguk University from here? 길을 알려주는 문장에서 'You will see Hanguk University on your right. (오른쪽에 한국 대학교가 보일 거예요.)'라는 것으로 보아 남자의 목적지는 한국 대학교이다.

11 (A) by bus: 버스로 on foot 걸어서, 도보로

12 ④ 한국 대학교에 가기 위해서 버스를 타면 5분 걸리고, 걸어서

19

20분 걸리므로 버스를 타는 것이 더 빠르다.

13 ① It is fun to speak in front of people. ② It is difficult to say which way the wind is blowing. ③ It was great to see the historical sites of this city from the park. ⑤ It is important to make plans in advance.

14 간접의문문의 어순은 '의문사+주어+동사'이며 의문사가 없는 경우는 'if[whether]+주어+동사'로 쓴다. 의문사가 주어인 경우에는 의문사가 주어 역할을 동시에 하므로 직접의문문처럼 '의문사+동사'의 어순임에 유의해야 하며, think 동사가 주절에 있을 경우 간접의문문의 의문사를 문장 맨 앞에 써야 함에도 유의한다.

15 'it ~ to 부정사' 구문을 이용하여 쓴다.

16 ③ 의문사 대신 if나 whether를 써야 한다.

17 주어가 'your field trips'이므로 were로 고치는 것이 적절하다.

18 ⓑ와 ①, ④: 명사적 용법, ② 형용사적 용법, ③, ⑤부사적 용법

19 국제시장에서 보수동 책방 거리까지 가는 데 얼마나 오래 걸렸는지는 대답할 수 없다. ① They went last week. ② It was interesting to see all the international goods there. ③ They ate many kinds of street food, such as Gimbap, fish cake, and Hotteok. ⑤ They sell used books.

20 ⓐ와 ①번: …와 같은(전치사), ②, ④: (…을) 좋아하다(동사), ③ [외관·형태·성질 등이] 같은(명사 shape를 수식하는 형용사), ⑤: 비슷한(명사 manner를 수식하는 형용사)

21 (A) '1.8-kilometer-long'이 형용사로 뒤에 나오는 명사를 꾸며주는 역할을 할 때는 단수로 써야 하므로 1.8-kilometer-long이 적절하다. (B) go ~ing: ~하러 가다 (C) 급류를 타면서 '동시에' 경치를 즐기는 것은 흥미진진했다고 해야 하므로 at the same time이 적절하다. at the same time: 동시에, one by one: 하나하나씩[차례차례]

22 학생들이 동굴 안의 소리에 '집중할 수' 있도록 모든 것을 '매우 어두워지게' 만들고 싶었기 때문이다.

23 남자 형제들과 수영을 했고, 해변에서 게를 좀 잡았고 아름다운 일몰을 보았다.

24 아름다운 일몰을 보는 것은 정말 '멋있었다'고 해야 하므로 awesome이 적절하다. awesome: 경탄할 만한, 어마어마한, 엄청난, awful: 끔찍한, 지독한

서술형 실전문제
p.102~103

01 Where are you planning to go?
Where are you going to go?
Where are you thinking of going?

02 It takes 10 and half hours.

03 Where are you going for your trip

---

04 I'm planning to visit[go to] museums.

05 (1) for my grandma to remember names
(2) for most of students to study English

06 (1) It is doubtful if[whether] Anna loves me.
(2) I'm not sure why Kate was so surprised.
(3) Cathy knows who broke the window yesterday.
(4) Which book can you imagine Jennifer bought?

07 (1) takes → to take (2) That → It
(3) Write → To write[Writing]
(4) when does the show start → when the show starts
(5) if does the bag have → if the bag has
(6) Do you think who → Who do you think

08 (A) How (B) markets (C) found

09 Seeing

10 (A) traditional markets, (B) different countries

01 Where are you planning to go?: 너는 어디에 갈 계획이니? Where are you going to go?: 너는 어디에 갈 거니? Where are you thinking of going?: 너는 어디에 갈 생각이니?

02 It takes 시간: (시간이) ~ 걸린다

03 where: 어디로 trip: 여행

04 museum: 박물관, 미술관 / 역사적이거나 예술적인 물건들이 전시되어 있는 건물 be planning to 동사원형: ~할 계획이다

05 (1) '이름을 기억하는 데 어려움이 있다'는 것을 '이름을 기억하기 어렵다'는 문장으로, (2) '영어 공부는 지루하다'는 것을 '영어를 공부하는 것은 지루하다'는 문장으로 'it ~ to 부정사' 구문을 이용하여 쓰고 to부정사의 의미상의 주어로 'for+목적격'을 쓴다.

06 간접의문문의 어순은 '의문사+주어+동사'이며 의문사가 없는 경우는 'if[whether]+주어+동사'로 쓴다. 의문사가 주어인 경우에는 직접의문문처럼 '의문사+동사'의 어순임에 유의해야 하며 imagine 동사가 주절에 있을 경우 간접의문문의 의문사를 문장 맨 앞에 써야 함에도 유의한다.

07 (1) 'it ~ to 부정사' 구문이 적절하다. (2) 가주어로는 that이 아니라 it을 쓴다. (3) to부정사나 동명사가 주어가 되도록 한다. (4) 간접의문문의 어순은 '의문사+주어+동사'이다. (5) 'if[whether]+주어+동사'의 어순이 되어야 한다. (6) think 동사가 주절에 있을 경우 간접의문문의 의문사를 문장 맨 앞에 써야 한다.

08 (A) 수학여행은 '어땠나요?'라고 해야 하므로 How가 적절하다. (B) one of the 복수명사: '~ 중의 하나'이므로 markets가 적절하다. (C) 만화책을 '발견했다'고 해야 하므로 found가 적절하다. find-found-found: 발견하다, found-founded-founded: 설립하다

09 진주어인 to부정사를 동명사 주어로 고치는 것이 적절하다.

10 그곳은 '전통 시장'을 방문하기를 좋아하는 사람들에게 좋은 장소이고, '여러 나라'에서 수입한 다양한 제품들을 파는 것으로 유명하다.

|모범답안|

01 What are you going[planning] to do next weekend? / to watch a movie / How can I get to the movie theater? / How long does it take to get[go] there? / takes 5 minutes on foot

02 (1) It is important to save water for environment.
　(2) It is necessary to prepare for the worst.
　(3) Do you know who won the prize?
　(4) I wonder if[whether] she loves me.

03 (A) Last summer　(B) swam　(C) caught
　(D) awesome　(E) beautiful sunset

01 next weekend: 다음 주말 What are you going to 동사원형 ~?: 너는 무엇을 할 거니? What are you planning to 동사원형 ~?: 뭐 할 계획이야? be planning to 동사원형: ~할 계획이다 How can[do] I get ~?: 어떻게 갈 수 있어? How long does it take to get ~?:~에 가는 데 얼마나 걸리나요? It takes 시간: (시간이) ~ 걸린다

 단원별 모의고사　p.105~108

01 ①

02 (h)istory / (s)cenery / (W)estern–style
　(1) scenery　(2) history　(3) Western–style

03 ④　　　04 field trip　05 ③　　　06 ④

07 ⑤

08 How do I get to Hanguk University from here?

09 (A) Go straight (for) two blocks, and then turn left.
　(B) your right

10 ③　　　11 ②　　　12 ④

13 (1) I know who won the race.
　(2) Do you know when the bus will come?
　(3) The man is asking her how long it takes to get to the mart.
　(4) I have no idea if[whether] they like it or not.
　(5) Who do you think will win the game?
　(6) What do you guess she wants to buy?

14 (1) It is important to protect our environment.
　(2) It is interesting to look around the traditional market.
　(3) It is exciting to ride the roller coaster.
　(4) It is necessary to get enough sleep.
　(5) I don't remember where the girl lived.
　(6) Anna asked me if[whether] I loved Angelina.

15 Do you know what it is famous for?

16 ②, ③　　　17 ④　　　18 ⓑ, ⓒ, ⓓ / ⓐ, ⓔ

19 in the cave　　　20 ③

21 (A) many (B) get (C) great　　　22 ④

01 turn off: (등, 전화기 등을) 끄다

02 (1) scenery: 풍경, 경치 / 자연의 아름다운 경치 / 우리는 해변에서 경치를 즐겼다. (2) history: 역사 / 과거에 발생한 사건들 / 나는 에펠탑의 역사를 알기 원한다. (3) Western-style: 서양풍의, 서양식의 / 서양 국가들과 관련된 특별한 방식이나 형식 / 나는 동양풍의 집보다 서양풍의 집을 선호한다.

03 여자아이는 현장 학습으로 미술관에 가고, 남자아이는 어디로 가는지 질문하자 놀이동산에 갈 것이라고 대답한다. 놀이동산에 가서 롤러코스터를 탈 생각으로 신난다고 하는 부분과 연결된다.

04 field trip: 견학 여행, 현장 학습 / 학생들과 선생님들이 무엇인가를 배우기 위해 방문하는 것

05 ⓐ Where ⓓ What ⓔ excited

06 ④ 남자아이가 놀이동산에 어떻게 갈 것인지는 언급되지 않았다. ① 언제 현장 학습에 가는가? ② 남자아이는 현장 학습으로 어디를 가는가? ③ 여자아이는 현장 학습으로 어디를 가는가? ⑤ 얼마나 많은 전시회가 지금 미술관에 있는가?

07 남자는 걸어서 가겠다고 말했다. 한국 대학교까지 버스를 타면 5분, 걸어가면 20분 걸린다.

08 How do I get to 장소: ~에 어떻게 가나요?

09 Go straight: 직진하세요 turn left: 좌회전하세요 It's on your right: 오른쪽에 있어요.

10 첫 문장에서는 진주어로 쓰인 to부정사가 적절하다. 두 번째 문장에서는 의문사 who가 적절하다.

11 ②번은 조건절에 쓰인 if이지만 나머지는 모두 간접의문문을 이끌고 있다.

12 ④ Is it possible to breathe under the water?

13 간접의문문의 어순은 '의문사+주어+동사'이며 의문사가 없는 경우는 'if[whether]+주어+동사'로 쓴다. think나 guess 동사가 주절에 있을 경우 간접의문문의 의문사를 문장 맨 앞으로 배치한다.

14 (1)~(4) 'it ~ to 부정사' 구문을 이용하여 쓴다. (5), (6) 간접의문문의 어순은 '의문사+주어+동사'이며 의문사가 없는 경우는 'if[whether]+주어+동사'로 쓴다.

15 'for'를 보충하고 간접의문문의 순서로 쓰는 것이 적절하다.

16 a variety of = various = diverse: 여러 가지의, 다양한, ① familiar: 익숙한, 친숙한, ⑤ common: 흔한

17 위 글은 강원도의 아름다운 자연에 관한 글이므로, 제목으로는 '강원도, 자연의 아름다움으로 가득한 곳'이 적절하다.

18 사실(fact)은 그것이 진실이라는 것을 입증할 수 있어야 한다. 반면에 견해(opinion)는 어떤 사람이 그렇게 믿거나 생각하고 있는 것이므로 그것이 진실이라는 보장이 없다. 따라서 사실은 모든 사람이 동일하게 인식하지만, 견해는 사람마다 다를 수 있다.

19 '동굴 안'을 가리킨다.

20 ③번 다음 문장의 the park에 주목한다. 주어진 문장의 Jayu Park를 가리키므로 ③번이 적절하다.

21 (A) 'Korea's firsts'가 복수이므로 many가 적절하다. (B) 'there'가 부사이므로 전치사 to 없이 get만 쓰는 것이 적절하다. get to+명사: ~에 도착하다, get there: 그곳에 도착하다, (C) 감각동사의 보어이므로 형용사 great이 적절하다.

22 ④ 자유 공원은 한국 최초의 '서구식' 공원이다. Eastern: 동양의

Lesson 7

On My Way to the Future

시험대비 실력평가
p.112

01 ②	02 ⑤	03 ③	04 ①
05 ④	06 ④	07 ②	08 ③

01 ② 이외의 보기는 직업에 관련된 단어들이다. ① cartoonist: 만화가 ② customer: 손님, 고객 ③ photographer: 사진작가, 사진사 ④ consultant: 상담가 ⑤ designer: 디자이너, 설계자

02 artificial: 인공적인, 인조의 / 이 음식에는 인공 색소가 들어 있지 않다.

03 develop: 발달시키다, 발전하다 / 어떻게 내 작문 실력을 발달시킬 수 있을까?

04 keep a diary: 일기를 쓰다 / 일기를 쓰는 것은 글 쓰는 연습을 하는 좋은 방법이다.

05 ① judge: 판사 ② writer: 작가 ③ artist: 예술가 ④ reviewer: (책·영화 등의) 논평가 ⑤ movie director: 영화 감독

06 노래를 부를 수 있느냐는 질문에 긍정의 대답을 했으므로 노래를 잘 부른다는 내용이 나와야 어울린다. 'I am good at+(동)명사'로 ~을 잘할 수 있음을 표현할 수 있다.

07 ② modeler: 모형 제작자 ① Sam은 매년 가을에 낙엽을 모으는 것을 좋아한다. ② 풍선 모형 제작자는 풍선으로만 만들어진 비행기를 보여줬다. ③ 체스는 문제 해결 능력을 길러 주는 것 같다. ④ 나뭇잎들은 오염을 줄여준다. ⑤ 나는 사람들의 사진을 찍는 데 재주가 있다고 생각한다.

08 specialist: 전문가 expert: 전문가 / 기상 전문가들은 장마가 10일 이상 지속될 거라고 말했다.

서술형 시험대비
p.113

01 (s)trength
02 keep
03 of
04 (1) emotion(s) (2) amount(s) (3) career (4) reason
05 fill out
06 (1) We need to analyze the cause of the failure.
　(2) You need to improve your English.
　(3) My strength is that I believe in myself.
　(4) My son has a talent for singing.
　(5) Do you want a late-night snack?

01 strength: 강점, 장점 strong point: 장점 / 내 직업의 장점은 높은 급료다.

02 keep+목적어+목적격보어(형용사): ~가 …한 상태로 유지하다 / 그 공원의 직원들은 그것들을 안전하게 보호하고 싶어 한다. keep a diary: 일기를 쓰다 / 너의 생각을 적을 수 있도록 일기를 써라.

03 take care of: ~을 돌보다 / 방과 후에 작은 딸을 보살펴 줄 사람이 필요하다 first of all: 무엇보다도 / 무엇보다도, 진정할 필요가 있다.

04 (1) emotion: 감정 / 너는 감정을 조절할 필요가 있다. (2) amount: 양, 총액 / 재활용은 많은 양의 에너지를 절약할 수 있다. (3) career: 진로, 직업 / 그 남자는 연기를 직업으로 선택했다. (4) reason: 이유, 원인 / 방문한 이유가 무엇입니까?

05 fill out: (서식 등을) 작성하다, (정보를) 기입하다, 채우다

06 (1) analyze: 분석하다 (2) improve: 개선하다, 향상시키다 (3) strength: 힘, 강점, 장점 (4) talent: (타고난) 재능, 재주 (5) late-night: 심야의

교과서
Conversation

핵심 Check
p.114~115

1 good at playing
2 Are you good at taking pictures / my brother is good at it
3 need to do to
4 How can I improve my English skills? / What do you suggest to improve my English skills?

교과서 대화문 익히기

Check(√) True or False
p.116

1 F　2 F　3 T　4 T　5 F　6 T

교과서 확인학습
p.118~119

Listen & Talk 1 A

play / not good / What are you / at playing / let's

Listen & Talk 1 B

to do / decide, What am / good at / good at singing / to play, Why don't you

Listen & Talk 1 C

need to fill out / wrote, and / be, P.E. teacher, watching, writing, strengths, What am I good / lots, First of, are good at, aren't you / I'm good at playing baseball / strengths / work, at listening to / You're good at

Listen & Talk 2 A

want to be, What / need to, develop, problem-solving

Listen & Talk 2 B

amazing / trying, to improve, writer / want, like, What do I, to / Reading makes your writing better / else / don't, keeping / advice

Listen & Talk 2 C

for / who want to be food / decorates, to look / to be a food stylist, What, need / need to learn, kinds / else / Creativity / Thank, for

시험대비 기본평가
p.120

| 01 ② | 02 ② | 03 ⑤ | 04 ⑤ |

01 상대방에게 조언을 구하는 질문에는 'What do I need to do?', 'What do you suggest?', 'What should I do?', 'What can I do?' 등이 있다.

02 푸드 스타일리스트가 되고 싶다는 상대방에게 어울리는 조언으로 다양한 종류의 음식에 대해서 배우라고 하는 것이 어울린다. ① 너는 쇼핑 리스트를 만들어야 해. ② 너는 많은 종류의 음식에 대해 배워야 해. ③ 너는 매일 운동을 해야 해. ④ 너는 한국 문화에 대한 블로그를 디자인해야 해. ⑤ 너는 문화에 대한 스타일을 설명해야 해.

03 'What are you good at?'은 상대방이 무엇을 잘하는지 묻는 표현이다. ① 나는 운동을 좋아하지 않아. ② 나는 그림 그리기를 잘 못해. ③ 나는 재능 있는 요리사가 아니야. ④ 나는 훌륭한 선생님이 될 거야.

04 상대방에게 조언을 구할 때는 'What do I need to do?', 'What do you suggest?', 'What should I do?' 등의 표현을 쓸 수 있다.

시험대비 실력평가
p.121~122

| 01 ④ | 02 ② | 03 ③ | 04 ③ |

05 You are good at so many things.

06 counseling 07 ⑤   08 ①   09 ③

10 ③   11 (A) ⓑ What are you good at?

    (B) ⓔ What do you want to be in the future?

01 상대방의 그림을 잘 그린다고 하는 말에 'No, thanks.(아니요, 됐습니다.)'라고 대답하는 것은 어울리지 않는다.

02 피아노를 잘 칠 수 있는 조언을 묻고 있는데, 조언이 아닌 상대방 의견에 동의를 하는 'I think you're right.(네가 옳다고 생각해.)'은 어색하다.

03 fill out: (서식 등을) 작성하다, (정보를) 기입하다, 채우다

04 (B)의 'strengths'는 '장점'이다. ③의 보기는 '힘'의 의미이고, 나머지 보기들은 장점의 의미이다. ① 자신감을 키우기 위해 여러분의 장점에 집중하세요. ② 장점을 이용하는 사람은 창조적이고, 활동적이며 생산적입니다 ③ 빙벽을 오르는 것은 많은 신체적인 힘을 요구한다. ④ 그의 장점은 정직한 점이다. ⑤ 그의 키는 농구 경기에 있어서 그의 장점이다.

05 be good at: ~을 잘하다 so: 매우, 아주

06 counseling: 상담 / 문제 해결을 돕기 위해 누군가에게 주어지는 조언

07 주어진 문장은 '조언 고마워.'란 뜻이다. G는 글을 잘 쓰고 싶어서 B에게 조언을 구하고 있다. 조언을 듣고 B에게 고맙다고 말하는 것이 자연스러우므로 ⑤가 적절하다.

08 글쓰기 기량을 발전시키려고 노력하고 있다는 말을 볼 때 남자아이는 작가가 되고 싶어 한다.

09 ③ What else: 그밖에 무엇을, What do I need to do?: 나는 뭘 해야 하니?

10 ③ Jason은 거의 매일 글을 쓰고 있다.

11 (A)에 대한 대답으로 자신이 잘하는 것에 대해 말했으므로 능력을 물어보는 질문이 어울린다. (B)는 미술가가 되고 싶다고 말했으므로 미래에 무엇이 되기를 원하는지 묻는 질문이 어울린다.

서술형 시험대비
p.123

01 (A) → (D) → (B) → (C)

02 (C) → (E) → (B) → (D) → (A)

03 good at playing basketball

04 I'm good at playing soccer.

05 What do I need to do?

06 Reading makes your writing better.

07 I'm not good at playing badminton.

01 (A)에서 조언을 구하는 질문을 하자 (D) 다양한 종류의 음식에 대해 배워야 한다고 대답한다. (B) 또 다른 것은 뭐가 필요한지 다시 질문하자 (C) 미술 공부도 해야 한다고 말하며 창의력이 중요하다고 덧붙인다.

02 (C) 잘하는 것이 무엇인지 묻자 (E) 사람들을 돌보는 것을 잘한다고 말한다. (B) 그러면 간호사가 되는 것이 어떻겠냐고 제안하자 (D) 좋은 생각이라고 말하며 상대방의 의견에 동의한다. 이어서 간호사가 되려면 뭘 해야 하는지 묻자 (A) 인간의 몸에 대해서 배워야 한다고 대답한다.

03 남자아이가 농구를 잘하지 못한다고 말하면서 '너는 잘하니?'라

고 묻고 있으므로 상대방이 농구를 잘하는지 묻는 질문을 한 것이다.

04 'Okay, then let's play soccer.(그래, 그러면 축구를 하자.)'라고 하는 것으로 보아 남자아이는 축구를 잘하는 것으로 추측할 수 있다.

05 'What do I need to do?'는 상대방에게 조언을 구할 때 하는 질문으로, '내가 뭘 해야 하니?'의 의미이다.

06 reading은 동명사 주어이다. make+목적어(your writing)+목적격보어(better): ~을 …하게 만들다

07 be not good at: ~을 잘하지 못하다, ~에 능숙하지 못하다

Grammar
[교과서]

핵심 Check
p.124~125

1 (1) to be (2) to return (3) to clear
2 to try
3 (1) if (2) rains (3) will come

시험대비 기본평가
p.126

01 (1) be → to be (2) to not lose → not to lose
   (3) aren't → are, 또는 unless → if
   (4) won't → don't   02 ②
03 (1) to give (2) to join (3) to do (4) do
04 (1) to try (2) If

01 (1) expect의 목적격보어로 to부정사가 적절하다. (2) to부정사의 부정은 'not to 동사원형'으로 쓴다. (3) unless는 'if ~ not'의 의미이므로 뒤에 나오는 aren't를 are로 고치거나 unless를 if로 고쳐야 한다. (4) 조건의 부사절에서는 실제로는 미래의 일을 나타내더라도 will을 쓰지 않고 현재시제를 쓰므로 won't를 don't로 고쳐야 한다.

02 조건의 부사절에서는 미래의 의미를 갖더라도 will을 쓰지 않고 현재시제를 쓴다.

03 (1), (2), (3) ask, want, tell의 목적격보어로 to부정사가 적절하다. (4) 사역동사 make의 목적격보어로 원형부정사가 적절하다.

04 (1) expect의 목적격보어로 to부정사가 적절하다. (2) '만약 ~한다면'이라는 뜻의 조건을 나타내는 부사절을 이끄는 접속사 If가 적절하다.

01 ⑤   02 ③   03 (1) to be (2) to study
   (3) smile
04 ②   05 ④   06 ①   07 ②
08 ③   09 ①   10 if
11 (A) to get (B) to do   12 ②
13 (1) I don't want you to tell anybody about that.
   (2) The doctor advised me to stop eating junk food.
   (3) If it rains tonight, I will stay at home.
   (4) Unless you know the answer, ask me.
14 ②   15 ②   16 ②   17 ④
18 Crossword puzzles are fun to do if you enjoy words. 또는 If you enjoy words, crossword puzzles are fun to do.
19 (1) My family expects me to come home by 9 p.m.
   (2) His illness forced him to cancel his visit.
   (3) Yesterday my boss even had me walk his dog.
   (4) We don't have enough people to get the work done.
   (5) If Mina teaches me English, I will help her with math.
   (6) If you keep looking ahead and dreaming big, your future will be bright.
   (7) I forget things unless I mark them down.

01 advised의 목적격보어로 to부정사가 적절하다.

02 ask의 목적격보어로 to부정사가 적절하다.

03 (1), (2) tell, want의 목적격보어로 to부정사가 적절하다. (3) 조건의 부사절에서는 미래의 의미를 갖더라도 will을 쓰지 않고 현재시제를 쓴다.

04 unless = if ~ not

05 order의 목적격보어로 to부정사가 적절하다.

06 조건절이 미래의 일을 나타낼 때에도 조건절의 시제는 현재형을 쓴다. If Hanbin joins our soccer club, I will play soccer with him.

07 make는 목적격보어로 to부정사가 아니라 원형부정사를 쓴다.

08 ① I asked the man to take my suitcase to the room. ② He advised me to see a doctor right away. ④ His mom allowed them to watch TV after dinner. ⑤ They made me say the same thing over and over again.

09 ② If you go to the aquarium, you can see a lot of fish and sea animals. ③ If you don't have lunch, you will feel hungry soon. ④ I don't know if she will come home next weekend. ⑤ The work will not be done unless you do it now. 또는 The work will be done if you do it now.

10 첫 번째 문장에서 wonder의 목적어로 명사절을 이끌고 두 번째

문장에서 조건절을 이끌 수 있는 if가 적절하다.

11 advise와 allow는 목적격보어로 to부정사를 쓴다.

12 ②번은 know의 목적어로 명사절을 이끌고 있으며 나머지는 모두 조건절을 이끄는 if이다.

13 (1), (2) want와 advise는 목적격보어로 to부정사를 쓴다. (3) 조건의 부사절에서는 미래의 의미를 갖더라도 will을 쓰지 않고 현재시제를 쓴다. (4) unless = if ~ not

14 tell은 목적격보어로 to부정사를 쓴다.

15 조건의 부사절에서는 미래의 의미를 갖더라도 will을 쓰지 않고 현재시제를 쓴다.

16 make는 사역동사이므로 목적격보어로 동사원형이 나와야 하며 나머지는 모두 목적격보어로 to부정사가 나와야 한다.

17 그의 차가 세차를 하는 것이 아니라 세차되는 것이므로 수동의 뜻을 갖는 과거분사 washed를 쓰는 것이 적절하다.

18 조건을 나타내는 말 앞에 접속사 if를 넣는다. if절이 앞에 올 경우, if절 뒤에 쉼표(,)를 써야 함에 주의한다.

19 (1), (2) expect, force의 목적격보어로 to부정사가 적절하다. (3) have는 사역동사이므로 목적격보어로 동사원형이 나와야 한다. (4) get의 목적격보어로 the work가 무엇을 행하는 것이 아니라 행해지는 것이므로 get the work done이 적절하다. (5), (6) 조건의 부사절에서는 미래의 의미를 갖더라도 will을 쓰지 않고 현재시제를 쓴다. 이때 주절의 시제는 미래시제를 쓰는 것에 주의한다. (7) unless = if ~ not

서술형 시험대비 p.130~131

01 (1) to go (2) to focus (3) to stop (4) not to go
   (5) to keep
02 (1) If Juhee comes to my birthday party
   (2) If you do volunteer work for a month
   (3) Unless you take the subway
03 (1) I want Jimin to come to school early.
   (2) The teacher told the students to respect each other
   (3) How much would it cost to have the camera repaired?
   (4) Her little black dress and pretty hat made her look chic.
   (5) If you don't hurry, you will miss the train.
   (6) You will achieve everything you want if you work hard.
   (7) If you don't have anything to wear, wear my coat. 또는 Unless you have anything to wear, wear my coat.
04 to start
05 (1) not to forget (2) to join (3) to leave
   (4) to exercise (5) to become

06 (1) joins, will give (2) will give (3) give, will make
07 (1) If (2) Unless
08 (1) If I don't come out at six tomorrow, please wake me up.
   (2) Unless I answer my phone, call my sister.
   (3) We will get there tomorrow if we walk all night.
   (4) I want my mom to buy me a new cell phone.
   (5) She asked me to become friends with her.
   (6) She encouraged her son to go to college.
   (7) Have him come here at five.

01 (1) allow (2), (3) advise (4) warn (5) encourage는 모두 목적격보어로 to부정사를 쓴다.

02 조건절에서는 현재시제로 미래시제를 대신한다.

03 (1), (2) want, tell의 목적격보어로 to부정사가 적절하다. (3) 사역동사 have의 목적격보어로 the camera가 수리하는 것이 아니라 수리되는 것이므로 repaired가 적절하다. (4) make는 사역동사로 목적격보어로 동사원형이 나와야 한다. (5), (6) 조건의 부사절에서는 미래의 의미를 갖더라도 will을 쓰지 않고 현재시제를 쓴다. 이때 주절의 시제는 미래시제를 쓰는 것에 주의한다. (7) unless는 'if ~ not'과 같은 뜻이다.

04 would like는 목적격보어로 to부정사를 쓴다.

05 warn, want, order, advise, expect의 목적격보어로 to부정사가 적절하다.

06 (1) 아직 일어나지 않은 미래의 일에 대한 조건을 나타내는 것이므로 조건절에는 현재시제를 쓰고 주절에는 미래시제를 쓴다. (2) 접속사 if가 명사절을 이끌고 있으므로 미래시제를 써야 한다. (3) unless도 'if ~ not'의 뜻으로 조건절을 이끄는 접속사이므로 조건절에는 현재시제를 쓰고 주절에는 미래시제를 쓴다.

07 명령문, + and ~: '~해라, 그러면'(= If ~), 명령문, + or ~: '~해라, 그렇지 않으면'(= Unless ~ = If not ~)

08 (1), (3) 조건의 부사절에서는 미래의 의미를 갖더라도 will을 쓰지 않고 현재시제를 쓴다. (4), (5), (6) want, ask, encourage는 목적격보어로 to부정사를 쓴다. (7) have는 사역동사이므로 목적격보어로 동사원형을 쓴다.

교과서
Reading

확인문제 p.132

1 T 2 F 3 F 4 T

확인문제 p.133

1 T 2 F 3 F 4 T 5 T 6 F

01 of the Future   02 be on the market
03 that   04 will print out
05 take space trips
06 under the sea, in floating cities
07 above   08 surprise
09 in the future   10 As, will appear
11 What kind of job   12 be like
13 looked ahead, chose jobs
14 Let's read   15 that Sujin made
16 was made from
17 upcycling designer
18 waste materials   19 in new ways
20 the amount of waste
21 To become, creative
22 Have you ever heard
23 works for, that makes
24 special software
25 specially for patients   26 are good at
27 to use   28 big data specialist
29 works on   30 For example
31 taxi use patterns, late-night travelers
32 analyzed, to create   33 working with
34 collecting data from
35 allows us to learn
36 develop, problem-solving skills
37 yourself, prepare for
38 keep looking, dreaming

1 Jobs of the Future
2 2020s: Self-driving cars will be on the market.
3 2030s: People will have robots that do everything for them.
4 2030s: 3D printers in every home will print out almost everything.
5 2050s: People will take space trips.
6 2050s: People will live under the sea or in floating cities.
7 Look at the pictures above.
8 Do these ideas surprise you?
9 You can see that our lives will be very different in the future.
10 As our lives change, many new jobs will appear.
11 What kind of job do you want?
12 What will your future life be like?

13 The following people looked ahead and chose jobs that will be important in the future.
14 Let's read about their jobs!
15 Do you see the flower pot that Sujin made?
16 It was made from old street flags.
17 She is an upcycling designer.
18 She works with waste materials to make new products.
19 Her products show people that old materials can be useful in new ways.
20 Upcycling can reduce the amount of waste in the future.
21 To become an upcycling designer, you should be creative and learn about art.
22 Have you ever heard of 3D modelers?
23 Taeho, a 3D modeler, works for a company that makes artificial hands and legs.
24 Taeho uses special software to print out new hands and legs.
25 They are made specially for patients.
26 If you are good at computer programming and art, you can be a 3D modeler.
27 Taeho wants more people to use 3D printed products in the future.
28 Jihye is a big data specialist.
29 She works on many projects.
30 For example, last year, she made bus routes.
31 To find the best night routes, she needed to collect smartphone use data and taxi use patterns from late-night travelers.
32 Then she analyzed this information to create the most useful routes.
33 Now Jihye is working with an online shopping mall.
34 She is collecting data from customers to find out the best styles for them.
35 She knows big data allows us to learn more about our daily lives.
36 If you want to become a big data specialist, you should develop your math and problem-solving skills!
37 Think about yourself and prepare for your future.
38 If you keep looking ahead and dreaming big, your future will be bright.

01 ③   02 (A) appear (B) What (C) ahead

03 under the sea, in floating cities

04 ④   05 what → that 또는 which

06 ①, ②, ④

07 (A) a 3D modeler

(B) works for a company that makes artificial hands and legs

(C) should be good at computer programming and art

08 ①, ④   09 customers

10 will keep → keep   11 ②   12 ③

13 ②

14 ⓐ excited ⓑ interested   15 a dream   16 ④

17 ⑤   18 people   19 ③   20 ④

21 to learn   22 She made bus routes.

23 at a software company   24 realized

25 She chose her job because she is interested in math and science.

01 ⓐ와 ③번: ~함에 따라(비례), ① ~ 때문에(이유), ② [보통 as ~ as ...로 형용사·부사 앞에서] ~와 같은 정도로 (앞의 as: 지시 부사, 뒤의 as: 접속사), ④ ~으로, ~이라고(전치사), ⑤ ~와 같이; ~하는 대로(양태·상태)

02 (A) 우리의 삶이 변화함에 따라 새로운 직업들이 많이 '생겨날 것'이라고 해야 하므로 appear가 적절하다. disappear: 사라지다, (B) 전치사 'like'의 목적어를 써야 하므로 What이 적절하다. (C) '앞을 내다보고' 미래에 중요하게 될 직업을 선택했다고 해야 하므로 ahead가 적절하다. look ahead: (앞일을) 내다보다, look behind: 뒤돌아보다; 회고하다

03 사람들은 육지뿐만 아니라 '바다 밑'이나 '수상 도시'에서 살 수 있을 것이다. not only A but also B: A뿐만 아니라 B도

04 ④ 당신은 미래에 우리의 삶이 매우 '달라진' 것을 볼 수 있다고 했다.

05 선행사인 a company가 있기 때문에 관계대명사 that이나 which로 고치는 것이 적절하다.

06 ⓑ와 ③, ⑤는 부사적 용법, ① 형용사적 용법 ②, ④ 명사적 용법

07 (A) 3D 모형 제작자이다. (B) 인공 손과 다리를 만드는 회사에서 일한다. (C) 컴퓨터 프로그래밍과 미술에 뛰어나야 한다.

08 ⓐ와 ①, ④번: 전문가, ② 비전문가, 아마추어, ③초보자, ⑤ 문외한

09 온라인 쇼핑몰의 '소비자들'을 가리킨다.

10 조건의 부사절에서는 현재시제가 미래시제를 대신한다.

11 수진은 거리의 낡은 깃발들로 화분을 만들었기 때문에, 폐기물을 가지고 새로운 제품을 만드는 '업사이클링 디자이너'라고 하는 것이 적절하다. ① 꽃집 주인[직원], ③ 쓰레기 수거인, ④ 재활용 프로그래머, ⑤ 쓰레기 봉투 디자이너

12 낡은 재료가 새로운 방식으로 유용해질 수 있다는 것을 보여주고 있기 때문에, 표어로는 '쓰레기를 낭비하지 마라'가 적절하다. ① environmental pollution: 환경오염, ⑤ disposable product: 일회용품

13 ② '화분 제작에 걸린 시간'은 알 수 없다. ① 낡은 거리 현수막, ③ 업사이클링 디자이너로서 폐기물을 가지고 새로운 제품을 만든다. ④ 낡은 재료가 새로운 방식으로 유용해질 수 있다는 것, ⑤ 창의적이어야 하며 미술을 배워야 한다.

14 감정을 나타내는 동사는 수식받는 주체가 감정을 느끼게 되는 경우에 과거분사를 써야 하므로 ⓐ excited와 ⓑ interested가 적절하다.

15 '꿈'을 가리킨다.

16 소인이 언제 일을 시작했는지는 대답할 수 없다. ① She is a computer programmer and works at a software company. ② She develops new software for computers. ③ People from different countries. ⑤ She studied computer science and developed her problem-solving skills.

17 우리의 삶이 변화함에 따라 새로운 직업들이 많이 생겨날 것이라는 말이 뒤에 이어지고 있으므로, 당신은 미래에 우리의 삶이 매우 '달라질' 것을 볼 수 있다고 하는 것이 적절하다. ③ similar: 비슷한, 유사한, ④ common: 흔한, 공통의

18 '사람들'을 가리킨다.

19 3D 프린터가 '거의' 모든 것을 출력해 낼 수 있다고 했을 뿐이므로, '모든' 것을 출력할 수 있는 3D 프린터가 인간도 출력할 수 있다는 진수의 생각은 올바르지 않다. ④ adventurous: 모험심이 강한, 모험을 즐기는

20 ⓐ the best styles for them: 그들(소비자)에게 맞는 최적의 스타일, ⓒ prepare for: ~을 준비하다

21 allow+목적어+to부정사: ~가 …하도록 허락하다

22 작년에 그녀는 버스 노선을 만들었다.

23 소프트웨어 회사에서

24 come true = be realized: 실현되다

25 수학과 과학에 관심이 있기 때문에 그녀의 직업을 선택했다.

01 ahead

02 In the 2030s, people will have robots that do everything for them and 3D printers in every home will print out almost everything.

03 Are you surprised at(또는 by) these ideas?

04 ⓐ old street flags ⓑ the flower pot

05 new → old, old → new

06 (A) an upcycling designer

(B) works with waste materials to make new products

(C) should be creative and learn about art

07 (A) works (B) that (C) at

08 artificial

09 using → to use

10 (A) looking (B) dreaming

11 (1) In order to find   (2) So as to find

12 She knows big data allows us to learn more about our daily lives.

13 (1) She needed to collect smartphone use data and taxi use patterns from late-night travelers.

(2) She analyzed this information.

01 미래에 무슨 일이 일어날지를 고려했다, foresee: 예견하다, 내다보다, look ahead: (앞일을) 내다보다

02 2030년대에 사람들은 그들을 위하여 모든 것을 하는 로봇을 갖게 될 것이고 모든 가정의 3D 프린터가 거의 모든 것을 출력해낼 것이다.

03 be surprised at/by: ~에 놀라다

04 ⓐ: '낡은 거리 깃발들', ⓑ: (수진이 만든) '화분'이 각각의 예에 해당한다.

05 거리의 낡은 깃발들로 화분을 만든 것이기 때문에, '낡은' 재료가 '새로운' 방식으로 유용해질 수 있다는 것을 보여준다고 하는 것이 적절하다.

06 (A) 업사이클링 디자이너이다. (B) 폐기물을 가지고 새로운 제품을 만든다. (C) 창의적이어야 하며 미술을 배워야 한다.

07 (A) Taeho와 a 3D modeler는 동격이므로 works가 적절하다. (B) 뒤에 불완전한 문장이 이어지므로 관계대명사 that이 적절하다. 관계부사 where+완전한 문장, (C) 컴퓨터 프로그래밍이나 미술에 '뛰어나다면'이라고 해야 하므로 at이 적절하다. be good at: ~에 능숙하다, ~을 잘하다, be good for: ~에 좋다

08 artificial = man-made: 인위적인, 인조의

09 want+목적어+to부정사: ~가 …하기를 원하다

10 keep ~ing: 계속해서 ~하다

11 in order to 동사원형 = so as to 동사원형 …하기 위하여(목적)

12 'to'를 보충하면 된다. allow+목적어+to부정사: ~가 …하도록 허락하다

13 (1) 최적의 심야 노선을 찾기 위하여, 그녀는 심야에 이동하는 사람들의 스마트폰 이용 정보와 택시 이용 패턴을 수집할 필요가 있었다. (2) 가장 유용한 노선을 만들기 위해 그녀는 그 정보를 분석했다.

영역별 핵심문제
p.145~149

01 consultant 02 ⑤

03 (1) decorate[to decorate] (2) allowed (3) apply

(4) float   04 ①   05 ⑤   06 apply

07 ②   08 ②

09 you need to develop your problem-solving skills

10 ⑤   11 ③, ⑤   12 (B) singing (C) sing

13 ⑤   14 ③

15 (1) If you don't take a shower first, you can't go into the pool.

(2) If you want to become an upcycling designer, you should be creative and learn about art.

(3) The grandfather wanted his grandson to visit him this weekend.

(4) I asked him to call me back tomorrow.

(5) I need you to do me a favor.

16 ②   17 not to fight, will be punished

18 ④

19 (1) unless you miss the bus

(2) if you tell a lie

20 If you go to Europe, you can see many old structures.

21 ⑤   22 ②, ④   23 ③

24 upcycling

25 Sujin(She) made it from old street flags.

26 ①   27 ③, ⑤   28 ②

29 collecting data, to find out

30 (A) big data (B) our daily lives

01 주어진 단어의 관계는 동사와 그 동사의 행위자의 관계이다. design: 디자인하다, 설계하다 designer: 디자이너, 설계자 consult: 상담하다 consultant: 상담가

02 collaborate: 협력하다

03 (1) decorate: 꾸미다, 장식하다 / 크리스마스 트리 장식하는 것 좀 도와줄래? (2) allow: 허락하다 / 누구도 여기서 담배 피는 것이 허락되지 않는다. (3) apply: 지원하다, 신청하다 / 나는 해외 자원 봉사 프로그램에 지원하게 되어 정말 기쁘다. (4) float: (물 위에) 뜨다, 떠다니다 / 그것들은 물에 집어넣으면 뜰 것이다.

04 route: 경로, 노선 / 두 장소 사이의 길

05 그림을 잘 그린다는 말과 보드게임을 잘한다는 말이 but으로 연결되는 것은 어색하다. I am good at drawing pictures. → I am not good at drawing pictures.

06 apply: 지원하다, 신청하다 / 어떤 것을 하기를 원한다고 말하는 서류를 제출하다

07 남자아이와 여자아이는 같은 행사가 아니라, 남자아이는 만화행사, 여자아이는 게임 행사에서 도움을 주기를 원한다.

08 상대방에게 조언을 구할 때 'What do I need to do?', 'What do you suggest?', 'What should I do to ~?', 'How can I ~?' 등을 사용할 수 있다.

09 develop: 발달시키다, 발전하다 problem-solving: 문제 해결의

10 주어진 문장은 밴드에서 록 음악을 연주할 계획이라고 말하는 내용이다. 이어서 노래를 잘하는 여자아이에게 밴드에서 노래하라고 제안하는 'Why don't you sing for us? (우리를 위해 노래해 주는 게 어때?)'라는 문장과 어울리므로 ⑤가 적절하다.

11 (A)에 대한 대답이 'You're good at dancing, aren't you?(춤 잘 추잖아, 그렇지 않니?)'이므로 자신이 무엇을 잘하는지에 대해 상대방에게 물어보는 것이 적절하다

12 be good at (동)명사: ~을 잘하다, Why don't you 동사원형 ~?: ~하는 게 어때?(제안하기)

13 ① We expect you to win the singing contest. ② The son asked his mom to give him more pocket money. ③ I want Juhee to come to my birthday party. ④ He ordered us to finish the project by Monday.

14 조건의 부사절에서는 미래의 의미를 갖더라도 will을 쓰지 않고 현재시제를 쓴다.

15 (1), (2) if는 조건을 나타내는 접속사로, 'if+주어+동사'로 쓰인다. if절이 앞에 올 경우, 부사절 뒤에 쉼표(,)를 붙인다. (3), (4), (5) want와 ask, need는 '동사+목적어+목적격보어(to부정사)'로 쓴다.

16 주어진 문장과 ②번은 조건을 나타내는 부사절을 이끌고 있다. ①, ③, ④번은 '~인지 아닌지'의 뜻으로 명사절을 이끌고 있다. ⑤ 가정법에 쓰인 if이다.

17 tell은 목적격보어로 to부정사가 나오며 싸우지 말라고 하는 것이 적절하므로 to부정사 앞에 not을 붙인다. If절에서는 현재시제를 쓰지만 내용상 미래의 일이므로 주절에는 미래시제를 쓴다. 또한 벌을 받는 것이므로 수동태로 써야 한다.

18 have는 사역동사이므로 목적격보어로 원형부정사가 나온다.

19 if는 조건을 나타내는 접속사로, 'if+주어+동사'로 쓰인다. if절이 앞에 올 경우 부사절 뒤에 쉼표(,)를 붙인다.

20 'If+주어+동사'로 쓰며 부사절 뒤에 쉼표(,)를 붙인다.

21 2050년대에 사람들은 '바다 밑'이나 '수상 도시'에서 살 것이다. ① be on the market = be offered for sale: 판매되고 있다, ④ take a trip = go on a trip: 여행을 가다

22 ⓑ와 ①, ③, ⑤: …와 비슷한(전치사), ② (…을) 좋아하다(동사), ④ [외관·형태·성질 등이] 같은(형용사)

23 '다음의 사람들은 앞을 내다보고 미래에 중요하게 될 직업을 선택하였습니다. 그들의 직업에 관하여 읽어 봅시다!'라고 했으므로, ③번이 적절하다.

24 부산물, 폐기물, 쓸모없는 혹은 원치 않는 제품들을 새로운 물질이나 더 좋은 품질의 환경적 가치를 가진 제품으로 변형시키는 과정, upcycle: (재활용품을) 더 나은 것으로 만들다 (= upgrade + recycle)

25 'Sujin(She)'을 주어로 해서 고치는 것이 적절하다.

26 3D 모형 제작자가 되기 위해서는 컴퓨터 프로그래밍과 미술에 뛰어나야 하므로, '보람'이가 적절하다.

27 ⓐ와 ③, ⑤번: 경험 용법, ① 결과 용법, ② 완료 용법, ④ 계속 용법

28 앞의 내용의 예가 나오고 있으므로 For example이 가장 적절하다. ① 그러므로, ④ 게다가, ⑤ 게다가, 더욱이

29 현재 그녀는 온라인 쇼핑몰의 소비자들에게 맞는 최적의 스타일을 '찾기 위하여' '데이터를 수집'하고 있다.

30 지혜에 따르면, '빅데이터'는 우리에게 '일상생활'에 관하여 더 많이 알게 해 준다.

단원별 예상문제
p.150~153

01 advice 02 out 03 ②
04 (C) – (B) – (A) – (D) 05 float 06 ③
07 (A) amazing (B) start 08 improve
09 ① 10 ② 11 (A) who (B) decorates
12 ③ 13 ③ 14 ④
15 (1) go → to go (2) to do → do
16 (A) old (B) waste (C) useful
17 (A) reduce (B) waste 18 ④ 19 ④
20 ⑤ 21 Self-driving cars
22 artificial hands and legs 또는 new hands and legs
23 ④
24 (1) 심야에 이동하는 사람들의 스마트폰 이용 정보와 택시 이용 패턴 수집
(2) 온라인 쇼핑몰 소비자들에게 맞는 최적의 스타일을 찾기 위한 데이터 수집
25 ②
26 We[I] need to keep looking ahead and dreaming big.

01 주어진 보기는 명사와 동사의 관계이다. analysis: 분석 analyze: 분석하다 advice: 충고, 조언 advise: 충고하다

02 help out: 도와주다, 거들다 / 내가 할 수 있으면 거들고 싶다. print out: 출력하다 / 이 문서를 출력해 주시겠어요?

03 space: 우주 / 과학자들은 사람들을 우주로 보냈다.

04 (C) 학교 재능 발표회에서 무엇을 할지 질문하자 (B) 아직 결정을 안 했다고 대답하면서 자신이 무엇을 잘하는지 상대방에게 질문한다. (A) 이에 대한 대답으로 춤을 잘 추지 않느냐고 말하자 (D) 자신은 노래를 잘한다고 대답한다.

05 float: (물 위에) 뜨다, 떠다니다 / 물 위에 머무르다

06 주어진 문장은 독서가 글쓰기를 더 좋게 만든다는 내용이다. 'You need to read a lot of books.(책을 많이 읽어야 해.)'의 내용과 연결되는 ③이 적절하다.

07 (A) amazing: 대단한, 멋진, It은 your paper(너의 글)를 받는 대명사로, 그 글이 대단한 것이므로 능동의 형태가 어울린다. (B) Why don't you 동사원형 ~?: ~하는 게 어때?

08 improve: 개선하다, 향상시키다 / 어떤 것을 더 좋게 만들다

09 Well, I need to study art history. → Well, you need to study art history.

10 주어진 질문에 ②번 다음에서 Sure.라고 답하고 있으므로 ②번이 적절하다.

11 (A) 주격 관계대명사의 자리이다. 선행사가 students로 사람이므로 who가 어울린다. decorate: 꾸미다, 장식하다

12 푸드 스타일리스트가 되기 위해서 가장 중요한 것은 무엇인지 언급되어 있지 않다. ① 소녀는 미래에 무엇이 되고 싶어 하는가? ② 소녀는 푸드 스타일리스트가 되기 위해서 무엇이 필요한가? ③ 푸드 스타일리스트가 되기 위해서 무엇이 가장 중요한가? ④ 푸드 스타일리스트는 무슨 일을 하는가? ⑤ 남자의 직업은 무엇인가?

13 allow의 목적격보어로 to부정사가 적절하다.

14 ① The father told his daughter to do her homework. ② I want Seri to watch the movie with us. ③ If something happens tomorrow, call me immediately. ⑤ I didn't expect you to get home so fast.

15 (1) request의 목적격보어로 to부정사가 나와야 한다. (2) let은 사역동사이므로 목적격보어로 동사원형이 나와야 한다.

16 (A) 거리의 '낡은' 깃발들로 만들어진 것이라고 해야 하므로 old가 적절하다. (B) '폐기물'을 가지고 새로운 제품을 만든다고 해야 하므로 waste가 적절하다. (C) 낡은 재료가 새로운 방식으로 '유용해질' 수 있다는 것을 보여준다고 해야 하므로 useful이 적절하다.

17 업사이클링은 '쓰레기'의 양을 '줄일 수' 있기 때문에, 환경 보호에 좋다고 말할 수 있다.

18 업사이클링은 미래에 쓰레기의 '양을 줄일 수 있다'고 했다.

19 ⓐ: 관계대명사 that, ⓑ: 목적어를 이끄는 접속사 that

20 ⑤ (새롭거나 뜻밖의 대상과) 접하다[마주치다], ⓒ와 나머지: 생기다, 발생하다, ① show up: 나타나다, ② emerge: 모습을 드러내다, 생겨나다, ③ come along: 생기다[나타나다], ④ turn up: 나타나다

21 2020년대에는 자율주행차들이 시장에 나올 것이다. be on the market: 판매하고 있다

22 '인공 손과 다리' 또는 '새 손과 다리'를 가리킨다.

23 태호가 누구와 함께 일하는지는 대답할 수 없다. ① He is a 3D modeler. ② He works for a company that makes artificial hands and legs. ③ He makes artificial hands and legs. ⑤ We[I] need to be good at computer programming and art.

24 (1) 지혜가 작년에 했던 작업, (2) 지혜가 현재 하고 있는 작업을 쓰면 된다.

25 ⓐ와 ②, ③, ⑤: 명사적 용법, ① 형용사적 용법, ④ 부사적 용법

26 만약 우리의 미래를 밝게 만들고 싶다면, '우리는 계속 앞을 내다보고 꿈을 크게 꿀 필요가 있다.'

01 planning

02 What am I good at?

03 ②I'm good at took care of people. → I'm good at taking care of people.

04 (1) her son to clean his room for himself
(2) him to stop smoking to live a life without pain
(3) John to pass the entrance exam

05 (1) What do you want me to do for you?
(2) Can you ask my prince to come to this tower?
(3) If you want to save us, throw a rope down to us.
(4) If Seri watches the movie with us, I will buy her some popcorn.

06 Unless, won't go

07 What will your future life be like?

08 No, it won't.

09 new jobs

10 (A) collect (B) daily (C) yourself

11 smartphone use data and taxi use patterns from late-night travelers

12 (A) a big data specialist
(B) math and problem-solving skills

01 be going to 동사원형: ~할 예정이다(= be planning to 동사원형)

02 What am I good at?: 나는 무엇을 잘하지? 'You're good at dancing, aren't you?(너 춤 잘 추잖아, 그렇지 않니?)'로 대답하기 위해서는 자신이 무엇을 잘하는지 질문하는 것이 적절하다.

03 능력을 말할 때 'be good at ~'을 사용해서 '~을 잘한다'는 의미를 나타낼 수 있다. 전치사 at 다음에는 명사나 동명사를 쓴다.

04 ask, warn, expect 등은 목적격보어로 to부정사를 쓴다.

05 (1) want (2) ask 등의 동사는 목적격보어로 to부정사가 나와야 한다. (3), (4) if는 조건을 나타내는 접속사로, if절이 앞에 올 경우 뒤에 쉼표(,)를 써야 한다. 또한 조건의 부사절에서는 미래시제 대신 현재시제를 쓴다.

06 unless=if ~ not

07 'like'를 보충하면 된다.

08 해석| '2040년대'가 아니라 '2050년대'에 사람들은 우주여행을 할 것이다.

09 미래에 우리의 삶은 오늘날의 그것과 같지 않을 것이다. 우리의 삶이 변화함에 따라 많은 '새로운 직업들'이 있게 될 것이다.

10 (A) '수집할' 필요가 있었다고 해야 하므로 collect가 적절하다. correct: 바로잡다, 정정하다, (B) '일상' 생활이라고 해야 하므로 daily가 적절하다. dairy: 낙농장, 유제품의, (C) 주어와 목적

어가 같으므로 재귀대명사 yourself가 적절하다.

11 '심야에 이동하는 사람들의 스마트폰 이용 정보와 택시 이용 패턴'을 가리킨다.

12 (A) 빅데이터 전문가이다. (B) 수학과 문제 해결 능력을 계발해야 한다.

창의사고력 서술형 문제 p.156

|모범답안|

01 What do I need to do to be / You need to[You should/Make sure you] study many recipes. / What else do I need to do?

02 (1) Mom expects me to get good grades.
   (2) Mom expects my sister to become a scientist.
   (3) Mom expects my dad not to smoke.

03 (A) a computer programmer (B) new software
   (C) from different countries
   (D) math and science (E) computer science

01 What do I need to do?: 저는 뭘 해야 하나요?, 저는 어떤 것을 해야 할까요? what else: 그 밖에 무슨 recipe: 요리법 dish: 요리

단원별 모의고사 p.157~160

01 ③

02 (1) collaboration (2) Creativity

03 (1) (a)ppeared (2) (a)pplied (3) (c)ounseling
   (4) (l)ook (a)head 04 ③ 05 ⑤

06 creativity

07 You need to learn about many kinds of food.

08 (A)at (B)of (C)about (D)about

09 develop

10 What skills do I need to develop? 11 ③, ④

12 I am not good at drawing pictures.

13 ② 14 ①, ②

15 (1) to win (2) not to be late

16 (1) The mother wanted her son to clean his room.
   (2) I expect Juho to exercise more.
   (3) The doctor advised me to stop eating junk food.
   (4) If you show us your hand, we will open the door.
   (5) If you don't sleep enough, you will be very tired.

17 (1) to go (2) rains 18 ③

19 If you keep looking ahead and dreaming big

20 ④ 21 creative 22 ② 23 ①, ④

24 the following people 25 ④

---

01 amount: 양, 총액 / 많은 양의 정보가 있었다.

02 (1) collaborate: 협력하다 collaboration: 공동 작업, 협동
   (2) creative: 창의적인 creativity: 창의력, 독창력

03 (1) appear: 나타나다, 보이기 시작하다 (2) apply: 지원하다, 신청하다 (3) counseling: 상담 (4) look ahead: (앞일을) 내다보다, 예견하다

04 talent: (타고난) 재능, 재주 / 어떤 것을 잘하는 타고난 능력

05 (A)의 대답으로 'A food stylist decorates food to look good for pictures or movies.(푸드 스타일리스트는 사진이나 영화에서 음식이 맛있어 보이도록 장식하는 일을 합니다.)'로 푸드 스타일리스트가 어떤 일을 하는지 얘기하고 있으므로 ⓒ가 어울린다. (B)와 (C)는 푸드 스타일리스트가 되기 위한 조언을 구하고 대답을 하고 있다. What do I need to do?: 뭘 해야 합니까?, 어떤 것을 해야 할까요? what else: 그 밖에 무슨

06 creativity: 창의력, 독창력 / 새로운 것을 생각해 내거나 만들어 내는 능력

07 need to 동사원형: ~할 필요가 있다 kind: 종류

08 (A) be good at: ~을 잘하다 (B) take care of: ~을 돌보다 (C) How about 동명사 ~?: ~하는 건 어때? (D) learn about: ~에 대해서 배우다

09 develop: 발달시키다, 발전하다 / 좀 더 진보된 상태로 되거나 변화되다

10 need to 동사원형: ~할 필요가 있다 skill: 기술

11 ⓐ looking ⓑ are needed ⓔ apply

12 be not good at: ~을 잘하지 못하다, ~에 능숙하지 못하다 draw: 그리다

13 persuade의 목적격보어로 to부정사가 적절하다.

14 빈칸이 있는 절은 현재시제이고 주절은 미래시제이므로, 빈칸은 시간이나 조건의 부사절이 되어야 한다. until은 '~(할 때)까지'라는 뜻의 시간을 나타내는 접속사이다.

15 encourage와 order는 목적격보어로 to부정사를 쓰고 to부정사의 부정은 not을 to 앞에 쓴다.

16 (1) want, (2) expect, (3) advise 등은 모두 목적격보어로 to부정사가 나와야 한다. (4) unless는 'if ~ not'이므로 unless를 if로 고쳐야 한다. (5) 조건의 부사절에서는 미래의 의미를 갖더라도 will을 쓰지 않고 현재시제를 쓴다.

17 (1) tell은 목적격보어로 to부정사를 쓴다. (2) 조건의 부사절에서는 미래시제 대신에 현재시제를 쓴다.

18 주어진 문장의 this information에 주목한다. ③번 앞 문장의 내용을 받고 있으므로 ③번이 적절하다.

19 keep ~ing: 계속해서 ~하다

20 지혜는 빅데이터가 우리에게 '일상생활'에 관하여 더 많이 알게 해 준다는 것을 알고 있다.

21 be동사의 보어이므로, create의 형용사 'creative'를 쓰는 것이 적절하다.

22 ⓐ와 ②번: 쓰레기(명사), ① …을 낭비하다(동사), ③ <기회 등을> 놓치다(동사), ④ 낭비(명사), ⑤ 쓸모가 없어진(형용사)

23 ⓐ와 ①, ④번: 관계대명사(뒤에 불완전한 문장이 나옴.), ②, ③, ⑤번: 접속사(뒤에 완전한 문장이 나옴.)

24 앞을 내다보고 미래에 중요하게 될 직업을 선택한 '다음의 사람들'을 가리킨다.

25 2060년대에 우리의 삶이 어떤 모습일지는 대답할 수 없다. ① Self-driving cars will be on the market. ② People will have robots that do everything for them and 3D printers in every home will print out almost everything. ③ In the 2050s. ⑤ Because our lives will change.

Lesson 8

Who Is Happy?

1 Who Is Happy?

2 Once upon a time, there was a crow who lived in a forest.

3 The crow was very happy with his life.

4 He always looked at himself in the water.

5 He thought no one was more beautiful than he was.

6 Then one day, the crow saw a swan on the lake.

7 "The swan is so white," he thought, "but I am so black.

8 I have never seen such a white bird before.

9 His beauty shines so brightly.

10 The swan must be the happiest bird in the world."

11 He went to the swan and expressed his thoughts.

12 "Actually," the swan said, "I thought that I was the happiest bird.

13 But then I saw a parrot.

14 Now I think the parrot is the happiest bird in the world."

15 The crow asked why he thought so.

16 The swan answered, "The parrot has colorful feathers.

17 He is more beautiful than I am.

18 He must be proud of his appearance."

19 The crow then flew to the parrot and said, "The swan said you are the happiest bird because you have colorful feathers."

20 The parrot explained, "I lived a very happy life until I saw a peacock.

21 My feathers are colorful, but the peacock's feathers are colorful, big, and gorgeous.

22 So he is loved by everyone."

23 The crow then visited the peacock at the zoo.

24 There were a lot of people around the peacock, and they praised him for his beauty.

25 The crow thought the peacock must be the happiest bird in the world.

26 After all the people left, the crow started to talk to the peacock.

27 "Peacock, you are so beautiful.

28 Many people come to see you every day.

29 On the other hand, when people see me, they chase me away.

30 I think you are the happiest bird in the world."

31 The peacock said, "I may be the most beautiful bird, but I'm not happy.

32 Because of my beauty, I am stuck in this zoo.

Check(√) True or False   p.164

1 T   2 F   3 F   4 T

Check(√) True or False   p.164

1 T   2 F   3 T   4 F   5 T   6 F

01 Who   02 Once upon a time

03 happy with   04 looked at himself

05 more beautiful than

06 on the lake   07 so white, so black

08 such a white bird

09 shines so brightly

10 must be   11 his thoughts   12 Actually

13 then   14 the happiest bird

15 why he thought so

16 colorful feathers

17 more beautiful than

18 must be proud of

19 flew, because   20 explained, until

21 the peacock's feathers, gorgeous

22 is loved by   23 at the zoo   24 praised, for

25 must be   26 started to talk

27 so beautiful   28 come to see

29 On the other hand, chase me away

30 in the world

31 the most beautiful

32 Because of, am stuck in   33 Unlike

34 be like

35 who the happiest bird was

36 thought to himself

37 free to fly

38 went back to

39 looked at himself

---

33 Unlike me, you aren't kept in a cage.

34 I want to be like you because you can go anywhere."

35 After the crow talked to the peacock, he started to think about who the happiest bird was.

36 The crow thought to himself, "The peacock's feathers are impressive, but he is stuck in a cage.

37 I don't have colorful feathers, but I'm free to fly anywhere."

38 The crow went back to the forest.

39 He looked at himself in the water again and saw the happiest bird in the world.

서술형 시험대비   p.170~175

01 (1) happiness   (2) beauty

02 is (s)tuck in

03 (1) (a)ppearance   (2) feathers   (3) shines
    (4) (t)houghts

04 (g)orgeous   05 (1) away   (2) of

06 of   07 so

08 I want to be free to come and go at anytime.

09 I'd like to travel around the world.

10 (d)irector   11 cage

12 (1) The crow thought if[whether] the swan was really white.
   (2) The man asks whose this bag is.
   (3) The peacock didn't know why people chased him away.
   (4) When do you think the crow visited the peacock?

13 There was a beautiful princess who[that] lived in a forest.

14 *Naruto* is an animation which[that] my brother loves watching.

15 That is the house in which Mariel lives. 또는 That is the house which[that] Mariel lives in.

16 Gabriel saw a boy and his dog that were playing together in the park.

17 such → so, so → such

18 throw away it → throw it away

19 She looked at herself in the mirror to straighten her own dress.

20 He must be stupid to ask such things.

21 I have never seen such a white bird before.

22 sure 또는 certain

23 the parrot is the happiest bird in the world

24 (A) more (B) than 또는 (A) as[so] (B) as

25 that

26 him → himself

27 flew

28 happily

29 everyone loves him

30 (A) Because of (B) because

31 chase away me → chase me away

32 어디든 갈 수 있다. / 사람들이 그를 보면, 쫓아낸다. / 아름다워서 매일 많은 사람이 그를 보러 온다. / 아름다움 때문에 동물원에 갇혀 있다.

33 (A) so (B) such (C) feathers

34 The swan must be the happiest bird in the world.

35 (A) black, (B) white, (C) colorful

36 thinking

37 The crow thought to himself

38 unhappiest → happiest

39 stuck

40 Though I may be the most beautiful bird, I'm not happy.

41 (A) chased, (B) anywhere, (C) most beautiful, (D)beautiful

01 (1) 전치사 다음에는 명사나 동명사가 올 수 있다. happy: 행복한 happiness: 행복, 만족 (2) beautiful: 아름다운 beauty: 아름다움

02 be stuck in: ~에 (갇혀) 있다

03 (1) appearance: 외모 (2) feather: (새의) 털, 깃털 (3) shine: 빛나다 (shine — shone — shone) (4) thought: 생각, 사고

04 gorgeous: 매력적인, 멋진 / 너 오늘 아주 멋져 보이네! 뭐 했니?

05 (1) chase away ~ : ~을 쫓아내다 / 나는 모든 모기들을 쫓아냈다. (2) be proud of: ~을 자랑으로 여기다 / 난 네가 정말 자랑스러워.

06 think of: ~을 생각하다 / 내가 배우가 되는 것을 생각해 본 적이 없다. because of: ~ 때문에 / 독감 때문에 일을 쉬고 집에 있었다.

07 so: (부) 너무나, 대단히, 그렇게 / 밤새 일해서 너무 피곤하다. 나는 너무 배고파서 더 이상 집중할 수 없다. 그 영화는 좀 슬펐어. 그렇게 생각하지 않니?

08 be free to 동사원형: 자유롭게 ~하다

09 around the world: 세계 곳곳에

10 director: 감독 / 어떤 것을 책임지는 사람

11 cage: 우리, 새장 / 동물을 가두기 위해 만들어진 상자

12 간접의문문의 어순은 '의문사+주어+동사'이며 의문사가 없는 경우는 'if[whether]+주어+동사'로 쓴다. think 동사가 주절

33

13 선행사가 사람이므로 주격 관계대명사 who나 that

14 선행사가 사물이므로 목적격 관계대명사 which나 that

15 목적격 관계대명사가 전치사의 목적어인 경우 전치사는 관계대명사절의 끝에 오거나 관계대명사 앞에 올 수 있으며 전치사가 관계대명사절의 끝에 올 경우에는 관계대명사를 생략할 수 있다. 전치사가 관계대명사 앞에 올 경우에는 관계대명사 that을 쓸 수 없으며 목적격 관계대명사는 생략될 수 있다.

16 선행사가 '사람+사물'이므로 관계대명사 that을 써야 한다.

17 so는 '매우, 무척, 대단히'라는 뜻의 부사로 쓰였고 'a+형용사+명사' 앞에는 so가 아니라 such가 적절하다. so는 'so+형용사+a+명사'의 어순으로 쓰인다.

18 '동사+인칭대명사 목적어+부사'의 어순에 주의한다.

19 자신의 옷매무새를 고치기 위해 거울을 본 것이므로 주어와 동사가 같기 때문에 재귀대명사가 나와야 한다.

20 have to는 추측의 의미로 쓰이지 않으므로 must를 써야 한다.

21 'before'를 보충하면 된다. such+a+형용사+명사

22 강한 추측의 의미를 나타내는 must는 I am sure[certain]를 사용하여 고치는 것이 적절하다.

23 까마귀는 왜 '앵무새가 세상에서 가장 행복한 새'라고 백조가 생각하는지를 물었다.

24 '부정주어+비교급 than = 부정주어+as[so]+원급+as: 최상급의 뜻을 가진다.

25 'who'는 선행사 a crow를 수식하는 주격 관계대명사이다. 우화에서는 동물을 의인화하기 때문에 선행사가 사람일 때 쓰는 'who'를 쓴 것이고, 'that'으로 바꾸어 쓸 수도 있다.

26 주어와 목적어가 같으므로 재귀대명사로 고치는 것이 적절하다.

27 fly의 과거시제를 쓰는 것이 적절하다. fly-flew-flown

28 동족목적어 a life를 없애는 경우, 형용사를 부사로 바꾸는 것이 적절하다.

29 'everyone'을 주어로 해서 고치는 것이 적절하다.

30 because of+구, because+절, (A)에는 Due to, Owing to도 가능, (B)에는 since, as도 가능

31 '동사+부사'인 이어동사의 목적어가 인칭대명사인 경우, 목적어는 부사 뒤에 쓸 수 없고 동사와 부사 사이에만 놓일 수 있다.

32 the crow는 어디든 갈 수 있지만, 사람들이 그를 보면, 그를 쫓아낸다. the peacock는 아름다워서 매일 많은 사람이 그를 보러 오지만 아름다움 때문에 동물원에 갇혀 있다.

33 (A) so+형용사[부사]이므로 so가 적절하다. (B) 'such+a+형용사+명사'이므로 such가 적절하다. (C) 앵무새는 형형색색의 '깃털'을 가졌다고 해야 하므로 feathers가 적절하다. feature: 특색, 특징, 특성

34 '백조가 세상에서 가장 행복한 새인 것이 틀림없다'를 가리킨다.

35 '검은색' 깃털을 가진 까마귀는 백조의 '하얀색' 깃털로 인해 백조의 아름다움이 환하게 빛난다고 말했지만, 백조는 '형형색색의' 깃털을 가진 앵무새가 자신보다 더 아름답다고 생각했다.

36 start는 to부정사나 동명사를 모두 목적어로 취하는 동사이다.

37 think to oneself: 조용히 생각하다, 마음속으로 생각하다

38 까마귀는 공작새와 대화한 후에, 누가 가장 행복한 새인지 생각하기 시작했고 둘의 삶의 장단점을 생각한 뒤에, 자신이 '가장 행복한' 새라고 생각하게 되었다고 하는 것이 적절하다.

39 be stuck in: ~에 (갇혀) 있다

40 but을 없애고, Though로 시작하는 것이 적절하다.

41 까마귀는 사람들에 의해 '쫓겨나지만' 우리에 갇혀 있지 않고 '어디든' 갈 수 있었다. 반면에 공작새는 '가장 아름다운' 새일지는 몰라도 '아름답기' 때문에 동물원에 갇혀 있었다.

단원별 예상문제 p.176~183

01 ⑤　　02 ②　　03 ④
04 (1) shining　(2) predict　(3) fly　(4) explain
05 ③
06 (1) (O)nce upon a time　(2) (a)nywhere
07 thought　08 bright
09 (1) director　(2) happiness　(3) until[till]
　　(4) explain　(5) express　10 ④
11 (1) He is unlike any other.
　　(2) The park has some gorgeous scenery.
　　(3) It's predicted that this summer will be hot.
　　(4) This article needs to be edited.
12 (e)xpress　13 (s)hine
14 (1) He has been to England twice.
　　(2) We should cool ourselves with the cold water.
　　(3) The game of football was invented by the English.
15 ③
16 ④
17 (1) The parrot was not sure who the happiest bird was.
　　(2) He saw a swan which[that] was so white on the lake.
　　(3) The peacock is loved by everyone because [as, since] his feathers are gorgeous.
　　(4) Shirley has gone to Paris.
18 ⑤
19 (1) An interesting toy was bought for my little sister by Mom.
　　(2) Sean lost the toy with which he used to play. 또는 Sean lost the toy (which/that) he used to play with.
　　(3) We have known each other for a long time.
　　(4) Patricia will ask you what you did last night.
　　(5) Don't put it off until tomorrow when you can do it today.

20 ④　　　　21 ②　　　　22 ③　　　　23 ③

24 ①, ④　　　　25 ⑤

26 (A) praised (B) Unlike (C) like

27 ①　　　　28 ③

29 The crow asked why he thought so.

30 ①, ⑤　　　　31 ⑤　　　　32 ④　　　　33 ②, ⑤

34 the peacock → he　　　　35 while → until[till]

36 gorgeous　37 So he is loved by everyone.

38 ⑤

39 the peacock must be the happiest bird in the
   world

40 ②　　　　41 colorful, big, gorgeous　42 ②, ⑤

43 ④　　　　44 ⑤　　　　45 ⓒ번, to → for

46 ③

01 on the other hand: 다른 한편으로는, 반면에 / 한편으로는 아이들을 사랑하지만 또 한편으로는 그들에게 너무 많은 시간을 쓰고 싶지 않다.

02 must+동사원형: ~임에 틀림없다(강한 추측) / 그렇게 줄곧 걸었으니 넌 틀림 없이 배가 고플 거야.

03 anywhere: 어느 곳이나, 어디든 / 우리는 그 강아지를 찾아 다녔지만 어디에서도 찾을 수가 없었다.

04 (1) shine: 빛나다 (shine-shone-shone) (2) predict: 예언하다, 예측하다 (3) fly: 날다 (fly-flew-flown) (4) explain: 설명하다

05 praise: 칭송하다, 칭찬하다

06 (1) once upon a time: 옛날 옛적에 / 옛날에, 한 나그네가 있었다. (2) anywhere: 어느 곳이나, 어디든 / 이러한 옷은 어디에서나 살 수 있다.

07 thought: 생각, 사고 / 새벽 5시에 일어나야 한다고 생각하니 참을 수가 없어.

08 bright: 밝은 / 빛으로 가득 찬 / Kate는 어느 밝은 방으로 들어갔다.

09 (1) director: 감독 (2) happiness: 행복, 만족 (3) until[till]: ~할 때까지 (4) explain: 설명하다 (5) express: 표현하다, 나타내다

10 because of: ~ 때문에 / 나는 어제 영어 시험 때문에 열심히 공부했다. find out: 알게 되다, 발견하다 / 나는 그게 뭔지 알아내려고 노력 중이다. chase away: ~을 쫓아내다 / 우리 집 고양이는 정원에 들어오는 어떤 개도 다 쫓아낸다.

11 (1) unlike: ~와 다른, ~와 달리 (2) gorgeous: 매력적인, 멋진 (3) predict: 예언하다, 예측하다 (4) edit: 편집하다

12 express: 표현하다, 나타내다 / 무언가에 대해 쓰거나 말하다

13 shine: 빛나다 (shine-shone-shone) / 빛을 방출하다

14 (1) 'have been to'는 경험을 나타낸다. (2) 주어와 목적어가 같은 대상일 경우 재귀대명사를 쓴다. (3) 발명된 것이므로 수동태가 적절하다.

15 '부정주어+비교급+than'은 최상급의 뜻을 갖는다. '비교급 than all the other ~'로 바꿔 쓸 수 있다.

16 목적격보어가 원형부정사인 경우 수동태 문장에서는 to부정사로 바뀐다.

17 (1) 간접의문문의 어순은 '의문사+주어+동사'이다. (2) 선행사가 동물이므로 주격 관계대명사 which나 that을 쓴다. (3) so는 결과를 이끌므로 원인을 이끄는 because로 바꿔 쓸 수 있다. '원인+so+결과' = '결과+because[as, since]+원인' (4) 현재완료의 결과 용법을 이용한다. have gone to: ~에 가버리고 없다

18 ⑤번은 주격 관계대명사이고 나머지는 모두 접속사이다. 관계대명사에 의해 이끌리는 절은 불완전하지만 접속사에 의해 이끌리는 절은 완전한 절임에 유의한다.

19 (1) buy는 수동태에서 간접목적어 앞에 전치사 for를 써야 한다. (2) 관계대명사 that은 전치사 다음에 쓸 수 없다. 전치사를 관계사절의 마지막에 쓰고 전치사의 목적격이므로 which나 that을 쓰면 된다. 또한 목적격 관계대명사이므로 생략할 수 있다. (3) since+시간 명사, for+기간 명사 (4) 간접의문문의 어순은 '의문사+주어+동사'이다. (5) '동사+대명사 목적어+부사'의 어순에 주의한다. (6) '부정주어+비교급 than'으로 최상급의 뜻을 가진다.

20 위 글은 '우화'이다. ① (책·연극·영화 등에 대한) 논평[비평], 감상문, ② 독후감, ③ 수필, ⑤ 요약, 개요

21 ② once in a while: 가끔[이따금], ⓐ와 나머지: 옛날 옛적에, 오래 전에

22 부정주어+비교급 than = 부정주어+as[so]+원급+as = 비교급+than anyone else: 최상급의 뜻을 가진다. ③은 others were more beautiful than he was의 뜻이다.

23 앵무새가 자신보다 더 아름답다고 했기 때문에, 그는 틀림없이 자신의 '외모'를 자랑스러워할 것이라고 하는 것이 적절하다. ② 영리함, ④ 인기, ⑤ 성격

24 ⓐ와 ①, ④번: ~임에 틀림없다(강한 추측), ②, ③, ⑤: [의무·명령·요망·충고를 나타내어] ~해야만 하다

25 누가 세상에서 가장 아름다운 새라고 백조가 생각했는지는 대답할 수 없다. ① He thought the swan was so white, and that his beauty shone so brightly. ② Because his beauty shone so brightly. ③ He thought that he was the happiest bird in the world. ④ Because the parrot had colorful feathers.

26 (A) 아름다움을 '칭송했다'고 해야 하므로 praised가 적절하다. praise: 칭찬하다, blame: 비난하다, (B) 나와 '달리' 너는 우리에 갇혀 있지 않다고 해야 하므로 Unlike가 적절하다. (C) 너'처럼' 되고 싶다고 해야 하므로 like가 적절하다.

27 ⓐ와 ②번: [가능성·추측] …일지도 모른다, ① 허락, ③ 목적, ④ may not: 가벼운 금지[부정], ⑤ [기원·바람·저주, may+주어+동사] (원컨대) …하여 주시옵기를

28 까마귀가 사람들을 쫓아다닌 것이 아니라, 사람들이 까마귀를 보면, 까마귀를 쫓아냈다. chase after: ~을 쫓다

29 Why did he think so?를 간접의문문으로 쓰는 것이 적절하다.

30 actually = in fact = as a matter of fact: 사실은, ② 정확히, ③ 즉시, ④ 틀림없이

31 The 'swan' is sure that the 'parrot' is proud of his appearance.

32 ④: 부사적 용법(목적), ⓐ와 나머지: 부사적 용법(형용사 수식)

33 이 글은 ② '다른 사람과 비교하지 마라.' ⑤ '자신이 가진 것에 만족해야 한다.'는 내용의 글이다. ① 유유상종(같은 유형의 사람들은 서로 함께 모이는 경향이 있다.) ③ 뜻이 있는 곳에 길이 있다. ④ 지혜나 지식이 가장 적은 자가 항상 가장 말이 많다.(빈 수레가 더 요란하다.)

34 그는 물에 비친 자신을 다시 보았고 세상에서 가장 행복한 새를 보았다고 했기 때문에, '자기'가 세상에서 가장 행복한 새라고 생각한 것이다.

35 나는 공작새를 보기 '전까지는' 매우 행복한 삶을 살았다고 하는 것이 적절하다.

36 gorgeous: 매력적인, 아주 멋진[아름다운/좋은]

37 be loved by: ~에게 사랑받다

38 앞에 나오는 내용과 상반되는 내용이 뒤에 이어지므로 On the other hand가 가장 적절하다. ① 그러므로, ② 게다가, ③ 즉, 다시 말해

39 must: ~임이 틀림없다'(강한 추측)

40 ②는 'the crow'이고, 나머지는 다 'the peacock'이다.

41 자신의 깃털은 '색이 다채롭지만', 공작새의 깃털은 색이 다채로운 데다 '크고' '화려하기'까지 하다고 생각했다.

42 ⓐ와 ①, ③, ④번: 동족목적어, 자동사와 형태가 같은 명사, 어원이 같은 명사가 목적어로 쓰일 때 동족목적어라 한다. ②, ⑤: 재귀목적어

43 앵무새와 공작새 중 어느 것이 더 행복한지는 알 수 없다.

44 주어진 문장의 Unlike me에 주목한다. ⑤번 앞 문장에서 묘사한 '공작새의 모습과는 달리'라는 뜻이므로 ⑤번이 적절하다.

45 praise A for B: B에 대해 A를 칭찬하다

46 공작새는 자신이 '가장 아름다운 새'일지는 모르지만 '행복하지' 않다고 말했다.

교과서 파헤치기

Lesson 5

단어 TEST Step 1
p.02

01 사고
02 명성
03 아름다움, 미(美)
04 순간, 잠깐
05 마음, 정신, 영혼
06 모으다, 수집하다
07 나이가 지긋한
08 살아남다, 생존하다
09 존경하다
10 (그) 다음의
11 친선 대사
12 조각상
13 깨닫다, 알아차리다
14 눈 먼, 장님의
15 국제적인
16 살아 있는, 존속하는
17 세계적인
18 먹이를 주다
19 항목, 물품
20 약
21 기부하다
22 운이 좋게도, 다행스럽게도
23 (음식을) 제공하다
24 양로원
25 자원봉사의; 자원 봉사자
26 집 없는, 노숙자의
27 칭찬하다
28 임무, 사명
29 들어 올리다, (자금을) 모으다
30 예우하다, 존중하다
31 전환점
32 속담, 격언
33 호의, 친절
34 지지하다, 원조하다
35 늘, 내내
36 넘어지다
37 나누어 주다
38 죽다, 사망하다
39 ~ 덕분에
40 ~을 치우다, 청소하다
41 ~을 돕다
42 ~을 찾다
43 ~을 돌보다

단어 TEST Step 2
p.03

01 respect
02 blind
03 saying
04 serve
05 worldwide
06 beauty
07 mission
08 moment
09 goodwill ambassador
10 favor
11 following
12 statue
13 hold
14 accident
15 raise
16 elderly
17 realize
18 collect
19 nursing home
20 spirit
21 fame
22 honor
23 alive
24 turning point
25 support
26 praise
27 luckily
28 grass
29 medicine
30 survive
31 donate
32 homeless
33 volunteer
34 feed
35 pass away
36 fall down
37 take care of
38 hand out
39 thanks to
40 give a hand
41 in need
42 clean up
43 all the time

단어 TEST Step 3
p.04

1 fame, 명성   2 blind, 눈 먼, 장님의   3 accident, 사고
4 collect, 모으다, 수집하다   5 praise, 칭찬하다
6 realize, 깨닫다, 알아차리다   7 support, 지지하다, 원조하다
8 respect, 존경하다   9 donate, 기부하다

---

10 turning point, 전환점   11 honor, 예우하다, 존중하다
12 mission, 임무, 사명   13 statue, 조각상
14 survive, 살아남다, 생존하다   15 volunteer, 자원 봉사자
16 nursing home, 양로원

대화문 TEST Step 1
p.05~06

Listen & Talk 1 A
can / help me move / What are, going to / going to donate

Listen & Talk 1 B
wrong with / broke it / happened / a hurry to catch, fell down / terrible, Is there, can do / can you help me carry

Listen & Talk 1 C
can you help, wash them / but, can't, to feed / Why don't you ask / ask you a favor / What / Can you help, wash / have to walk / Thank you

Listen & Talk 2 A
What kinds of volunteer / don't we clean up / right, Let's

Listen & Talk 2 B
As you know, was, Why don't we raise, at, on May, bring your items, donate, give all the money to, give a hand, in need

Listen & Talk 2 C
cleaned up, we going to / don't we visit, nursing home, clean it up / bad idea, to do something fun, Why don't we hold / What / can serve / how about playing / can play the cello / sounds like

Do It Yourself A
want to do on that day / Why don't, volunteer activities, help others, make, better / sounds great, is / who has volunteered a lot / has volunteered, help us find / usually search for, don't we check / good idea

대화문 TEST Step 2
p.07~08

Listen & Talk 1 A
B: Mia, can you help me move these books?
G: Sure. What are you going to do with them?
B: I'm going to donate them to a children's library.

Listen & Talk 1 B
B: Hey, Minji! What's wrong with your leg?
G: I broke it last week.
B: Really? What happened?

G: I was in a hurry to catch a train. But I fell down in the street.

B: Oh, that's terrible! Is there anything I can do for you?

G: Well, can you help me carry this bag?

B: Sure.

Listen & Talk 1 C

B1: Wow! These dogs are so dirty. Jay, can you help me wash them?

B2: Allen, I'm sorry, but I can't. I have to feed the cats now. Why don't you ask Nicky?

B1: Okay! Nicky, can I ask you a favor?

G: Sure, Allen. What is it?

B1: Can you help me wash these dogs?

G: Sure. But I have to walk these dogs first. After that, I will help you.

B1: All right! Thank you.

Listen & Talk 2 A

G: What kinds of volunteer activities can we do?

B: Why don't we clean up our town's streets?

G: All right! Let's do it.

Listen & Talk 2 B

G: Good morning, students! As you know, there was a big fire in Mapletown. Why don't we raise money and help the people there? Come to our special event at the school grounds on May 3! Please bring your items and donate them. We will sell your items. Then, we will give all the money to Mapletown. Please give a hand to people in need.

Listen & Talk 2 C

B1: Next Wednesday is Volunteer Day. We cleaned up the park last time. What are we going to do this time?

G: Why don't we visit a nursing home and clean it up?

B2: That's not a bad idea. But I want to do something fun. Why don't we hold a party for the people there?

G: That's a good idea. What can we do at the party?

B1: We can serve some food.

B2: And how about playing some music? I can play the piano.

G: And I can play the cello.

B1: It sounds like a good plan.

Do It Yourself A

G1: We have a class activity day next Friday. What do you want to do on that day?

B: Why don't we do some volunteer activities? We can

help others and make our community better.

G1: That sounds great, but choosing a good place is not easy.

B: We need someone who has volunteered a lot.

G1: I know Sumin has volunteered a lot. Sumin, can you help us find some good places?

G2: Sure. I usually search for information on the internet. Why don't we check the volunteering website for teens?

B: That's a good idea.

본문 TEST Step 1   p.09~10

01 Spirit, Audrey 02 During, little, were

03 that, find was 04 felt scared, time

05 Luckily, thanks to

06 groups, helped, was

07 Later, became, worldwide

08 Her name

09 When, up, beauty

10 because of, such as

11 which, wore, even   12 still love, style

13 turning point, life

14 went, international, festival

15 donated money, went

16 Thanks to, more, than

17 realized, fame, others   18 went to, in

19 There, brought, to

20 shocked because, lives

21 After, volunteered, other

22 visited, hand out, support

23 to, passed away, following

24 praised, beauty, real, heart

25 To honor, statue

26 respect, keep, alive

27 favorite saying, mission

28 *As, get, remember*

29 *One, yourself, other, others*

본문 TEST Step 2   p.11~12

01 Spirit of Audrey

02 During, little, were hungry, sick

03 The only, that, was

04 felt scared all the time

05 Luckily, thanks to, others

06 One of the groups that, was

07 a worldwide movie star

08 Her name was

09 grew up, a symbol of beauty

10 because of, such as

11 which she wore, is famous

12 still love her style   13 a turning point

14 an international music festival

15 donated money, to UNICEF

16 Thanks to, collected more, than

17 realized that, help others, a UNICEF Goodwill Ambassador

18 went to Ethiopia

19 brought, to hungry children

20 was shocked because, lives

21 volunteered in other countries

22 to hand out medicine, support

23 to, passed away, following year

24 praised, real beauty was her heart

25 To honor, made a statue

26 who respect, keep, alive

27 favorite saying, her mission

28 *As*, *get older*

29 *One*, *yourself*, *the other*, *others*

1 오드리의 정신

2 제2차 세계 대전 동안, 한 어린 소녀와 그녀의 어머니는 굶주리고 아팠다.

3 그들이 찾을 수 있었던 유일한 음식은 풀뿐이었다.

4 어린 소녀는 내내 겁에 질려 있었다.

5 다행히도, 소녀는 다른 사람들의 도움 덕분에 살아남았다.

6 그녀를 도왔던 단체 중 하나는 유니세프(국제 연합 아동 기금)였다.

7 후에, 소녀는 세계적인 영화배우가 되었다.

8 그녀의 이름은 오드리 헵번이었다.

9 그녀가 자랐을 때, 헵번은 아름다움의 상징이 되었다.

10 그녀는 〈마이 페어 레이디〉와 〈로마의 휴일〉과 같은 흥행 영화들로 인해 매우 인기가 있었다.

11 그녀가 영화에서 입었던 아담한 검은 드레스는 심지어 오늘날까지도 유명하다.

12 많은 사람이 여전히 그녀의 스타일을 사랑한다.

13 1987년 가을은 헵번의 인생 전환점이었다.

14 그녀는 마카오의 한 국제 음악 축제에 갔다.

15 많은 사람이 축제에서 돈을 기부했고, 그 돈은 유니세프로 보내졌다.

16 그녀의 명성 덕분에, 유니세프는 어느 때보다도 더 많은 돈을 모았다.

17 헵번은 자신의 명성이 다른 사람들을 도울 수 있다는 것을 깨닫고, 유니세프 친선 대사가 되었다.

18 먼저, 헵번은 1988년에 에티오피아로 갔다.

19 그곳에서, 그녀는 굶주린 아이들에게 음식을 가져다주었다.

20 그녀는 그들의 삶이 매우 어려웠기 때문에 충격을 받았다.

21 그 후, 그녀는 다른 나라들에서도 봉사하였다.

22 1990년, 그녀는 의약품을 나눠 주고 깨끗한 식수 프로그램을 지원하기 위하여 베트남을 방문하였다.

23 그녀의 마지막 여행은 1992년 소말리아에 간 것이었으며, 이듬해 그녀는 사망하였다.

24 많은 사람이 그녀의 아름다움과 스타일을 칭송했지만, 헵번의 진정한 아름다움은 그녀의 마음이었다.

25 그녀를 기리기 위해, 유니세프는 '오드리의 정신'이라는 동상을 만들었다.

26 그녀를 존경하는 사람들이 그녀의 사명을 이어 나가고 있다.

27 그녀가 가장 좋아했던 구절은 그녀의 사명을 보여 준다.

28 나이가 들어갈수록, 당신에게 손이 두 개가 있다는 것을 기억하라.

29 한 손은 자신을 돕기 위한 것이고, 다른 한 손은 타인을 돕기 위한 것이다.

1 The Spirit of Audrey

2 During World War II, a little girl and her mother were hungry and sick.

3 The only food that they could find was grass.

4 The little girl felt scared all the time.

5 Luckily, the girl survived, thanks to the help of others.

6 One of the groups that helped her was UNICEF.

7 Later, the girl became a worldwide movie star.

8 Her name was Audrey Hepburn.

9 When she grew up, Hepburn became a symbol of beauty.

10 She was very popular because of her hit movies, such as *My Fair Lady* and *Roman Holiday*.

11 The little black dress which she wore in a movie is famous even today.

12 Many people still love her style.

13 The autumn of 1987 was a turning point in Hepburn's life.

14 She went to an international music festival in Macau.

15 Many people donated money at the festival, and the money went to UNICEF.

16 Thanks to her fame, UNICEF collected more money than ever before.

17 Hepburn realized that her fame could help others, so she became a UNICEF Goodwill Ambassador.

18 First, Hepburn went to Ethiopia in 1988.

19 There, she brought food to hungry children.

20 She was shocked because their lives were very difficult.

21 After that, she volunteered in other countries.

22 In 1990, she visited Vietnam to hand out medicine and support clean drinking water programs.

23 Her last trip was to Somalia in 1992, and she passed away the following year.

24 Many people praised her beauty and style, but Hepburn's real beauty was her heart.

25 To honor her, UNICEF made a statue, *The Spirit of Audrey*.

26 People who respect her keep her mission alive.

27 Her favorite saying shows her mission.

28 *As you get older, remember you have two hands.*

29 *One is for helping yourself, and the other is for helping others.*

Presentation Time

1. a great person
2. priest, also
3. built, for
4. took care of, taught classes
5. From, that, should help, in need

After You Read B

1. How, during
2. tell me about
3. terrible, were hungry, sick
4. survived thanks to, others
5. begin to work
6. changed my life
7. that, could help other people
8. After that, did, do
9. visited some countries, volunteered there

Culture Link

1. Talking Books
2. program that makes, blind
3. was started
4. record your voice
5. are given, for free

Presentation Time

1. Lee Taeseok was a great person.
2. He was a priest and also a doctor.
3. He built hospitals and schools for the people of Tonj.
4. He took care of them and taught classes.
5. From this person, I learned that I should help people in need.

After You Read B

1. Reporter: How was your life during World War II?
2. Can you tell me about it?
3. Audrey: It was terrible. My family and I were hungry and sick.
4. We survived thanks to the help of others.
5. Reporter: How did you begin to work for UNICEF?
6. Audrey: In 1987, a musical festival in Macau changed my life.
7. I learned that my fame could help other people.
8. Reporter: After that, what did you do?
9. Audrey: I visited some countries in Africa and Asia and volunteered there.

Culture Link

1. Talking Books Program
2. This is a program that makes audiobooks for blind people.
3. It was started in 1931 in the United States.
4. You just read books and record your voice.
5. These audiobooks are given to blind people for free.

단어 TEST Step 1 — p.21

01 발표　　　　　02 전망

03 휴식을 취하다, 느긋이 쉬다　　　　04 매우 멋진

05 (여행 중) 머무른 곳, 멈춤, 정거장　　06 만화책

07 상태, 상황　　08 견학 여행, 현장 학습

09 놀라운, 멋진　　10 미술관　　11 역사

12 목적, 목표　　13 놀이공원　　14 외국의

15 길거리 음식　　16 하이킹하다, 도보 여행하다

17 똑바로, 일직선으로　　18 휴가, 공휴일, 휴일

19 국제적인　　20 마을

21 미술 전시회　　22 역사적인, 역사상의

23 장소　　24 자연의　　25 그림

26 상품, 물건　　27 계획하다; 계획　　28 래프팅, 급류 타기

29 가을　　30 거친, 파도가 심한　　31 풍경, 경치

32 대학교　　33 박물관, 미술관

34 방문하다, 찾아가다　　35 동시에, 한꺼번에

36 걸어서, 도보로　　37 ~할 수 있다　　38 내리다, 하차하다

39 더 이상 ~하지 않는　　40 여러 가지의, 다양한

41 (~에) 집중하다, 초점을 맞추다　　42 ~ 앞에서

43 버스로

단어 TEST Step 2 — p.22

01 comic book　02 scenery　03 international

04 straight　05 condition　06 presentation

07 museum　08 amazing　09 art museum

10 view　11 stop　12 rough

13 field trip　14 hike　15 relax

16 history　17 village　18 foreign

19 university　20 purpose　21 autumn

22 visit　23 historical　24 site

25 holiday　26 amusement park

27 street food　28 goods　29 art show

30 natural　31 rafting　32 awesome

33 painting　34 plan　35 focus on

36 on foot　37 get off　38 a variety of

39 by bus　40 in front of　41 no longer

42 be able to 동사원형　　43 at the same time

단어 TEST Step 3 — p.23

1 condition, 상태, 상황　　2 awesome, 매우 멋진

3 goods, 상품, 물건　　4 scenery, 풍경, 경치

5 amusement park, 놀이공원　6 autumn, 가을

7 relax, 휴식을 취하다, 느긋이 쉬다

8 stadium, 경기장, 스타디움　9 foreign, 외국의

10 history, 역사　11 purpose, 목적, 목표

12 rough, 거친　13 rafting, 래프팅, 급류 타기

14 stop, (여행 중) 머무른 곳

15 field trip, 견학 여행, 현장 학습

16 museum, 박물관, 미술관

대화문 TEST Step 1 — p.24~25

Listen & Talk 1 A

What are you, this weekend / going to go / What, you planning to do / I'm planning to

Listen & Talk 1 B

have, this, have any / going / What, planning to, with / I'm planning, with them / about, plans for / going, stay home, relax / good idea

Listen & Talk 1 C

Where, field trip / We are going to / interesting, planning to see / are, right now. I'm planning to see, Where, going / We are going to, amusement, excited to ride / sounds fun, good trip

Listen & Talk 2 A

How, get to school / by bus / How long, take to get / It takes

Listen & Talk 2 B

pictures, beautiful, Where, take / were lots of, should / to, How, get, from / Get on, get off, see, in front of / long, take to get / takes minutes / next weekend

Listen & Talk 2 C

How do I get to / go there by bus or on foot / How long, take to get / by, on foot / will walk, Can you tell how to get / Go straight, turn, on your right / Go, for, turn left

Do It Yourself A

What, planning to do this / to go to / Are you, to see / will, I'm planning to visit / How long, to get / an hour and 40 minutes by / much faster than, have, good trip

대화문 TEST Step 2 — p.26~27

Listen & Talk 1 A

B: What are you going to do this weekend?

G: I'm going to go to Jeju-do.

B: What are you planning to do there?

G: I'm planning to go hiking on Hallasan.

B: We have a long holiday this month. Do you have any plans?

G: I'm going to visit my grandparents in Jeonju.

B: Oh, really? That's nice. What are you planning to do with them?

G: I'm planning to go to Hanok Village with them. How about you? What are your plans for the holiday?

B: I'm going to stay home and relax.

G: That's also a good idea!

Listen & Talk 1 C

B: Hi, Nuri. Where is your class going for the field trip tomorrow?

G: Hello, Mike. We are going to the art museum.

B: Sounds interesting. What are you planning to see there?

G: There are three art shows right now. I'm planning to see Vincent van Gogh's paintings. Where is your class going?

B: We are going to the amusement park. I'm excited to ride a roller coaster!

G: That sounds fun. Have a good trip!

Listen & Talk 2 A

G: How do you get to school?

B: I go to school by bus.

G: How long does it take to get there?

B: It takes 15 minutes.

Listen & Talk 2 B

B: Wow, these pictures are so beautiful. Where did you take them?

G: At Riverside Park. There were lots of flowers. You should go there!

B: I want to. How do I get there from our school?

G: Get on bus number 135 and get off at the Riverside Stadium stop. You can see the park in front of the bus stop.

B: How long does it take to get there?

G: It takes 30 minutes.

B: Thanks. I'll go there next weekend.

Listen & Talk 2 C

B: Excuse me. How do I get to Hanguk University from here?

W: You can go there by bus or on foot.

B: How long does it take to get there?

W: It takes five minutes by bus and 20 minutes on foot.

B: Oh, then I will walk there. Can you tell me how to get there?

W: Go straight for two blocks, and then turn left. You will see Hanguk University on your right.

B: Go straight for two blocks and turn left. Thank you!

Do It Yourself A

G: What are you planning to do this weekend?

B: I'm planning to go to a baseball game in Daegu.

G: Are you going to see the All-Star Game?

B: Yes. It will be fun. Also, I'm planning to visit my friend there.

G: Nice. How long does it take to get there?

B: It takes an hour and 40 minutes by express train.

G: Wow, it's much faster than I thought. I hope you have a good trip!

B: Thank you.

본문 TEST Step 1   p.28~29

01 Best Moment, Field

02 How, trip, tell us   03 Market Heaven

04 traditional markets   05 Then go, in

06 one, most famous markets

07 what, famous for

08 selling, variety of, different

09 interesting, all, international goods

10 kinds of, such as

11 Then, walked to

12 Many bookstores, used books

13 excited because, found   14 nice, relax, read

15 Full, Natural Beauty

16 place like, nature   17 First, went to

18 cave, in, condition

19 amazing, natural beauty

20 Near, turned off, minute

21 became, able, focus on

22 most amazing experience

23 Our next stop   24 went rafting

25 excting, rough, view, same   26 City of Firsts

27 where, first, is 28 How about   29 answer, is

30 place, many, firsts   31 To get, went

32 next to, station

33 learned about, history

34 walked around, Western–style

35 view from, awesome

36 great, historical sites

37 places sound great

38 all, done, on, presentations

01 The Best Moment, Field Trip

02 How were, last week, Please tell us

03 Market Heaven

04 traditional markets   05 Then go to

06 one of the most famous markets

07 what it is famous for

08 is famous for, a variety of goods

09 It, to see all the international goods

10 also ate many kinds of, such as

11 Then, walked to

12 sell used books

13 really excited because, found

14 to relax, read   15 Full of Natural Beauty

16 no place like, beautiful nature   17 First, went to

18 in good condition

19 so amazing, natural beauty

20 cave tour, turned off, for a minute

21 were able to focus on

22 the most amazing experience

23 Our next stop   24 went rafting

25 exciting to ride, at the same time

26 Firsts   27 where, is   28 How about

29 The answer   30 many of Korea's firsts

31 To get there, went   32 next to

33 the history of *Jajangmyeon*

34 the first Western-style park

35 view from, awesome

36 to see the historical sites   37 sound great

38 on your presentations

1 수학여행에서의 가장 좋았던 순간

2 교사: 안녕하세요, 여러분! 지난주 수학여행은 어땠나요? 얘기해 봅시다!

3 부산, 시장 천국

4 전통 시장을 좋아하세요?

5 그렇다면 부산에 있는 국제시장으로 가세요.

6 그곳은 부산에서 가장 유명한 시장 중 하나입니다.

7 그곳이 무엇으로 유명한지 아세요?

8 그 시장은 여러 나라에서 온 다양한 제품들을 파는 것으로 유명합니다.

9 그곳에서 세계 곳곳의 제품들을 모두 볼 수 있어서 흥미로웠습니다.

10 우리는 또한 김밥, 어묵 그리고 호떡과 같은 여러 종류의 길거리 음식을 먹었습니다

11 그리고 나서 우리는 보수동 책방 거리로 걸어갔습니다.

12 그곳의 많은 서점에서는 중고 책을 팝니다.

13 우리는 몇 권의 오래된 만화책을 발견해서 정말 신이 났습니다!

14 카페에서 휴식을 취하며 그 책들을 읽는 것이 좋았습니다.

15 강원도, 자연의 아름다움으로 가득한 곳

16 아름다운 자연에 관한 한 강원도만 한 곳이 없습니다.

17 우선, 우리는 백룡동굴로 갑니다.

18 이 1.8킬로미터 길이의 동굴은 여전히 잘 보존된 상태입니다.

19 그곳의 자연의 아름다움을 보는 것은 매우 놀라웠습니다.

20 동굴 관광의 끝 무렵, 안내인이 동굴 안의 불을 잠시 껐습니다.

21 모든 것이 매우 어두워져서, 우리는 그곳의 소리에 집중할 수 있었습니다.

22 그것은 여행에서 가장 경이로운 경험이었습니다!

23 우리의 다음 여행지는 동강이었습니다.

24 우리는 래프팅을 하러 갔습니다!

25 급류를 타면서 동시에 경치를 즐기는 것은 흥미진진했습니다.

26 인천, '최초의 것'들의 도시

27 한국 최초의 기차역이 어디인지 아세요?

28 첫 번째 자장면은요?

29 그 답은 인천입니다!

30 이곳에는 한국의 최초의 것들이 많이 있습니다.

31 그곳으로 가기 위하여, 우리는 인천역으로 갔습니다.

32 자장면 박물관은 역 옆에 있습니다.

33 우리는 그곳에서 자장면의 역사에 대하여 배웠습니다.

34 다음에는, 한국 최초의 서구식 공원인 자유 공원을 거닐었습니다

35 공원에서 바라본 경치는 정말 멋있었습니다!

36 공원에서 이 도시의 역사적인 장소들을 바라보는 것은 아주 좋았습니다.

37 교사: 와, 이곳들은 멋지게 들리네요!

38 여러분 모두 발표를 훌륭하게 잘했어요!

1 The Best Moment of the Field Trip

2 Teacher: Good morning, everyone! How were your field trips last week? Please tell us about them!

3 Busan, Market Heaven

4 Do you like traditional markets?

5 Then go to Gukje Market in Busan.

6 It is one of the most famous markets in Busan.

7 Do you know what it is famous for?

8 It is famous for selling a variety of goods from different countries.

9 It was interesting to see all the international goods there.

10 We also ate many kinds of street food, such as *Gimbap*, fish cake, and *Hotteok*.

11 Then we walked to Bosu-dong Book Street.

12 Many bookstores there sell used books.

13 We were really excited because we found some old comic books!

14 It was nice to relax in a café and read them.

15 Gangwon-do, Full of Natural Beauty

16 There is no place like Gangwon-do for beautiful nature.

17 First, we went to Baengnyong Cave.

18 This 1.8-kilometer-long cave is still in good condition.

19 It was so amazing to see its natural beauty.

20 Near the end of our cave tour, the guide turned off the lights in the cave for a minute.

21 Everything became very dark, so we were able to focus on the sounds there.

22 It was the most amazing experience of the tour!

23 Our next stop was Donggang.

24 We went rafting!

25 It was exciting to ride on the rough water and enjoy the view at the same time.

26 Incheon, A City of Firsts

27 Do you know where the first train station in Korea is?

28 How about the first *Jajangmyeon?*

29 The answer is Incheon!

30 This place has many of Korea's firsts.

31 To get there, we went to Incheon Station.

32 The Jajangmyeon Museum is next to the station.

33 We learned about the history of *Jajangmyeon* there.

34 Later, we walked around Jayu Park, the first Western-style park in Korea.

35 The view from the park was awesome!

36 It was great to see the historical sites of this city from the park.

37 Teacher: Wow, these places sound great!

38 You all have done a wonderful job on your presentations!

구석구석지문 TEST Step 1 p.38

After You Read D

1. live in
2. There is, railway
3. no longer used
4. take pictures of, scenery

Think & Write Step 3

1. Autumn Walk
2. Last autumn, went to, with
3. rode, to the middle of
4. Then, hiked to

5. At the top, autumn scenery, took, pictures

6. It, amazing, exciting to see

Culture Link

1. Eco
2. take trips, without hurting
3. it, to protect nature
4. Volunteer
5. go on trips, special purposes
6. to do volunteer work
7. local communities, during
8. History Trip
9. On this trip, historical sites, learn about
10. During, can understand, lives, in the past

구석구석지문 TEST Step 2 p.39

After You Read D

1. I live in Hang-dong, Seoul.
2. There is an old railway.
3. It is no longer used.
4. You can walk there and take pictures of beautiful scenery.

Think & Write Step 3

1. Autumn Walk in Naejangsan
2. Last autumn, I went to Naejangsan with my family.
3. I rode a cable car to the middle of the mountain.
4. Then , I hiked to the top.
5. At the top, I saw beautiful autumn scenery. I took many pictures .
6. It was amazing and exciting to see beautiful autumn leaves.

Culture Link

1. Eco Trip
2. Some people take trips in nature without hurting the environment.
3. They think it is important to protect nature.
4. Volunteer Trip
5. Some people go on trips for special purposes.
6. They travel to do volunteer work.
7. They help local communities or wild animals during their trips.
8. History Trip
9. On this trip , people visit historical sites and learn about history.
10. During this trip, people can understand the lives of people in the past .

단어 TEST Step 1   p.40

01 양, 총액   02 진로, 직업   03 공동 작업, 협동

04 자율주행차   05 모으다, 수집하다

06 나타나다, 보이기 시작하다   07 상담가

08 발달시키다, 발전하다   09 감정

10 분석하다   11 (물 위에) 뜨다, 떠다니다

12 상담   13 인공적인, 인조의

14 개선하다, 향상시키다   15 통역사

16 힘, 강점, 장점   17 심야의

18 지원하다, 신청하다   19 (타고난) 재능, 재주

20 환자   21 쓰레기, 폐기물   22 전문가

23 협력하다   24 경로, 노선   25 꾸미다, 장식하다

26 창의력, 독창력   27 줄이다, 감소시키다

28 우주, 공간   29 손님, 고객   30 문제 해결의

31 다음[아래]에 나오는[언급되는]

32 (폐품 등을) 다시 쓸 수 있게 만들다

33 (책, 영화 등의) 논평가   34 창의적인

35 무엇보다도   36 ~을 돌보다   37 (앞일을) 내다보다,

38 예견하다   39 ~을 잘하다   40 그 외에, 그 밖에

41 이루어지다, 실현되다

42 (서식 등을) 작성하다, (정보를) 기입하다, 채우다

43 일기를 쓰다   44 출력하다

단어 TEST Step 2   p.41

01 advice   02 career   03 skill

04 reduce   05 talent   06 reviewer

07 counseling   08 specialist   09 collaborate

10 apply   11 decorate   12 interpreter

13 analyze   14 emotion   15 consultant

16 artificial   17 float   18 strength

19 collaboration   20 following   21 improve

22 late-night   23 creative   24 patient

25 amount   26 problem-solving

27 allow   28 reason   29 customer

30 route   31 develop   32 appear

33 creativity   34 space   35 keep a diary

36 look ahead   37 print out   38 take care of

39 what else   40 fill out   41 come true

42 be good at   43 first of all

단어 TEST Step 3   p.42

1 late-night, 심야의   2 analyze, 분석하다

3 route, 경로, 노선   4 improve, 개선하다, 향상시키다

5 specialist, 전문가   6 patient, 환자

7 float, (물 위에) 뜨다, 떠다니다

8 artificial, 인공적인, 인조의   9 strength, 강점, 장점

10 counseling, 상담   11 talent, (타고난) 재능, 재주

12 creativity, 창의력, 독창력

13 develop, 발달시키다, 발전하다   14 career, 진로, 직업

15 apply, 지원하다, 신청하다

16 reviewer, (책 · 영화 등의) 논평가

대화문 TEST Step 1   p.43~44

Listen & Talk 1 A

Let's play / not good at / What are you good at /
good at playing / let's play

Listen & Talk 1 B

are, going to do / decide, What am, good at / good at
dancing, aren't / good at singing, singing / planning to
play / Why don't you / love to

Listen & Talk 1 C

need to fill out / career counseling / wrote, and / be,
P.E. teacher, watching, writing, strengths, What am I
good / lots, First of, are good at, aren't you / I'm good
at playing baseball / other strengths / work, other
people, at listening to / You're good at / Thanks

Listen & Talk 2 A

want to be, What, need to do / need to, develop,
problem-solving skills

Listen & Talk 2 B

amazing / Thank, for saying, trying, to improve, writing
skills, writer / want, like, What do I, to / a lot of, Reading
makes your writing better / else, need to / every day,
don't, keeping / Thank, for, advice

Listen & Talk 2 C

Thank, for / problem / who want to be food, about
your job / decorates, to look / to be a food stylist,
What, need / need to learn, kinds / What else, need
to do / too Creativity / Thank, for

대화문 TEST Step 2   p.45~46

Listen & Talk 1 A

G: Let's play basketball.

B: Well... I'm not good at playing basketball. Are
you?

G: Yes, I think I am. What are you good at?

B: I'm good at playing soccer.

G: Okay, then let's play soccer.

Listen & Talk 1 B

B: Jessica, what are you going to do for the school talent show?

G: I didn't decide yet. What am I good at?

B: You're good at dancing, aren't you?

G: Not really. But I think I'm good at singing. I like singing very much.

B: Really? Actually, I'm planning to play rock music with my band. Why don't you sing for us?

G: Sure, I'd love to.

Listen & Talk 1 C

B: Mom, I need to fill out this form for tomorrow's career counseling program. Could you help me?

W: Sure. Let me see. You already wrote your dream job and hobby.

B: Yes, I want to be a P.E. teacher, and my hobby is watching sports games. But writing my strengths is hard. What am I good at?

W: Well, I think you have lots of strengths. First of all, you are good at playing baseball, aren't you?

B: Oh, yes. I'm good at playing baseball.

W: And you have many other strengths.

B: You're right. I also work well with other people. And I'm good at listening to people.

W: Right! You're good at so many things.

B: Thanks, Mom.

Listen & Talk 2 A

B: I want to be a scientist. What do I need to do?

W: You need to study science. And you need to develop your problem-solving skills.

Listen & Talk 2 B

G: Jason, I read your paper. It was so amazing!

B: Thank you for saying that. I'm trying hard to improve my writing skills. I want to be a writer someday.

G: Really? I want to write well like you. What do I need to do?

B: You need to read a lot of books. Reading makes your writing better.

G: What else do I need to do?

B: Well, I write almost every day. Why don't you start keeping a diary?

G: Thank you for your advice. I'll start today.

Listen & Talk 2 C

G: Hello, Mr. Watson! Thank you for doing this interview.

M: Sure, no problem.

G: This interview is for students who want to be food stylists. Can you tell me about your job?

M: Sure. You may see pictures of food in books or on TV. A food stylist decorates food to look good for pictures or movies.

G: I want to be a food stylist like you. What do I need to do?

M: You need to learn about many kinds of food.

G: What else do I need to do?

M: You need to study art, too. Creativity is important.

G: All right! Thank you for your time, Mr. Watson.

본문 TEST Step 1

p.47~48

01 Jobs of, Future

02 be on, market

03 robots that, everything

04 every, print out almost

05 take space trips

06 under, floating cities

07 Look at, above

08 Do, ideas surprise

09 lives, different, future

10 As, change, appear

11 What kind, job

12 will, be like

13 following, looked ahead, chose

14 Let's read, their

15 pot that, made

16 made from, flags

17 upcycling designer

18 waste materials, products

19 that, useful in, ways

20 Upcycling, reduce, waste

21 become, creative, learn

22 Have, ever heard

23 works for, makes artificial

24 special software, print out

25 made specially, patients

26 good at, modeler

27 use, printed, future

28 big data specialist

29 works on, projects

30 For example, last, routes

31 collect, use, late-night travelers

32 analyzed, create, useful

33 working with, online

34 collecting, from, find out

35 allows, learn, daily

36 specialist, develop, problem-solving
37 Think, yourself, prepare for
38 keep looking ahead, dreaming

01 of the Future   02 Self-driving, be on the market
03 that, everything
04 will print out almost everything
05 take space trips
06 under the sea, in floating cities
07 Look at, above   08 these, surprise
09 our lives, in the future
10 As, change, ill appear
11 What kind of job
12 What will, be like
13 The following, looked ahead, chose jobs, be important
14 Let's read   15 flower pot that Sujin made
16 was made from, flags
17 upcycling designer
18 waste materials, products
19 can be useful in new ways
20 reduce the amount of waste
21 To become, upcycling designer, creative
22 Have you ever heard, modelers
23 works for, that makes artificial
24 special software
25 specially for patients
26 are good at, be a 3D modeler
27 wants, to use, in the future
28 big data specialist   29 works on
30 For example, bus routes
31 taxi use patterns, late-night travelers
32 analyzed, to create, useful routes
33 working with
34 collecting data from, find out
35 allows us to learn, our daily lives
36 specialist, develop, problem-solving skills
37 Think, yourself, prepare for
38 keep looking, dreaming, be bright

1 미래의 직업
2 2020년대: 자율주행차들이 시장에 나올 것이다.
3 2030년대: 사람들은 그들을 위하여 모든 것을 하는 로봇을 갖게 될 것이다.

4 2030년대: 모든 가정의 3D 프린터가 거의 모든 것을 출력해 낼 것이다.
5 2050년대: 사람들은 우주여행을 할 것이다.
6 2050년대: 사람들은 바다 밑이나 수상 도시에서 살 것이다.
7 위의 그림들을 보세요.
8 이 생각들이 놀랍습니까?
9 당신은 미래에 우리의 삶이 매우 달라질 것을 볼 수 있습니다.
10 우리의 삶이 변화함에 따라 새로운 직업들이 많이 생겨날 것입니다.
11 당신은 어떤 직업을 원하세요?
12 미래의 당신 삶은 어떤 모습일까요?
13 다음의 사람들은 앞을 내다보고 미래에 중요하게 될 직업을 선택하였습니다.
14 그들의 직업에 관하여 읽어 봅시다!
15 수진이 만든 화분이 보이시나요?
16 이것은 거리의 낡은 깃발들로 만들어진 것입니다.
17 그녀는 업사이클링 디자이너입니다.
18 그녀는 새로운 제품을 만들기 위해 폐기물을 가지고 작업합니다.
19 그녀의 제품들은 낡은 재료가 새로운 방식으로 유용해질 수 있다는 것을 사람들에게 보여줍니다.
20 업사이클링은 미래에 쓰레기의 양을 줄일 수 있습니다.
21 업사이클링 디자이너가 되려면 당신은 창의적이어야 하며 미술을 배워야 합니다.
22 3D 모형 제작자에 관하여 들어 본 적이 있으신가요?
23 3D 모형 제작자인 태호는 인공 손과 다리를 만드는 회사에서 일합니다.
24 태호는 새 손과 다리를 출력하기 위하여 특별한 소프트웨어를 사용합니다.
25 그것들은 환자를 위하여 특별히 제작됩니다.
26 만약 당신이 컴퓨터 프로그래밍이나 미술을 잘한다면, 3D 모형 제작자가 될 수 있습니다.
27 태호는 미래에 더 많은 사람들이 3D 프린터로 출력된 제품들을 사용하기를 원합니다.
28 지혜는 빅데이터 전문가입니다.
29 그녀는 많은 프로젝트에서 일합니다.
30 예를 들어, 작년에 그녀는 버스 노선을 만들었습니다.
31 최적의 심야 노선을 찾기 위하여, 그녀는 심야에 이동하는 사람들의 스마트폰 이용 정보와 택시 이용 패턴을 수집할 필요가 있었습니다.
32 그런 다음 그녀는 그 정보를 분석하여 가장 유용한 노선을 만들었습니다.
33 현재 지혜는 온라인 쇼핑몰과 작업하고 있습니다.
34 그녀는 소비자들에게 맞는 최적의 스타일을 찾기 위하여 그들로부터 데이터를 수집하고 있습니다.
35 그녀는 빅데이터가 우리에게 일상생활에 관하여 더 많이 알게 해 준다는 것을 알고 있습니다.
36 만약 당신이 빅데이터 전문가가 되고 싶다면, 수학과 문제 해결 능력을 계발해야 합니다!

37 자신에 대하여 생각해 보고 미래를 준비하세요.

38 만약 당신이 계속 앞을 내다보고 꿈을 크게 꾼다면, 당신의 미래는 밝을 것입니다.

1 Jobs of the Future

2 2020s: Self-driving cars will be on the market.

3 2030s: People will have robots that do everything for them.

4 2030s: 3D printers in every home will print out almost everything.

5 2050s: People will take space trips.

6 2050s: People will live under the sea or in floating cities.

7 Look at the pictures above.

8 Do these ideas surprise you?

9 You can see that our lives will be very different in the future.

10 As our lives change, many new jobs will appear.

11 What kind of job do you want?

12 What will your future life be like?

13 The following people looked ahead and chose jobs that will be important in the future.

14 Let's read about their jobs!

15 Do you see the flower pot that Sujin made?

16 It was made from old street flags.

17 She is an upcycling designer.

18 She works with waste materials to make new products.

19 Her products show people that old materials can be useful in new ways.

20 Upcycling can reduce the amount of waste in the future.

21 To become an upcycling designer, you should be creative and learn about art.

22 Have you ever heard of 3D modelers?

23 Taeho, a 3D modeler, works for a company that makes artificial hands and legs.

24 Taeho uses special software to print out new hands and legs.

25 They are made specially for patients.

26 If you are good at computer programming and art, you can be a 3D modeler.

27 Taeho wants more people to use 3D printed products in the future.

28 Jihye is a big data specialist.

29 She works on many projects.

30 For example, last year, she made bus routes.

31 To find the best night routes, she needed to collect smartphone use data and taxi use patterns from late-night travelers.

32 Then she analyzed this information to create the most useful routes.

33 Now Jihye is working with an online shopping mall.

34 She is collecting data from customers to find out the best styles for them.

35 She knows big data allows us to learn more about our daily lives.

36 If you want to become a big data specialist, you should develop your math and problem-solving skills!

37 Think about yourself and prepare for your future.

38 If you keep looking ahead and dreaming big, your future will be bright.

After You Read D

1. reviewer, writers articles
2. chose, because, watching movies
3. To get, improve, writing skills
4. many different types

Culture Link

1. Personal, Consultant
2. creates, their customers
3. unique strengths
4. by using, personality, knowledge, skills
5. To get, need to, communication skills

Do It Yourself A

1. looking at
2. are needed
3. help out, good at drawing
4. help out
5. Why don't we apply
6. not good at, good at playing
7. help out
8. Let's, apply to become

After You Read D

1. Taehun Kim is a movie reviewer . He writers articles about new movies.
2. He chose this job because he loves watching movies .
3. To get this job, he read many books to improve his writing skills .
4. He also watched many different types of movies.

Culture Link

1. Personal Brand Consultant
2. A personal brand consultant creates a personal brand for their customers.
3. They find the customer's unique strengths.
4. Then they build a personal brand by using the customer's personality , knowledge , and skills.
5. To get this job, you need to have great communication skills.

Do It Yourself A

1. B: Hey, Mandy. What are you looking at ?
2. G: Hey, Edward. Look! Some volunteers are needed for the school festival.
3. B: Really? I want to help out. You know I'm good at drawing pictures. I think I can do something for the festival.
4. G: I think you can help out at the cartoon event.
5. B: Right! Why don't we apply together?
6. G: Well, I am not good at drawing pictures. But I'm good at playing board games.
7. B: You can help out at the game event then.
8. G: Okay. Let's go and apply to become volunteers.

Lesson 8

01 아름다움	02 ~를 뒤쫓다, 추적하다	
03 날다	04 ~할 때까지	
05 빛나는, 반짝거리는		06 설명하다
07 어느 곳이나, 어디든		08 칭송하다, 칭찬하다
09 외모	10 색채가 다양한, 형형색색의	
11 숲	12 표현하다, 나타내다	
13 매력적인, 멋진	14 감독	15 예언하다, 예측하다
16 행복, 만족	17 (사물·사람이) 인상적인, 인상 깊은	
18 앵무새	19 밝게	20 (새의) 털, 깃털
21 편집하다	22 빛나다	23 우리, 새장
24 공작(새)	25 백조	26 생각, 사고
27 ~와 다른, ~와 달리		28 동물원
29 호수, 연못	30 까마귀	31 너무나, 대단히, 그렇게
32 조용히 생각하다, 마음속으로 생각하다		
33 ~에 (갇혀) 있다	34 반면에	35 ~을 쫓아내다
36 자유롭게 ~하다	37 옛날 옛적에	38 ~을 자랑으로 여기다
39 세계 곳곳에	40 ~ 때문에	41 알게 되다, 발견하다
42 ~로 돌아가다	43 ~임에 틀림없다(강한 추측)	
44 어느 날		

01 cage	02 shine	03 unlike
04 anywhere	05 crow	06 director
07 explain	08 feather	09 shiny
10 peacock	11 swan	12 forest
13 zoo	14 praise	15 brightly
16 until	17 fly	18 appearance
19 gorgeous	20 edit	21 happiness
22 express	23 impressive	24 lake
25 parrot	26 chase	27 colorful
28 beauty	29 predict	30 so
31 thought	32 on the other hand	
33 go back to	34 around the world	
35 be proud of	36 once upon a time	
37 be stuck in	38 think to oneself	
39 because of	40 chase ~ away	41 find out
42 one day	43 think of	43 be free to 동사원형

1 gorgeous, 매력적인, 멋진   2 shine, 빛나다

3 unlike, ~와 다른, ~와 달리

4 anywhere, 어느 곳이나, 어디든   5 bright, 밝은

6 cage, 우리, 새장   7 until, ~할 때까지

8 director, 감독   9 edit, 편집하다

10 express, 표현하다, 나타내다

11 happiness, 행복, 만족   12 explain, 설명하다

13 swan, 백조   14 forest, 숲

15 feather, (새의) 털, 깃털   16 predict, 예언하다, 예측하다

01 Who, Happy   02 Once, time, forest

03 crow, with, life 04 looked at himself

05 thought, more, than   06 one, swan, lake

07 so, thought, black

08 seen such, before

09 beauty, so brightly

10 must be, happiest

11 went, expressed, thoughts

12 Actually, thought, happiest, bird

13 then, saw   14 parrot, bird, world

15 asked why, thought

16 swan, colorful feathers

17 more beautiful than

18 must, proud, appearance

19 flew, happiest, because, feathers

20 explained, until, peacock

21 colorful, feathers, gorgeous

22 So, loved by   23 crow, peacock zoo

24 lot, around praised, beauty

25 thought, must be

26 After, left, started

27 so beautiful   28 Many, every day

29 On, hand, chase, away

30 happiest bird, world

31 may, most beautiful, happy

32 Because of, stuck

33 Unlike, kept, cage

34 like, because, anywhere

35 talked, started, think, was

36 himself, impressive, stuck

37 colorful, free, fly   38 went back to

39 looked at himself, saw

01 Who, Happy   02 Once upon a time, lived, forest

03 happy with his life

04 always looked at himself

05 thought, more beautiful than

06 on the lake   07 so white, so black

08 such a white bird

09 beauty shines so brightly

10 must be, happiest

11 expressed his thoughts   12 Actually

13 then, saw   14 the happiest bird

15 asked why he thought so

16 colorful feathers

17 more beautiful than

18 must be proud of, appearance

19 flew, because, colorful feathers

20 explained, lived, life until

21 the peacock's feathers, colorful, big, gorgeous

22 is loved by everyone   23 at the zoo

24 around praised, for, beauty

25 must be   26 After, left, started to talk

27 so beautiful   28 come to see

29 On the other hand, chase me away

30 in the world

31 the most beautiful, not happy

32 Because of, am stuck in

33 Unlike, aren't kept

34 be like

35 think about who the happiest bird was

36 thought to himself, impressive, is stuck

37 free to fly anywhere

38 went back to

39 looked at himself

1 누가 행복한가?

2 옛날 옛적에 숲에 사는 까마귀 한 마리가 있었다.

3 그 까마귀는 그의 삶에 매우 행복했다.

4 그는 항상 자신의 모습을 물에 비춰 보았다.

5 그는 자신보다 더 아름다운 새는 없다고 생각했다.

6 그러던 어느 날 까마귀는 호수에서 백조를 보았다.

7 "백조는 정말 하얗구나." 그는 생각했다. "그런데 나는 너무 까매.

8 나는 저렇게 하얀 새를 전에 본 적이 없어.

9 그의 아름다움은 정말 환하게 빛나는구나.

10 백조가 세상에서 가장 행복한 새인 것이 틀림없어."

11 그는 백조에게 가서 그의 생각을 표현했다.

12 "사실은," 백조가 말했다. "나는 내가 가장 행복한 새라고 생각했어.

13 하지만 곧 앵무새를 보았지.

14 이제 난 앵무새가 세상에서 가장 행복한 새라고 생각해."

15 까마귀는 그가 왜 그렇게 생각하는지 물었다.

16 백조는 대답했다. "앵무새는 형형색색의 깃털을 가졌거든.

17 그는 나보다 더 아름다워.

18 그는 틀림없이 자신의 외모를 자랑스러워할 거야."

19 까마귀는 그 다음에 앵무새에게 날아가서 말했다. "백조가 말하기를 당신이 형형색색의 깃털을 가졌기 때문에 가장 행복한 새래요."

20 앵무새는 설명했다. "나는 공작새를 보기 전까지는 매우 행복한 삶을 살았어.

21 내 깃털은 색이 다채롭지만, 공작새의 깃털은 색이 다채로운 데다 크고 화려하기까지 하거든.

22 그래서 그는 모든 사람에게 사랑받지."

23 까마귀는 그래서 동물원의 공작새에게 갔다.

24 공작새 주변에는 많은 사람이 있었고, 그들은 그의 아름다움을 칭송했다.

25 까마귀는 공작새가 세상에서 가장 행복한 새가 틀림없다고 생각했다.

26 모든 사람이 떠난 후, 까마귀는 공작새에게 말을 걸기 시작했다.

27 "공작새님, 당신은 참 아름다워요.

28 매일 많은 사람이 당신을 보러 와요.

29 반면에 사람들은 저를 보면, 저를 쫓아내요.

30 나는 당신이 세상에서 가장 행복한 새라고 생각해요."

31 공작새는 말했다. "내가 가장 아름다운 새일지는 모르지만 나는 행복하지 않아.

32 나의 아름다움 때문에 내가 이 동물원에 갇혀 있거든.

33 나와 달리 너는 우리에 갇혀 있지 않잖아.

34 너는 어디든 갈 수 있으니 나는 너처럼 되고 싶어."

35 까마귀는 공작새와 대화한 후에, 누가 가장 행복한 새인지 생각하기 시작했다.

36 까마귀는 조용히 생각했다. "공작새의 깃털은 인상적이지만 그는 우리에 갇혀 있어.

37 나는 형형색색의 깃털은 없지만, 어디든 자유롭게 날아갈 수 있어."

38 까마귀는 숲으로 돌아갔다.

39 그는 물에 비친 자신을 다시 보았고 세상에서 가장 행복한 새를 보았다.

1 Who Is Happy?

2 Once upon a time, there was a crow who lived in a forest.

3 The crow was very happy with his life.

4 He always looked at himself in the water.

5 He thought no one was more beautiful than he was.

6 Then one day, the crow saw a swan on the lake.

7 "The swan is so white," he thought, "but I am so black.

8 I have never seen such a white bird before.

9 His beauty shines so brightly.

10 The swan must be the happiest bird in the world."

11 He went to the swan and expressed his thoughts.

12 "Actually," the swan said, "I thought that I was the happiest bird.

13 But then I saw a parrot.

14 Now I think the parrot is the happiest bird in the world."

15 The crow asked why he thought so.

16 The swan answered, "The parrot has colorful feathers.

17 He is more beautiful than I am.

18 He must be proud of his appearance."

19 The crow then flew to the parrot and said, "The swan said you are the happiest bird because you have colorful feathers."

20 The parrot explained, "I lived a very happy life until I saw a peacock.

21 My feathers are colorful, but the peacock's feathers are colorful, big, and gorgeous.

22 So he is loved by everyone."

23 The crow then visited the peacock at the zoo.

24 There were a lot of people around the peacock, and they praised him for his beauty.

25 The crow thought the peacock must be the happiest bird in the world.

26 After all the people left, the crow started to talk to the peacock.

27 "Peacock, you are so beautiful.

28 Many people come to see you every day.

29 On the other hand, when people see me, they chase me away.

30 I think you are the happiest bird in the world."

31 The peacock said, "I may be the most beautiful bird, but I'm not happy.

32 Because of my beauty, I am stuck in this zoo.

33 Unlike me, you aren't kept in a cage.

34 I want to be like you because you can go anywhere."

35 After the crow talked to the peacock, he started to think about who the happiest bird was.

36 The crow thought to himself, "The peacock's feathers are impressive, but he is stuck in a cage.

37 I don't have colorful feathers, but I'm free to fly anywhere."

38 The crow went back to the forest.

39 He looked at himself in the water again and saw the happiest bird in the world.

적중 **100** + 특별부록

Plan B

우리학교
최신기출

능률 · 김성곤

◎ 선택형 문항의 답안은 컴퓨터용 수정 싸인펜을 사용하여 OMR 답안지에 바르게 표기하시오.
◎ 서술형 문제는 답을 답안지에 반드시 검정 볼펜으로 쓰시오.
◎ 총 30문항 100점 만점입니다. 문항별 배점은 각 문항에 표시되어 있습니다.

[경기 ○○중]

01 다음 단어의 사전적 정의가 적절하지 <u>않은</u> 것은? (3점)

① fame: the state of being famous
② honor: to treat someone with respect
③ praise: to say nice things about someone
④ collect: to live after something bad happens
⑤ support: to give help or assistance to someone

[서울 강북구 ○○중]

02 다음 글의 밑줄 친 ⓐ~ⓔ 중 어휘의 의미가 문맥 안에서 가장 바르게 해석된 것은? (2점)

<Talking Books Program>
This is a program that makes audiobooks for ⓐ<u>blind</u> people. It was started in 1931 in the United States. You just read books and ⓑ<u>record</u> your voice. These audiobooks are given to blind people for free.

<Terry Fox School Run>
In Canada, some schools ⓒ<u>hold</u> a running event every year. When you run, you can raise money for cancer ⓓ<u>studies</u>. The event was started in 1981 by Terry Fox. He lost his leg because of cancer. He ran across Canada with an ⓔ<u>artificial</u> leg.

① ⓐ : 청각 장애가 있는
② ⓑ : 녹화하다
③ ⓒ : 지지하다
④ ⓓ : 연구
⑤ ⓔ : 자연스러운

[강원 ○○중]

03 다음 중 밑줄 친 부분의 쓰임이 <u>어색한</u> 것은? (3점)

① She was so <u>disappointed</u> with her test score.
② I felt very <u>tired</u> all day because I didn't sleep well last night.
③ The movie was very <u>excited</u> and I became interested in hocky.
④ The boy was very <u>scared</u> of the crocodile and began to cry.
⑤ Listening to classical music makes me <u>relaxed</u>.

[서울 강동구 ○○중]

04 다음 <보기>에 이어질 대화의 순서로 알맞은 것은? (3점)

> 보기
> Hey, Jane! What's wrong with your leg?

(A) I was in a hurry to catch a train. But I fell down in the street.
(B) Really? What happened?
(C) Oh, that's terrible! Is there anything I can do for you?
(D) I broke it last week.

① (A) - (B) - (D) - (C)
② (B) - (D) - (A) - (C)
③ (B) - (D) - (C) - (A)
④ (D) - (B) - (A) - (C)
⑤ (D) - (B) - (C) - (A)

Good morning, students! As you know, there was a big fire in Mapletown. Why don't we raise money and help the people there? Come to our special event at the school grounds on May 3! Please bring your items and donate them. We will sell your items. Then, we will give all the money to Mapletown. (A)Please give a hand to people in need.

05 위 글을 읽고 알 수 있는 것은? (3점)

① 행사장까지 가는 방법
② 행사 수익금의 사용처
③ 행사장에 방문할 수 있는 횟수
④ 행사에 기부 가능한 물품의 종류
⑤ 행사장에 한 번에 방문할 수 있는 인원

06 위 글의 밑줄 친 (A)를 우리말로 옮기시오. (3점)

→ _____

07 다음 빈칸에 알맞은 것은? (4점)

Sumi was _____ because her math test score was bad.

① disappoint
② disappoints
③ disappointed
④ disappointing
⑤ to disappoint

08 다음 중 fact(사실)와 opinion(의견)이 잘못 짝지어진 것은? (4점)

① The view from the park was awesome. (opinion)
② Many bookstores there sell used books. (fact)
③ The Jajangmyeon Museum is next to the station. (fact)
④ It was the most exciting experience of the tour. (opinion)
⑤ We ate many kinds of street food such as Gimbap, fish cake and Hotteok. (opinion)

09 다음 대화의 흐름이 자연스럽도록 우리말 뜻에 맞게 대화 속의 문장들을 활용하여 빈칸 (A), (B)에 들어갈 문장들을 각각 영어로 쓰시오. (6점)

A: Mr. Kim, I will tell you a secret. That man is a spy. You met him yesterday. Be careful.
B: What? Are you sure that (A)_____ _____?
A: Yes! Do you see this? This is the ID. The spy used it before.
B: Oh no! Do you mean that (B)_____ _____?
A: That's right!

(A) 내가 어제 만난 저 남자는 스파이이다. (8 words)
(B) 이것은 그 스파이가 전에 사용했던 그 ID이다.(9 words)

(A)_____
(B)_____

A: Next Wednesday is Volunteer Day. We cleaned up the park last time. What are we going to do this time?

B: Why don't we (A)[visit / visiting] a nursing home and clean it up?

C: That's not a bad idea. But I want to do something fun. Why don't we (B)[hold / holding] a party for the people there?

B: That's a good idea. What can we do at the party?

A: We can serve some food.

C: And how about (C)[play / playing] some music? I can play the piano.

B: And I can play the cello.

A: It sounds like a good plan.

[서울 관악구 ○○중]

10 위 대화의 괄호 (A), (B), (C) 안에서 순서대로 알맞게 짝지은 것은? (3점)

	(A)	(B)	(C)
①	visit	hold	playing
②	visit	holding	play
③	visiting	hold	playing
④	visiting	hold	play
⑤	visiting	holding	play

[서울 관악구 ○○중]

11 What will the students do on Volunteer Day? (3점)

① They will visit the park.

② They will clean the park.

③ They will clean the nursing home.

④ They will hold a party at the park.

⑤ They will hold a party at the nursing home.

B1: Wow! These dogs are so dirty. Hey, Jay. ⓐ이 개들을 씻게 나를 도와줄 수 있니?

B2: Allen, I'm sorry, but I can't. I have to feed the cats now. Why don't you ask Nicky?

B1: Okay! Nicky, ⓑcan I ask you a favor?

G: Sure. Allen. What is it?

B1: ⓐ이 개들을 씻게 나를 도와줄 수 있니?

G: Sure. But I have to walk these dogs first. After that, I will help you.

B1: All right! Thank you.

[서울 성북구 ○○중]

12 위 대화가 일어나고 있는 장소로 가장 적절한 곳은? (3점)

① nursing home

② movie theater

③ school cafeteria

④ children's hospital

⑤ animal care center

[서울 성북구 ○○중]

13 위 대화의 ⓐ의 의미가 되도록 7단어로 영작하시오. (3점)

→ ＿＿＿＿ ＿＿＿＿ ＿＿＿＿ ＿＿＿＿ ＿＿＿＿
＿＿＿＿ ＿＿＿＿

[서울 성북구 ○○중]

14 위 대화의 ⓑ와 바꾸어 쓸 수 있는 것은? (정답 2개) (3점)

① may I help you?

② can I give you a hand?

③ can you do me a favor?

④ can you give me a hand?

⑤ do you want me to help you?

15 위 대화의 내용과 일치하는 것은? (3점)

① Jay는 Nicky의 부탁을 거절했다.

② Allen은 고양이 먹이를 주어야 한다.

③ Allen과 Nicky는 함께 개를 씻길 것이다.

④ Jay는 자신의 부탁을 들어줄 사람을 찾고 있다.

⑤ Nicky는 고양이들에게 먹이를 준 후에 씻길 예정이다.

16 다음 글의 제목으로 가장 적절한 것은? (4점)

Talking Books Program is a program that makes audiobooks for blind people. It was started in 1931 in the United States. You just read books and record your voice. These audiobooks are given to blind people for free.

In Canada, some schools hold a running event every year. When you run, you can raise money for cancer studies. The event was started in 1981 by Terry Fox. He lost his leg because of cancer. He ran across Canada with an artificial leg.

Caps for Good is a Save the Children program. Every year, many babies die in their first month of life. By making hats, you can save their lives. Thanks to the hat you made, babies will be warm and safe.

① Nothing Is Impossible

② Volunteer: Sharing One's Talents

③ Great Events for the Blind People

④ New Ways to Make a Better World

⑤ Talking, Running, Making: New Items for the Future

[17~19] 다음 글을 읽고 물음에 답하시오.

"Father, Father!"

The people of Tonj, South Sudan, were all crying. Some children were walking with pictures of a man. They had lost a very special person. The man in the picture was Father Lee Taeseok, a Korean priest and doctor.

In 2001, Father Lee Taeseok visited Tonj to help the sick and poor people there. Life in Tonj was very difficult, so he soon returned to Korea. ⓐ_____, he could not forget the people there. So he flew to Tonj again later that year. From then on, Father John Lee, as the villagers called him, worked ⓑ_____ as a doctor, teacher, and musician. First, he built a hospital and treated 300 people a day. Then he built a school. He even taught math and music and made a band with the villagers. When the music filled the air, the village was filled with hopes and dreams too.

ⓒ_____, in 2008 Father Lee Taeseok discovered that he had cancer. He tried to fight it, but he passed away two years later at the age of 48. (A)_____. Today, he is admired for his great love for others.

17 위 글의 ⓐ, ⓑ, ⓒ에 들어갈 말을 쓰시오. ⓑ, ⓒ는 주어진 단어를 변형시켜 쓰시오. (6점)

→ ⓐ_____

　 ⓑ_____ (tire)

　 ⓒ_____ (fortunate)

18 위 글의 빈칸 (A)에 들어갈 말로 가장 적절한 것은? (3점)

① The people in Tonj tried to forget him.

② Everyone does not remember his achievements.

③ Many people were very sad to hear of his death.

④ All the dreams disappeared because of his death.

⑤ The hospital and the school he made were destroyed.

19 위 글의 내용과 일치하는 것은? (3점)

① 이태석 신부는 Tonj에 도착한 후 가장 먼저 학교를 세웠다.

② 이태석 신부는 2008년 48세의 나이로 세상을 떠났다.

③ 이태석 신부는 학교의 학생들과 음악 밴드를 만들었다.

④ 이태석 신부는 학교에서 수학과 음악을 직접 가르쳤다.

⑤ 이태석 신부는 2001년 첫 방문 후 Tonj에 계속 거주했다.

[20~25] 다음 글을 읽고 물음에 답하시오.

During World War Ⅱ, a little girl and her mother were hungry and sick. The only food Ⓐthat they could find was grass. The little girl felt ⓐ_____ all the time. Luckily, the girl survived, thanks to the help of others. One of the groups Ⓑthat helped her was UNICEF. Later, the girl became a worldwide movie star. Her name was Audrey Hepburn.

When she grew up, Hepburn became a symbol of beauty. She was very popular ⓑ_____ her hit movies, such as *My Fair Lady and Roman Holiday*. (가)그녀가 영화에서 입었던 작은 검정색 드레스는 심지어 지금도 유명하다. Many people still love her style.

(A) The autumn of 1987 was a turning point in Hepburn's life. (B) Many people donated money at the festival, and the money went to UNICEF. (C) Thanks to her fame, UNICEF collected more money than ever before. (D) Hepburn realized Ⓒthat her fame could help others, so she became a UNICEF Goodwill Ambassador. (E)

20 위 글의 내용과 일치하지 <u>않는</u> 것은? (3점)

① 오드리 햅번은 자라서 아름다움의 상징이 되었다.

② 오드리 햅번은 어렸을 때 UNICEF로부터 큰 도움을 받았다.

③ UNICEF는 오드리 햅번 덕분에 1987년 페스티벌에서 더 많은 돈을 모금하였다.

④ 세계 2차 대전이 일어났을 때, 오드리 햅번과 그녀의 딸은 궁핍한 생활을 하였다.

⑤ 오드리 햅번은 자신의 명성을 이용하여 다른 사람들을 도울 수 있다는 것을 깨달았다.

21 위 글의 (A)~(E) 중 다음의 문장이 들어갈 곳은? (3점)

> She went to an international music festival in Macau.

① (A) ② (B) ③ (C)

④ (D) ⑤ (E)

23 위 글의 ⓐ와 ⓑ에 들어갈 단어로 알맞게 짝지어진 것은? (3점)

	ⓐ	ⓑ
①	afraid	because
②	scared	because of
③	scared	because
④	excited	because
⑤	excited	because of

24 위 글의 내용을 바탕으로 3번째 단락의 요약문을 완성하시오. (7단어) (4점)

→ Hepburn began to work for UNICEF because she _____ _____ _____ _____ _____ _____ _____.

22 위 글의 밑줄 친 Ⓐ~Ⓒ의 that과 같은 용법으로 쓰인 것을 〈보기〉에서 각각 골라 알맞게 분류한 것은? (4점)

보기

㉠ Pass me that salt on the table.

㉡ I like the song that you sang yesterday.

㉢ The computer that you bought was amazing.

㉣ Jake owned the robot that cleaned the room by itself.

㉤ They have thought that fish are healthy food.

㉥ Sunmi read the book that her mother recommended.

	Ⓐ	Ⓑ	Ⓒ
①	㉠, ㉣	㉤	㉡, ㉥
②	㉡	㉣	㉢, ㉥, ㉤
③	㉢	㉥, ㉤	㉡, ㉣
④	㉡	㉤	㉠, ㉢, ㉣, ㉥
⑤	㉡, ㉢, ㉥	㉣	㉤

25 위 글의 밑줄 친 (가)를 가장 바르게 영작한 것은? (3점)

① She wore a black small dress which was famous in the movie.

② The small black dress who she wore in a movie is famous today.

③ The black little dress which she wears in a movie were famous today.

④ Even today, the little black dress that she wore in a movie is famous.

⑤ Today, she is wearing the little black dress which she wore in the movie.

First, Hepburn went to Ethiopia in 1988. There, she brought food to ⓐhungry children. She was shocked (A)_____ their lives were very difficult. After that, she ⓑvolunteered in other countries. In 1990, she visited Vietnam to hand out medicine and support ⓒclean drinking water programs. Her last trip was to Somalia in 1992, and she ⓓpassed away the following year. Many people praised her beauty and style, (B)_____ Hepburn's real beauty was her heart. To honor her, UNICEF made a statue, *The Spirit of Audrey*. People who ⓔenvy her keep her mission alive. Her favorite saying shows her mission.

As you get older, remember you have two hands. (가)_____ is for helping yourself, and (나)_____ is for helping others.

26 위 글의 Hepburn에 대한 설명으로 바른 것은?　　(3점)

① Her real beauty was heart.

② She passed away in 1992.

③ Her first trip was to Somalia.

④ She brought food to Vietnam.

⑤ She went to Ethiopia to clean water.

27 위 글의 빈칸 (가), (나)에 알맞은 것은?　　(3점)

① One – the other

② One – some

③ The other – one

④ Some – another

⑤ Some – the others

28 위 글의 빈칸 (A), (B)에 들어갈 가장 적절한 연결사는?　(3점)

	(A)	(B)
①	because	or
②	so	or
③	because	but
④	so	but
⑤	since	or

29 위 글을 읽고 답할 수 없는 질문은?　　(3점)

① When did Hepburn go to Ethiopia?

② Why did Hepburn visit Vietnam in 1990?

③ What did she do in Somalia?

④ What did UNICEF make to honor Hepburn?

⑤ What is Hepburn's favorite saying?

30 위 글의 ⓐ~ⓔ 중, 문맥상 쓰임이 적절하지 않은 것은?　(3점)

① ⓐ　　　　② ⓑ　　　　③ ⓒ

④ ⓓ　　　　⑤ ⓔ

2학년 영어 2학기 중간고사(5과) 2회

문항수 : 선택형(25문항) 서술형(5문항)   20 . . .

◎ 선택형 문항의 답안은 컴퓨터용 수정 싸인펜을 사용하여 OMR 답안지에 바르게 표기하시오.
◎ 서술형 문제는 답을 답안지에 반드시 검정 볼펜으로 쓰시오.
◎ 총 30문항 100점 만점입니다. 문항별 배점은 각 문항에 표시되어 있습니다.

[서울 강남구 ○○중]

01 다음 각 단어의 영영풀이가 올바른 것은?   (3점)

① praise : to say nice things about someone
② waste: useful materials that are kept well
③ mission: an impossible task to be done by agents
④ in need: having enough things that are necessary for life
⑤ public transportation: ways of traveling that a few rich people can use

[강원 ○○중]

02 다음 중 어법상 <u>어색한</u> 문장은?   (3점)

① I'll give you the dragonflies I caught yesterday.
② This is my uncle whom I told you about.
③ Amy bought the car which I wanted.
④ A baguette is a type of bread is popular in France.
⑤ The book he was reading is missing.

[인천 ○○중]

03 다음 빈칸에 들어갈 말로 적절한 것은?   (3점)

> Yumi and Jisu are _____ about watching a movie on Saturday night.

① excited   ② exciting
③ to excite   ④ having exciting
⑤ having to excite

[서울 강남구 ○○중]

04 Which is the question that we can not find the answer to from the dialog?   (4점)

> B1: Hey, Jungtae! What's wrong with your leg?
> B2: I broke it last week.
> B1: Really? What happened?
> B2: I was in a hurry to catch my bus. But I fell down in the street.
> B1: Oh, that's terrible! Is there anything I can do for you?
> B2: Well, can you help me carry my bag?
> B1: Sure.

① What happened to Jungtae?
② When did the accident happen?
③ Why did Jungtae fall down in the street?
④ What does Jungtae ask his friend to do?
⑤ How long will Jungtae have to stay in hospital?

[서울 중구 ○○중]

05 다음 짝지어진 대화 중 <u>어색한</u> 것은?   (3점)

① A: Can you do me a favor?
   B: Sure. What is it?
② A: How do you get to school?
   B: I go to school by bus.
③ A: Why don't you clean up your room?
   B: All right. Let's do it now.
④ A: Can you tell me how to get there?
   B: Go straight two blocks. And you can see it on your left.
⑤ A: What are you planning to do there?
   B: I'm planning to go hiking on Hallasan.

[6~8] 다음 대화를 읽고 물음에 답하시오.

A: Next Wednesday is Volunteer Day. We cleaned up the park last time. ⓐWhat are we going to do this time?
B: ⓑHow about visiting a nursing home and cleaning it up?
C: That's not a bad idea. ⓒBut I want to do something fun. Let's throw a party for the people there.
B: That's a good idea. What can we do at the party?
A: ⓓWe can help others and make our community better.
C: And what about playing some music? I can play the piano.
B: And I can play the cello.
A: ⓔIt sounds like a good plan.

08 What will the speakers do? (3점)

① A will go to a park next Wednesday.
② A and B will cook some food for a party.
③ C will visit and clean up a nursing home.
④ A and C are going to buy B a new cello.
⑤ C will play the piano at a party for people at a nursing home.

06 Choose the sentence which is not natural considering the context of the dialog. (3점)

① ⓐ   ② ⓑ   ③ ⓒ
④ ⓓ   ⑤ ⓔ

[9~10] 다음 글을 읽고 물음에 답하시오.

It was a long day. I felt very ⓐtired all day because I didn't sleep well last night. The first class was social studies, and we got our exams back. I failed the test. I was so ⓑdisappointed. My best friend Kevin was ⓒworrying about me and took me to a movie after school. We watched a movie about a hockey team. It was very ⓓexciting and I became ⓔinteresting in hockey! I'm going to join a hockey team tomorrow.

07 위 대화의 주제로 가장 적절한 것은? (4점)

① cleaning a nursing home
② the schedule of last volunteer day
③ the volunteer plan at a nursing home
④ playing music on a volunteer day
⑤ the ideas to make a home party better

09 위 글의 내용과 일치하지 않는 것은? (3점)

① 지난밤에 잠을 잘 못 자서 피곤했다.
② 체육 시간에 시험지를 돌려받았다.
③ 시험을 못 봐서 실망했다.
④ 학교가 끝나고 영화를 보러 갔다.
⑤ 내일 하키팀에 가입할 것이다.

10 위 글의 ⓐ~ⓔ 중 어법상 <u>어색한</u> 표현을 2개 골라 고쳐 쓰시오. (5점)

(1)_____ → _____

(2)_____ → _____

[12~14] 다음 대화를 읽고 물음에 답하시오.

> Allen: Wow! These dogs are so dirty. Jay, can you help me wash them?
> Jay: ⓐ_____ I have to feed the cats now. Why don't you ask Nicky?
> Allen: Okay! Nicky, can you give me a hand?
> Nicky: Sure, Allen. What is it?
> Allen: Can you help me wash these dogs?
> Nicky: ⓑ_____ But I have to walk these dogs first. After that, I will help you.
> Allen: All right! Thank you.

11 다음 대화의 내용과 일치하는 것은? (4점)

> James: Next Wednesday is Volunteer Day. We cleaned up the park last time. What are we going to do this time?
> Emma: Why don't we visit a nursing home and clean it up?"
> Liam: That's not a bad idea. But I want to do something fun. Why don't we hold a party for the people there?
> Emma: That's a good idea. What can we do at the party?
> James: We can serve some food.
> Liam: And how about playing some music? I can play the piano.
> Emma: And I can play the cello.
> James: It sounds like a good plan.

① James suggested playing music at the party.

② James wants to clean up the park for this Volunteer Day.

③ They'll serve some food and play music at the party.

④ Liam thinks holding a party for the sick children would be fun.

⑤ Following Emma's idea, they are going to clean up a nursing home.

12 위 대화의 장소로 가장 알맞은 것은? (3점)

① a zoo

② a pet shop

③ a nursing home

④ an animal care center

⑤ an animal hospital

13 위 대화의 빈칸 ⓐ와 ⓑ에 들어갈 말이 바르게 짝지어진 것은? (3점)

	ⓐ	ⓑ
①	Sure.	No problem.
②	Why not?	Of course not.
③	Sorry, but I can't.	I'm sorry.
④	I'm sorry?	Not at all.
⑤	I'm afraid not.	Sure, I can.

14 위 대화의 내용과 일치하는 것은? (3점)

① The dogs are sick.

② Allen asked Jay and Nicky for help.

③ Jay didn't want to wash dirty dogs.

④ Jay and Nicky refused to help Allen.

⑤ Nicky will help Allen to walk the dogs.

16 위 글의 목적으로 알맞은 것은? (3점)

① to sell goods for donation

② to give a warning about a fire

③ to invite students to a donation event

④ to raise money for students in Mapletown

⑤ to teach students how to help people in need

17 위 글의 밑줄 친 ⓐ와 같은 의미로 쓰인 것은? (4점)

① We will <u>raise</u> funds to build a school.

② The news started to <u>raise</u> fears of war.

③ <u>Raise</u> your hand if you know the answer.

④ My boss doesn't want to <u>raise</u> my salary.

⑤ Do you <u>raise</u> chickens and pigs on your farm?

[15~17] 다음 글을 읽고 물음에 답하시오.

Good morning, students! As you know, there was a big fire in Mapletown. Why don't we ⓐ <u>raise</u> money and help the people there? Come to our special event at the school grounds on May 3! Please bring your items and donate them. (A)_____ Then, we will give all the money to Mapletown. Please give a hand to people in need.

15 위 글의 빈칸 (A)에 들어갈 말로 가장 적절한 것은? (3점)

① We will fix your items.

② We will buy your items.

③ We will sell your items.

④ We will save your items.

⑤ We will clean your items.

18 다음 문장에서 나타내는 감정으로 가장 적절한 것은? (3점)

I heard that James got into an accident this morning!

① sleepy ② shocked

③ lonely ④ satisfied

⑤ confident

① Lee Taeseok's Three Jobs

② Lee Taeseok's Trip to Tonj

③ Lee Taeseok's Volunteer Work

④ Lee Taeseok's Hospital in Tonj

⑤ Lee Taeseok's Friendship with Villagers

[인천 ○○중]

19 다음 빈칸에 들어갈 수 있는 말을 보기에서 모두 고르면? (3점)

> A: Minji, _____
> B: Sure. What is it?
> A: Can you help me move these books?
> B: Okay. What are you going to do with them?
> A: I'm going to donate them to a children's library.

보기

> • Can I ask you a favor?
> • Can you do me a favor?
> • What's wrong with you?
> • Can you give me a hand?
> • Why don't we go to a children's library?

① 1개   ② 2개   ③ 3개

④ 4개   ⑤ 5개

[서울 강남구 ○○중]

20 다음 글의 제목으로 알맞은 것은?   (3점)

> In 2001, Father Lee Taeseok visited Tonj to help the sick and poor people there. Life in Tonj was very difficult, so he soon returned to Korea. However, he could not forget the people there. So he flew to Tonj again later that year.
>
> From then on, Father John Lee, as the villagers called him, worked tirelessly as a doctor, teacher, and musician. First, he built a hospital and treated 300 people a day. Then he built a school. He even taught math and music and made a band with the villagers. When the music filled the air, the village was filled with hopes and dreams too.

[21~25] 다음 글을 읽고 물음에 답하시오.

> ⓐDuring World War II, a little girl and her mother were hungry and sick. (A)The only food that they could find was grass. (B)그 작은 소녀는 항상 무서움을 느꼈다. ⓑLuckily, the girl survived, thanks to the help of others. One of the groups that helped her was UNICEF. Later, the girl became a worldwide movie star. Her name was Audrey Hepburn.
>
> When she grew up, Hepburn became a ⓒsymbol of beauty. She was very popular because of her hit movies, ⓓsuch My Fair Lady and Roman Holiday. (C)The little black dress (is, she, famous, in, wore, a movie). ⓔeven today. Many people still love her style.

[서울 동작구 ○○중]

21 위 글의 흐름상, 밑줄 친 단어들 중 어색한 것은?   (3점)

① ⓐ   ② ⓑ   ③ ⓒ

④ ⓓ   ⑤ ⓔ

22 위 글의 밑줄 친 (A)의 형태를 이용하여, 〈보기〉의 두 문장을 주어진 우리말 뜻에 맞게 하나의 영어 문장으로 연결하여 쓰시오. (4점)

> **보기**
> • The man is going to meet the students.
> • He taught them a long time ago.

그 남자는 그가 오래 전에 가르친 학생들을 만날 예정이다.

→ _____

23 위 글의 밑줄 친 (B)의 우리말을 주어진 단어들을 모두 이용하여 영어로 옮기시오. (단, 필요하다면 단어의 형태를 변형할 수 있음) (4점)

all the time / feel / the little girl / scare

→ _____

24 위 글을 읽고 학생들이 나눈 대화에서 위 글을 바르게 이해한 학생들로만 묶인 것은? (3점)

가영: Hepburn은 어렸을 때 배가 고프고 아팠어.
진수: 맞아. 하지만 그녀를 도와준 유일한 단체인 UNICEF 덕분에 살아남을 수 있었어.
민아: 그녀가 성장했을 때, 그녀의 히트작들 때문에 매우 인기가 있었어.
해영: 그녀는 축제에서 검은색 드레스를 입고 나와서 큰 화제가 되었어.
정민: 많은 사람들이 최근에 들어서 Hepburn의 스타일을 모방하고 있어.

① 가영, 진수
② 가영, 민아
③ 가영, 해영
④ 진수, 정민
⑤ 민아, 정민

25 위 글의 밑줄 친 (C)가 "그녀가 한 영화에서 입었던 작은 검은색 드레스는 오늘날까지도 유명하다."의 뜻이 되도록 관계대명사 하나를 추가하여 괄호 안의 어구를 올바른 순서로 배열하시오. (3점)

→ _____

[26~30] 다음 글을 읽고 물음에 답하시오.

The autumn of 1987, she went to an international music festival in Macau. ⓐMany people donated money at the festival, and the money went to UNICEF. ⓑBecause of her, UNICEF collected more money than ever before. Hepburn realized that her fame could help others, so she became a UNICEF Goodwill Ambassador.

First, Hepburn went to Ethiopia in 1988. There, she brought food to hungry children. ⓒShe was shocked because of their lives were very difficult. After that, she volunteered in other countries. ⓓIn 1990, she visited Vietnam to hand out medicine and support clean drinking water programs.

Her last trip was to Somalia in 1992, and she passed (A)_____ the following year. Many people praised her beauty and style, but Hepburn's real (가)_____ was her heart.

(B)_____ honor her, UNICEF made a statue, *The Spirit of Audrey*. ⓔPeople whom respect her keep her mission alive. Her favorite saying shows her mission.

As you get older, remember you have two hands.

One is (C)_____ helping yourself, and the other is (C)_____ helping others.

26 위 글의 ⓐ~ⓔ 중, 어법상 <u>어색한</u> 문장은 <u>모두</u> 몇 개인가?

(3점)

① 1개 ② 2개 ③ 3개

④ 4개 ⑤ 5개

29 위 글의 내용과 일치하는 것은? (3점)

① 1987년 헵번은 마카오에서 음악 축제를 열었다.

② 축제에서 많은 사람들이 헵번에게 돈을 기부하였다.

③ 헵번의 마지막 여행은 에티오피아로 떠난 것이었다.

④ 헵번은 외모와 마음 모두 아름다운 사람이었다.

⑤ 지금까지도 헵번은 많은 사람을 돕고 있다.

27 위 글의 빈칸 (가)에 들어갈 말로 가장 적절한 것은? (3점)

① honor

② mission

③ beauty

④ money

⑤ volunteer

28 위 글의 (A)~(C)에 들어갈 말이 바르게 짝지어진 것은? (4점)

	(A)	(B)	(C)
①	from	To	for
②	from	For	on
③	away	To	for
④	away	For	on
⑤	away	In	for

30 위 글에서 질문의 답을 찾아 영어 한 문장으로 쓰시오. (4점)

> Why did Hepburn become a UNICEF Goodwill Ambassador?

→ _____

◎ 선택형 문항의 답안은 컴퓨터용 수정 싸인펜을 사용하여 OMR 답안지에 바르게 표기하시오.
◎ 서술형 문제는 답을 답안지에 반드시 검정 볼펜으로 쓰시오.
◎ 총 30문항 100점 만점입니다. 문항별 배점은 각 문항에 표시되어 있습니다.

[부산 ○○중]

01 다음 문장의 빈칸에 들어갈 표현으로 가장 적절한 것은? (3점)

Hyori is _____ her breathing in the yoga class.

① turning off
② focusing on
③ hanging out
④ giving away
⑤ searching for

[서울 강북구 ○○중]

02 다음 우리말을 참고하여 (A)를 완성할 때 ⓒ에 들어갈 단어는? (3점)

어떤 사람들은 특별한 목적을 위해 여행을 간다.

(A)Some people (ⓐ) on (ⓑ) (ⓒ) (ⓓ) (ⓔ). They travel to do volunteer work. They want to help local communities or wild animals during their trips.

① go
② purposes
③ for
④ trips
⑤ special

[전북 ○○중]

03 다음 대화의 빈칸에 알맞은 것은? (3점)

A: How do you get to school?
B: I go to school by bus.
A: _____
B: It takes 20 minutes.

① What time do you leave for school?
② How long does it take to get there?
③ How much time do you need to get there?
④ When will you take it?
⑤ How many pictures do you take?

[서울 송파구 ○○중]

04 다음 중 짝지어진 대화가 자연스러운 것은? (3점)

① A: How do you get to school?
　B: I go to school by my feet.
② A: Where did you take these beautiful pictures?
　B: At Riverside Park. You should go there.
③ A: How far is it from our school to the zoo?
　B: Get on bus 135 and get off at the Riverside stop.
④ A: How long does it take to get there?
　B: It takes 5 minutes by bus and 20 minutes on walk.
⑤ A: Can you tell me how to get to Baker Middle School?
　B: Go straight for 2 blocks, and then turn left. You will miss it.

[5~6] 다음 대화를 읽고 물음에 답하시오.

Jay: Wow, these pictures are so beautiful. Where did you take them?

Tom: At Riverside Park. There were lots of flowers. You should go there!

Jay: I want to. How can I get there from our school?

Tom: Get (A)_____ the bus number 135 and get off at the Riverside Stadium stop. You can see the park in front of the bus stop.

Jay: (B)얼마나 오래 걸려?

Tom: It takes about 30 minutes on foot and 15 minutes by bus.

05 위 대화의 (A)와 다음 문장들의 빈칸에 들어갈 전치사가 같은 것은? (3점)

① Let's clean _____ our town's streets.

② I felt nervous but, _____ the same time, excited.

③ I have a plan _____ Valentine's Day.

④ I went to Hanguk University _____ bus.

⑤ I learned the lives of people _____ the past.

06 위 대화의 밑줄 친 (B)를 주어, 동사를 갖춘 완전한 영어 문장으로 작성하시오. (5 words) (4점)

→ _____

07 다음 중 밑줄 친 부분의 쓰임이 <u>다른</u> 것은? (3점)

① <u>It</u> is exciting to watch baseball games.

② <u>It</u> is not easy to have meals in space.

③ <u>It</u> is difficult to read English novels.

④ <u>It</u> is about two hours from here to the beach.

⑤ <u>It</u> is dangerous for her to climb the mountain.

08 다음 빈칸 (A), (B), (C)에 들어갈 제목으로 알맞은 것은? (4점)

(A)_____ Trip

On this trip, people visit historical sites and learn about history. During this trip, people can understand the lives of people in the past.

(B)_____ Trip

Some people go on a trip for special purposes. They travel to work for people in need. They help local communities or wild animals during their trips.

(C)_____ Trip

Some people take trips in nature without hurting the environment. They think it is important to protect nature.

	(A)	(B)	(C)
①	Eco	Volunteer	History
②	History	Eco	Volunteer
③	Volunteer	History	Eco
④	Eco	History	Volunteer
⑤	History	Volunteer	Eco

09 다음 대화의 빈칸에 들어갈 말로 알맞지 <u>않은</u> 것은? (3점)

A: What are you planning to do on Chuseok?

B: _____

① I'm planning to eat Songpyeon.

② I have been to Jeju-do with my family.

③ I'm going to visit Korean Folk Village.

④ I'm supposed to go fishing in Daebu-do.

⑤ I don't have any plans. I'm going to watch TV.

[10~11] 다음 대화를 읽고 물음에 답하시오.

B: We have a long holiday this month. Do you have any plans?

G: I'm going to visit my grandparents in Jeonju.

B: Oh, that's nice. What are you (A)_____ to do with them?

G: I'm planning to go to Hanok Village with them. How about you? What are your (B)_____ for the holiday?

B: I'm going to stay home and relax.

G: That's also a good idea!

*B: Boy G: Girl

[경기 ○○중]

10 위 대화의 (A), (B)에 들어갈 단어를 바르게 짝지은 것은? (3점)

	(A)	(B)
①	plan	planning
②	plan	plans
③	planning	planning
④	planning	plans
⑤	plans	plans

[경기 ○○중]

11 위 대화를 읽고 답할 수 없는 질문은? (3점)

① Where do the girl's grandparents live?

② How many days will the girl stay in Jeonju?

③ Does the boy want to take a rest this holiday?

④ Will the girl go to Hanok Village this holiday?

⑤ What is the purpose of her visit to Jeonju this holiday?

[경기 ○○중]

12 다음 대화를 읽고 빈칸 (A), (B)를 완성하시오. (6점)

B: Excuse me. (A)_____ _____ _____ _____ _____ the airport?

W: You can go there by taxi.

B: (B)_____ _____ _____ _____ _____ to get there?

W: It takes 20 minutes by taxi.

(A)_____

(B)_____

[부산 ○○중]

13 다음 대화의 내용상 밑줄 친 표현이 적절하지 못한 것은? (4점)

G: ⓐWhat are you planning to do this weekend?

B: ⓑI'm planning to go to a baseball game in Daegu.

G: ⓒWho will you see in the game?

B: Yes. It will be fun. Also, I'm planning to visit my friend there.

G: Nice. How long does it take to get there?

B: It takes 40 minutes.

G: ⓓWow, it's much faster than I thought. I hope you have a good trip!

B: ⓔThank you.

① ⓐ　　② ⓑ　　③ ⓒ　　④ ⓓ　　⑤ ⓔ

B: Hi, Nuri. Where is your class going for the field trip tomorrow?

G: Hello, Mike. We are going to the art museum. (A)

B: Sounds interesting. (B) What are you planning to see there?

G: There are three art shows right now. (C) I'm planning to see Vincent van Gogh's paintings. Where is your class going?

B: We are going to the amusement park. (D) I'm excited to ride a roller coaster!

G: (E) Have a good trip!

[충남 ○○중]

14 위 대화의 (A)~(E) 중 다음 문장이 들어갈 위치로 가장 알맞은 곳은? (3점)

> That sounds fun.

① (A) ② (B) ③ (C)
④ (D) ⑤ (E)

[충남 ○○중]

15 위 대화의 내용과 일치하지 <u>않는</u> 것은? (3점)

① Nuri will go on a field trip tomorrow.

② Nuri's class will visit the art museum.

③ Nuri will meet Vincent van Gogh.

④ Mike will go to the amusement park.

⑤ Mike is planning to ride a roller coaster.

Busan, Market Heaven

(A) Then we walked to Bosu-dong Book Street. Many bookstores there sell (a)<u>used</u> books. We were really excited because we found some old comic books! It was nice to relax in a café and read them.

(B) It is famous for selling a variety of goods from different countries. It was interesting to see all the international goods there. We also ate many kinds of street food, such as *Gimbap*, fish cake, and *Hotteok*.

(C) Do you like traditional markets? Then go to Gukje Market in Busan. It is one of the most famous markets in Busan. Do you know what it is famous for?

[충북 ○○중]

16 위 글의 (A)~(C)를 자연스럽게 이어지도록 순서대로 배열한 것은? (4점)

① (A) - (B) - (C)
② (A) - (C) - (B)
③ (B) - (C) - (A)
④ (C) - (A) - (B)
⑤ (C) - (B) - (A)

[충남 ○○중]

17 위 글에서 다음 제시된 질문에 대한 답을 찾아 한 문장으로 쓰시오. (4점)

> Q: What is Gukje Market famous for?

→ _____

18 위 글의 내용과 일치하지 <u>않는</u> 것은? (3점)

① 많은 종류의 길거리 음식을 먹었다.

② 국제시장은 부산에서 가장 유명하다.

③ 국제시장은 다른 나라의 물건들을 판다.

④ 보수동의 많은 서점들이 중고책을 판다.

⑤ 오래된 만화책을 몇 권 찾아서 신이 났다.

19 위 글을 읽고 알 수 <u>없는</u> 것은? (3점)

① 국제시장에서 파는 물건

② 길거리 음식의 종류

③ 중고책을 파는 서점이 있는 곳

④ 카페에서 읽은 책의 종류

⑤ 중고책의 가격

20 위 글의 (a)와 같은 의미로 쓰인 것은? (3점)

① I'm looking for a <u>used</u> car.

② He <u>used</u> a knife to cut some bread.

③ She <u>used</u> beautiful colors in her painting.

④ I <u>used</u> up my pocket money in three days.

⑤ Most students <u>used</u> smart phones or computers.

[21~25] 다음 글을 읽고 물음에 답하시오.

Gangwon-do, Full of Natural Beauty

There is no place like Gangwon-do for beautiful nature. ⓐFirst, we went to Baengnyong Cave. This 1.8-kilometer-long cave is still in good condition. ⓑ<u>It was so amazing to see its natural beauty.</u> Near the end of our cave tour, the guide turned off the lights in the cave for a minute. ⓒ <u>Without a guide, you cannot tour the cave.</u> Everything became very dark, so we (A)<u>were able to</u> focus on the sounds there. ⓓ<u>It was the most amazing experience of the tour!</u> Our next stop was Donggang. ⓔ<u>We went rafting!</u> (B)_____ on the rough water and enjoy the view at the same time.

21 위 글의 내용과 일치하지 <u>않는</u> 것은? (3점)

① 강원도는 자연이 아름답다.

② 백룡동굴은 상태가 좋다.

③ 동굴 탐험 전 안내원이 전등을 껐다.

④ 모든 것이 어두워져 소리에 집중하였다.

⑤ 동굴 탐험 다음 목적지는 동강이었다.

22 위 글의 흐름으로 보아 ⓐ~ⓔ 중 <u>어색한</u> 문장은? (4점)

① ⓐ　　② ⓑ　　③ ⓒ　　④ ⓓ　　⑤ ⓔ

23 위 글의 밑줄 친 (A)와 바꿔 쓸 수 있는 것은? (3점)

① may　　② can　　③ must

④ could　　⑤ had to

24 위 글의 빈칸 (B)를 아래 주어진 단어를 모두 사용하여 완성하시오. (3점)

> was / to / it / exciting / ride

→ _____

27 위 글의 밑줄 친 ⓐIt과 쓰임이 같은 것은? (3점)

① How's <u>it</u> going?

② <u>It</u> is raining outside.

③ <u>It</u> looks good on you.

④ <u>It</u> is nice to meet you again.

⑤ <u>It</u> is 2 kilometers from here to the library.

25 위 글의 분위기로 가장 적절한 것은? (3점)

① fun   ② rude   ③ scary

④ silly   ⑤ nervous

28 위 글의 빈칸에 가장 적절한 것은? (3점)

① Firsts   ② Trains

③ Food   ④ Parks

⑤ City Lights

[26~30] 다음 글을 읽고 물음에 답하시오.

Incheon, A City of _____

(가)한국 최초의 기차역이 어디인지 아시나요? How about the first *Jajangmyeon*? The answer is Incheon! (A) This place has many of Korea's firsts. (B) The *Jajangmyeon* Museum is next to the station. (C) We learned about the history of *Jajangmyeon* there. (D) Later, we walked around Jayu Park, the first Western-style park in Korea. (E) The view from the park was awesome! ⓐIt was great to see the historical sites of this city from the park.

29 위 글의 (A)~(E) 중, 다음 문장이 들어갈 위치로 가장 적절한 것은? (3점)

> To get there, we went to Incheon Station.

① (A)   ② (B)   ③ (C)

④ (D)   ⑤ (E)

30 위 글의 내용과 <u>다른</u> 것은? (3점)

① 한국 최초의 기차역은 인천에 있다.

② 자장면 박물관은 기차역 옆에 있다.

③ 박물관에서 자장면의 역사를 배웠다.

④ 자유 공원 옆에 서양식 공원이 있다.

⑤ 자유 공원에서 보이는 경치는 멋지다.

26 위 글의 밑줄 친 (가)의 우리말을 영작할 때, 7번째 올 단어로 알맞은 것은? (4점)

① first   ② know   ③ train

④ station   ⑤ Korea

2학년 영어 2학기 중간고사(6과) 2회

문항수 : 선택형(23문항) 서술형(7문항)　　　20 ． ． ．

◎ 선택형 문항의 답안은 컴퓨터용 수정 싸인펜을 사용하여 OMR 답안지에 바르게 표기하시오.
◎ 서술형 문제는 답을 답안지에 반드시 검정 볼펜으로 쓰시오.
◎ 총 30문항 100점 만점입니다. 문항별 배점은 각 문항에 표시되어 있습니다.

[경기 ○○중]

01 다음 중 단어의 뜻이 적절하지 <u>않은</u> 것은? (3점)

① relax: 일하다
② on foot: 걸어서
③ presentation: 발표
④ a variety of: 다양한
⑤ at the same time: 동시에

[서울 송파구 ○○중]

02 다음 대화 중 어법상 <u>어색한</u> 것을 고르면? (3점)

① A: Why do the leaves turn red in autumn?
　B: I don't know why the leaves turn red in autumn.
② A: How much does the book cost?
　B: I don't know. I will ask my mom how the book cost much.
③ A: Selena got an A on her math test. How long did Selena study yesterday?
　B: Do you want me to ask her how long she studied yesterday?
④ A: Who did MJ talk to during English class?
　B: I was studying. So I don't know exactly who he talked to.
⑤ A: Why is Jenny always late?
　B: Well, I don't know why Jenny is always late.

[3~4] 다음 대화를 읽고 물음에 답하시오.

B: Excuse me. How do I ⓐget to Hanguk University from here?
W: You can go there ⓑby bus or on foot.
B: How long does it take to get there?
W: It ⓒtakes five minutes by bus and 20 minutes ⓓon foot.
B: Oh, then _____. Can you tell me how to get there?
W: Go ⓔstraight for two blocks, and then turn left. You will see Hanguk University on your right.
B: Go straight for two blocks and turn left. Thank you!

[충남 ○○중]

03 다음 밑줄 친 단어의 뜻이 올바르게 연결되지 <u>않은</u> 것은? (3점)

① ⓐget to: ~에 도착하다
② ⓑby bus: 버스로
③ ⓒtakes: 기다리다
④ ⓓon foot: 걸어서
⑤ ⓔstraight: 직진하여

[경기 ○○중]

04 위 대화의 흐름상 빈칸에 들어갈 말로 가장 적절한 것은? (3점)

① I'll take a bus
② the faster, the better
③ I'm going to take a taxi
④ I'm going to go there on foot
⑤ you had better go there with me

[5~7] 다음 대화를 읽고 물음에 답하시오.

Jinsu: Wow, these pictures are so beautiful. Where did you take them? (A)

Sue: At Riverside Park. There were lots of flowers. You should go there! (B)

Jinsu: I want to. (C)

Sue: Get on bus number 135 and get off at the Riverside Stadium stop. You can see the park in front of the bus stop. (D)

Jinsu: (a)<u>거기 가는 데 시간이 얼마나 걸리니?</u> (E)

Sue: It takes 30 minutes.

Jinsu: Thanks. I'll go there next weekend.

05 위 대화가 자연스럽게 이어지도록 〈보기〉 문장이 들어갈 곳은? (3점)

> 보기
> How do I get there from our school?

① (A) ② (B) ③ (C)

④ (D) ⑤ (E)

06 위 대화의 내용과 일치하는 것은? (3점)

① They are looking at the flowers in a park.

② Both of them have been to Riverside Park.

③ Sue and Jinsu will go to Riverside Park next weekend.

④ They need to take bus No. 135 to get to Riverside Park.

⑤ Jinsu knew how long it takes to get to the Riverside Park.

07 위 대화의 (a)의 우리말에 맞게 다음 괄호 안에 주어진 단어에 하나의 단어를 더 추가하여 영작하시오. (4점)

> (long, it, to, there, how, does, get)

→ _____

08 다음 중 대화의 흐름상 어색한 것은? (3점)

B: We have a long holiday this month. Do you have any plans?

G: ⓐI'm going to visit my grandparents in Jeonju.

B: ⓑOh, really? That's nice. ⓒWhat is your plan there?

G: My plan is to go to Hanok Village with my grandparents. How about you? ⓓ When did you plan for the holiday?

B: I'm going to stay home and relax.

G: ⓔThat's also a good idea!

① ⓐ ② ⓑ ③ ⓒ

④ ⓓ ⑤ ⓔ

09 다음 소개하는 것과 가장 관계가 깊은 것은? (3점)

> Some people take trips in nature without hurting the environment. They think it is important to protect nature.

① Eco Trip

② Volunteer Trip

③ History Trip

④ Culture Trip

⑤ Field Trip

10 다음 주어진 문장을 활용하여 간접의문문을 완성하시오. (6점)

> (1) Do you know _____?
>   (When did the show start?)
> (2) Can you tell me _____?
>   (What movie does she like?)
> (3) I'm not sure _____.
>   (Is Tom at home?)

(1)_____

(2)_____

(3)_____

11 다음 〈보기〉에서 필요한 단어를 사용하여 주어진 우리말에 맞게 문장을 완성하시오. (5점)

> 보기
> difficult / possible / important / interesting /
> live / give up / a smart phone

(1) It _____.

　(스마트폰 없이 사는 것은 어렵다.)

(2) It _____.

　(포기하지 않는 것은 중요하다.)

[12~13] 다음 대화를 읽고 물음에 답하시오.

> B: Hi, Nuri. Where is your class going for the field trip tomorrow?
> G: Hello, Mike. _____
> B: Sounds interesting. _____
> G: There are three art shows right now. I'm planning to see Vincent van Gogh's paintings. Where is your class going?
> B: _____ I'm excited to go hiking.
> G: That sounds fun. Have a good trip!

12 위 대화가 자연스럽도록 빈칸에 들어갈 가장 알맞은 말을 〈보기〉에서 골라 순서대로 나열한 것은? (3점)

> 보기
> (A) We are going to the amusement park.
> (B) We are going to Halla Mountain in Jeju.
> (C) What are you planning to ride there?
> (D) What are you planning to see there?
> (E) We are going to the art museum.

① (A) - (B) - (D)　　② (A) - (C) - (E)

③ (C) - (A) - (D)　　④ (E) - (C) - (B)

⑤ (E) - (D) - (B)

13 위 대화의 내용과 일치하지 않는 것은? (3점)

① 누리와 마이크는 같은 학급의 학생이다.

② 마이크는 하이킹 가는 것을 기대하고 있다.

③ 누리는 현장 학습을 미술관에 갈 것이다.

④ 미술관에서는 세 가지의 전시를 하고 있다.

⑤ 누리와 마이크는 내일 현장 학습을 간다.

14 다음 글의 내용과 일치하지 않은 것은? (3점)

> Autumn Walk in Naejangsan
>
> Last summer, I went to Naejangsan with my family. I rode a cable car to the middle of the mountain. Then, I hiked to the top. At the top, I saw beautiful autumn scenery. I took many pictures. It was amazing and exciting to see beautiful autumn leaves.

① 내장산에서 많은 사진을 찍었다.

② 산꼭대기에서 케이블카를 탔다.

③ 아름다운 단풍을 보는 것은 놀라웠다.

④ 산에서 아름다운 가을 풍경을 보았다.

⑤ 지난여름 가족과 함께 내장산에 갔다.

Incheon, ⓐ_____

Do you know ⓑ한국의 첫 기차역이 어디인지? How (A)_____ the first *Jajangmyeon*? The answer is Incheon! This place has many of Korea's firsts. (B)_____ get there, we went to Incheon Station. The *Jajangmyeon* Museum is next (C)_____ the station. We learned about the history of *Jajangmyeon* there. Later, we walked around Jayu Park, the first Western-style park in Korea. The view from the park was awesome! It was great to see the historical sites of this city from the park.

[서울 동작구 ○○중]

15 위 글의 제목으로 빈칸 ⓐ에 들어갈 말로 가장 적절한 것은? (3점)

① A City of Firsts
② A City of Jajangmyeon
③ A City of Train Stations
④ A City of Historical Sites
⑤ A City of Western-style Park

[서울 동작구 ○○중]

16 위 글의 빈칸 (A)~(C)에 들어갈 단어들로 바르게 묶인 것은? (3점)

	(A)	(B)	(C)
①	about	For	to
②	of	To	to
③	about	To	to
④	of	For	of
⑤	about	To	of

[부산 ○○중]

17 위 글을 읽고 답할 수 <u>없는</u> 질문은? (3점)

① When was Jayu Park built?
② Did they walk around Jayu Park?
③ Where is the Jajangmyeon Museum?
④ Where is the first train station in Korea?
⑤ What did the students learn from the Jajangmyeon Museum?

[서울 동작구 ○○중]

18 위 글의 글쓴이의 생각으로 알맞지 <u>않은</u> 것은? (3점)

① 박물관은 찾아가기 쉬운 위치에 있었어.
② 자장면은 역사가 있는 음식이었어.
③ 한국 전통식 공원은 놀라웠어.
④ 공원에서 보이는 경치가 훌륭했어.
⑤ 인천은 역사를 간직한 도시였어.

[서울 동작구 ○○중]

19 위 글의 밑줄 친 ⓑ의 우리말을 주어진 단어를 모두 배열하여 쓰시오. (4점)

train station / is / where / in Korea / the first

→ Do you know _____?

[서울 강동구 ○○중]

20 위 글의 학생들의 발표를 듣고 선생님이 할 말로 알맞지 <u>않은</u> 것은? (3점)

① This place sounds great!
② You have done a wonderful job!
③ Wow, I also want to go there someday.
④ Can you tell me the history of Jajangmyeon?
⑤ I'm sorry that you did not go to Incheon station.

Teacher: Good morning, everyone! How were your (A)_____ last week? Please tell us about them!

Busan, Market Heaven

Do you like traditional markets? Then go to Gukje Market in Busan. It is one of the most famous markets in Busan. ⓐDo you know what is it famous for? (B)그것은 다른 나라에서 온 다양한 제품들을 파는 것으로 유명하다. It was interesting to see all the international goods there. We also ate many kinds of street food, such as *Gimbap*, fish cake, and *Hotteok*. Then we walked to Bosu-dong Book Street. Many bookstores there sell used books. We were really excited because we found some old comic books! It was nice to relax in a café and read them.

[충북 ○○중]

21 위 글의 밑줄 친 ⓐ를 어법상 올바른 간접의문문으로 고치시오. (3점)

→ _____

[서울 동작구 ○○중]

22 위 글의 빈칸 (A)에 들어갈 말로 적절한 것은? (3점)

① field trips
② problems
③ meanings
④ classes
⑤ meals

[서울 동작구 ○○중]

23 위 글에서 글쓴이가 경험한 내용과 다른 것은? (4점)

① Gukje Market is a traditional market.
② I had some fast food on the street of the market.
③ I went from Gukje Market to Bosu-dong on foot.
④ I sold books at the bookstores in Bosu-dong.
⑤ I read comic books in a café.

[서울 동작구 ○○중]

24 위 글의 밑줄 친 (B)의 우리말을 주어진 단어들을 모두 사용하고, 다른 단어를 추가하여 영어로 옮겨 쓰시오. (4점)

variety / countries / famous / goods / different / selling

→ _____

[서울 강동구 ○○중]

25 위 글에서 가주어 it이 사용된 문장의 개수는? (3점)

① 0개 ② 1개 ③ 2개
④ 3개 ⑤ 4개

[26~30] 다음 글을 읽고 물음에 답하시오.

<Gangwon-do, Full of Natural Beauty>

There is no place like Gangwon-do for beautiful nature. First, we went to Baengnyong Cave. This 1.8-kilometer-long cave is still in good ⓐcondition. It was so amazing to see its ⓑnatural beauty. Near the end of our cave tour, the guide ⓒturned off the lights in the cave for a minute. Everything became very dark, so we _____ focus on the sounds there. It was the most amazing experience of the tour! Our next stop was Donggang. We went rafting! It was exciting to ride on the ⓓrough water and enjoy the ⓔview at the same time.

[경기 ○○중]

26 위 글의 빈칸에 들어갈 말로 적절한 것은? (3점)

① able
② are able
③ are able to
④ were able
⑤ were able to

[전북 ○○중]

27 위 글을 읽고 답할 수 없는 질문은? (3점)

① Is Gangwon-do a good place for travel?
② How long is Baengyong Cave?
③ Why did the guide turn off the lights?
④ Was the rafting exciting?
⑤ How long did it take to finish rafting?

[서울 강북구 ○○중]

28 위 글의 ⓐ~ⓔ 중, 어휘의 의미가 문맥상 어색하게 해석된 것은? (3점)

① ⓐ : 상태
② ⓑ : 자연의
③ ⓒ : 껐다
④ ⓓ : 거친
⑤ ⓔ : 견해

[부산 ○○중]

29 위 글의 내용과 일치하지 않는 것은? (3점)

① The students had a Baengnyong Cave tour.
② Baengnyong Cave is the longest cave in Korea.
③ Gangwon-do is famous for its beautiful nature.
④ The students rode on the rough water in Donggang.
⑤ The students went to Baengnyong Cave and Donggang in Gangwon-do.

[서울 강북구 ○○중]

30 위 글을 읽고 다음 주어진 질문을 조건에 맞춰 영어로 답하시오. (4점)

질문
What was the most amazing experiences of the tour?

조건
• '동굴', '소리' 2단어를 모두 넣을 것.
• 완전한 문장으로 답을 작성할 것.

→ _____

◎ 선택형 문항의 답안은 컴퓨터용 수정 싸인펜을 사용하여 OMR 답안지에 바르게 표기하시오.
◎ 서술형 문제는 답을 답안지에 반드시 검정 볼펜으로 쓰시오.
◎ 총 30문항 100점 만점입니다. 문항별 배점은 각 문항에 표시되어 있습니다.

[울산 ○○중]
01 다음 영영풀이에 해당하는 단어는? (4점)

the ability to think of or create something new

① career ② strength
③ creativity ④ emotion
⑤ reason

[서울 성북구 ○○중]
02 다음 빈칸에 단어 'reduce'가 들어가기에 가장 자연스럽지 않은 문장은? (3점)

① Mike, _____ speed now.
② Crying helps _____ stress.
③ I have to _____ for the test.
④ They tried to _____ food waste.
⑤ What can I do to _____ pollution?

[서울 관악구 ○○중]
03 다음 빈칸에 알맞은 말끼리 짝지은 것은? (3점)

• Once upon a time, there _____ a crow with black feathers.
• I have never _____ such a white bird before.

① are - seen
② is - saw
③ was - see
④ was - seen
⑤ was - saw

[서울 관악구 ○○중]
04 다음 대화의 흐름상 빈칸에 가장 적절한 말은? (3점)

A: I want to be a music producer. What should I do?
B: I think that you should _____.

① play soccer a lot
② take a walk every day
③ draw a lot of pictures
④ take pictures of animals
⑤ listen to many kinds of music

[서울 성북구 ○○중]
05 다음 중 어법상 옳은 문장은? (3점)

① I want go there.
② Do you want tall?
③ They want to money.
④ Jake wants you have the ball.
⑤ Kate wants me to help her.

[경북 ○○중]
06 다음 문장의 빈칸에 가장 알맞은 것은? (3점)

If _____, you will miss the train.

① you will hurry
② you don't hurry
③ don't you hurry
④ will not you hurry
⑤ you will not hurry

G: Hello, Mr. Watson! Thank you for doing this interview.

M: (a)_____

(A) I want to be a(n) (가)_____ like you. What do I need to do?

(B) What else do I need to do?

(C) This interview is for students who want to be a(n) (가)_____. Can you tell me about your job?

(D) Sure. You may see pictures of food in books or on TV. A(n) (가)_____ decorates food to look good for pictures or movies.

(E) You need to learn about many kinds of food.

M: You need to study art, too. Creativity is important.

G: All right! Thank you for your time, Mr. Watson.

07 위 대화의 빈칸 (a)에 들어갈 말로 적절치 <u>않은</u> 것은? (3점)

① You're welcome.

② Sure, no problem.

③ Don't mention it.

④ Not at all.

⑤ Of course.

08 위 대화의 빈칸 (가)에 들어갈 직업으로 가장 적절한 것은? (3점)

① cook   ② artist

③ teacher   ④ photographer

⑤ food stylist

09 위 대화의 (A)~(E)를 가장 자연스럽게 이어지도록 배열한 것은? (4점)

① (A)-(C)-(B)-(D)-(E)

② (A)-(E)-(B)-(C)-(D)

③ (C)-(E)-(A)-(D)-(B)

④ (C)-(D)-(A)-(E)-(B)

⑤ (E)-(B)-(D)-(A)-(C)

10 다음 중 대화가 <u>어색한</u> 것은? (3점)

① A: How often do you play the guitar a week?
B: Almost every day.

② A: How do you get to school from your house?
B: I usually walk to school.

③ A: What do I need to do to be a counselor?
B: You need to be creative and learn about math.

④ A: How do you spend on your free time?
B: I watch old movies downloaded to my computer.

⑤ A: What are you going to do for school talent show?
B: Well, I didn't decide yet.

[11~13] 다음 대화를 읽고 물음에 답하시오.

B: Mom, I need to fill out this form for tomorrow's career counseling program. Could you help me?

M: Sure. Let me see. You already wrote your dream job and hobby.

B: Yes, I want to be a P.E. teacher, and my hobby is watching sports games. But writing my strengths is hard. _____

M: Well, I think you have lots of strengths. First of all, you are good at playing baseball, aren't you?

B: Oh, yes. I'm good at playing baseball.

M: And you have many other strengths.

B: You're right. I also work well with other people. And I'm good at listening to people.

M: Right! You're good at so many things.

B: Thanks, Mom.

*B: Boy, M: Mom

12 위 대화의 빈칸에 알맞은 것은? (3점)

① Are you good?

② Am I good at?

③ Are you good at?

④ What am I good at?

⑤ What are you good at?

13 위 대화의 주제로 가장 적절한 것은? (3점)

① 소년의 장점

② 소년의 단점

③ 소년의 취미

④ 소년의 장래 희망

⑤ 소년의 직업 상담 프로그램

14 다음 중 어법상 어색한 것은? (3점)

① If you want to save me, throw a rope down to me.

② I will go shopping if it won't snow tomorrow.

③ We will open the door if you show us your hand.

④ If you don't hurry, you'll miss the train.

⑤ If I don't answer my phone, call my sister.

11 위 대화의 아들에 대한 설명으로 가장 알맞은 것은? (4점)

① 직업 상담 프로그램을 만들어야 한다.

② 장래 희망을 정하지 못했다.

③ 농구를 잘한다.

④ 청력이 좋은 편이다.

⑤ 자신에게 강점이 있다는 것을 깨달았다.

15 다음 글의 앞에 올 내용으로 가장 적절한 것은? (3점)

Look at the pictures above. Do these ideas surprise you? You can see that our lives will be very different in the future. As our lives change, many new jobs will appear. What kind of job do you want? What will your future life be like? The following people looked ahead and chose jobs that will be important in the future.

① Lives of the Future
② Jobs of the Past
③ Cities of the Future
④ Schools of the Future
⑤ Interesting Jobs Around Us

17 다음 글의 내용과 일치하지 <u>않는</u> 것은? (4점)

Have you ever heard of *miniature figure painters? They paint plastic models of movie or animation characters. Jack, a miniature figure painter, works for a company that produces the figures that he paints.

Jack has always loved painting. His childhood hobby was figure painting. As he got older, he took pictures of the miniature figures that he painted and put them on his blog. He really enjoyed painting them, and he got better and better at it. People loved his work and he got many fans. Finally, a miniature figure company saw his blog and offered him his current job!

It's amazing how a hobby can turn into a job opportunity! If you want to become a miniature figure painter, you should be passionate about painting.

*miniature figure: 정밀 모형

① Jack's current job is a miniature figure painter.
② People liked the works that Jack put on his blog.
③ In Jack's case, his hobby has changed into a career.
④ After Jack got a job, he started posting his works on his blog.
⑤ We should be passionate about painting to become a miniature figure painter.

16 다음 두 문장이 같도록 to부정사를 이용하여 문장을 완성하시오. (4점)

· He told us that we should get some rest.
  = He advised _____.

[18~19] 다음 글을 읽고 물음에 답하시오.

Today, I'll talk about my job. ⓐMy name is Sujin Kim and I am a computer programmer. I work at a software company. I develop new software for computers there. ⓑI work with many people from different countries. ⓒI chose this job because I'm interested in math and science. ⓓReading makes your writing better. ⓔTo become a computer programmer, I studied computer science and developed my problem-solving skills.

18 위 글의 내용과 일치하는 것으로 가장 옳은 것은? (3점)

① 수진은 컴퓨터 게임 프로그래머이다.

② 수진은 컴퓨터 게임을 개발하는 회사에 다닌다.

③ 수진은 다국적 출신의 사람들과 함께 일을 한다.

④ 수진은 현재 직업을 갖고 난 후에 수학에 관심이 생겼다.

⑤ 수진은 문제 해결 능력을 지금도 계속 개발하는 중이다.

19 위 글의 ⓐ~ⓔ 중 흐름상 어색한 문장은? (3점)

① ⓐ 　　② ⓑ 　　③ ⓒ

④ ⓓ 　　⑤ ⓔ

20 다음 글에 바로 이어질 내용으로 가장 알맞은 것은? (4점)

You can see that our lives will be very different in the future. As our lives change, many new jobs will appear. What kind of job do you want? What will your future life be like? The following people looked ahead and chose jobs that will be important in the future.

① 미래의 다양한 직업

② 변화된 미래의 생활

③ 미래의 유망 직종

④ 미래에 다가올 로봇의 변화

⑤ 장래의 유망한 직업을 찾은 사람들

[21~25] 다음 글을 읽고 물음에 답하시오.

(가) Do you see the flower pot (A)_____ Sujin made? It was made from old street flags. She is an upcycling designer. She works with waste materials to make new products. Her products show people that old materials can be useful in new ways. Upcycling can reduce the amount (B)_____ waste in the future. To become an upcycling designer, you should be creative and learn about art.

(나) Have you ever heard of 3D modelers? Taeho, a 3D modeler, works for a company that makes artificial hands and legs. Taeho uses special software to print out new hands and legs. They (C)_____ specially for patients. If you are good at computer programming and art, you can be a 3D modeler.

21 위 글의 빈칸 (A)~(C)에 들어갈 말이 바르게 짝지어진 것은?
(4점)

	(A)	(B)	(C)
①	that	for	made
②	who	of	made
③	who	for	are made
④	who	for	made
⑤	that	of	are made

22 위 글의 (A)와 (B) 두 단락에 공통으로 들어 있는 각 직업에 대한 내용은?
(3점)

① 소개, 필요한 능력

② 소개, 인기도

③ 이름, 연봉

④ 필요한 역량, 취업률

⑤ 이름, 관련 취미 활동

23 위 글의 내용과 일치하는 것은?
(3점)

① Sujin은 패션 디자이너이고, Taeho는 모델이다.

② Sujin은 헌 옷을 가지고 화분을 만들었다.

③ 업사이클링 디자이너가 되려면 미술을 배워야 한다.

④ 인조 손, 다리는 건강한 사람들을 위해 만들어진다.

⑤ 3D 모형 제작자가 되려면 인내심이 있어야 한다.

24 위 글을 읽고 답할 수 없는 질문은?
(3점)

① What is Sujin's job?

② Why does Sujin use new materials?

③ How can upcycling help the environment?

④ What did Sujin use to make the flower pot?

⑤ What does Sujin use to make new products?

25 위 글에서 upcycling designer가 되기 위해 필요한 두 가지를 찾아 우리말로 쓰시오.
(5점)

(1) _____

(2) _____

[26~30] 다음 글을 읽고 물음에 답하시오.

Have you ever heard of 3D modelers? Taeho, a 3D modeler, works for a company that makes artificial hands and legs. Taeho uses special software to print out new hands and legs. They are made specially for patients. **(A)**[If / Before] you are good at computer programming and art, you can be a 3D modeler. Taeho wants more people to use 3D printed products in the future.

Jihye is a big data specialist. She works on many projects. **(B)**[For example / However], last year, she made bus routes. To find the best night routes, she needed to collect smartphone use data and taxi use patterns from late-night travelers. Then she analyzed this information to create the most useful routes. Now Jihye is working with an online shopping mall **(C)**[find / to find] out the best styles for them. She knows big data allows us to learn more about our daily lives. If you want to become a big data specialist, you should develop your math and problem-solving skills!

26 위 글의 (A)~(C)에 들어갈 말이 알맞게 짝지어진 것은? (3점)

	(A)	(B)	(C)
①	If	For example	to find
②	If	However	find
③	Before	For example	to find
④	Before	For example	find
⑤	Before	However	to find

28 위 글의 빅데이터 전문가가 하는 일의 핵심은? (3점)

① to draw the best bus routes

② to collect and analyze a lot of data

③ to create an online shopping mall

④ to find out the best styles for people

⑤ to learn more about our daily lives

29 What do you need to become a big data specialist? (3점)

① 창의력, 미적 감각

② 프로그래밍 기술, 미술

③ 정보통신 기술, 창의력

④ 계산 능력, 의사소통 능력

⑤ 수학 능력, 문제 해결 능력

27 위 글의 내용으로 보아 Taeho가 본인의 시점에서 자신에 관해 한 말로 가장 적절하지 않은 것은? (4점)

① My company makes artificial hands and legs for patients.

② I am a 3D modeler who uses 3D printers to make artificial body parts.

③ Before choosing my job, I thought about the changes in the future.

④ In order to print out artificial hands and legs, I use special software.

⑤ I hope people use 3D printing machines more often because they are amazing at making things.

30 위 글을 읽고 답할 수 없는 질문은? (3점)

① What did Jihye make last year?

② What kind of company does Taeho work for?

③ What 3D printed products do people use the most?

④ What skills are needed to be a big data specialist?

⑤ What does Taeho use to print out new hands and legs?

반		점수	
이름			

문항수 : 선택형(27문항) 서술형(3문항)　　20 ． ． ．

◎ 선택형 문항의 답안은 컴퓨터용 수정 싸인펜을 사용하여 OMR 답안지에 바르게 표기하시오.
◎ 서술형 문제는 답을 답안지에 반드시 검정 볼펜으로 쓰시오.
◎ 총 30문항 100점 만점입니다. 문항별 배점은 각 문항에 표시되어 있습니다.

[서울 관악구 ○○중]

01 다음 밑줄 친 말과 반대의 의미를 가진 단어는?　　(4점)

> Scientists made <u>artificial</u> skin a long time ago.

① dark　　　② useful

③ creative　　④ colorful

⑤ natural

[서울 관악구 ○○중]

02 다음 빈칸에 가장 알맞은 말은?　　(2점)

> Please allow me _____ into the town.
> 제가 마을로 들어가는 것을 허락해 주세요.

① go

② going

③ to go

④ had gone

⑤ having gone

[경북 ○○중]

03 다음 중 어법상 가장 <u>어색한</u> 문장은?　　(3점)

① My mother allowed me to watch TV.

② The boy made the woman to go first.

③ What do you want me to do for you?

④ The father told his daughter to do her homework.

⑤ The son asked his mom to give him more pocket money.

[인천 ○○중]

04 다음 빈칸에 들어갈 알맞은 말은?　　(3점)

> _____ designs and creates a theme park and attractions. They choose the theme of the park and the colors, lights, and special effects of the attractions.

① An architect

② An investigator

③ A pet food taster

④ A theme park designer

⑤ A personal brand consultant

[서울 성북구 ○○중]

05 다음 대화의 빈칸에 들어갈 말로 가장 적절한 것은?　　(3점)

> A: I am a food stylist.
> B: I want to be a food stylist like you. What do I need to do?
> A: _____

① You need to read books about science.

② You like to see pictures of food in books.

③ You need to learn about many kinds of food.

④ You need to develop your problem–solving skills.

⑤ You like to decorate food to look good for pictures or movies.

06 다음 대화의 내용과 일치하지 <u>않는</u> 것은? (4점)

> Sue: Thank you for doing this interview.
> Tom: No problem.
> Sue: This interview is for students who want to be food stylists. Can you tell me about your job?
> Tom: Sure. You may see pictures of food in books or on TV. A food stylist decorates food to look good for pictures or movies.
> Sue: I want to be a food stylist like you. What do I need to do?
> Tom: You need to learn about many kinds of food.
> Sue: What else do I need to do?
> Tom: You need to study art, too. Creativity is important.
> Sue: All right! Thank you for your time.

① Sue wishes to be a food stylist.

② Tom explains about a food stylist.

③ A food stylist makes food delicious.

④ Creativity is needed to become a food stylist.

⑤ This interview helps students understand about food stylists.

[7~8] 다음 대화를 읽고 물음에 답하시오.

> Jenny: Congratulations on winning the first place at the speech contest. I liked the topic of your speech.
> Jason: Thank you. I hope it made you think about the environment more.
> Jenny: It really did. I want to help protect the environment just like you. (A)_____
> Jason: You don't have to be a super hero to help the environment. You can start by taking the stairs instead of the elevator.
> Jenny: That's a good idea.
> Jason: You could also start carrying around your own cup. So you don't have to use paper cups.
> Jenny: Wow! Simple actions can really save the environment! Thank you for your advice.

07 위 대화를 통해 알 수 있는 사실들로만 짝지은 것은? (4점)

> ⓐ Jason participated in the speech contest.
> ⓑ Jason offers his opinion about recycling paper.
> ⓒ After the conversation, Jenny won't use paper cups.
> ⓓ Jason has given Jenny a piece of advice on protecting the environment.
> ⓔ Jenny is asking Jason for some advice on writing an eco-travel essay.
> ⓕ In order to protect the environment, you need to make a big effort and take big actions.

① ⓐ, ⓓ   ② ⓑ, ⓓ

③ ⓒ, ⓔ   ④ ⓓ, ⓕ

⑤ ⓔ, ⓕ

08 위 대화의 빈칸 (A)에 들어갈 말로 가장 적절한 것은? (3점)

① What do I need to do?

② What can you be planning?

③ Can I become a super hero?

④ What do you think about this?

⑤ What are you planning to ride?

10 Which is not correct about the conversation above? (3점)

① Jason은 가끔 글을 쓴다.

② Jason의 장래 희망은 작가이다.

③ Jason은 글쓰기 능력을 향상하기 위해 노력한다.

④ 상대방은 Jason의 조언을 긍정적으로 받아들이고 있다.

⑤ Jason은 글을 잘 쓰기 위해 책을 많이 읽어야 한다고 생각한다.

[9~10] 다음 대화를 읽고 물음에 답하시오.

> A: Jason, I read your paper. It was so amazing!
> B: Thank you for saying that. I'm trying hard to improve my writing skills. I want to be a writer someday.
> A: Really? I want to write well like you. What do I need to do?
> B: You need to read a lot of books. Reading makes your writing better.
> A: What else do I need to do?
> B: Well, I write almost every day. (A)How about starting keeping a diary?
> A: Thank you for your advice. I'll start today.

09 위 대화의 밑줄 친 (A)와 바꿔 쓸 수 있는 말은? (3점)

① Don't start keeping a diary.

② What about starting telling a diary?

③ You shouldn't start to keep a dairy.

④ Why don't you start keeping a diary?

⑤ You don't have to start keeping a diary.

[11~12] 다음 대화를 읽고 물음에 답하시오.

> Brian : Mom, I need to fill out this form for tomorrow's career counseling program. Could you help me?
> Mom : Sure. Let me see. You already wrote your dream job and hobby.
> Brian : Yes, I want to be a P.E. teacher, and my hobby is to watch sports games. But (A)저의 장점들을 쓰는 것이 어려워요. What am I good at?
> Mom : Well, I think you have lots of strengths. First of all, you are good at playing baseball, aren't you?
> Brian : Oh, yes. I'm good at playing baseball.
> Mom : And you have many other strengths.
> Brian : You're right. I also work well with other people. And I'm good at listening to people.
> Mom : Right! You're good at so many things.
> Brian : Thanks, Mom.

11 위 대화의 Brian에 대한 설명으로 바르지 <u>않은</u> 것은?　(3점)

① He is a good listener.

② He plays baseball well.

③ He enjoys watching sports games.

④ He works well with other people.

⑤ He is strong enough to do many things.

12 위 대화의 밑줄 친 (A)의 우리말을 가주어 it을 사용하여 영작하시오.　(4점)

→ _____

13 다음 대화의 빈칸에 차례로 들어갈 가장 알맞은 말은?　(3점)

B: Jessica, what are you going to do for the school talent show?

G: I didn't decide yet. What am I good at?

B: You're good at dancing, aren't you?

G: Not really. But I think I'm good at (A)_____. I like (B)_____ very much.

B: Really? Actually, I'm planning to play rock music with my band. Why don't you (C)_____ for us?

G: Sure, I'd love to.

*B: Boy, G: Girl

	(A)	(B)	(C)
①	songs	to sing	singing
②	sing	singing	to sing
③	sing	to sing	sing
④	singing	to sing	to sing
⑤	singing	singing	sing

14 다음 Job Opening에 관한 안내문의 내용과 일치하는 것은?　(4점)

Job: Personal Brand Consultant

What this person does:
- Create a personal brand for the customers.
- Find the customer's unique strengths.
  (customer's personality, knowledge, and skills)

You need to:
- Have great communication skills.

More information
- Call to 888-8888.

To apply this job:
- Send an Email to Yokgok@ms.kr by December 15th.

① 기업 브랜드 상담가를 구하고 있다.

② 고객의 고민을 해결해 주는 직업이다.

③ 고객의 성격, 지식, 직장 경력을 바탕으로 채용한다.

④ 높은 의사소통 능력을 요구한다.

⑤ 12월 15일까지 전화하여 지원해야 한다.

15 다음 밑줄 친 ⓐ~ⓔ 중 어법상 올바른 것의 개수는? (4점)

Hello, everyone. My name is Doona Kim. ⓐI'm exciting to tell you about my job. I am a computer programmer, and I ⓑwork to a software company. I develop new software for computers there. I ⓒwork with many people ⓓfrom different countries. I chose this job because ⓔI am interested with math and science. To become a computer programmer, I studied computer science and developed my problem-solving skills.

① 1개   ② 2개   ③ 3개
④ 4개   ⑤ 5개

[16~17] 다음 글을 읽고 물음에 답하시오.

Hootak is an upcycling designer. ⓐHe works with waste materials to make new products. ⓑHis products show people that old materials can be (A)_____ in new ways. ⓒThey are made specially for patients. ⓓUpcycling can (B)_____ the amount of waste in the future. ⓔHootak wants more people to know about upcycling. To become an upcycling designer, you should be creative and learn about art.

16 위 글의 (A), (B)에 들어갈 말이 바르게 짝지어진 것은? (4점)

	(A)	(B)
①	use	reduce
②	useful	reduce
③	used	be reduced
④	useful	be reduced
⑤	used	be reducing

17 위 글에서 전체 흐름과 관계없는 문장은? (3점)

① ⓐ   ② ⓑ   ③ ⓒ
④ ⓓ   ⑤ ⓔ

[18~21] 다음 글을 읽고 물음에 답하시오.

- Self-driving cars will be ⓐ시장에 나와 있는.
- People will have robots that do everything for them.
- 3D printers in every home will ⓑ출력하다 almost everything.
- People will live under the sea or in ⓒ수상도시들.
- People will take ⓓ우주여행들.

Do the ideas above surprise you? You can see that our lives will be very different in the future. (A)As our lives change, many new jobs will appear. What kind of job do you want? What will your future life be like? The following people ⓔ앞을 내다보았다 and chose jobs that will be important in the future. Let's read about their jobs!

18 위 글의 ⓐ~ⓔ의 뜻에 대응되는 어구로 바르게 연결되지 않은 것은? (3점)

① ⓐ: on the market
② ⓑ: print out
③ ⓒ: floating cities
④ ⓓ: space trips
⑤ ⓔ: looked back

19 위 글의 밑줄 친 (A)와 문장 내에서 같은 뜻으로 쓰인 것은?

(4점)

① I listen to music <u>as</u> I'm studying.

② <u>As</u> I like him, I'll go there with him.

③ <u>As</u> it was too cold, they stayed home.

④ <u>As</u> she grows up, she learns more about life.

⑤ <u>As</u> they watched the movie, they heard a strange sound.

20 위 글의 내용과 일치하지 <u>않는</u> 것은? (3점)

① 미래에는 로봇이 사용될 것이다.

② 가정에서 3D 프린터를 사용하는 모습을 볼 수 있을 것이다.

③ 사람들은 바다 속에서 살 것이다.

④ 우리의 삶은 미래에 매우 다를 것이다.

⑤ 우리 삶이 바뀌면서 많은 직업들이 사라질 것이다.

21 위 글의 다음에 나올 내용으로 가장 적절한 것은? (3점)

① Jobs that the robots will have

② Ways to make self-driving cars

③ People who went to other planets

④ Jobs that will be important in the future

⑤ People who changed their jobs for the future

Do you see the flower pot that Sujin made? It was made from old street flags. She is an upcycling designer. She works with waste materials to make new products. Her products show people that old materials can be used in new ways. (A)업사이클링은 미래에 쓰레기의 양을 줄일 수 있다. To become an upcycling designer, you should be creative and learn about art.

Have you ever heard of 3D modelers? Taeho, a 3D modeler, works for a company that makes artificial hands and legs. Taeho uses special software to print out new hands and legs. They are made specially for patients. If you are good at computer programming and art, you can be a 3D modeler. (B)태호는 더 많은 사람들이 3D 프린터로 출력된 제품들을 미래에 사용하기를 원한다.

22 위 글을 읽고 답할 수 <u>없는</u> 질문은? (4점)

① From what did Sujin make the flower pot?

② What do Sujin's products show people?

③ What kind of company does Taeho work for?

④ How can upcycling help the environment?

⑤ Why should we use 3D printers?

23 위 글을 읽고 옳은 것만 고른 것은? (4점)

> ⓐ Sujin works with waste materials to make new products.
> ⓑ To become an upcycling designer, you should learn about the computer programming.
> ⓒ The software that Taeho uses was made specially for old people.
> ⓓ If you are good at computer programming and art, you can be a 3D modeler.

① ⓐ, ⓑ
② ⓐ, ⓓ
③ ⓑ, ⓒ
④ ⓑ, ⓓ
⑤ ⓒ, ⓓ

24 위 글의 (A)의 우리말을 〈보기〉에 주어진 말을 바르게 배열하여 영어로 옮기시오. (3점)

> 보기
>
> reduce / in the future / upcycling / waste / can / the amount of

업사이클링은 미래에 쓰레기의 양을 줄일 수 있다.

→ _____

25 위 글의 (B)의 우리말을 영어로 옮기시오. 〈보기〉에 주어진 말은 모두 쓰되, 다른 말을 추가하여 쓰시오. (3점)

> 보기
>
> more people / 3D printed products

태호는 더 많은 사람들이 3D 프린터로 출력된 제품들을 미래에 사용하기를 원한다.

→ Taeho wants _____ .

[26~30] 다음 글을 읽고 물음에 답하시오.

Do you see the flower pot (A)that Sujin made? It (가)_____ old street flags. She is an upcycling designer. She works with waste materials (B)to make new products. Her products show people (C)that old materials can be useful in new ways.

Upcycling can ⓐreduce the amount of waste in the future. To become an upcycling designer, you should be ⓑcreative and learn about art.

Jihye is a big data ⓒspecialist. She works on many projects. For example, last year, she made bus routes. (D)To find the best night routes, she needed to collect smartphone use data and taxi use patterns from late-night travelers. Then she ⓓ analyzed this information to create the (E)useful routes. Now Jihye is working with an online shopping mall. She is collecting data from ⓔ customers to find out the best styles for them. She knows (F)_____ big data allows us (G)learn more about our daily lives. If you want to become a big data specialist, you should develop your math and problem-solving skills!

Think about yourself and prepare for your future. (나)Your future will be bright if you keep looking ahead and dreaming big.

26 위 글의 빈칸 (가)에 들어갈 가장 알맞은 형태는? (3점)

① made of
② is made to
③ makes from
④ was made from
⑤ was made into

27 위 글의 밑줄 친 @~ⓔ 중 단어의 뜻이 바르게 연결되지 <u>않은</u> 것은? (2점)

① @: 줄이다
② ⓑ: 인공적인
③ ⓒ: 전문가
④ ⓓ: 분석했다
⑤ ⓔ: 고객

29 위 글의 (A)~(G)에 대한 설명으로 옳은 것을 <u>모두</u> 고른 것은? (4점)

> ㉠ (A)는 생략 가능하며 which로 바꿔 쓸 수 있다.
> ㉡ (B), (D)는 모두 '~하기 위해서'로 해석한다.
> ㉢ (C)는 people을 꾸며주는 관계대명사이다.
> ㉣ (E)의 최상급은 usefulest이다.
> ㉤ (F)에는 관계대명사 that이 생략되어 있다.
> ㉥ (G)는 learning으로 바꿔야 한다.

① ㉠, ㉡
② ㉠, ㉤
③ ㉡, ㉢, ㉣
④ ㉢, ㉤, ㉥
⑤ ㉢, ㉣, ㉤, ㉥

28 위 글의 밑줄 친 문장 (나)의 if와 그 쓰임과 의미가 같은 것은? (3점)

① I am wondering if it will rain tonight.
② Do you know if the library is still open?
③ Can you tell me the right answer if I'm wrong?
④ You should figure out if he is telling the truth.
⑤ I'm not sure if I can wake up at six tomorrow.

30 위 글의 내용과 일치하지 <u>않는</u> 것은? (4점)

① 지혜는 버스 노선을 만들었다.
② 업사이클링은 환경에 도움이 된다.
③ 수진이는 오래된 깃발을 사용하여 화분을 만들었다.
④ 지혜는 소비자들에게 맞는 스타일을 찾기 위해 데이터를 수집한다.
⑤ 빅데이터 전문가가 되기 위해서 수학적 능력과 미적 감각을 키워야 한다.

2학년 영어 2학기 기말고사(8과) 1회

문항수 : 선택형(25문항) 서술형(5문항) | 20 . . .

◎ 선택형 문항의 답안은 컴퓨터용 수정 싸인펜을 사용하여 OMR 답안지에 바르게 표기하시오.

◎ 서술형 문제는 답을 답안지에 반드시 검정 볼펜으로 쓰시오.

◎ 총 30문항 100점 만점입니다. 문항별 배점은 각 문항에 표시되어 있습니다.

[대구 ○○중]

01 다음 중 두 단어의 관계가 나머지 넷과 <u>다른</u> 것은?　(3점)

① freedom : free

② beauty : beautiful

③ happiness : happy

④ appearance : appear

⑤ impression : impressive

[경북 ○○중]

02 다음은 각 영영풀이에 알맞은 단어를 빈칸으로 표시한 것이다. 모형 '♥' 안에 들어갈 알파벳을 순서대로 배열한 것은?　(4점)

♥ _ _ _ _ _	a light and soft thing that covers a bird's body
_ _ _ _ ♥ _ _	to say what will happen in the future
_ _ _ ♥	a box made to hold birds or animals
_ ♥ _ _ _	a large area of fresh water, surrounded by land
♥ _ _ _ _ _ _ _	a person in charge of something

① force

② field

③ ocean

④ owner

⑤ house

[대구 ○○중]

03 다음 대화가 가장 <u>어색한</u> 것은?　(3점)

① A: I'd like to pay by credit card.

　B: Sorry. We take cash only.

② A: Do we discuss in groups or in pairs?

　B: Please do it in Paris with your partner.

③ A: I decided to join the Summer English camp.

　B: Did you already sign up for it?

④ A: I want to withdraw some money.

　B: I'd rather put the money in my bank account.

⑤ A: I want to get a full refund.

　B: Go to the customer service center with the receipt.

The crow then visited the peacock at the zoo. There were a lot of people around the peacock, and ⓐthey praised him for his beauty. The crow thought ⓑthe peacock must be the happiest bird in the world. After all the people left, the crow started **(a)**to talk to the peacock. "Peacock, nice **(b)**to see you. You are so beautiful. Many people come **(c)**to see you every day. On the other hand, when people see me, they chase me away. I think you are the happiest bird in the world." The peacock said, "I may be the most beautiful bird, but I'm not happy. Because of my beauty, I am stuck in this zoo. ⓒLike me, you aren't kept in a cage. I want **(d)**to be like you because you can go anywhere."

After the crow talked **(e)**to the peacock, ⓓhe started to think about **(A)**[the / bird / happiest / who / was]. The crow thought to himself, "The peacock's feathers are impressive, but he sticks in a cage. I don't have colorful feathers, but ⓔI'm free to fly anywhere." The crow went back to the forest. He looked at him in the water again and saw the happiest bird in the world.

04 위 글의 (A)의 단어들을 바르게 배열하시오. (3점)

→ _____

05 위 글에서 어색한 부분 2곳을 찾아 바르게 고치시오. (6점)

(1) _____ → _____

(2) _____ → _____

06 위 글의 ⓐ~ⓔ 중 흐름상 가장 어색한 문장은? (3점)

① ⓐ   ② ⓑ   ③ ⓒ
④ ⓓ   ⑤ ⓔ

07 Which is true according to the text? (3점)

① The peacock lived in the forest.

② The peacock wants to be like the crow because the crow is black.

③ Many people come to the zoo to see the crow.

④ Because of his beauty, the peacock was kept in the zoo and he was not happy.

⑤ The crow looked at himself in the water again and was not happy with his appearance.

08 위 글의 밑줄 친 to의 용법 중 그 쓰임이 같은 것끼리 묶은 것은? (3점)

① (a), (c)   ② (a), (d)
③ (c), (d)   ④ (b), (e)
⑤ (d), (e)

09 Which is <u>incorrect</u> according to the passage above? (3점)

① The crow can go anywhere freely.

② The people praised the peacock's beauty.

③ The peacock said he wanted to be like the crow.

④ The peacock was satisfied with people's attention.

⑤ The crow was envious of the peacock's appearance at first.

[11~13] 다음 글을 읽고 물음에 답하시오.

Then one day, the crow saw a swan on the lake. "The swan is so white," he thought, "but I am so black. I (A)<u>have never seen</u> such a white bird before. His beauty shines so brightly. The swan must be the happiest bird in the world." He went to the swan and expressed his thoughts. "Actually," the swan said, "I thought that I was the happiest bird. But then I saw a parrot. Now I think the parrot is the happiest bird in the world." The crow asked (B)<u>왜 그가 그렇게 생각했는지를</u>. The swan answered, "The parrot has colorful feathers. He is more beautiful than I am. He must be proud of his appearance."

11 위 글의 밑줄 친 (A)와 쓰임이 <u>다른</u> 것은? (3점)

① Amy <u>has visited</u> Jeonju Hanok Village before.

② I <u>have heard</u> the song twice.

③ <u>Have</u> you ever <u>seen</u> the actor?

④ She <u>has searched</u> for him for 5 days.

⑤ Cheolsoo <u>has</u> never <u>caught</u> a fish.

10 위 글의 peacock의 생각과 일치하는 것은? (3점)

① Beauty brings luck and happiness to everyone.

② 'Being beautiful' just means you can live a happier life.

③ Being loved by other people is important for building confidence and power.

④ Happiness depends on freedom. Being stuck in a place which I don't want to be in is awful.

⑤ The color of our skin and hair is an important factor. People prefer a lighter skin and brighter hair color.

12 위 글의 밑줄 친 (B)를 알맞게 영작한 것은? (3점)

① why he thought so

② why he thinks so

③ why does he think so

④ why did he think so

⑤ why he so thinks

13 Why did the crow think the swan was the happiest bird?

(3점)

① Because the swan was healthy.

② Because the swan was so white.

③ Because the swan had colorful feathers.

④ Because the swan had beautiful legs.

⑤ Because the swan was wiser than the crow.

14 다음 글을 읽고 (A), (B)에 들어갈 단어로 알맞은 것은? (4점)

Dear Advisor,

I am a second year middle school student. These days, everyone around me looks happy on social media. For example, my cousin Jessie posts a lot of selfies. I guess she can enjoy taking selfies because she is pretty. My friend Toby has a rich father. He usually posts pictures of his new toys. They look expensive. I think their lives are full of happiness. I can't find anything special about my life. Help me, please.

Unhappy Girl

Dear Unhappy Girl,

A lot of people feel the same way. Here are some things you can do to feel better. First, remember that many people post only the good things that happen in their lives. They don't talk about the sad things that happen much. Everyone has ups and downs in his or her own life. So try not to envy other people's lives too much. Second, look for your own true happiness. Think about anything that brings you joy in your everyday life and write it down. It can be your loving family, friends, your dreams, and even hobbies. You will find that happiness is already in your heart!

<Problem>

An unhappy girl is a second year middle student. She thinks everyone around her looks happy on social media. Also, she thinks their lives are always happy. But she can't find (A)_____ about her life. So she needs a help from the advisor.

↓

<Solution>

The advisor suggests she should try not to (B)_____ other people's lives too much. Also she should always think her joy in her everyday life and write it down.

	(A)	(B)
①	happiness	- be proud of
②	dream	- predict
③	happiness	- envy
④	life	- be free from
⑤	dream	- do her work

[15~16] 다음 글을 읽고 물음에 답하시오.

After the crow talked to the peacock, ⓐhe started to think about who was the happiest bird. ⓑThe crow thought to himself, ⓒ"The peacock's feathers are impressive, but he is stuck in a cage. I don't have colorful feathers, ⓓbut I'm free to flying anywhere." ⓔThe crow went back to the forest. He found out that he was the happiest bird in the world.

15 위 글의 밑줄 친 ⓐ~ⓔ 중 어법상 옳은 문장의 개수는? (4점)

① 1개   ② 2개   ③ 3개

④ 4개   ⑤ 5개

16 What is the best appropriate lesson of this story? (3점)

① No pain, no gain.

② Life is short, but art is long.

③ The difficulty in life is the choice.

④ Comparing myself to others is stupid.

⑤ A bad workman finds fault with his tools.

17 다음 글의 내용에 가장 잘 어울리는 옛 속담은? (3점)

> The crow then flew to the parrot and said, "The swan said you are the happiest bird because you have colorful feathers." The parrot explained, "I lived a very happy life until I saw a peacock. My feathers are colorful, but the peacock's feathers are colorful, big, and gorgeous,"

① 백지장도 맞들면 낫다.

② 남의 떡이 더 커 보인다.

③ 고래 싸움에 새우 등 터진다.

④ 황소 뒷걸음치다가 쥐 잡는다.

⑤ 호미로 막을 것을 가래로 막는다.

[18~24] 다음 글을 읽고 물음에 답하시오.

Once upon a time, there was a crow who lived in a forest. The crow was very happy with his life. He always looked at **(A)**[him / himself] in the water. He thought (가)<u>no one was more beautiful than he was</u>.

Then one day, the crow saw a swan on the lake. "The swan is so white," he thought, "but I am so black. I have never seen **(B)**[so / such] a white bird before. His beauty shines so brightly. The swan (나)<u>must</u> be the happiest bird in the world." He went to the swan and expressed his thoughts. "Actually," the swan said, "I thought that I was the happiest bird. But then I saw a parrot. Now I think the parrot is the happiest bird in the world." The crow asked why ⓐ<u>he</u> thought (다)<u>so</u>. The swan answered, "The parrot has colorful feathers. ⓑ<u>He</u> is more beautiful than I am. He must be proud of ⓒ<u>his</u> appearance."

The crow then flew to ⓓ<u>the parrot</u> and said, "The swan said you are the happiest bird because ⓔ<u>you</u> have colorful feathers." The parrot explained, "I lived a very happy life **(C)**[after / until] I saw a peacock. My feathers are colorful, but the peacock's feathers are colorful, big, and gorgeous. So he is loved by everyone."

18 위 글의 밑줄 친 ⓐ~ⓔ 중 가리키는 대상이 나머지 넷과 <u>다른</u> 것은? (3점)

① ⓐ   ② ⓑ   ③ ⓒ

④ ⓓ   ⑤ ⓔ

[충남 ○○중]

19 위 글의 밑줄 친 (가)와 같은 의미의 문장은? (3점)

① all the crows were beautiful

② he was not a beautiful bird

③ there were no beautiful birds

④ he was the least beautiful bird

⑤ he was the most beautiful bird

[대구 ○○중]

20 위 글의 밑줄 친 (나)must와 같은 용법으로 쓰인 것은? (3점)

① You <u>must</u> come earlier tomorrow.

② You <u>must</u> keep quiet in the library.

③ You <u>must</u> be tired after your long walk.

④ We <u>must</u> turn off our phones for takeoff.

⑤ There are some places where you <u>must</u> wear a mask.

[대구 ○○중]

21 위 글의 괄호 (A), (B), (C)에 들어갈 말이 가장 알맞게 연결된 것은? (4점)

	(A)	(B)	(C)
①	him	such	until
②	him	so	after
③	himself	so	after
④	himself	such	after
⑤	himself	such	until

[울산 ○○중]

22 위 글의 밑줄 친 (다)so가 의미하는 것으로 가장 알맞은 것은? (3점)

① 까마귀가 세상에서 가장 아름답다.

② 까마귀가 세상에서 가장 행복한 새다.

③ 백조가 세상에서 가장 행복한 새다.

④ 앵무새가 세상에서 가장 행복한 새다.

⑤ 앵무새가 세상에서 가장 인기 있는 새다.

[부산 ○○중]

23 위 글을 읽고 답할 수 <u>없는</u> 것은? (3점)

① Where did the crow see the swan?

② What did the parrot feel about a crow's appearance?

③ What did the swan think of himself before he saw a parrot?

④ Why did the swan think that the parrot was the happiest bird?

⑤ How did the crow feel about his life before seeing a swan?

[충북 ○○중]

24 위 글의 내용과 일치하도록, 주어진 단어를 변형 없이 모두 사용하고 필요한 단어를 추가하여 다음 질문에 대한 답을 문장으로 완성하시오. (4점)

the parrot, beautiful, because, his colorful feathers

What does the swan think of the parrot's beauty?

→ The swan thinks (that) _____
_____.

→ _____

[25~30] 다음 글을 읽고 물음에 답하시오.

The crow then visited the peacock at the zoo. There were a lot of people around the peacock, and they praised him (A)for his beauty. The crow thought the peacock must be the happiest bird in the world. After all the people left, the crow started (B)to talk to the peacock. "Peacock, you are so beautiful. Many people come to see you every day. (가)_____, when people see me, they (C)chase away me. I think you are the happiest bird in the world." The peacock said, "I may be the most beautiful bird, but I'm not happy. (D)Because of my beauty, I am stuck in this zoo. Unlike me, you (E)aren't kept in a cage. I want to be like you because you can go anywhere."

After the crow talked to the peacock, ⓐhe started to think about who the happiest bird was. The crow thought to himself, "The peacock's feathers are impressive, but ⓑhe is stuck in a cage. ⓒI don't have colorful feathers, but I'm free to fly anywhere." ⓓThe crow went back to the forest. He looked at himself in the water again and saw ⓔthe happiest bird in the world.

[서울 관악구 ○○중]

25 위 글의 밑줄 친 (A)~(E) 중 어법상 바르지 <u>못한</u> 것은? (3점)

① (A)　　　② (B)　　　③ (C)
④ (D)　　　⑤ (E)

[충남 ○○중]

26 위 글의 밑줄 친 ⓐ~ⓔ 중 가리키는 대상이 <u>다른</u> 것은? (3점)

① ⓐ　　　② ⓑ　　　③ ⓒ
④ ⓓ　　　⑤ ⓔ

[충남 ○○중]

27 위 글의 빈칸 (가)에 들어갈 말이 가장 자연스러운 것은? (3점)

① So　　　　　　② Of course
③ For example　　④ For the first time
⑤ On the other hand

[충남 ○○중]

28 위 글에서 다음 빈칸에 들어갈 단어를 각각 찾아 쓰시오. (4점)

"The peacock may be the most (A)_____ bird, but I am the (B)_____ bird in the world."

(A)_____

(B)_____

[충남 ○○중]

29 위 글을 참고하여 다음 질문에 대한 답을 완전한 영어 문장으로 쓰시오. (6 words) (4점)

Why did the peacock want to be like the crow?

→ _____

[충남 ○○중]

30 위 글의 내용과 일치하지 <u>않는</u> 것은? (3점)

① The peacock wanted to be free.
② The peacock was happy in the cage.
③ People liked the peacock because he was beautiful.
④ The crow was not the most beautiful bird, but he was happy.
⑤ The peacock thought that the crow was happier than he was.

◎ 선택형 문항의 답안은 컴퓨터용 수정 싸인펜을 사용하여 OMR 답안지에 바르게 표기하시오.
◎ 서술형 문제는 답을 답안지에 반드시 검정 볼펜으로 쓰시오.
◎ 총 29문항 100점 만점입니다. 문항별 배점은 각 문항에 표시되어 있습니다.

[대구 강북중 기출]

01 다음 영영풀이에 해당하는 단어는? (4점)

a thing that is used with other foods in the preparation of a particular dish

① paste
② cooker
③ cutting board
④ recipe
⑤ ingredient

[충남 ○○중]

02 다음 대화를 읽고, 두 사람이 겪고 있는 상황으로 가장 적절한 것은? (3점)

W: Oh, what happened?
M: I think it is a blackout.
W: Again?
M: Yeah. I heard thunder a second ago.
W: Don't worry. I bought a flashlight just in case it happened.
M: That's good.
W: Well, I thought I put in this drawer, but I can't find it.
M: Then, I'll look for some candles on the kitchen.

① 홍수　　　　　② 화재
③ 정전　　　　　④ 지진
⑤ 폭풍

[경기 ○○중]

03 다음 문장의 빈칸에 들어갈 단어의 풀이를 〈보기〉에서 찾을 수 없는 것은? (6점)

보기
• This means that you make something smaller in size or amount, or less in degree.
• This means that you make something more attractive by adding things to it.
• This is the act of working together to produce a piece of work, especially a book or some research.
• This is the word to describe the situation that is fixed tightly in a particular position and is unable to move.
• This means that you give someone confidence, for example by letting them know that what they are doing is good and telling them that they should continue to do it.

① Everybody will _____ for her performance.
② She said her car was _____ in the heavy snow.
③ The new technique will _____ the cost of production.
④ He wanted to _____ his room with pictures of all his favorite sports figures.
⑤ Jake will _____ her to his parents.

(가) Once upon a time, there was a crow who lived in a forest. The crow was very happy with his life. He always looked at himself in the water. He thought (A)그는 숲에서 자신이 가장 아름다운 새라고.

(나) Then one day, the crow saw a swan on the lake. "The swan is so white," he thought. "but I am so black. ⓐI have never seen so a white bird before. ⓑHis beauty shine so brightly. The swan must be the happiest bird in the world." He went to the swan and expressed his thoughts. "Actually," the swan said, "ⓒI thought that I was the happiest bird. But then I saw a parrot. Now I think the parrot is the happiest bird in the world." ⓓThe crow asked why did he thought so. The swan answered, "He is more beautiful than I am. ⓔHe must be proud of his appearance."

(다) The crow then flew to the parrot and said, "The swan said you are the happiest bird because you have Ⓐ＿＿＿＿＿＿＿ feathers." The parrot explained, "I lived a very happy life until I saw a peacock. My feathers are Ⓐ＿＿＿＿＿＿＿, but the peacock's feathers are Ⓐ＿＿＿＿＿＿＿, big, and gorgeous. So he is loved by everyone."

05 위 글의 밑줄 친 (A)의 우리말을 바르게 영작한 것을 <u>2개</u> 고르면? (4점)

① he was the most beautiful bird in the forest.

② he was as beautiful as some other birds in the forest.

③ he was less beautiful than any other bird in the forest.

④ no bird was more beautiful than he was in the forest.

⑤ no bird was as beautiful as all the other birds in the forest.

04 위 글의 빈칸 Ⓐ에 공통으로 들어갈 말은? (3점)

① horrible

② various

③ black

④ colorful

⑤ impossible

06 위 글 (나)의 밑줄 친 ⓐ~ⓔ 중에서 문법적으로 옳은 문장끼리 묶인 것은? (3점)

① ⓑ, ⓔ

② ⓒ, ⓔ

③ ⓐ, ⓑ, ⓒ

④ ⓑ, ⓓ, ⓔ

⑤ ⓒ, ⓓ, ⓔ

07 Which is true according to the text? (3점)

① The crow is loved by everyone.

② The swan thinks he is the happiest bird.

③ The crow saw a lot of people in the forest.

④ The swan saw a peacock and he asked if the parrot was proud of himself.

⑤ The parrot lived a happy life until he saw a peacock.

08 위 글과 관련된 영어 속담은? (4점)

① Every Jack has his Jill.

② The pot calls the kettle black.

③ Birds of a feather flock together.

④ A man is known by the company he keeps.

⑤ The grass is greener on the other side of the fence.

[9~13] 다음 글을 읽고 물음에 답하시오.

The crow then flew to the parrot and said, "The swan said you are the happiest bird because ㉮you have colorful feathers." The parrot explained, "I lived a very happy life ㉠_____ I saw a peacock. My feathers are colorful, but the peacock's feathers are colorful, big, and gorgeous. So ⓐeveryone loves him.

(A) After the crow talked to the peacock, he started to think about ⓑwho were the happiest bird. The crow thought to himself, "The peacock's feathers are impressive, but ㉯he is stuck in a cage. I don't have colorful feathers, but I'm free to fly anywhere."

(B) After all the people left, the crow started to talk to the peacock. "Peacock, you are so beautiful. ⓒMany people come to seeing you every day. On the other hand, when people see me, ㉰they chase me away. I think you are the happiest bird in the world."

(C) The crow went back to the forest. He looked at ㉱himself in the water again and saw the happiest bird in the world.

(D) The crow then visited the peacock at the zoo. ⓓThere was a lot of people around the peacock, and they praised ㉲him for his beauty. The crow thought the peacock must be the happiest bird in the world.

(E) The peacock said, "I may be the most beautiful bird, but I'm not happy. ㉡_____ my beauty, I was stuck in this zoo. Unlike me, ⓔyou aren't keep in a cage. I want to be like you because you can go anywhere."

09 위 글의 흐름에 맞게 (A)~(E)를 바르게 연결한 것은? (4점)

① (C) - (A) - (B) - (E) - (D)
② (D) - (E) - (A) - (C) - (B)
③ (D) - (B) - (E) - (A) - (C)
④ (E) - (D) - (C) - (A) - (B)
⑤ (E) - (C) - (D) - (B) - (A)

12 위 글의 ㉮~㉺ 중 가리키는 것이 어색한 것은? (3점)

① ㉮ parrot
② ㉯ swan
③ ㉰ people
④ ㉱ crow
⑤ ㉲ peacock

10 위 글에 대한 설명으로 어색한 것은? (3점)

① 백조는 까마귀와 달리 새장에 갇혀 있다.
② 앵무새는 공작의 깃털이 화려하다고 생각한다.
③ 까마귀는 앵무새의 이야기를 들은 후에 공작에게 갔다.
④ 까마귀는 사람들이 떠나간 후에 공작과 이야기했다.
⑤ 까마귀는 공작과 이야기한 후에 자신이 가장 행복한 새라고 생각했다.

13 위 글의 밑줄 친 ⓐ~ⓔ 중 어법상 올바른 문장은? (3점)

① ⓐ
② ⓑ
③ ⓒ
④ ⓓ
⑤ ⓔ

14 다음 글의 흐름으로 보아, 주어진 문장이 들어가기에 가장 적절한 곳은? (3점)

> On the other hand, when people see me, they chase me away.

> The crow then visited the peacock at the zoo. There were a lot of people around the peacock, and they praised him for his beauty. (A) The crow thought the peacock must be the happiest bird in the world. (B) After all the people left, the crow started to talk to the peacock. (C) "Peacock, you are so beautiful. (D) Many people come to see you every day. (E) I think you are the happiest bird in the world."

① (A)
② (B)
③ (C)
④ (D)
⑤ (E)

11 위 글의 ㉠, ㉡에 들어갈 단어를 바르게 연결한 것은? (3점)

	㉠	㉡
①	after	because
②	after	because of
③	until	because
④	when	because
⑤	until	because of

After the crow talked to the peacock, he started to think about who the happiest bird was. The crow thought to himself, "The peacock's feathers are impressive, (A)_____ he is stuck in a cage. I don't have colorful feathers, (B)_____ I'm free to fly anywhere." The crow went back to the forest. He looked at himself in the water again (C)_____ saw the happiest bird in the world.

[전북 ○○중]

15 What is impressive's meaning? (3점)

① very attractive
② to be unable to get out of something
③ causing a feeling of admiration and respect
④ up to a certain time
⑤ at some point in the past

[전북 ○○중]

16 위 글 바로 앞에 올 내용으로 알맞은 것은? (3점)

① 까마귀가 공작을 방문한 이유
② 공작의 아름다움
③ 공작이 행복하다고 느끼지 못하는 이유
④ 까마귀와 공작의 대화
⑤ 공작 깃털과 까마귀 깃털의 차이

[서울 성북구 ○○중]

17 Why did the crow become happy? (3점)

① He could think to himself.
② He was free to fly anywhere.
③ He could talk to the peacock.
④ His feathers were impressive.
⑤ He looked at himself in the water.

[서울 성북구 ○○중]

18 위 글의 문맥상 (A)~(C)에 들어갈 가장 적절한 표현은? (3점)

	(A)	(B)	(C)
①	but	but	but
②	but	but	and
③	but	and	and
④	and	but	but
⑤	and	and	but

[서울 관악구 ○○중]

19 위 글의 내용과 일치하도록 빈칸에 가장 적합한 문장은? (4점)

The crow started to feel happy about his life again, because _____.

① people don't like him at all
② he can fly anywhere when he wants to
③ people will come to see him every day
④ he is the most beautiful bird in the world
⑤ he doesn't like people around the peacock

[경기 ○○중]

20 위 글을 읽고 다음 질문에 답이 될 수 있는 것을 〈보기〉에서 고른 것은? (4점)

What is the lesson of the story?

보기
(A) Slow and steady wins the race.
(B) Don't compare yourself to others.
(C) The early bird catches the worm.
(D) Be satisfied with the things you have.
(E) Heaven helps those who help themselves.

① (A), (B)   ② (A), (C)
③ (B), (D)   ④ (C), (E)
⑤ (D), (E)

The crow then ⓐ<u>visited</u> the peacock at the zoo. There were a lot of people around the peacock, and they ⓑ<u>praised</u> him for his beauty. The crow thought the peacock must be the happiest bird in the world. After all the people left, the crow started to talk to the peacock. "Peacock, many people come to see you every day (A)_____ you are so ⓒ<u>beautiful</u>. On the other hand, when people see me, they ⓓ<u>chase me away</u>. I think you are the happiest bird in the world." The peacock said, "I may be the most beautiful bird, but I'm not happy. (B)_____ my beauty, I am stuck in this zoo. ⓔ<u>Like me</u>, you aren't kept in a cage. I want to be like you (C)_____ you can go anywhere."

21 위 글의 ⓐ~ⓔ 중 흐름상 <u>어색한</u> 표현은? (3점)

① ⓐ　　　② ⓑ　　　③ ⓒ

④ ⓓ　　　⑤ ⓔ

22 위 글의 내용과 일치하는 것은? (정답 2개) (3점)

① 공작새는 까마귀를 부러워한다.

② 공작새는 숲에서 벗어날 수 없었다.

③ 까마귀의 주변에는 사람들이 많았다.

④ 공작새는 자신이 행복하다고 느꼈다.

⑤ 사람들은 공작새의 아름다움을 칭찬했다.

23 위 글의 문맥상 (A)~(C)에 들어갈 표현으로 가장 적절한 것은? (3점)

	(A)	(B)	(C)
①	because	Because	because of
②	because	Because of	because of
③	because	Because of	because
④	because of	Because	because
⑤	because of	Because of	because

24 위 글의 주제로 가장 적절한 것은? (3점)

① Animals are helping each other.

② Happiness depends on one's mind.

③ We should admit our weaknesses.

④ The true value of life lies in beauty.

⑤ Animals should be allowed to live freely.

25 위 글을 다음과 같이 요약할 때, 글의 내용과 일치하도록 밑줄 친 (1)~(3)을 알맞게 고쳐 쓰시오. (6점)

The crow visits the peacock. The peacock is the most beautiful bird. But because of his beauty, (1)<u>the crow</u> is stuck in the zoo. People (2)<u>like</u> the crow, but he can go (3)<u>nowhere</u>.

→ (1)_____

　(2)_____

　(3)_____

Once upon a time, there was a crow ㉠that lived in a forest. The crow was very happy with his life. He always looked at himself in the water. He thought he was the most beautiful bird in the world.

Then one day, the crow saw a swan on the lake. "The swan is so white," ⓐhe thought, "but I am so black. I have never see such a white bird ago. His beauty shines so brightly. The swan must be the happiest bird in the world." ⓑHe went to the swan and expressed his thoughts. "Actually," the swan said, "I thought that I was the happiest bird. But then I saw a parrot. Now I think the parrot is the happiest bird in the world." The crow asked why ⓒhe thought so. The swan answered, "The parrot has colorful feathers. ⓓHe is more beautiful than I am. ⓔHe must be proud of (A)his appearance."

[대구 ○○중]

26 위 글의 밑줄 친 ㉠과 쓰임이 같은 것은? (3점)

① We all know that the earth is round.

② I have a friend that plays baseball very well.

③ His car is more expensive than that of my uncle.

④ You didn't have to give him that much money.

⑤ He realized the fact that he had made a mistake.

[경기 ○○중]

27 위 글의 (A)가 가리키는 문장을 본문에서 찾아 〈조건〉에 맞게 쓰고, 그 의미를 우리말로 해석하시오. (4점)

> **조건**
> • 'his'가 가리키는 대상을 포함한 완전한 영어 문장으로 쓸 것.
> • 'appearance'의 특징을 구체적으로 쓸 것.

영어: _____

_____

해석: _____

_____

[서울 성북구 ○○중]

28 위 글의 ⓐ~ⓔ가 가리키는 것으로 옳지 않은 것은? (3점)

① ⓐ - crow

② ⓑ - crow

③ ⓒ - swan

④ ⓓ - parrot

⑤ ⓔ - swan

[서울 성북구 ○○중]

29 위 글의 밑줄 친 문장에서 어색한 부분 두 곳을 찾아 어법에 맞게 고쳐서 다시 쓰시오. (단, 전체 문장을 다시 쓸 것, 단어를 빠뜨릴 경우 감점함) (3점)

→ _____

정답 및 해설

Lesson 5 (중간) 1회

```
01 ④  02 ④  03 ③  04 ④  05 ②
06 도움이 필요한 사람을 도와줘.      07 ③  08 ⑤
09 (A) the man I met yesterday is a spy
   (B) this is the ID which[that] the spy used before
10 ①  11 ⑤  12 ⑤  13 Can you help me wash these dogs?
14 ③, ④      15 ③  16 ②
17 ⓐ: However ⓑ: tirelessly ⓒ: Unfortunately
18 ③  19 ④  20 ②  21 ②  22 ⑤  23 ②
24 realized that her fame could help others
25 ④  26 ①  27 ①  28 ③  29 ③  30 ⑤
```

01 collect는 '수집하다'라는 뜻을 갖는 단어이다. '나쁜 일이 일어난 후에 살아 남다'라는 영영풀이가 가리키는 것은 survive(생존하다)이다.

02 ⓐ 눈이 먼, ⓑ 녹음하다, ⓒ 개최하다, ⓔ 인공적인

03 영화가 사람을 신나게 하는 것이므로 과거분사 ③ excited를 현재분사 exciting으로 고쳐야 어법상 적절한 문장이 된다.

04 A가 Jane(B)에게 다리에 무슨 일이 생긴 거냐고 묻자, B는 지난주에 다리를 다쳤다고 대답한다. A는 무슨 일이 벌어진 것이냐고 묻고, B는 기차를 잡으려다 거리에서 넘어졌다고 설명한다. 이에 A는 자신이 도와줄 일이 있냐고 묻는 순서로 이어지는 것이 대화의 흐름상 가장 적절하다.

05 위 글에서는 Mapletown을 위해 모금한 돈을 Mapletown 사람들에게 줄 것이라고 언급했다.

06 give a hand 도움을 주다 / people in need 어려움에 처한 사람들

07 감정을 나타내는 타동사의 과거분사는 '어떤 감정을 느끼는'이라는 의미로, 주로 사람을 주어로 한다.

08 '우리는 김밥이나 어묵, 호떡과 같은 많은 종류의 길거리 음식을 먹었다'('We ate many kinds of street food such as *Gimbap*, fish cake and *Hotteok*.')는 문장은 의견이 아니라 사실을 나타낸다.

09 두 문장을 연결할 때 겹치는 부분을 선행사로 만들고 관계대명사를 이용해 연결할 수 있다. 이때 관계대명사가 이끄는 절에서 관계대명사 who[whom], which 또는 that이 목적어 역할을 할 때 생략 가능하다.

10 (A), (B) 상대방에게 무언가를 제안할 때, "~하는 게 어때?"라는 의미의 "Why don't we + 동사원형 ~?" 표현을 사용할 수 있다.

(C) "how about ~?"이라고 물을 때는 뒤에 명사나 동명사형을 쓴다.

11 학생들은 봉사활동의 날에 양로원 사람들을 위해 파티를 열 것이라고 언급했다.

12 위 대화에서는 다양한 동물들을 돌보고 있으므로, 위 대화가 일어나는 장소로는 ⑤ animal care center(동물 돌봄 센터)가 가장 적절하다.

13 help가 사용될 경우 목적보어로는 to부정사나 동사원형을 쓴다.

14 "Can I ask you a favor?"는 상대방에게 도움을 요청하는 표현으로 "Can you do me a favor?", "Can you give me a hand?"와 같은 표현으로 바꿔 쓸 수 있다.

15 개를 함께 씻기자는 Allen의 부탁에 Nicky가 승낙했으므로 함께 개를 씻길 것이다.

16 위 글에서는 시각 장애인을 위해 책을 읽거나, 암 연구를 위해 모금을 하거나 혹은 신생아들을 위해 모자를 만드는 등의 자원 봉사활동에 대해서 이야기 하고 있다. 따라서 위 글의 제목으로 가장 적절한 것은 ② Volunteer: Sharing One's Talents(봉사 활동: 재능 나누기)이다.

17 ⓐ 한국으로 돌아갔지만 Tonj 사람들을 잊을 수 없었다는 내용이므로 However가 적절하다. / ⓑ tirelessly 지칠 줄 모르고 / ⓒ unfortunately 운이 나쁘게도

18 Tonj에서 자원 봉사 활동을 하던 이태석 신부가 48세의 나이에 암으로 사망했다고 했으므로 이에 이어질 내용으로 가장 적절한 것은 ③ Many people were very sad to hear of his death.(많은 사람들이 그의 죽음을 듣고 매우 슬퍼했다.)이다.

19 이태석 신부는 심지어 수학과 음악을 가르쳤다('He even taught math and music')고 언급되어 있다.

20 세계 2차 대전이 일어났을 때, 오드리 햅번과 그녀의 어머니는 궁핍한 생활을 하였다.

21 '그녀는 마카오의 국제 음악 축제에 갔다'는 문장이 들어가기에 가장 적절한 곳은 많은 사람들이 축제에서 돈을 기부했다는 내용이 나오는 (B)이다.

22 Ⓐ that은 목적격 관계대명사, Ⓑ that은 주격 관계대명사, Ⓒ that은 접속사로 사용되었다. ㉠ 한정사, ㉡, ㉢, ㉥ 목적격 관계대명사, ㉣ 주격 관계대명사, ㉤ 접속사이다.

23 ⓐ scared 무서워하는
ⓑ because of+명사(구) ~ 때문에

24 세 번째 문단에서, 'Hepburn realized that her fame could help others, so she became a UNICEF Goodwill Ambassador.'라고 언급되어 있다.

25 the little black dress를 선행사로 쓰고 목적격 관계대명사 that/which를 이용해 the little black dress that she wore in a movie is famous.라는 문장으로 영작할 수 있다.

26 위 글에서는 헵번이 스타일과 아름다움으로 유명했지만 그녀의 진정한 아름다움은 다른 사람들을 도우려는 아름다운 마음씨였다는 것에 대해서 이야기 하고 있다.

27 one ~, the other ~ (두 개 중에) 하나는 ~, 다른 하나는 ~

28 (A) because+절(주어+동사) ~이기 때문에
(B) but 그러나

29 ③ What did she do in Somalia?(소말리아에서 그녀는 무슨 활동을 했는가?)에 대해서는 위 글에서 언급되어 있지 않다.

30 문맥상 ⓔenvy(부러워하다)는 resptect(존경하다)로 고쳐야 적절하다.

Lesson 5 (중간)

```
01 ①  02 ④  03 ①  04 ⑤  05 ③  06 ④  07 ③  08 ⑤
09 ②
10 (1) ⓒ worrying → worried (2) ⓔ interesting → interested
11 ③  12 ④  13 ⑤  14 ②  15 ③  16 ③  17 ①  18 ②
19 ③  20 ③  21 ④
22 The man is going to meet the students who[whom] he
   taught a long time ago.
23 The little girl felt scared all the time.       24 ②
25 which she wore in a movie is famous    26 ③  27 ③
28 ③  29 ④
30 Because Hepburn realized that her fame could help others.
```

01 praise는 '칭찬하다'라는 뜻을 가진 단어로 '어떤 사람에 대해 좋은 말을 하다'라는 영영풀이와 의미가 같다.

02 ④ is popular → that is popular로 고쳐야 어법상 적절한 문장이 된다.

03 과거분사 excited는 '흥분한', '신난'이라는 뜻을 지닌 단어이다.

04 ⑤ How long will Jungtae have to stay in hospital?(정태는 얼마나 오래 병원에 머물러 있어야 하는가?)에 대해서는 위 대화에서 언급되어 있지 않다.

05 "네 방을 치우는 게 어떠니?"라는 A의 말에 대해 "좋아, 지금 청소하자."라는 B의 대답은 흐름상 자연스럽지 않다.

06 B가 "파티에서 무엇을 할 수 있을까?"라고 물었으므로 이에 대한 A의 대답인 "우리는 다른 사람들을 돕고 우리 사회를 더 낫게 만들 수 있어."라는 대답은 문맥상 적절하지 않다.

07 위 대화에서는 자원 봉사의 날을 맞이하여 양로원 사람들을 위해 그곳에서 파티를 여는 것에 대해서 이야기하고 있다. 따라서 위 대화의 주제로 가장 적절한 것은 ③ the volunteer plan at a nursing home(양로원에서의 봉사활동 계획)이다.

08 C는 "And what about playing some music? I can play the piano."(음악을 연주하는 건 어때? 난 피아노를 연주할 수 있어.)라고 언급한 바 있다.

09 위 글에 따르면, 시험지를 돌려받은 것은 체육 시간이 아니라 사회 시간이다.

10 ⓒ worrying 걱정시키는, worried 걱정을 하는
ⓔ interesting (어떤 일이)흥미롭게 하는, interested (사람이)흥미로워하는

11 위 대화의 후반부에서 볼 수 있듯이, James, Liam, Emma는 양로원 사람들을 위한 파티에서 음식을 제공하고 음악을 연주하기로 했다.

12 위 글에서는 여러 동물들을 돌보고 보호하고 있는 내용이므로 ④ an animal care center(동물 돌봄 센터)가 위 대화의 장소로 가장 적절하다.

13 ⓐ Jay는 고양이에게 밥을 주고 있기 때문에 Allen의 도움 요청을 거절했다. 따라서 "I'm afraid not." 또는 "Sorry, but I can't."가 빈칸에 적절하다. / ⓑ Nicky는 Allen의 도움 요청을 수락했기 때문에 "Sure, I can." 또는 "No problem."이라고 대답하는 것이 자연스럽다.

14 위 대화에 따르면, Allen은 더러워진 개를 씻기 위해 Jay와 Nicky에게 도움을 요청했다.

15 위 글에서는 화재가 난 Mapletown을 위해 사람들이 기부한 옷을 판매해서 모금하려고 하고 있다. 따라서 빈칸에 들어갈 말로 가장 적절한 것은 ③ We will sell your items.이다.

16 위 글에서는 화재가 난 Mapletown을 위해 사람들이 기부한 옷을 판매해서 모금하려고 하고 있다. 따라서 글의 목적으로 가장 적절한 것은 ③ to invite students to a donation event(기부 행사에 학생들을 초대하기 위해)이다.

17 ⓐraise는 '모금하다'라는 뜻으로 사용되었다. 이와 같은 의미로 사용된 문장은 ① We will raise funds to build a school.(우리는 학교를 짓기 위해 돈을 모금할 것이다.)이다.

18 주어진 문장은 "James가 오늘 아침에 사고를 당했다고 들었어!"라는 뜻이다. 따라서 이에 대한 반응으로 가장 적절한 것은 ② shocked(충격을 받은)이다.

19 상대방에게 도움을 요청할 때는, "Can I ask you a favor?", "Can you do me a favor?", "Can you give me a hand?"와 같은 표현을 사용할 수 있다.

20 위 글에서는 이태석 신부가 Tonj에서 봉사활동을 한 내용에 대해서 이야기 하고 있다. 따라서 위 글의 제목으로 가장 적절한 것은 ③ Lee Taeseok's Volunteer Work(이태석 신부의 봉사활동)이다.

21 오드리 헵번의 히트한 영화의 종류에 대해서 설명하고 있으므로 ⓓsuch는 ⓓsuch as(~와 같은)가 되어야 어법상 적절하다.

22 주어진 문장은 목적격 관계대명사가 쓰인 문장으로, 선행사가 관

계대명사 절에서 목적어 역할을 할 때 쓰인다. 이때 선행사가 사람이므로 관계대명사 who나 whom을 쓴다.

23 주어가 사람이고 무서움을 느끼게 된 것이므로 feel scared라고 표현할 수 있다.

24 위 글에 따르면, 오드리 헵번은 아프고 배고팠으며(a little girl and her mother were hungry and sick), 히트한 영화들로 인해 인기가 많았다(She was very popular because of her hit movies)고 언급되어 있다.

25 주어진 문장은 목적격 관계대명사가 쓰인 문장으로, 선행사가 관계대명사 절에서 목적어 역할을 할 때 쓰인다. 이때 선행사는 The little black dress라는 사물이기 때문에 which 또는 that을 사용할 수 있다.

26 ⓑ Because of → Thanks to / ⓒ because of → because / ⓔ whom → who로 고쳐야 어법상 적절한 문장이 된다.

27 위 글에서는 오드리 헵번이 가난하고 배고팠던 어린 시절을 거쳐 스타가 된 후 자신의 유명세를 통해 자선 활동을 한 내용에 대해서 이야기하고 있다. 따라서 빈칸에 들어갈 내용으로 가장 적절한 것은 그녀의 진짜 아름다움은 그녀의 마음이라는 내용이므로 ③ beauty이다.

28 (A) pass away 사망하다
(B) to honor her 그녀를 기리기 위해
(C) for ~를 위한, 위해

29 위 글에 따르면, 오드리 헵번의 미모와 스타일을 사람들이 칭송했지만 그녀의 진정한 아름다움은 그녀의 마음이라고 언급되어 있다.

30 첫 문단에 언급되어 있듯이, 오드리 헵번은 그녀의 유명세가 다른 사람들을 돕는 데 사용될 수 있다고 깨달았다.

Lesson 6 (중간)   1회

01 ② 02 ③ 03 ② 04 ② 05 ③
06 How long does it take? 07 ④ 08 ⑤ 09 ② 10 ④
11 ② 12 (A) How can I get[go] to (B) How long does it take
13 ③ 14 ⑤ 15 ③ 16 ⑤
17 It is famous for selling a variety of goods from different countries.
18 ② 19 ⑤ 20 ① 21 ③ 22 ③ 23 ④
24 it was exciting to ride 25 ① 26 ③ 27 ④ 28 ①
29 ② 30 ④

01 빈칸에는 문맥상 ② focusing on(집중하고 있다)이 가장 적절하다.

02 주어진 우리말을 영작하면, 'Some people go on trips for special purposes.'라는 문장이 된다. 따라서 ⓒ에 들어갈 말로

가장 적절한 것은 ③ for이다.

03 B의 대답이 "20분 걸려요."인 것으로 미루어 볼 때, A의 말로 가장 적절한 것은 ② How long does it take to get there?(거기까지 얼마나 걸리니?)이다.

04 이 아름다운 사진들을 어디서 찍었냐는 A의 질문에 대해, 리버사이드 공원에서 찍었다고 말하면서 "너도 거기 꼭 가 봐."라는 B의 대답은 흐름상 자연스럽다.

05 문맥상 (A)에는 '~에 타다'라는 의미의 get on이 들어가야 자연스럽다. 따라서 전치사 on이 들어갈 문장으로 가장 적절한 것은 ③ 'I have a plan on Valentine's Day.'이다.

06 어떤 일을 하는 데 소요되는 시간을 물을 때는 'How long does it take?'를 사용한다.

07 ④번은 거리를 나타내는 비인칭주어이고, 나머지는 모두 가주어로 쓰인 it이다.

08 (A)에서는 역사적인 장소를 방문해서 역사에 대해서 배운다고 했으므로 History가 들어가는 것이 적절하다. / (B)에서는 어떤 사람들이 어려움에 처한 사람들을 돕기 위한 특별한 목적을 갖고 여행한다고 했으므로 빈칸에는 Volunteer가 적절하다. / (C)에서는 사람들이 환경을 해치지 않고 자연에서 여행을 한다고 했으므로 빈칸에는 Eco가 적절하다.

09 A가 추석에 무엇을 할 계획이냐고 물었다. 따라서 이에 대한 B의 대답으로 적절하지 않은 것은 ② I have been to Jeju-do with my family.(난 가족들이랑 제주도에 가 본 적이 있어.)이다.

10 (A) 계획을 물을 때는 동사 plan을 써서 "What are you planning to+동사원형 ~?"으로 물을 수 있다.
(B) "What are you planning to do?"와 같은 표현으로는 "What's your plan for ~?" 등이 있다.

11 ② How many days will the girl stay in Jeonju?(소녀는 전주에서 며칠이나 묵을 것인가?)에 대해서는 위 글에서 언급된 바 없다.

12 (A) 여성의 대답인 "택시를 타고 그곳에 갈 수 있어요."라는 문장으로 미루어 볼 때, (A)에는 "How can I get to ~?"(~에 어떻게 갈 수 있나요?)라는 문장이 자연스럽다. (B)에서 여성의 대답인 "택시를 타고 20분 걸려요."라는 문장으로 미루어 볼 때, 빈칸에는 "How long does it take?"(시간이 얼마나 걸리나요?)가 들어가는 것이 문맥상 적절하다.

13 ⓒWho will you see in the game?(야구 경기에서 넌 누구를 볼 거니?)라는 문장은 문맥상 자연스럽지 않다.

14 "그거 재밌게 들린다."라는 문장이 들어가기에 가장 적절한 곳은 놀이공원에 가서 롤러코스터를 탈 것이라고 말하는 Mike에 대해 대답하고 있는 (E)이다.

15 누리는 반 고흐를 만나러 가는 것이 아니라 그의 그림을 보러 갈 것이라고 했다.

16 부산이 시장들의 천국이라고 언급한 뒤, 전통 시장을 좋아하냐고 물으면서, 국제 시장에 가보라고 추천한다. 국제 시장은 다른 나라에서 온 다양한 물건들을 파는 것으로 유명하다고 이야기하면서, 그곳에서 길거리 음식을 먹었다고 한다. 마지막으로 보수동 책방 골목에 가서 오래된 만화책을 발견했고 카페에서 쉬면서 그것들을 읽는 것이 즐거웠다고 이야기하는 순서로 이어지는 것이 흐름상 가장 자연스럽다.

17 두 번째 문단에 언급되어 있듯이, 국제 시장은 다른 나라에서 온 다양한 물건들을 파는 걸로 유명하다고 한다.

18 국제 시장이 부산에서 가장 유명한 시장 중에 하나라고 언급했다.

19 중고책의 가격에 대해서는 위 글에서 언급되지 않았다.

20 (a)used는 '중고의'라는 뜻을 가진 단어이다. 따라서 이와 같은 의미로 쓰인 문장은 ① I'm looking for a used car.(나는 중고차를 찾고 있다.)이다.

21 안내원이 전등을 끈 것은 동굴 투어가 거의 끝나갈 때쯤이었다.

22 투어에서 무엇을 했는지에 대해서 이야기하고 있으므로 ⓒ Without a guide, you cannot tour the cave.(안내자가 없으면 동굴 투어를 할 수 없다.)라는 문장은 문맥상 자연스럽지 않다.

23 'be able to ~'는 '~할 수 있다'라는 뜻으로, 이 문장에서는 과거형으로 쓰였기 때문에 ④ could(~할 수 있었다)로 바꿔 쓸 수 있다.

24 문장의 주어로 쓰인 to부정사가 수식어로 인해 길어진 경우, 보통 to부정사를 뒤로 보내고 대신 주어 자리에 가주어 it을 둔다.

25 위 글에선 강원도의 동굴 투어와 동강에서 래프팅을 했던 경험에 대해 이야기하면서 놀라웠던 경험이라고 언급했다. 따라서 위 글의 분위기로 가장 적절한 것은 ① fun(재미있는)이다.

26 주어진 우리말을 영작하면, 'Do you know where the first train station in Korea is?'가 된다.

27 ⓐIt은 가주어 It으로 to부정사 구문을 대신한다. 따라서 이와 쓰임이 같은 것은 ④ It is nice to meet you again.이다.

28 위 글에 따르면, 인천은 한국 최초로 기차나 자장면 등이 생긴 곳('This place has many of Korea's firsts.')이라고 한다. 따라서 위 글의 빈칸에 들어갈 말로 가장 적절한 곳은 ① Firsts(최초의 것들)이다.

29 '그곳에 가기 위해, 우리는 인천역으로 갔다'라는 문장이 들어가기에 가장 적절한 곳은 자장면 박물관이 인천역 옆에 있다고 이야기하고 있는 (B)이다.

30 서양식 공원이라고 언급한 곳은 자유 공원이다.

Lesson 6 (중간)

01 ① **02** ② **03** ③ **04** ④ **05** ③ **06** ④

07 How long does it take to get there?　　　**08** ④ **09** ①

10 (1) when the show started (2) what movie she likes
　　(3) if[whether] Tom is at home

11 (1) It is difficult to live without a smart phone.
　　(2) It is important not to give up.

12 ⑤ **13** ① **14** ② **15** ① **16** ③ **17** ① **18** ③

19 where the first train station in Korea is　　**20** ⑤

21 Do you know what it is famous for?　　**22** ① **23** ④

24 It is famous for selling a variety of goods from different countries.

25 ③ **26** ⑤ **27** ⑤ **28** ⑤ **29** ②

30 The most amazing experiences of the tour were the cave and sounds.

01 relax는 '긴장을 풀다'라는 뜻을 갖는 단어이다.

02 ②에서 B의 대답인 'I will ask my mom how the book cost much.'는 'I will ask my mom how much the book costs.'로 고쳐야 어법상 적절한 문장이다.

03 ⓒtakes는 '시간이 걸리다'라는 뜻으로 사용되었다.

04 위 대화에서, 여성이 한국 대학교에 버스로 가면 5분, 걸어서 가면 20분이라고 말해 주었고 또한 뒤에서 가는 법을 상세하게 이야기해 주고 있다. 따라서 빈칸에 들어갈 말로 가장 적절한 것은 ④ I'm going to go there on foot.(저는 걸어서 갈게요.)이다.

05 "우리 학교에서 그곳에는 어떻게 가니?"라는 문장이 들어가기에 가장 적절한 곳은 Sue가 진수에게 리버사이드 공원에 갈 것을 추천하자 진수가 자신도 가보고 싶다고 말하고 있는 (C)이다.

06 Sue는 리버사이드에 가는 방법으로 135번 버스를 타야 한다고 언급했다.

07 어떤 곳에 가는 데 소요되는 시간을 물을 때, "How long does it take to get there?"를 사용한다.

08 위 대화의 화자들은 휴가 계획에 대해서 이야기하고 있는데, ⓓ When did you plan for the holiday?(넌 언제 휴일을 계획했니?)라는 문장은 문맥상 자연스럽지 않다.

09 위 글에 따르면, 어떤 사람들은 환경을 해치지 않고 자연 속에서 여행을 하며 그들은 자연을 보호하는 것을 중요하게 생각한다고 한다. 따라서 이와 가장 관계가 깊은 것은 ① Eco Trip(환경 친화적인 여행)이다.

10 의문문이 문장 안에서 쓰인 경우 간접의문문의 형태로 만들어야 어법상 적절하다. 간접의문문은 의문문이 '의문사+주어+동사' 형태로 다른 문장 안에서 주어, 목적어, 보어 역할을 하는 것을 말한다.

11 문장의 주어로 쓰인 to부정사가 수식어로 인해 길어진 경우, 보통

to부정사를 뒤로 보내고 대신 주어 자리에 가주어 it을 둔다. 이때 쓰인 it은 가주어이므로 구체적인 뜻이 없으며, '…하는 것은 ~하다'로 해석한다.

12 (1) Mike가 누리에게 현장 학습을 어디로 가냐고 물어봤고, 그러자 누리는 반 고흐 전시를 볼 것이라고 했으므로 대답은 (E) We are going to the art museum.이 적절하다. (2) Mike는 누리가 미술관에 간다고 대답하자, (D) What are you planning to see there?라고 물어 본다. (3) 누리가 Mike에게 어디로 현장 학습을 가냐고 물어보자, Mike는 등산을 하게 돼서 신난다고 대답했으므로 (B) We are going to Halla Mountain in Jeju.라는 대답이 빈칸에 가장 적절하다.

13 누리와 마이크는 다른 학급의 학생이라 서로 다른 곳으로 현장 학습을 가는 것에 대해서 이야기하고 있다.

14 케이블카를 탄 것은 산중턱이라고('I rode a cable car to the middle of the mountain.') 언급되어 있다.

15 위 글에 따르면, 인천은 한국 최초로 기차나 자장면 등이 생긴 곳('This place has many of Korea's firsts.')이라고 한다. 따라서 제목으로 가장 적절한 것은 ① A City of Firsts(최초의 것들의 도시)이다.

16 (A) How about ~? ~은 어때?
(B) to부정사의 부사적 용법; ~하기 위해
(C) next to ~의 옆에

17 ① When was Jayu Park built?(자유 공원이 언제 지어졌는가?)에 대해서는 위 글에서 언급된 바 없다.

18 위 글에서 언급된 공원인 자유 공원은 한국 최초의 서양식 공원(Jayu Park, the first Western-style park in Korea.)이라고 한다.

19 간접의문문은 의문문이 '의문사+주어+동사' 형태로 다른 문장 안에서 주어, 목적어, 보어 역할을 하는 것을 말한다.

20 위 글에 따르면, 학생들은 자장면 박물관을 가기 위해 인천역에 갔다고 언급했기 때문에 선생님의 반응으로 ⑤ I'm sorry that you did not go to Incheon station.(너희들이 인천역에 가지 못해서 유감이구나.)는 적절하지 않다.

21 간접의문문은 '의문사+주어+동사' 형태로 쓴다.

22 위 글에서는 학생들이 현장 학습을 갔다 온 경험에 대해서 선생님, 친구들과 공유하고 있다. 따라서 빈칸에 들어갈 말로 가장 적절한 것은 ① field trips(현장 학습)이다.

23 글쓴이는 보수동에서 책을 판매한 것이 아니라 책을 구매했다.

24 be famous for ~로 유명하다 / a variety of 다양한

25 to부정사 구문을 대신하는 가주어 it이 사용된 문장은 'It was interesting to see all the international goods there.'와 'It was nice to relax in a cafe and read them.'이다.

26 '과거에 ~할 수 있었다'는 내용이므로 과거형을 쓴 ⑤ were able

to가 빈칸에 가장 적절하다.

27 ⑤ How long did it take to finish rafting?(래프팅을 하는 데 시간이 얼마나 걸렸는가?)에 대해서는 위 글에서 언급된 바 없다.

28 ⓔview는 문맥상 '경치', '경관'이라고 해석한다.

29 강원도 백룡 동굴이 한국에서 가장 큰 동굴인지에 대해서는 위 글에서 언급된 바 없다.

30 투어 중에 무엇이 가장 놀라운 경험이었냐고 물어봤으므로, 대답은 'The most amazing experiences of the tour were ~'라고 답한다.

Lesson 7 (기말)

01 ③　02 ③　03 ④　04 ⑤　05 ⑤　06 ②　07 ⑤　08 ⑤
09 ④　10 ③　11 ⑤　12 ④　13 ①　14 ②　15 ①
16 us to get some rest　17 ④　18 ①　19 ④　20 ⑤　21 ⑤
22 ①　23 ③　24 ②
25 (1) 창의적이어야 함 (2) 미술을 배워야 함　26 ①　27 ⑤
28 ②　29 ⑤　30 ③

01 '어떤 새로운 것을 만들거나 생각해 내는 능력'이라는 영영풀이가 가리키는 것은 ③ creativity(창의력)이다.

02 reduce는 '줄이다', '감소시키다'라는 뜻을 가진 단어이다.

03 there is/are 문장에서의 동사는 그 뒤에 오는 명사의 수에 따라 결정된다. 따라서 was가 적절하다. / 현재완료 시제가 쓰인 문장이므로 과거분사 seen이 적절하다.

04 A가 자신은 음악 제작자가 되고 싶다고 하면서 조언을 구하고 있다. 따라서 이에 대한 B의 조언으로 가장 적절한 것은 ⑤ listen to many kinds of music이다.

05 ① go → to go / ② tall → to be tall / ③ to money → money / ④ you have → you to have 로 고쳐야 어법상 적절한 문장이 된다.

06 if는 '만약 ~한다면'이라는 뜻의 조건을 나타내는 부사절을 이끄는 접속사로 한 문장을 다른 문장에 연결해 준다. if절이 앞에 올 경우, 부사절 뒤에 쉼표(,)를 붙인다. 시간이나 조건의 접속사가 이끄는 부사절에서는 실제로는 미래의 일을 나타내더라도 will을 쓰지 않고 현재시제를 쓴다.

07 G가 M에게 인터뷰를 해주어서 고맙다고 했으므로 이에 대한 대답으로 적절하지 않은 것은 ⑤ Of course.(당연하지.)이다.

08 위 대화의 흐름상, 빈칸에 들어갈 직업으로 가장 적절한 것은 ⑤ food stylist(푸드 스타일리스트)이다.

09 위 글에서는 Watson을 인터뷰하고 있는 중으로, 인터뷰는 이 인터뷰가 푸드 스타일리스트가 되고 싶은 학생들을 위한 것이라고 말하면서 직업에 대해서 이야기해 달라고 한다(C). 이에

Watson은 푸드 스타일리스트는 사진이나 영화에서 음식을 맛있게 보이도록 장식하는 역할을 한다고 대답한다(D). 이에 인터뷰어는 자신도 푸드 스타일리스트가 되고 싶은데 어떻게 해야 하냐고 조언을 구하자(A), Watson은 많은 음식에 대해서 배워야 한다고 대답한다. 이에 인터뷰어는 또 달리 해야 하는 건 무엇이냐고 묻자(B) Watson이 미술을 공부하라고 대답하는 순서로 이어지는 것이 가장 자연스럽다.

10 상담가가 되기 위해선 무엇을 해야 하냐는 A의 질문에 대해, "창의력을 키우고 수학을 배워야 돼."라는 B의 대답은 문맥상 적절하지 않다.

11 위 대화에서 소년은 직업 상담 프로그램을 위해 엄마와 함께 문서를 작성하면서 야구를 잘하는 것과 다른 사람의 이야기를 잘 들어주고 그들과 일을 잘하는 것 등 자신의 강점을 깨달았다.

12 엄마의 답변인 "너는 강점이 많단다."로 미루어 볼 때, 빈칸에 들어갈 말로 가장 적절한 것은 ④ What am I good at?(전 뭘 잘하죠?)이다.

13 위 대화에서 소년은 직업 상담 프로그램을 위해 엄마와 함께 문서를 작성하면서 자신의 장점에 대해서 이야기하고 있다.

14 ② won't snow → doesn't snow로 고쳐야 어법상 적절한 문장이 된다.

15 위 글의 초반부에, 위 그림을 보라고 이야기하고 우리의 삶이 미래에는 달라질 것이라고 언급한다. 따라서 위 글의 앞에 올 내용으로 가장 적절한 것은 ① Lives of the Future(미래의 삶)이다.

16 동사 advise는 to부정사를 목적보어로 취한다. 따라서 'He advised us to get some rest.'라는 문장이 되는 것이 적절하다.

17 Jack이 블로그에 그의 작품 사진을 올리고 난 후, 회사에서 제안이 들어와 직업을 갖게 되었다고 언급되어 있다.

18 다른 나라에서 온 많은 사람들과 함께 일한다('I work with many people from different counties.')고 언급되어 있다.

19 위 글에서는 컴퓨터 프로그래머인 수진이 자신의 직업에 대해서 이야기 하고 있다. 따라서 ⓓReading makes your writing better.(독서는 당신의 글쓰기 능력을 길러준다.)라는 문장은 문맥상 적절하지 않다.

20 위 글의 후반부에, 앞을 내다보고 미래에 중요해질 직업을 택한 사람들의 이야기를 들어보자고 했다. 따라서 위 글의 다음에 바로 이어질 내용으로 가장 적절한 것은 ⑤ '장래의 유망한 직업을 찾은 사람들'이다.

21 (A) 선행사가 사물인 the flower pot이므로 that이나 which가 적절하다.

(B) the amount of ~의 양

(C) 인공 손과 다리를 가리키는 대명사 They가 주어이므로 동사는 수동태형인 are made가 적절하다.

22 위 글에서는 공통적으로 직업에 대한 소개와 그 직업을 갖기 위해

필요한 능력들에 대해서 이야기하고 있다.

23 업사이클링 디자이너가 되기 위해선, 창의적이 되어야 하고, 미술에 대해서 배워야 한다('To become an upcycling designer, you should be creative and learn about art.')고 언급되어 있다.

24 ② Why does Sujin use new materials?(왜 수진이는 새로운 물질을 이용하는가?)라는 질문은, 수진이가 오래된 물건이나 쓰레기를 이용한다는 내용과는 일치하지 않는다.

25 업사이클링 디자이너가 되기 위해선 창의적이어야 하고, 미술에 대해서 배워야 한다('To become an upcycling designer, you should be creative and learn about art.')고 언급되어 있다.

26 (A) if는 '만약 ~한다면'이라는 뜻의 조건을 나타내는 부사절을 이끄는 접속사로 한 문장을 다른 문장에 연결해 준다. (B) For example 예를 들어 (C) to부정사의 부사적 용법인 to find가 들어가야 어법상 적절하다.

27 ⑤ I hope people use 3D printing machines more often because they are amazing at making things.(전 사람들이 3D 프린트 기계를 더 자주 사용했으면 좋겠어요. 왜냐면 그건 물건을 만드는 데 좋으니까요.)라는 말은 위 글에서 언급된 바 없다.

28 위 글에 따르면, 빅데이터 전문가는 많은 데이터를 모으고 분석해서 실생활에 사용한다고 언급되어 있다.

29 빅데이터 전문가가 되고 싶다면, 당신은 수학과 문제 해결 능력을 길러야 한다('If you want to become a big data specialist, you should develop your math and problem-solving skills!')고 언급되어 있다.

30 ③ What 3D printed products do people use the most?(어떤 3D 프린트로 만든 제품을 사람들이 가장 자주 이용하는가?)라는 질문에 대한 내용은 위 글에서 언급된 바 없다.

Lesson 7 (기말) 2회

01 ⑤	02 ③	03 ②	04 ④	05 ③	06 ③	07 ①	08 ①
09 ④	10 ①	11 ⑤	12 It is hard to write my strengths.				
13 ⑤	14 ④	15 ②	16 ②	17 ③	18 ⑤	19 ④	20 ⑤
21 ④	22 ⑤	23 ②					

24 Upcycling can reduce the amount of waste in the future.

25 more people to use 3D printed products in the future

26 ④	27 ②	28 ③	29 ①	30 ⑤

01 artificial은 '인공적인'이라는 뜻을 가진 단어로 이와 반대의 의미를 가진 단어는 ⑤ natural(자연적인)이다.

02 동사 allow는 목적보어로 to부정사를 취한다. 따라서 빈칸에 들어

갈 단어의 형태로 가장 적절한 것은 ③ to go이다.

03 사역동사 make는 목적보어로 동사원형을 취한다. 따라서 ② to go를 go로 고쳐야 어법상 적절한 문장이 된다.

04 위 글에 따르면, 이 직업은 놀이공원을 만들고 놀이기구를 디자인한다고 했으므로, 빈칸에 들어갈 말로 가장 적절한 직업은 ④ A theme park designer(놀이공원 디자이너)이다.

05 A처럼 푸드 스타일리스트가 되고 싶다는 B에게 A가 해 줄 수 있는 말로 가장 적절한 것은 ③ You need to learn about many kinds of food.(많은 종류의 음식에 대해서 배워야 해.)이다.

06 푸드 스타일리스트가 하는 일은 음식을 좋아 보이게 장식하는 일이라고("A food stylist decorates food to look good for pictures or movies.") 언급되어 있다.

07 Jason이 말하기 대회에 참여해 1등을 했다고 언급되어 있다. 또한 Jenny는 Jason에게 환경을 보호하는 방법에 대해 물어보자 Jason은 엘레베이터 대신 계단을 이용하라는 등의 방법을 알려 주었다.

08 Jenny가 Jason에게 자신도 Jason처럼 환경을 보호하고 싶다고 말하고 있고, 이에 대해 Jason은 환경을 보호하는 것에 대해서 조언을 하고 있다. 따라서 빈칸에 들어갈 말로 가장 적절한 말은 ① What do I need to do?(내가 무엇을 해야 할까?)이다.

09 "How about ~?"은 "~는 어때?"라는 의미로 상대방에게 무언가를 제안할 때 쓸 수 있는 표현이다. 따라서 이와 바꿔 쓸 수 있는 표현은 ④ Why don't you start keeping a diary?이다.

10 Jason은 거의 매일 글을 쓴다고("I write almost every day.") 언급되어 있다.

11 Brian이 많은 일을 할 만큼 강하다는 이야기는 위 대화에서 언급되어 있지 않다.

12 문장의 주어로 쓰인 to부정사가 수식어로 인해 길어진 경우, 보통 to부정사를 뒤로 보내고 대신 주어 자리에 가주어 it을 둔다. 이때 쓰인 it은 가주어이므로 구체적인 뜻이 없으며, '…하는 것은 ~하다'로 해석한다.

13 (A) be good at+(동)명사 ~를 잘하다
(B) 동사 like는 to부정사와 동명사형 모두를 목적보어로 취한다.
(C) Why don't you+동사원형 ~? ~하는 게 어때?

14 위 공고문에 따르면, 퍼스널 브랜드 상담가는 높은 의사소통 능력이 필요하다고("You need to have great communication skills") 언급되어 있다.

15 ⓐ exciting → excited / ⓑ work to → work for[at] / ⓔ interested with → interested in으로 고쳐야 어법상 적절한 문장이 된다.

16 (A) 문맥상 빈칸에는 형용사 useful이 들어가야 한다. (B) 조동사가 쓰였으므로 빈칸에는 동사원형 reduce가 들어가야 어법상 적절하다.

17 ⓒThey are made specially for patients.(그것들은 환자들을 위해 특별히 만들어졌다.)라는 문장은 쓰레기를 이용해 새로운 물건을 만들어 낸다는 업사이클링에 대한 내용의 흐름상 적절하지 않다.

18 look back은 '뒤를 돌아보다'라는 뜻으로 사용된다. ⓔ '앞을 내다보다'라는 단어로는 look ahead가 적절하다.

19 (A)as는 '~함에 따라'라는 의미로 사용되었다. 이와 같은 뜻으로 쓰인 문장은 ④ As she grows up, she learns more about life.(그녀가 성장함에 따라, 그녀는 인생에 대해 더 많이 배워간다.)이다.

20 위 글에 따르면, 미래에 우리의 삶이 변화함에 따라, 많은 직업들이 생겨날 것('many new jobs will appear.')이라고 한다.

21 위 글의 후반부에서는 미래를 내다보고 미래에 중요해질 직업을 선택한 사람들에 대해서 이야기해 보자고 했다. 따라서 위 글의 다음에 나올 내용으로 가장 적절한 것은 ④ Jobs that will be important in the future이다.

22 ⑤ Why should we use 3D printers?(왜 우리는 3D 프린터를 사용해야 하는가?)에 대해서는 위 글에서 언급되지 않았다.

23 위 글에 따르면, 수진이는 쓰레기를 이용해 새로운 물건들을 만들고 있다. 또한 컴퓨터 프로그래밍과 미술을 잘하면, 3D 모형 제작자가 될 수 있다고 언급되어 있다.

24 reduce 줄이다, 감소시키다
the amount of ~의 양

25 동사 want는 목적보어로 to부정사를 취한다. 따라서 주어진 우리말을 영작하면, 'Taeho wants more people to use 3D printed products in the future.'가 된다.

26 be made from ~로부터 만들어지다

27 ⓑcreative는 '창의적인'이라는 뜻을 가진 단어이다.

28 (나) 문장에서 쓰인 if는 '만약 ~한다면'이라는 뜻의 조건을 나타내는 부사절을 이끄는 접속사로 한 문장을 다른 문장에 연결해 준다. 따라서 이와 쓰임이 같은 문장은 ③ Can you tell me the right answer if I'm wrong?(내가 틀린다면 네가 정확한 답을 말해줄래?)이다.

29 (A)that은 사물인 선행사를 수식하는 목적격 관계대명사이기 때문에 생략 가능하다. 또한 (B), (D)의 to부정사는 부사적 용법이기 때문에, '~하기 위해'로 해석한다.

30 빅데이터 전문가가 되고 싶다면, 수학적 능력과 문제 해결 능력을 길러야 한다('If you want to become a big data specialist, you should develop your math and problem-solving skills!')라고 언급되어 있다.

Lesson 8 (기말) 1회

01 appearance는 '출현, 외모'라는 뜻을 가진 명사이며, appear는 '나타나다'라는 뜻을 가진 동사이다. 나머지는 모두 명사와 형용사의 관계이다.

02 위에서부터 순서대로, feather, predict, cage, lake, director라는 단어가 들어간다.

03 그룹으로 혹은 짝을 지어 토론을 하냐는 A의 질문에 대해 파트너와 함께 파리에서 토론하라는 B의 대답은 흐름상 자연스럽지 않다.

04 간접의문문은 의문문이 다른 문장 안에서 주어, 목적어, 보어 역할을 하는 것으로, '의문사+주어+동사' 형태로 쓰인다.

05 (1) 공작새가 갇혀 있는 것이므로 수동태인 is stuck이 들어가는 것이 적절하다.
(2) himself 그 자신

06 까마귀는 공작새와는 달리 동물원의 새장에 갇혀 있지 않다. 따라서 ⓒLike me, you are kept in a cage.는 ⓒUnlike me, you aren't kept in a cage.가 되어야 문맥상 적절하다.

07 위 글에 따르면, 공작새는 자신의 아름다운 외양 때문에 동물원에 갇혀 있고 자유롭게 날 수 없어서 행복하지 않다고 한다.

08 (a), (d)는 모두 to부정사의 명사적 용법이다. (b), (c)는 to부정사의 부사적 용법, (e)는 '~에게'라는 의미의 전치사이다.

09 공작새는 자신의 미모 때문에 동물원의 새장에 갇혀 있기 때문에 행복하지 않다고 언급했다.

10 공작새는 자신의 미모 때문에 동물원에 갇혀 자유롭게 날 수 없어서 행복하지 않다고 언급했다. 따라서 공작새의 생각과 일치하는 것은 ④ Happiness depends on freedom. Being stuck in a place that I don't want to be in is awful.(행복은 자유로움에 달려 있다 자신이 원하지 않는 장소에 갇혀 있는 것은 끔찍하다.) 이다.

11 (A)는 현재완료 시제의 경험적 용법이 사용된 것이다. 이와 쓰임이 같지 않은 것은 현재완료 시제의 계속적 용법으로 사용된 ④ She has searched for him for 5 days.(그녀는 그를 5일간 찾아 다녔다.)이다.

12 간접의문문은 의문문이 다른 문장 안에서 주어, 목적어, 보어 역할

13 까마귀는 백조가 자신과 다르게 하얀 깃털을 가졌기 때문에 가장 행복한 새라고 생각했다고 언급되어 있다.

14 위 글의 내용에 따르면, 소녀는 자신이 가진 것에 만족하지 못하고 다른 사람이 가진 것을 부러워해 행복하지 못하다고 이야기했다. 이에 대해 조언자는 다른 사람의 삶을 부러워하지 말라고 조언했다. 따라서 (A)에는 happiness, (B)에는 envy가 들어가는 것이 적절하다.

15 ⓐhe started to think about who was the happiest bird는 he started to think about who the happiest bird was로, ⓓbut I'm free to flying anywhere.는 but I'm free to fly anywhere.로 바꿔야 어법상 적절하다.

16 위 글에서는 자신을 다른 새와 비교하면서 자신이 가진 것에 만족하지 못하던 까마귀가 비교를 그만두면서 행복함을 느끼게 된 것에 대해서 이야기하고 있다. 따라서 위 글의 교훈으로 가장 적절한 것은 ④ Comparing myself to others is stupid.(나를 다른 사람과 비교하는 것은 어리석은 짓이다.)이다.

17 위 글에서는 자신을 다른 새와 비교하면서 자신이 가진 것에 만족하지 못하던 까마귀에 대해서 이야기하고 있다. 따라서 위 글과 가장 어울리는 속담은 ② '남의 떡이 더 커 보인다.'이다.

18 ⓐhe는 백조를 가리킨다. 나머지는 모두 앵무새를 가리킨다.

19 '누구도 그보다 더 아름답지 않았다'라는 의미의 문장이므로 최상급인 ⑤ He was the most beautiful bird.와 의미가 같다.

20 (나)must는 '~임에 틀림 없다'는 의미의 조동사로 사용되었다. 이와 쓰임이 같은 것은 ③ You must be tired after your long walk.(오래 걷고 난 후에 넌 피곤하겠구나.)이다.

21 (A) himself 그 자신 / (B) such a(n)+형용사+명사 그렇게 … 한 ~ / (C) until ~할 때까지

22 so는 앞서 언급된 문장인 'the parrot is the happiest bird in the world.'를 가리킨다.

23 ② What did the parrot feel about a crow's appearance? (앵무새는 까마귀의 외양에 대해 어떻게 생각했는가?)라는 질문에 대한 내용은 위 글에서 언급되어 있지 않다.

24 백조는 앵무새의 아름다움에 대해, 앵무새의 다양한 색의 깃털을 보고 그가 자신보다 더 아름답다고 생각한다고 언급했다.

25 (C)chase away me는 chase me away로 고쳐야 어법상 적절하다.

26 ⓑ는 공작새를 가리킨다. 나머지는 모두 까마귀를 가리킨다.

27 위 글에서는, 공작새는 아름다워서 사람들이 보러 오지만, 사람들이 까마귀를 보면 쫓아낸다고 이야기하고 있다. 따라서 빈칸에 들어갈 말로 가장 적절한 것은 ⑤ On the other hand(반면에)이다.

28 위 글에 따르면, 까마귀는 공작새가 가장 아름다운 새일지도 모르지만 가장 행복한 새는 자신일 것이라고 언급했다.

29 위 글에 따르면, 공작새는 까마귀가 어디든지 날아갈 수 있어서 그처럼 되고 싶다고 말했다.

30 공작새는 동물원의 새장에 갇혀서 자유롭게 날 수 없기 때문에 행복하지 않다고 언급했다.

Lesson 8 (기말)

01 ⑤ **02** ③ **03** ⑤ **04** ④ **05** ①, ④ **06** ② **07** ⑤
08 ⑤ **09** ③ **10** ① **11** ⑤ **12** ② **13** ① **14** ⑤ **15** ③
16 ④ **17** ② **18** ② **19** ② **20** ③ **21** ⑤ **22** ①, ⑤
23 ③ **24** ②
25 (1) the peacock (2) don't like (3) anywhere **26** ②
27 영어: The parrot has colorful feathers.
　　해석: 앵무새는 알록달록한 깃털을 가지고 있다.
28 ⑤ **29** I have never seen such a white bird before.

01 '특별한 음식을 준비할 때 다른 음식과 함께 쓰이는 것'이라는 영영풀이가 가리키는 것은 ⑤ ingredient(재료)이다.

02 위 대화에 따르면, blackout(정전)이 일어났다고 언급되어 있다.

03 영영풀이는 순서대로, reduce, decorate, cooperate, stuck, praise를 가리킨다. 또한 주어진 문장은 빈칸 위에서부터 순서대로, praise, stuck, reduce, decorate, introduce이 들어가야 문맥상 적절하다.

04 위 글에 따르면, 백조와 까마귀는 앵무새가 아름답고 색깔이 다양한 깃털을 갖고 있어서 부러워한다고 언급되어 있다.

05 '그가 숲에서 가장 아름다운 새'라는 의미의 문장은 최상급 표현을 이용해 he was the most beautiful bird in the forest라고 할 수 있다. 혹은 비교급 문장을 이용해 no bird was more beautiful than he was in the forest.라고 영작할 수 있다.

06 ⓐ so → such / ⓑ shine → shines / ⓓ why did he thought so → why he thought so로 고쳐야 어법상 적절한 문장이 된다.

07 위 글에 따르면, 앵무새는 공작새를 보기 전까지는 행복한 삶을 살았다고 언급되어 있다.

08 위 글에서는 자신을 다른 새와 비교하면서 자신이 가진 것에 만족하지 못하는 까마귀에 대해서 이야기하고 있다. 따라서 위 글과 가장 어울리는 속담은 ⑤ The grass is greener on the other side of the fence.(남의 떡이 더 커 보인다.)이다.

09 자신에게 만족하던 까마귀가 처음 백조를 보고 흰 깃털을 부러워하게 된다. 이후 백조가 앵무새의 깃털이 더 멋지다고 말하고, 앵무새를 찾아가 본 까마귀는 다양한 색깔을 가진 앵무새의 깃털을 부러워하게 된다. 이후 앵무새로부터 공작새의 깃털이 멋지다는 이야기를 듣고 난 후, 공작새를 보러 가지만 아름다운 외모 때문에 동물원에 갇히게 된 이야기를 듣고 누가 가장 행복한 새인지에 대해 다

시 생각해 보게 되었다는 순서로 이어지는 것이 흐름상 가장 자연스럽다.

10 새장에 갇혀 있는 것은 백조가 아니라 공작새이다.

11 ㉠ until ~할 때까지, ㉡ because of+명사(구) ~때문에

12 ㉘는 공작새를 가리킨다.

13 ⓑ who were the happiest bird → who the happiest bird was / ⓒ to seeing → to see / ⓓ was → were / ⓔ keep → kept로 고쳐야 어법상 적절한 문장이 된다.

14 '반면에, 사람들이 나를 보면, 나를 내쫓는다.'라는 문장이 들어가기에 가장 적절한 곳은 까마귀가 공작새에게 사람들은 공작새를 보러 온다고 이야기하고 있는 (E)이다.

15 impressive는 '인상적인'이라는 뜻을 가진 단어이다.

16 위 글에서는 까마귀가 공작새와 이야기한 후 누가 세상에서 가장 행복한 새인지 생각해 보게 되었다고 언급한다. 따라서 위 글의 앞에 올 내용으로 가장 적절한 것은 ④ '까마귀와 공작의 대화'이다.

17 위 글에 따르면, 까마귀는 자신이 어디든지 날 수 있는 자유가 있기 때문에 행복하다고 느꼈다.

18 (A) but 그러나 (B) but 그러나 (C) and 그리고

19 위 글에 따르면, 까마귀는 자신이 어디든지 날 수 있는 자유가 있기 때문에 행복하다고 느꼈다.

20 위 글의 교훈으로 가장 적절한 것은 (B) Don't compare yourself to others.(자신을 남과 비교하지 말아라.)와 (D) Be satisfied with the things you have.(자신이 가진 것에 만족하라.)이다.

21 ⓔLike는 Unlike(~와 달리)로 고쳐야 문맥상 자연스럽다.

22 위 글에 따르면, 공작새는 까마귀가 자유롭게 날 수 있어서 부러워했다. 또한 공작새의 깃털이 아름다워서 사람들은 공작새를 보러 가서 아름다움을 칭찬했다.

23 (A) because+주어+동사: ~이기 때문에
(B) because of+명사(구): ~ 때문에
(C) because+주어+동사: ~이기 때문에

24 위 글에서는 다른 새와 자신을 비교하는 까마귀의 이야기를 통해 자신이 가진 것에 만족하면 행복하다고 이야기하고 있다. 따라서 위 글의 주제로 가장 적절한 것은 ② Happiness depends on one's mind.(행복은 마음에 달려 있다.)이다.

25 동물원의 새장에 갇혀 있는 것은 공작새이며, 사람들은 까마귀가 아니라 공작새를 좋아한다. 또한 까마귀는 어디든지 날아갈 수 있다고 언급되어 있다.

26 ㉠that은 주격 관계대명사 that으로 사용되었다. 이와 쓰임이 같은 것은 ② I have a friend that plays baseball very well.(나는 야구를 매우 잘하는 친구가 있다.)이다.

27 위 글에 따르면, (A)his appearance는 앵무새의 외모를 가리킨다. 앵무새의 외모는 색깔이 다양한 깃털을 갖고 있다고 한다.

28 ⓔ는 앵무새를 가리킨다.

29 '~한 적이 있다/없다'를 표현할 때 현재완료 시제(have p.p.)를 이용할 수 있다.